2019

FEDERAL LAW SUMMARY FOR MPJE
ALL TOPICS IN THE EXAM BULLETIN

The Written Material for the RxPrep MPJE Online Law Review course, at www.rxprep.com

KAREN SHAPIRO, PHARMD, BCPS

PRIMARY SOURCES

Food and Drug Administration, at www.fda.gov

National Association of Boards of Pharmacy, at https://nabp.pharmacy/

DEA's Pharmacist's Manual, at www.deadiversion.usdoj.gov/pubs/manuals/pharm2/

U.S. Pharmacopeia Chapters, at www.usp.org

Welcome to the RxPrep
MPJE EXAM
REVIEW

This manual is to be used with RxPrep's online MPJE® course. The course includes videos that explain and summarize each topic. The videos correspond with the online test bank sections. You will be able to test your knowledge retention with the test banks.

Several of the tables in the text contain information that may have changed (such as requirements for intern hours or continuing education). If you are aware of updates in your state, or have questions for the instructors, you are welcome to send an email to instructors@rxprep.com.

If RxPrep has prepared updates based on revisions to the exam requirements or the competency statements, the updates will be posted on the RxPrep website at www.rxprep.com. Announcements about updates are sent to the RxPrep mobile application on your phone or tablet, and are posted to the Announcement section on the student dashboard page on the RxPrep website.

We wish you the best for your MPJE® preparation.

The RxPrep Team
www.rxprep.com

RXPREP BY THE NUMBERS

53

STATE-SPECIFIC INFORMATION PACKETS

100+

FACULTY YEARS OF PHARMACY EXPERIENCE

6

ONLINE MPJE COURSE VIDEOS

300+

MPJE TEST BANK QUESTIONS

TABLE OF CONTENTS

CHAPTER ONE

01

INTRODUCTION
TO THE MPJE

MPJE Questions are Based on Competency Statements 2
    The Questions come from the Competency Statements................................. 2
    The Candidate Bulletin includes both Exams: NAPLEX and MPJE 2
        RxPrep MPJE Course Updates... 2
    The Law Exams are State-Specific; NAPLEX is Not 2
    MPJE Scores Cannot be Transferred 3
    Each State will have a Different Version of the MPJE...................................... 3
    Discrepancies in Federal and State Law.. 3
    The Fill-in Spaces in this Manual for State-Specific Information 4
    The Possibility of Additional State Requirements 4
    Practice Where You Preach... 4
    State Information can be Located Online 4

Steps to be Well-Prepared 5
    1. Learn with the Video Course 5
    2. Master the Online Test Bank Questions 5
    3. Complete and Learn the Fill-In Spaces in this Manual 5
    4. Learn any State-Specific (Unique) Requirements.. 5
    5. Don't Worry, Be Happy 6
    6. Take the MPJE Practice Test Before You Test 6

Applying to Take The Exam 6
    Complete NABP's Two-Step MPJE Application Process.................................... 6
    Testing at a Pearson VUE Center.. 6

General Information about the Exam 6

Agencies Governing Pharmacy Law 11

MPJE Competency Statements 12
    The State Boards of Pharmacy 12

CHAPTER TWO

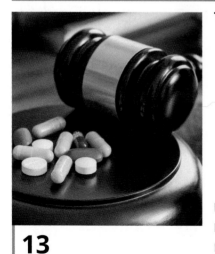

13

PHARMACY
LAWS AND
REGULATIONS

The Food and Drug Administration...14
    The Drug Approval Process... 14
    Prescribing Information Approval... 16
    The Over-the-Counter Drug Approval Process... 17
    Generic Drug Approval and the Abbreviated New Drug Application 17
    FDA Adverse Event Reporting System and MedWatch.................................. 17
    Unapproved Drugs Remain on the Market.. 18
    Direct-to-Consumer Advertising for Drugs 18
    Drug Recalls 19
    Market Withdrawal.. 19
    Counterfeit Drugs.. 19

Pure Food and Drug Act of 1906 (The Wiley Act)...20

Food, Drug and Cosmetic Act of 1938 20

Durham-Humphrey Amendment of 1951...23

Kefauver-Harris Amendment of 1962 23

Controlled Substances Act of 1970 24

Poison Prevention and Packaging Act of 1970..25

Drug Listing Act of 1972...25

Federal Anti-Tampering Act of 1982...25

Orphan Drug Act of 1983...26

Hatch-Waxman Act (Drug Price Competition and Patent Term Restoration Act) of 1984............26

Prescription Drug Marketing Act of 1987 27

Omnibus Budget Reconciliation Act of 1990 27

Dietary Supplement Health and Education Act of 1994..28

FDA Modernization Act of 1997..28

The Drug Addiction Treatment Act of 2000 29

FDA Amendments Act of 2007...29

Affordable Care Act of 2010...30

The Biologics Price Competition and Innovation Act of 2010.......................................30

Drug Quality and Security Act of 2013 31

Pregnancy and Nursing Labeling Final Rule 2014...31

Comprehensive Addiction and Recovery Act of 2016..32

CHAPTER THREE

33

PHARMACY
OPERATIONS

Licensure, Registration and Certifications 34

Pharmacist 34

Continuing Pharmacy Education 36

Pharmacist Intern...40

Pharmacy Technician..42

Controlled Substance Registrants 44

Disciplinary Actions Against Pharmacy Staff..46

**Recovery Programs for Drug and Alcohol Abuse or
Psychological Illness** 47

Renaming, Relocating, or Closing a Pharmacy 48

Inspection of a Pharmacy...48

Drug Supply Chain Integrity 49

Space and Equipment 49

Temporary Absence of the Pharmacist 50

Advertising and Signage 53

Pharmacy Security 54

Policies and Procedures 54

Libraries 54

Display of Licenses 55

Drug Storage in a Pharmacy Setting...55

Controlled Substance Storage 55

Investigational New Drug Storage...55

Repackaged and Resold Drug Storage 55

Drug Recalls 55

Expired (Outdated) Drug 55

Drug Samples 56

Drug Delivery 57

Drug Delivery Through Mail or by a Pharmacy Employee 57

Vacuum Tubes 58

Drive-up Windows 58

Quality Assurance and Medication Error Reporting..............................59

Notification of Potential Terrorist Events..60

Reporting Physical Abuse 60

Treatment for Tuberculosis 60

CHAPTER FOUR

62

PHARMACY
PRACTICE

Fundamental Responsibilities of the Pharmacy Staff **64**

The Pharmacist..64

Collaborative Practice Agreement..65

The Pharmacist-in-Charge..65

The Pharmacist Intern 66

The Pharmacy Technician 67

The Pharmacy Clerk 68

Requirements for Valid Prescriptions **68**

Written, Oral, Electronic, and Faxed Prescriptions...............................68

Healthcare Providers Authorized to Prescribe Medications...............69

Valid Prescriber/Patient Relationship 69

Self Prescribing and Prescribing for Family Members..........................69

Prescriptions from Retired or Deceased Prescribers 70

Prescriptions from Other States or Territories......................................70

Prescriptions from Foreign Countries 71

Off-Label Promotion by Manufacturers 71

Off-Label Prescribing 71

Correcting Errors and Omissions on Prescriptions **71**

Prescription Refills **72**

Emergency Refills without the Prescriber's Authorization **72**

Prescription Transfers **73**

Information Required on Multiple Unit/Dose Prescription Labels **74**

Formatting Standards for Multiple Unit/Dose Prescription Labels **74**

Expiration Dates Versus Beyond-Use Dates..**76**

Child-Resistant Packaging..**76**

Drugs That Require C-R Packaging..77

Drugs That Do Not Require C-R Packaging 77

Single Dose (Unit-Dose) Prescription Labels **79**

Unit Dose Beyond Use Date **80**

Customized Patient Packaging for Adherence **80**

Drug Utilization Reviews **82**

Written Material that is Included as Part of the Package Labeling **84**

Consumer Medication Information 84

Patient Package Inserts 84

Medication Guides 84

Risk Evaluation and Mitigation Strategy 85

Examples of REMS Requirements 86

**Patient Identification Prior to Dispensing or Administering
Prescription Drugs** **86**

Patient Counseling..**87**

Counseling Face-to-Face...87

Counseling When the Patient is Not Present..88

Counseling the Limited-English Proficient Patient................................88

Exemptions for Patient Counseling 88

Counseling Requirements by State..89

Health Insurance Portability and Accountability Act **90**

The Notice of Privacy Practices 92

Drug Substitution or Selection **93**

Generic Drug Substitution 93

Using the Orange Book 93

Narrow Therapeutic Index Drug Substitution 94

Biologics and Biosimilars 95

Pharmacy & Therapeutics Committee 95

Drug Formularies 95

Therapeutic Interchange 96

Pharmacy Compounding **97**

Traditional Compounding and Section 503A 97

Outsourcing Facilities and Section 503B 98

Compounding Versus Manufacturing 98

Non-Sterile Compounding 99

Sterile Compounding 99

Master Formulation Record 100

The Compounding Record or Log Book 100

Compounded Product Labels 101

Staff Training Requirements for Compounding 101

Beyond Use Dating and Expiration Dates for Compounded Products 101

Handling Hazardous Drugs 102

Dispensing Under Special Circumstances **103**

Conscience or Moral Clauses 103

Requirements for Death with Dignity 103

Medication Provisions During Declaration of Disaster or Emergency 104

Telepharmacy 105

Vaccine Administration **105**

Return, Disposal, or Reuse of Medications **106**

Returning or Disposing Prescription Medication to the Supplier 106

Returns from the Pharmacy Will Call (Pick Up) Area 106

Charitable Programs 107

Drug Donations to Cancer or Other Repository Programs 107

Patients Returning Previously Dispensed Medications to the Pharmacy 107

Disposal of Prescription Medication by the Ultimate User 108

Manufacturer Drug Samples Given to Prescribers to Provide to Patients **109**

Resale of Discounted Prescription Drugs **109**

Prescription Medication Loss or Theft **110**

Recordkeeping of Prescription Medication **111**

Maintaining Pedigrees to Ensure the Quality of Drugs **111**

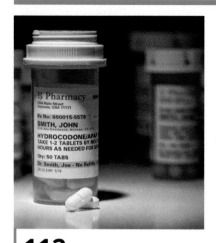

CHAPTER FIVE

112

CONTROLLED
SUBSTANCES

Laws, Rules, and Regulations 114
  Controlled Substances Act 114
  Classification of Controlled Substances 115
  Federal Controlled Substance Schedules............................. 116
  Drugs Scheduled Differently than the DEA........................ 118
  Maximum Limits and Set Opioid Amounts 121

Ordering Controlled Substances **121**
  DEA Form 222 121
  Requesting DEA Form 222 122
  Ordering Schedule II Drugs with DEA Form 222 122
  Cancelling or Voiding DEA Form 222 124
  Lost or Stolen DEA Form 222 125
  Electronic Controlled Substance Ordering System 126
  Ordering Controlled Substances with CSOS 127
  Cancelling or Voiding Electronic Orders......................... 127
  Theft or Loss of Controlled Substance Orders 128
  Granting the Power of Attorney 128
  Ordering Schedule III – V Drugs..................................... 130

Prescribing and Filling Controlled Substances **130**
  Healthcare Providers Authorized to Prescribe Controlled Substances......... 130
  Prescribing Controlled Substances for Oneself or Immediate Family Members.. 131
  Checking the Validity of a DEA Number 131
  Validity of Prescriptions for Controlled Substances........ 133
  Written Prescriptions for Controlled Substances............ 133
  Oral (Phone) Prescriptions for Controlled Substances.... 135
  Faxed Prescriptions for Controlled Substances 135
  Electronic Prescriptions for Controlled Substances........ 136
  Multiple Prescriptions for Schedule II Drugs 137
  Pre-signing and Post-signing Prescriptions for Controlled Substances 138
  Errors or Omissions on a Controlled Substance Prescription 139

The Prescriber's and Pharmacist's Corresponding Responsibility **140**
  Recognizing Red Flags to Prevent Drug Diversion 140
  Prescription Drug Monitoring Programs......................... 141

Refills of Controlled Substances....................................... **142**
  Controlled Substances Eligible for Refills....................... 142
  Paper Recordkeeping Requirements for Refills of Schedule III – IV Drugs ... 142
  Electronic Recordkeeping Requirements for Refills of Schedule III – IV Drugs 142
  Processing Schedule III – IV Refills When the Computer System is Down 143

Partial Filling of Controlled Substances **144**
  Partial Fills of Schedule III – V Prescriptions.................. 144
  Partial Fills of Schedule II Prescriptions......................... 145

Emergency Refilling/Filling of Controlled Substances **146**
  Emergency Refilling of Schedule III – V Drugs without Prescriber's Authorization................................ 146
  Emergency Filling of Schedule II Drugs........................... 147

Label Requirements for Controlled Substances **148**

Labeling Requirements for All Controlled Substances 148

DEA-Required Warning Statement on Label 148

Additional Label Requirement for Central Fill Pharmacies 148

Exemptions to Labeling Requirements 148

Transferring Controlled Substance Prescriptions **149**

Transferring Schedule III – V Prescriptions 149

Transferring Schedule II Prescriptions 150

Patient Identification Prior to Dispensing Controlled Substances **150**

Dispensing Non-Prescription Controlled Substances **151**

Delivering Controlled Substances to Patients **152**

Compounding or Repackaging Controlled Substances **152**

Dispensing Controlled Substances in Long-term Care Facilities **152**

Partial Filling of Schedule II Drugs for LTCF Patients 152

Automated Dispensing Systems in LTCFs 152

Emergency Kits for LTCFs 153

Internet Pharmacies and the Ryan Haight Amendments **153**

Treatment of Opioid Overdose and Dependence **154**

The Opioid Epidemic 154

Naloxone 154

Pharmacists and Naloxone Distribution 154

Opioid Treatment Programs 155

Opioid Dependence Treatment in an Office-Based Setting 155

Distribution of Controlled Substances Between DEA Registrants **156**

Pharmacy Going Out of Business 156

Pharmacy Selling Controlled Substances 156

Disposal of Controlled Substances **157**

Registrants Returning Controlled Substances to the Wholesaler 157

Registrants Sending Controlled Substances to a Reverse Distributor 157

Patients Disposing of Controlled Substances 158

Disposal of Controlled Substance Wastage in an Institutional Setting 159

Controlled Substance Loss or Theft 159

Reporting In-Transit Losses of Controlled Substances 160

Breakage, Damage, or Spillage of Controlled Substances **162**

Recordkeeping of Controlled Substances **162**

Paper Prescription Recordkeeping System 163

Electronic Prescription Recordkeeping System 163

Institutional Medication Records 163

DEA Controlled Substances Inventory 164

Nonprescription Products with Restricted Sales **164**

Pseudoephedrine, Ephedrine, Phenylpropanolamine, and Norpseudoephedrine 164

Dextromethorphan 168

Drug Paraphernalia **168**

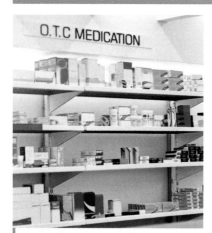

CHAPTER SIX

Labeling Requirements for Nonprescription Drugs.......................................170
OTC Labeling for Sodium, Calcium, Magnesium, and Potassium.............172
OTC Emergency Contraception...172
Behind the Counter Drugs..174

169

DISPENSING
**NONPRESCRIPTION
DRUGS**

Index 175
Image Credits 177

175

INDEX

ONE | INTRODUCTION
TO THE MULTISTATE PHARMACY JURISPRUDENCE EXAM

CHAPTER CONTENTS

MPJE Questions are Based on Competency Statements..2
    The Questions come from the Competency Statements..2
    The Candidate Bulletin includes both Exams: NAPLEX and MPJE..2
      RxPrep MPJE Course Updates..2
    The Law Exams are State-Specific; NAPLEX is Not..2
    MPJE Scores Cannot be Transferred..3
    Each State will have a Different Version of the MPJE..3
    Discrepancies in Federal and State Law..3
    The Fill-in Spaces in this Manual for State-Specific Information..4
    The Possibility of Additional State Requirements..4
    Practice Where You Preach..4
    State Information can be Located Online..4

Steps to be Well-Prepared...5
    1. Learn with the Video Course..5
    2. Master the Online Test Bank Questions..5
    3. Complete and Learn the Fill-In Spaces in this Manual..5
    4. Learn any State-Specific (Unique) Requirements..5
    5. Don't Worry, Be Happy..6
    6. Take the MPJE Practice Test Before You Test..6

Applying to Take The Exam...6
    Complete NABP's Two-Step MPJE Application Process..6
    Testing at a Pearson VUE Center..6

General Information about the Exam..6

Agencies Governing Pharmacy Law..11

MPJE Competency Statements..12
    The State Boards of Pharmacy..12

ONE

INTRODUCTION
TO THE MULTISTATE PHARMACY JURISPRUDENCE EXAM

MPJE QUESTIONS, COMPETENCY STATEMENTS & THE BULLETIN

THE QUESTIONS COME FROM THE COMPETENCY STATEMENTS

The MPJE includes test questions based on the <u>Competency Statements</u> that the National Association of Boards of Pharmacy (NABP) publishes in the <u>Candidate Registration Bulletin</u>. The bulletin can be found on the National Association of Boards of Pharmacy (NABP) website.[1] In order to pass, a candidate must demonstrate competence in these items (e.g., *Competency Statement #1.4.6, Requirements for Labelling,* requires the candidate to know what information should be on a prescription label). The <u>Competency Statements</u> are included at the <u>end</u> of this chapter.

THE CANDIDATE BULLETIN INCLUDES BOTH EXAMS: NAPLEX AND MPJE

In addition to the Competency Statements, the Candidate's Bulletin covers the registration process, exam scheduling, exam results and the test design for both the NAPLEX and the MPJE. Both exams are provided by the National Association of Boards of Pharmacy (NABP), which is why many of the processes you are likely familiar with from the NAPLEX will be the same, such as the testing center locations and some of the question types. The exam format is described in more detail at the end of this chapter.

RxPrep MPJE Course Updates

If RxPrep has prepared updates to the course, they will be posted with your online course access, and can be printed out when logged into your account on the RxPrep website through a web browser.

THE LAW EXAMS ARE STATE-SPECIFIC; NAPLEX IS NOT

In order to become licensed, a pharmacist has to demonstrate competency in clinical topics (the NAPLEX) <u>and</u> in pharmacy law (in most states, by passing the MPJE). A handful of states have additional testing requirements to become licensed as a pharmacist, such as a compounding exam. Drug treatment does not vary state-by-state, and all states and commonwealths require

---

1   https://nabp.pharmacy/programs/mpje/(accessed 2019 Jan 15).

passing the NAPLEX, with the exception of Puerto Rico, where candidates can take either the NAPLEX or the Puerto Rico clinical exam.

A few states and jurisdictions develop their own law exams and do not use the MPJE (Arkansas, California, and Puerto Rico). For licensure in Puerto Rico, candidates can take the MPJE or the Puerto Rico law exam.

MPJE SCORES CANNOT BE TRANSFERRED

The MPJE is specific to the law in an individual state or commonwealth, and scores received in one area will not be valid in another. A separate MPJE must be taken for each state or commonwealth in which a candidate wishes to become licensed. The NAPLEX, by comparison, can be transferred (reciprocated) to most areas. If it is within 90 days of taking the NAPLEX, the score can be transferred. If not, most states accept the license through a process called reciprocity.

There are some discrepancies between current legal requirements and state board law resources; if you contact the state board for clarification, you should ask for the name of the person verifying the information in the event that follow-up is needed.

EACH STATE WILL HAVE A DIFFERENT VERSION OF THE MPJE

While NABP defines the competency statements, the correct responses to questions can change according to the state's law. Most differences are due to the scheduling of controlled substances, described in the next section. In a state that was a center of the methamphetamine epidemic, the requirements for pseudoephedrine are likely to be more stringent. Some states permit schedule V cough syrups to be sold behind the pharmacy counter, without a prescription; most do not. Some states require the person picking up controlled drugs to have a valid government ID; most do not require ID to pick up any prescription. Even the requirements for information present on a prescription for a pet toy poodle will be more stringent in one state versus another.

DISCREPANCIES IN FEDERAL AND STATE LAW

Federal law is followed for the majority of pharmacy practice, and consequently makes up the bulk of most of the MPJE questions. Most differences between federal and state law concern scheduling controlled substances. When state and federal pharmacy law differ, candidates must answer the question based on the stricter state law.

Butalbital, acetaminophen and caffeine (*Fioricet*) is a good example of this type of discrepancy. Fioricet contains acetaminophen, butalbital and caffeine, which is not federally classified as a controlled substance. *Fioricet with Codeine* is federally scheduled as schedule III because of the codeine component.

Interestingly, a similar drug that contains butalbital, aspirin and caffeine (*Fiorinal*) is federally scheduled as schedule III. The only reason to schedule both drugs would be the butalbital component. Some of the states went ahead and scheduled *Fioricet* as schedule III.

Butalbital-acetaminophen & caffeine (Fioricet) is not federally-scheduled, but is scheduled in some states.

Federal schedules for controlled substances are set by the Drug Enforcement Administration (DEA). If a candidate is testing in a state where *Fioricet* is scheduled, the candidate should answer the MPJE questions on *Fioricet* according to the assigned schedule in that state. The schedule will be stricter than the federal requirement. States are not permitted to weaken federal schedules.

THE FILL-IN SPACES IN THIS MANUAL FOR STATE-SPECIFIC INFORMATION

RxPrep can provide you with the state-specific information to complete the fill-in lines in this manual. For each fill-in line, enter your state's requirement. Email the RxPrep Support Team at support@rxprep.com. Let us know the one or two states where you plan to take the MPJE.

THE POSSIBILITY OF ADDITIONAL STATE REQUIREMENTS

The state board of pharmacy website may list recommended study materials for the MPJE. You must check the state board's website to confirm that additional materials are (or are not) required for the state's version of the MPJE. The RxPrep legal team is happy to help with any law item that is confusing; email support@rxprep.com with your question/s.

To find the state board in which you wish to become licensed, click on the state on the NABP's website listing of state boards[2] or search online for "pharmacy board" and "name of state".

PRACTICE WHERE YOU PREACH

Many questions on the MPJE are asked in reference to specific drugs, or as practice scenarios (e.g., *Which drugs should be ordered on a DEA Form 222?*) It is helpful to complete your intern hours in the state in which you plan to become licensed in order to become familiar with how the pharmacy law applies in practice. It is not a requirement, because most of the law will be federal law, but it is useful if you can. Practice in any dispensing location will be helpful; rather than abstractly memorizing what is required on a unit-dose label (i.e., the amount required for one dose of a medication, such as a small package that contains 1 tablet of 100 mcg levothyroxine), it is helpful to have prepared unit-dose packages.

STATE INFORMATION CAN BE LOCATED ONLINE

NABP conducts a survey of all 50 states, the District of Columbia, Guam and Puerto Rico. The Survey includes questions about many aspects of pharmacy law, such as the state's requirements for intern hours, the exam requirements to become a pharmacist, the continuing pharmacist education (CPE) requirements, and many others. The Survey provides a quick and easy way to review select legal requirements for those areas in which the candidate wishes to become licensed. Pharmacy graduates of U.S. ACPE-certified schools should receive a copy of the Survey prior to graduation. U.S. pharmacy graduates should contact their school to obtain the survey if they did not receive it. The survey can be purchased on the NABP website for $195 and downloaded. State-specific information can be searched using the online site NABPLAW online, which is typically used by businesses.

STEPS TO BE WELL-PREPARED

Follow the steps to make sure you are well-prepared prior to taking your law exam.

1. LEARN WITH THE VIDEO COURSE

Watch the videos with this manual in front of you. Highlight what you need to review, study, then proceed to the MPJE Test Bank for that section. The Test Banks match to the chapters in this manual.

2. MASTER THE ONLINE TEST BANK QUESTIONS

Mastering the test bank questions that come with this course completely (with an understanding of "why" the answer is correct) will help you master the material and achieve a passing score. The questions can be accessed via a computer browser or through the RxPrep App.

Important: Do not skip over questions you miss in the test banks. RxPrep's instructions for what to do when a question is missed on the NAPLEX work just as nicely for law. Find them under the Student Resources tab at www.rxprep.com. Click on ACE Your Exams. The instructions also include guidance on creating a schedule. Preparing a schedule will help avoid the perpetual problem reported as: *Help! I ran out of time!* It is important to test only when the preparation has been completed. If not, the exam date should be rescheduled.

3. COMPLETE AND LEARN THE FILL-IN SPACES IN THIS MANUAL

Some of the information in this manual varies by state (e.g., in some states, a technician can make the offer to counsel, and in others, only the pharmacist can ask the patient if they would like to receive counseling). The information that varies state-by-state will have "fill-in" spaces in this manual. RxPrep can help with the fill-in information for one or two states. Send a request to support@rxprep.com. Please include the name of the state (or two states) that you need.

4. LEARN ANY STATE-SPECIFIC (UNIQUE) REQUIREMENTS

There may be details that are unique in a state and are not included in this manual (e.g., Florida does not permit pharmacists to be involved with the promotion or advertising of controlled drugs; this restriction does not apply to non-controlled drugs. This requirement is present in only a few states.)

The requirements for testing will be listed under the exam information on the state board's website. State boards usually spell out how an applicant should prepare. Typically, the requirements can be found by clicking on a link such as *Pharmacy Statutes* or *Pharmacy Law*. Most of the state links contain federal law, which is in this manual. You need to identify any content that is unique to the state. Fortunately, not all states have additional tested content.

5. DON'T WORRY, BE HAPPY

That's easy to say, but here's a thought that should help: the amount of material required to do well on the MPJE is much less than the amount required to do well on the NAPLEX. A big difference is that the content is completely different; some students try to wing the law exam, but except for the most-aware intern who has practiced in a dispensing setting, this is not a good idea. Learn the material. The amount you need to learn is manageable.

We have found that most students are able to cram for the exam for several weeks (minimally, full-time) and do well.

6. TAKE THE MPJE PRACTICE TEST BEFORE YOU TEST

After mastering the Test Bank questions (with an understanding of why the answer is correct—and without any questions skipped) take the practice exam. If you have mastered the questions, the score will be high. Do not consider taking the MPJE until the score is high, with a minimal score of 80%.

APPLYING TO TAKE THE EXAM

COMPLETE NABP'S TWO-STEP MPJE APPLICATION PROCESS

When the state's requirements have been met (e.g., the intern hours requirement), log into the NABP website with your e-profile. If you have not set up an e-profile, do that first. Submit the MPJE application with the initial fee. NABP will confirm your eligibility to sit for the exam and notify you via email when you can submit the completed application, with another fee.

TESTING AT A PEARSON VUE CENTER

Pearson VUE, the company that runs the testing centers used for both NAPLEX and MPJE, will receive notification that you are eligible to test from NABP. They will send you the information needed to schedule the test date on the Pearson VUE website.

GENERAL INFORMATION ABOUT THE EXAM

There are three competency areas tested on the exam:

- Area I tests on legal aspects of pharmacy practice (83%)

- Area II tests on licensure, registration, certification, and operational requirements (15%)

- Area III tests general regulatory processes (2%)

The MPJE is a 2.5-hour, 120 question, computer-adaptive examination. "Adaptive" means that the exam questions will adapt to the tester's ability level. Of the 120 questions, 100 questions count towards the grade. The other 20 questions are pretest questions and do not count. The board uses the pretest questions to determine if they are appropriate for use in future exams. These are dispersed throughout the test and there is no way to tell if a specific question will be counted. It is important to answer each question as best as possible.

The question types include <u>multiple-choice</u>, <u>select all that apply</u> (SATA), "<u>K-type</u>" (which include single or multiple correct responses, such as selecting options I, II and III) and <u>ranking</u> questions (the steps for a procedure are presented out of order, and the tester has to move them into the correct order). It is not possible to go back and change previously selected answer choices.

To receive an MPJE score, 107 exam questions must be completed. If more than 107 but less than 120 questions are answered, a penalty will be applied to the score. It is best to be well prepared and be able to complete the exam. A passing score is 75 points.

MPJE

MPJE Competency Statements

The MPJE Competency Statements provide a blueprint of the topics covered on the examination. They offer important information about the knowledge, judgment, and skills you are expected to demonstrate while taking the MPJE. A strong understanding of the Competency Statements will aid you in your preparation to take the examination.

Your formal education, training, practical experience, and self-study prepare you for the MPJE. The MPJE has been designed to assess how well you apply your knowledge, skills, and abilities to evaluate situations involving the applicable federal and state laws and regulations that govern the practice of pharmacy in the state in which you are seeking licensure. Additional information may also be obtained from the state board of pharmacy where you are seeking licensure.

 Note: No distinction is made in the examination between federal and state jurisprudence questions. You are required to answer each question in terms of the prevailing laws of the state in which you are seeking licensure.

Area 1   Pharmacy Practice (Approximately 83% of Test)
- **1.1**   *Legal responsibilities of the pharmacist and other pharmacy personnel*
  - **1.1.1**   Unique legal responsibilities of the pharmacist-in-charge (or equivalent), pharmacists, interns, and pharmacy owners
    - Responsibilities for inventory, loss and/or theft of prescription drugs, the destruction/disposal of prescription drugs and the precedence of Local, State, or Federal requirements
  - **1.1.2**   *Qualifications, scope of duties, and conditions for practice relating to pharmacy technicians and all other non-pharmacist personnel*
    - Personnel ratios, duties, tasks, roles, and functions of non-pharmacist personnel
- **1.2**   *Requirements for the acquisition and distribution of pharmaceutical products, including samples*
  - **1.2.1**   Requirements and record keeping in relation to the ordering, acquiring, and maintenance of all pharmaceutical products and bulk drug substances/excipients
    - Legitimate suppliers, pedigrees and the maintenance of acquisition records
  - **1.2.2**   *Requirements for distributing pharmaceutical products and preparations, including the content and maintenance of distribution records*
    - Legal possession of pharmaceutical products (including drug samples), labeling, packaging, repackaging, compounding, and sales to practitioners
- **1.3**   *Legal requirements that must be observed in the issuance of a prescription/drug order*
  - **1.3.1**   Prescription/order requirements for pharmaceutical products and the limitations on their respective therapeutic uses
    - Products, preparations, their uses and limitations applicable to all prescribed orders for both human and veterinary uses
  - **1.3.2**   Scope of authority, scope of practice, and valid registration of all practitioners who are authorized under law to prescribe, dispense, or administer pharmaceutical products, including controlled substances
    - Federal and State registrations, methadone programs, office-based opioid treatment programs, regulations related to retired or deceased prescribers, internet prescribing, limits on jurisdictional prescribing
  - **1.3.3**   Conditions under which the pharmacist participates in the administration of pharmaceutical products, or in the management of patients' drug therapy
    - Prescriptive authority, collaborative practice, consulting, counseling, medication administration (including immunization, vaccines), ordering labs, medication therapy management, and disease state management

1.3.4   Requirements for issuing a prescription/order
- Content and format for written, telephonic voice transmission, electronic facsimile, computer and internet, during emergency conditions, and tamper-resistant prescription forms.

1.3.5   Requirements for the issuance of controlled substance prescriptions/orders
- Content and format for written, telephonic voice transmission, electronic facsimile, computerized and internet, during emergency conditions, conditions for changing a prescription, time limits for dispensing initial prescriptions/drug orders, and requirements for multiple Schedule II orders

1.3.6   Limits of a practitioner's authority to authorize refills of a pharmaceutical product, including controlled substances

1.4   *Procedures necessary to properly dispense a pharmaceutical product, including controlled substances, pursuant to a prescription/drug order*

1.4.1   Responsibilities for determining whether prescriptions/orders were issued for a legitimate medical purpose and within all applicable legal restrictions
- Corresponding responsibility, maximum quantities, restricted distribution systems, red flags/automated alerts, controlled substances, valid patient / prescriber relationship, and due diligence to ensure validity of the order

1.4.2   Requirements for the transfer of existing prescription/order information from one pharmacist to another

1.4.3   Conditions under which a prescription/order may be filled or refilled
- Emergency fills or refills, partial dispensing of a controlled substance, disaster or emergency protocol, patient identification, requirement for death with dignity, medical marijuana, and conscience /moral circumstances

1.4.4   Conditions under which prospective drug use review is conducted prior to dispensing
- Patient-specific therapy and requirements for patient-specific documentation

1.4.5   Conditions under which product selection is permitted or mandated
- Consent of the patient and/or prescriber, passing-on of cost savings, and appropriate documentation

1.4.6   Requirements for the labeling of pharmaceutical products and preparations dispensed pursuant to a prescription/order
- Generic and therapeutic equivalency, formulary use, auxiliary labels, patient package inserts, FDA medication guides, and written drug information

1.4.7   Packaging requirements of pharmaceutical products, preparations, and devices to be dispensed pursuant to a prescription/order
- Child-resistant and customized patient medication packaging

1.4.8   Conditions under which a pharmaceutical product, preparation, or device may not be dispensed
- Adulteration, misbranding, and dating

1.4.9   Requirements for compounding pharmaceutical products
- Environmental controls, release checks and testing, beyond use date (BUD), initial and ongoing training

1.4.10   Requirements for emergency kits
- Supplying, maintenance, access, security, and inventory

1.4.11   Conditions regarding the return and/or reuse of pharmaceutical products, preparations, bulk drug substances/excipients, and devices
- Charitable programs, cancer or other repository programs, previously dispensed, and from ""will call"" areas of pharmacies

1.4.12   Procedures and requirements for systems or processes whereby a non-pharmacist may obtain pharmaceutical products, preparations, bulk drug substances/excipients, and devices
- Pyxis (vending), after hour's access, telepharmacies, and secure automated patient drug retrieval centers

1.4.13   Procedures and requirements for establishing and operating central processing and central fill pharmacies
- Remote order verification

1.4.14   Requirements for reporting to PMP, accessing information in a PMP and the maintenance of security and confidentiality of information accessed in PMPs

1.4.15   Requirements when informed consent must be obtained from the patient and/or a duty to warn must be executed
- Collaborative practice and investigational drug therapy

1.5   *Conditions for making an offer to counsel or counseling appropriate patients, including the requirements for documentation*

1.5.1   Requirements to counsel or to make an offer to counsel

1.5.2   Required documentation necessary for counseling

1.6 *Requirements for the distribution and/or dispensing of non-prescription pharmaceutical products, including controlled substances*

   1.6.1   Requirements for the labeling of non-prescription pharmaceutical products and devices

   1.6.2   Requirements for the packaging and repackaging of non-prescription pharmaceutical products and devices

   1.6.3   Requirements for the distribution and/or dispensing of poisons, restricted, non-prescription pharmaceutical products, and other restricted materials or devices
- Pseudoephedrine, dextromethorphan, emergency contraception, and behind the counter products as appropriate

1.7 *Procedures for keeping records of information related to pharmacy practice, pharmaceutical products and patients, including requirements for protecting patient confidentiality*

   1.7.1   Requirements pertaining to controlled substance inventories

   1.7.2   Content, maintenance, storage, and reporting requirements for records required in the operation of a pharmacy
- Prescription filing systems, computer systems and backups, and prescription monitoring programs

   1.7.3   Requirements for protecting patient confidentiality and confidential health records
- HIPAA requirements and conditions for access and use of information

1.8 *Requirements for handling hazardous materials such as described in USP <800>*

   1.8.1   Requirements for appropriate disposal of hazardous materials

   1.8.2   Requirements for training regarding hazardous materials
- Reverse distributors, quarantine procedures, comprehensive safety programs, Material Safety Data Sheets

   1.8.3   Environmental controls addressing the proper storage, handling, and disposal of hazardous materials
- Ventilation controls, personal protective equipment, work practices, and reporting

   1.8.4   Methods for the compounding, dispensing and administration of hazardous materials
- All hazardous materials including sterile and non-sterile compounding

Area 2 – Licensure, Registration, Certification, and Operational Requirements (15%)

2.1 *Qualifications, application procedure, necessary examinations, and internship for licensure, registration, or certification of individuals engaged in the storage, distribution, and/or dispensing of pharmaceutical products (prescription and non-prescription)*

   2.1.1 Requirements for special or restricted licenses, registration, authorization, or certificates
- Pharmacists, pharmacist preceptors, pharmacy interns, pharmacy technicians, controlled substance registrants, and under specialty pharmacist licenses (Nuclear, Consultant etc.)

   2.1.2   Standards of practice related to the practice of pharmacy
- Quality assurance programs (including peer review), changing dosage forms, therapeutic substitution, error reporting, public health reporting requirements (such as notification of potential terrorist event, physical abuse, and treatment for tuberculosis), and issues of conscience and maintaining competency

   2.1.3   Requirements for classifications and processes of disciplinary actions that may be taken against a registered, licensed, certified, or permitted individual

   2.1.4   Requirements for reporting to, and participating in, programs addressing the inability of an individual licensed, registered, or certified by the Board to engage in the practice of pharmacy with reasonable skill and safety
- Impairment caused by the use of alcohol, drugs, chemicals, or other materials, or mental, physical, or psychological conditions

2.2 *Requirements and application procedure for the registration, licensure, certification, or permitting of a practice setting or business entity*

   2.2.1   Requirements for registration, license, certification, or permitting of a practice setting
- In-state pharmacies, out-of-state pharmacies, specialty pharmacies, controlled substance registrants, wholesalers, distributors, manufacturers/repackagers, computer services providers, and internet pharmacies

   2.2.2   Requirements for an inspection of a licensed, registered, certified, or permitted practice setting

   2.2.3   Requirements for the renewal or reinstatement of a license, registration, certificate, or permit of a practice setting

2.2.4   Classifications and processes of disciplinary actions that may be taken against a registered, licensed, certified, or permitted practice setting

2.3   *Operational requirements for a registered, licensed, certified, or permitted practice setting*

    2.3.1   Requirements for the operation of a pharmacy or practice setting that is not directly related to the dispensing of pharmaceutical products
- Issues related to space, equipment, advertising and signage, security (including temporary absences of the pharmacist), policies and procedures, libraries and references (including veterinary), and the display of licenses

    2.3.2   Requirements for the possession, storage, and handling of pharmaceutical products, preparations, bulk drug substances/excipients, and devices, including controlled substances
- Investigational new drugs, repackaged or resold drugs, sample pharmaceuticals, recalls, and outdated pharmaceutical products

    2.3.3   Requirements for delivery of pharmaceutical products, preparations, bulk drug substances/excipients, and devices, including controlled substances
- Issues related to identification of the person accepting delivery of a drug, use of the mail, contract delivery, use of couriers, use of pharmacy employees, use of kiosks, secure mail boxes, script centers, use of vacuum tubes, and use of drive-up windows

Area 3 – General Regulatory Processes (2%)

3.1   *Application of regulations*

    3.1.1   Laws and rules that regulate or affect the manufacture, storage, distribution, and dispensing of pharmaceutical products, preparations, bulk drug substances/excipients, and devices, (prescription and non-prescription), including controlled substances
- Food, Drug, and Cosmetic Act(s) and Regulations, the Controlled Substances Act(s) and Regulations, OBRA 90's Title IV Requirements, Practice Acts and Rules, other statutes and regulations, including but not limited to, dispensing of methadone, child-resistant packaging, tamper resistant packaging, drug paraphernalia, drug samples, pharmacist responsibilities in Medicare-certified skilled-nursing facilities, NDC numbers, and schedules of controlled substances

MPJE Sample Questions

The following are examples of question types that examinees may encounter when taking the MPJE. These questions are presented as examples to familiarize examinees with their formats and are not intended to represent content areas on the MPJE. Every examinee is presented with the opportunity to take a tutorial at the testing center prior to initiating the MPJE. The tutorial instructs examinees on how to respond to all of the types of questions that could be presented on the examination. NABP strongly encourages each examinee to take the tutorial in order to become familiar with how to submit responses in the computer-based examination.

Multiple-Choice Question Format

How many total continuing pharmacy education hours are required to be completed upon the second renewal of a pharmacist's license in this jurisdiction?

A.   15

B.   20

C.   25

D.   30

E.   40

Multiple-Response Question Format

Which of the following medications are classified as Schedule II controlled substances in this jurisdiction? (Select **ALL** that apply.)

A.   Strattera

B.   Lisdexamfetamine

C.   Meprobamate

D.   Amphetamine

E.   Dexmethylphenidate

Ordered-Response Question Format

Place the following in the order in which they would expire according to federal regulations, starting with the earliest.

(**ALL** options must be used.)

Left-click the mouse to highlight, drag, and order the answer options.

Unordered Options	Ordered Response
A partially filled methylphenidate prescription for a patient not in a long-term care facility	
A phoned-in, emergency oxycodone prescription	
A written bupropion prescription	
An electronic alprazolam prescription	
A partially filled morphine prescription for a patient in a long-term care facility	

AGENCIES GOVERNING PHARMACY LAW

It is not possible to find a law book published by one federal agency that combines all federal requirements for the legal practice of pharmacy because there are different independent agencies involved in setting the requirements. In addition to federal requirements, the pharmacist will need to follow the statutes and regulations set by the state in which the pharmacist is licensed. A few examples of agencies that set and/or enforce the federal requirements for pharmacy practice include the:

- Federal Food and Drug Administration (drug approval with package inserts, drug manufacturing/distribution, and drug safety)

- Federal Drug Enforcement Administration (controlled drugs, with schedule categories, and enforcement)

- Consumer Product Safety Commission [OTC labeling, Child-Resistant (C-R) packaging]

- Federal Trade Commission (FTC) (OTC advertising)

- Department of Health and Human Services (DHHS) (oversees areas involving "health", including the FDA and CMS)

- Centers for Medicare and Medicaid Services (CMS) (responsible for insurance coverage for elderly, low-income and disabled)

- State boards of pharmacy (any revisions to federal law, with any additional state requirements)

MPJE COMPETENCY STATEMENTS

THE STATE BOARDS OF PHARMACY

Each state and jurisdiction has a board of pharmacy (or a similar body) whose primary purpose is to protect the patients. The board is responsible for granting and revoking professional licenses for pharmacists and other licensed personnel in the state who practice in a pharmacy. The board sets the requirements for the intern hours required to sit for licensure, and the continuing pharmacy education (CPE) hours and requirements that must be maintained by licensed pharmacists. The board will meet on a scheduled basis to review the rules and regulations set by the state and amend these, or add new requirements, when it is necessary.

The board may consist of public and professional members who serve for a certain length of time. The board will oversee pharmacy inspectors who inspect the individual pharmacies to ensure compliance with federal and state laws and regulations.

How many public members (non-pharmacists) serve on the board of pharmacy in your state?

_____

How many pharmacist members serve on the board of pharmacy in your state? _____

What is the term of service (length of years)? _____

3   https://nabp.pharmacy/programs/mpje/ (accessed 2019 Jan 13).

TWO # PHARMACY
LAWS AND REGULATIONS

CHAPTER CONTENTS

The Food and Drug Administration **14**
   The Drug Approval Process 14
   Prescribing Information Approval 16
   The Over-the-Counter Drug Approval Process 17
   Generic Drug Approval and the Abbreviated New Drug Application 17
   FDA Adverse Event Reporting System and MedWatch 17
   Unapproved Drugs Remain on the Market 18
   Direct-to-Consumer Advertising for Drugs 18
   Drug Recalls 19
   Market Withdrawal 19
   Counterfeit Drugs 19
Pure Food and Drug Act of 1906 (The Wiley Act) **20**
Food, Drug and Cosmetic Act of 1993 .... **20**
Durham-Humphrey Amendment of 1951 .... **23**
Kefauver-Harris Amendment of 1962 .... **23**
Controlled Substances Act of 1970 .... **24**
Poison Prevention and Packaging Act of 1970 .... **25**
Drug Listing Act of 1972 .... **25**
Federal Anti-Tampering Act of 1982 .... **25**
Orphan Drug Act of 1983 .... **26**
Hatch-Waxman Act (Drug Price Competition and Patent Term Restoration Act) of 1984 .... **26**
Prescription Drug Marketing Act of 1987 .... **27**
Omnibus Budget Reconciliation Act of 1990 .... **27**
Dietary Supplement Health and Education Act of 1994 .... **28**
FDA Modernization Act of 1997 .... **28**
The Drug Addiction Treatment Act of 2000 .... **29**
FDA Amendments Act of 2007 .... **29**
Affordable Care Act of 2010 .... **30**
The Biologics Price Competition and Innovation Act of 2010 .... **30**
Drug Quality and Security Act of 2013 .... **31**
Pregnancy and Nursing Labeling Final Rule 2014 .... **31**
Comprehensive Addiction and Recovery Act of 2016 .... **32**

TWO | PHARMACY
LAWS AND REGULATIONS

Laws are enacted through a federal or state legislative process. Regulations, or rules, provide specific details to help implement the law, and are issued by state regulatory agencies. In pharmacy, most of the rules and regulations are enacted through the state boards of pharmacy. This section discusses the history and practical use of drug laws and regulations in the United States, beginning with the FDA and the U.S. drug approval process.

THE FOOD AND DRUG ADMINISTRATION

The Food and Drug Administration (FDA), in its own words, is "responsible for protecting the public health by assuring the safety, efficacy and security of human and veterinary drugs, biological products, medical devices, our nation's food supply, cosmetics, and products that emit radiation".[4] The FDA splits up the responsibilities among six centers. The largest center is the one that is most important for pharmacy—the Center for Drug Evaluation and Research (CDER). CDER reviews the drug data provided by the manufacturer in order to make sure that the drugs marketed in the U.S. are safe and effective.

THE DRUG APPROVAL PROCESS

The drug approval process begins with <u>pre-clinical</u> testing on animals, which are generally rodents. This is called "pre-clinical" research because it comes before the "clinical" research that uses human subjects. If the pre-clinical animal research appears to indicate a relatively <u>safe</u> drug with a <u>potential therapeutic use</u>, the manufacturer will file an investigational new drug (IND) application with the FDA. The IND approval represents the FDA's permission to begin the Phase I clinical studies in human subjects. All phases of the clinical trial will involve the drug's safety. If a drug is found to be particularly unsafe at any phase, the FDA may halt the clinical trial entirely.

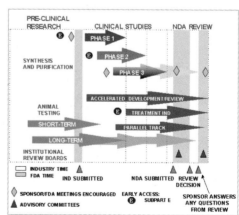

Timeline of the FDA's drug approval process.

---

4   http://www.fda.gov/AboutFDA/WhatWeDo/ (accessed 2019 Jan 15).

PHASE	SUBJECTS	PURPOSE
Pre-Clinical	Animals	Relative safety, therapeutic potential
Phase I	Healthy subjects ~ 20 – 80	Safety, side effects, adverse effects Pharmacokinetics and pharmacodynamics
Phase II	Patients ~ 35 – 100	Safety and efficacy Dosing range studied
Phase III	Patients ~ 300 – 3,000	Efficacy for treating the condition compared to a placebo or gold-standard treatment If completed successfully the manufacturer files an NDA or BLA
Phase IV	Patients	Post-marketing surveillance

Phase I studies determine if a drug is safe. Side effects, adverse events, and the drug's pharmacokinetics and pharmacodynamics are studied.

Phase II studies determine if the drug is safe and effective. In other words, is the drug safe and does it work? The subjects in the phase II trials have the indicated condition; for example, if a new agent has been developed to remove plaque in patients with coronary artery disease, the subjects in phase II will have coronary artery disease. This is when dose-ranging is analyzed. The trial will be designed to determine the optimum dose (or dose range) for the given condition.

Phase III studies determine if the drug is better (safer or more effective) than a standard drug treatment. Placebos may be used in some phase III studies, but they are never used alone if there is a treatment available that works. If the phase III study has promising results, the next step is to submit an application to the FDA. The new drug application (NDA) is used for drugs and a biologics license application (BLA) is used for biologics.

The NDA or BLA will include all the collected animal data, human data, the pharmacokinetic and pharmacodynamic analysis, including drug interaction studies, and a complete review of the manufacturing process. This material will be evaluated by the FDA through CDER. In accordance with the Prescription Drug User Fee Act (PDUFA), CDER is expected to review 90% of applications for standard drugs within 10 months of receiving the application, and within 6 months for priority drugs.

Phase IV studies, commonly referred to as post-marketing surveillance studies, may be conducted after the drug is approved and released for use. The FDA might request a post-marketing phase IV study to examine the risks and benefits of the new drug in a different population or to conduct special monitoring in a high-risk population that showed concern during the clinical testing. Alternatively, a phase IV study might be initiated by the manufacturer to assess such issues as the long-term effects of drug exposure.

To change a label, add a new indication, add new dosage or strength of a drug, or change the way it manufactures a drug, a company must submit a supplemental new drug application (sNDA).

PRESCRIBING INFORMATION APPROVAL

When a drug is approved, the prescribing information (the "package insert") is approved concurrently. The top section contains the prescribing information "Highlights", followed by the detailed information. The labeling must include these categories:

- Indications and Usage
- Dosage and Administration
- Dosage Forms and Strengths
- Boxed Warnings, if present
- Contraindications
- Warnings and Precautions
- Adverse Reactions
- Drug Interactions

- Use in Specific Populations (including pregnancy, nursing, pediatrics and geriatrics)
- Description
- Clinical Pharmacology
- Clinical Studies
- References
- How Supplied/Storage and Handling
- Patient Counseling Information

HIGHLIGHTS OF PRESCRIBING INFORMATION
These highlights do not include all the information needed to use EVISTA safely and effectively. See full prescribing information for EVISTA.

EVISTA (raloxifene hydrochloride) Tablet for Oral Use
Initial U.S. Approval: 1997

WARNING: INCREASED RISK OF VENOUS THROMBOEMBOLISM AND DEATH FROM STROKE

See full prescribing information for complete boxed warning.

- **Increased risk of deep vein thrombosis and pulmonary embolism have been reported with EVISTA (5.1). Women with active or past history of venous thromboembolism should not take EVISTA (4.1).**
- **Increased risk of death due to stroke occurred in a trial in postmenopausal women with documented coronary heart disease or at increased risk for major coronary events. Consider risk-benefit balance in women at risk for stroke (5.2, 14.5).**

-----------------------RECENT MAJOR CHANGES------------------------

Contraindications, Pregnancy (4.2)	06/2018
Warnings and Precautions, Premenopausal Use (5.4)	06/2018

----------------------------INDICATIONS AND USAGE--------------------------

EVISTA® is an estrogen agonist/antagonist indicated for:
- Treatment and prevention of osteoporosis in postmenopausal women. (1.1)
- Reduction in risk of invasive breast cancer in postmenopausal women with osteoporosis. (1.2)
- Reduction in risk of invasive breast cancer in postmenopausal women at high risk for invasive breast cancer. (1.3)

Important Limitations: EVISTA is not indicated for the treatment of invasive breast cancer, reduction of the risk of recurrence of breast cancer, or reduction of risk of noninvasive breast cancer. (1.3)

----------------------DOSAGE AND ADMINISTRATION----------------------

60 mg tablet orally once daily. (2.1)

--------------------DOSAGE FORMS AND STRENGTHS---------------------

Tablets (not scored): 60 mg (3)

-----------------------------CONTRAINDICATIONS----------------------------

- Active or past history of venous thromboembolism, including deep vein thrombosis, pulmonary embolism, and retinal vein thrombosis. (4.1)

- Pregnancy. (4.2, 8.1)

----------------------WARNINGS AND PRECAUTIONS----------------------

- *Venous Thromboembolism*: Increased risk of deep vein thrombosis, pulmonary embolism, and retinal vein thrombosis. Discontinue use 72 hours prior to and during prolonged immobilization. (5.1, 6.1)
- *Death Due to Stroke*: Increased risk of death due to stroke occurred in a trial in postmenopausal women with documented coronary heart disease or at increased risk for major coronary events. No increased risk of stroke was seen in this trial. Consider risk-benefit balance in women at risk for stroke. (5.2, 14.5)
- *Cardiovascular Disease*: EVISTA should not be used for the primary or secondary prevention of cardiovascular disease. (5.3, 14.5)
- *Premenopausal Women*: Use is not recommended. (5.4)
- *Hepatic Impairment*: Use with caution. (5.5)
- *Concomitant Use with Systemic Estrogens*: Not recommended. (5.6)
- *Hypertriglyceridemia*: If previous treatment with estrogen resulted in hypertriglyceridemia, monitor serum triglycerides. (5.7)

------------------------------ADVERSE REACTIONS-----------------------------

Adverse reactions (>2% and more common than with placebo) include: hot flashes, leg cramps, peripheral edema, flu syndrome, arthralgia, sweating. (6.1)

To report SUSPECTED ADVERSE REACTIONS, contact Eli Lilly and Company at 1-800-545-5979 or FDA at 1-800-FDA-1088 or www.fda.gov/medwatch

------------------------------DRUG INTERACTIONS-----------------------------

- *Cholestyramine*: Use with EVISTA is not recommended. Reduces the absorption and enterohepatic cycling of raloxifene. (7.1, 12.3)
- *Warfarin*: Monitor prothrombin time when starting or stopping EVISTA. (7.2, 12.3)
- *Highly Protein-Bound Drugs*: Use with EVISTA with caution. Highly protein-bound drugs include diazepam, diazoxide, and lidocaine. EVISTA is more than 95% bound to plasma proteins. (7.3, 12.3)

-----------------------USE IN SPECIFIC POPULATIONS-----------------------

- Pediatric Use: Safety and effectiveness not established. (8.4)

See 17 for PATIENT COUNSELING INFORMATION and Medication Guide

Revised: 06/2018

The Highlights of the Prescribing Information for Evista. The complete labeling information, with all the information required, will be included on the following pages of the package insert.

THE OVER-THE-COUNTER DRUG APPROVAL PROCESS

Over-the-counter (OTC) drugs are approved either with the same NDA process used for prescription drugs, or can be approved through the simpler OTC drug monograph process. The OTC monograph approval process has three steps, which the FDA calls a "three-phase public rulemaking process". Each phase requires a publication in the *Federal Register*, the federal government's daily 'newspaper', which is used to keep the public informed. The final version is the drug monograph.

In the first phase of the OTC monograph approval process, the FDA forms advisory review panels to review the active ingredients and determine whether they are "generally recognized as safe and effective" for use in self-treatment. The panels recommend appropriate labeling, including therapeutic indications, dosage instructions, and warnings about side effects and how to prevent misuse. The conclusions are published in the *Federal Register* in the form of an advanced notice of proposed rulemaking (ANPR). After publication of the ANPR, a period of time is given for any interested parties to submit comments or data in response to the proposal.

The second phase is the agency's review of active ingredients in each class of drugs, the public comments, and any new data that has become available. The FDA publishes its conclusions in the *Federal Register* in the form of a tentative final monograph (TFM). After publication of the TFM, a period of time is allotted for interested parties to submit comments or data in response to the monograph.

The publication of the final OTC drug monograph is the third and final phase of the OTC monograph approval process. The monograph will establish the conditions under which the OTC drug has been recognized as safe and effective. If a drug cannot comply with the drug monograph requirements, an IND and subsequent NDA review process will be required for the OTC drug to be approved, and released to the market. OTC drugs are discussed in a separate section.

GENERIC DRUG APPROVAL AND THE ABBREVIATED NEW DRUG APPLICATION

Generic drug approval requires an Abbreviated New Drug Application (ANDA). The ANDA process requires a review of the generic product's chemistry, the manufacturing controls, and the labeling. The review is abbreviated because it does not require pre-clinical animal studies and clinical studies with human subjects. The bioavailability data required with an NDA is replaced with a simpler bioequivalency analysis.

FDA ADVERSE EVENT REPORTING SYSTEM AND MEDWATCH

All drugs cause some adverse events, which should be reported to the FDA's MedWatch program. The name implies the purpose of the program: MedWatch is designed to "watch" the medication use in the public and find the adverse events that were not found in the clinical trials. The "eyes" of MedWatch are healthcare professionals, including pharmacists. Reporting and responding to adverse events is part of the professional responsibility of a pharmacist. Patients can report to MedWatch directly. Healthcare professionals and patients can also report adverse events to the drug manufacturer, who is required to send the collected reports at quarterly intervals for the first 3 years after drug approval, including a special report for any serious and unexpected events. This is considered part of the phase IV post-marketing surveillance.

Even the most well-designed phase III studies cannot possibly uncover every problem that could become apparent once a product is used in the real world. This is due to a variety of reasons, including an adverse event with a rare incidence (which may not have appeared in the trial subjects), adverse reactions that affect patients who were excluded from the trials, effects from long-term drug exposure that were not observed within the duration of the clinical trials, and a lack of rigorous lab monitoring. If the FDA gathers enough adverse reaction reports linked to the drug, the package labeling will be amended to incorporate the concern. If the adverse reactions are serious enough, the FDA may mandate a risk evaluation and mitigation strategy (REMS) or have the drug removed from the market.

UNAPPROVED DRUGS REMAIN ON THE MARKET

There are still unapproved drugs on the market because they were available before the FDA approval process was established in year 1938. Initially, these drugs were "grandfathered" into the law, meaning they were not required to go through the same approval process as new drugs. Over time, the FDA has been bringing these older drugs into the approval process, starting with those medications that pose the greatest health risk to the public.[5] For example, levothyroxine is a narrow therapeutic index drug with a long history of product inconsistency. The FDA required all levothyroxine products to submit an NDA by August 2001, and all levothyroxine products have since been FDA-approved or withdrawn from the market due to safety concerns. An unapproved drug will have an NDC number but will not be listed in the FDA's *Approved Drug Products with Therapeutic Equivalence Evaluations,* commonly known as the Orange Book.

DIRECT-TO-CONSUMER ADVERTISING FOR DRUGS

Prescription drug advertising is regulated primarily by the FDA. OTC drug advertising is regulated primarily by the Federal Trade Commission (FTC). In previous years, drug marketing was targeted primarily towards healthcare professionals. Now, manufacturers spend billions of dollars each year on direct-to-consumer (DTC) advertising, which is the promotion of drugs aimed directly at the patient, primarily through television commercials and magazine advertisements. Unfortunately, patients may be persuaded to request a treatment based on advertisements that may not be the best option for their condition.

The advertisement does not have to be FDA-approved, but the FDA will get involved if the information is false, misleading, or lacking fair balance. "Fair balance" means that the positive information about the drug must be balanced with the negative information. The side effect and safety concerns must be presented in a manner designed to have as similar an impact on the viewer as the drug's benefit for treating the stated condition.

5   https://www.fda.gov/Drugs/GuidanceComplianceRegulatoryInformation/EnforcementActivitiesbyFDA/ SelectedEnforcementActionsonUnapprovedDrugs/ucm118990.htm (accessed 2019 Jan 15).

The FDA's minimum requirements for what an advertisement must contain[6]:

- The name of the drug (brand and generic)

- At least one FDA-approved use for the drug

- The most significant risks of the drug

There are different types of advertisements (e.g., product claim ads, reminder ads, help-seeking ads) with different requirements.

If the ad is found to violate the law, the FDA will get involved to have the ad pulled. Violations typically include making unsupportable claims, leaving out risk information, failing to include an adequate provision, misrepresenting study data, overstating the benefits, or promoting use in patient groups that have not been studied. Any false or misleading statements in the advertisement could be considered misbranding.

DRUG RECALLS

Drug recalls are made for a variety of reasons, such as contamination, variability of drug concentration, incomplete product labeling and stability concerns.

Recalls involve a drug that poses a danger; thus, classifying the recall properly and taking an action commensurate with the risk is required.

MARKET WITHDRAWAL

Manufacturers may withdraw a drug from the market for many reasons, which can be due to safety issues or decreased market demand. The drug is not making enough money or extensive monitoring is required, which may prove to be too costly.

COUNTERFEIT DRUGS

Counterfeit drugs are fake, illegal drugs that are often misbranded and adulterated. The drug strength may be different than what is stated on the label or may not even contain the active ingredient at all. Excipients may be harmful. Current Good Manufacturing Practices (CGMPs) may not have been followed in the manufacturing of the counterfeit drugs. Counterfeit drugs have a higher likelihood of contamination and other quality concerns.

The FDA is responsible for investigating reports of counterfeit drugs. The most newsworthy drugs with recent counterfeit drugs include some of the erectile dysfunction drugs, the cancer drug *Avastin*, the stimulant *Adderall* and the emergency contraception product *Plan B One-Step*. Counterfeit drugs can be identified by differences on the product labeling. For example, a counterfeit *Cialis* bottle did not include an NDC number, did not have the tablet strength in a colored box, had different patterns and colors, had misspellings in the name. Consumers and healthcare providers must be diligent about ordering drugs from reputable sources to avoid using counterfeit drugs.

---

6   https://www.fda.gov/Drugs/ResourcesForYou/Consumers/PrescriptionDrugAdvertising/ucm072077.htm#other_materials (accessed 2019 Jan 15).

PURE FOOD AND DRUG ACT OF 1906 (THE WILEY ACT)

The Pure Food and Drug Act was the first legislation in the U.S. that offered protection to consumers from drug misuse. Pressure on President Roosevelt to improve the safety of food and drugs had been building for years but got a final boost with the release of *The Jungle* by Upton Sinclair, which exposed the horrific conditions in the meat-packing industry. On June 30, 1906, President Roosevelt signed the Pure Food and Drug Act, otherwise known as the Wiley Act, which established both a meat inspection law and a comprehensive food and drug law.

The basis of the law involving drugs was to mandate accurate product labeling and to require that the ingredients used in drugs met the standards of strength, quality, and purity in the *United States Pharmacopoeia* (USP) and the *National Formulary (NF)*. The law required that the food or drug label <u>could not be false or misleading</u>, and the presence and amount of eleven dangerous ingredients, including alcohol, heroin, and cocaine, had to be listed.

The law required that <u>no adulterated or misbranded drugs</u> could be sent through interstate commerce. Adulteration means the drug itself is bad (drug quality is not up to standard) and misbranding means the label is inaccurate.

FOOD, DRUG AND COSMETIC ACT OF 1938

In 1937, diethylene glycol was used as a solvent for an elixir preparation of sulfanilamide, an older sulfonamide antibiotic. This resulted in 107 deaths, most of which were children. The solvent in the untested product was a chemical analogue of antifreeze. The public outcry led to requirements for drugs to demonstrate safety prior to release. Congress enacted the Food, Drug, and Cosmetic Act (FDCA) in 1938, marking the birth of the modern FDA. The new act required that the manufacturer (not the FDA) prove the <u>safety</u> of a drug before it could be marketed. It authorized the FDA to conduct manufacturer and distributor inspections, and established penalties for using misleading labeling. From this point forward, the product claims must be accurate, and all ingredients must be listed on the label so that the public is aware of what they are ingesting. The amendments to the FDCA described on the following pages addressed deficiencies in the original act.

U. S. Races Death to Save 700 From Elixir

Recovery of Pint Bottles Sold to Patients Goal as Deaths From Poison Reach 36

Diethylene glycol, used as a solvent in an oral preparation, resulted in fatalities.

The definitions for food, drugs, dietary supplements and devices were defined by the FDCA for use in humans and other animals. Cosmetics were defined for human use only.

TERM	DEFINITION
Food	Items used for food or drink, the components in the food or drink, and chewing gum.
Drugs	Items recognized as drugs by the USP, NF and the official Homoeopathic Pharmacopoeia, and their supplements; Items used to diagnosis, cure, mitigate, treat or prevent disease; Items (other than food) intended to affect the structure or any function of the body.
Dietary Supplements	A product (other than tobacco) intended to supplement the diet that bears or contains one or more of the following ingredients: a vitamin, mineral, herb or other botanical, or amino acid, and their concentrates and extracts. These can be in combination; A dietary substance meant to supplement the diet by increasing the dietary intake and which is not used as the conventional food or as the sole item of a meal or the diet.
Devices	An instrument, apparatus, implement, machine, contrivance, implant, in vitro reagent, or similar that is recognized by USP; An item intended to be used in the diagnosis of disease or other conditions, or in the cure, mitigation, treatment, or prevention of disease; An item intended to affect the structure or any function of the body, and which does not achieve its primary intended purposes through chemical action and which is not dependent upon being metabolized.
Cosmetics	Items that are intended to be rubbed, poured, sprinkled, sprayed on, introduced into, or otherwise applied to the human body for cleansing, beautifying, promoting attractiveness, or altering the appearance, and the components of cosmetics, except soap (which is not a cosmetic).

The FDCA prohibited adulterated or misbranded drugs in interstate commerce. Adulteration involves the drug itself (the quality) and misbranding involves incorrect or missing information on the container or labeling. These are important concepts for the exam, since this involves giving unsafe drug.

Causes of Drug Adulteration:

■ It is <u>filthy, putrid, or decomposed</u>.

■ It has been prepared, packed, or stored under <u>unsanitary conditions</u> where it may have become <u>contaminated</u> with filth, or where it can become dangerous to a person's health. This includes a lack of adequate controls during the manufacturing process or a lack of tests that confirmed the quality and purity.

■ It contains a drug recognized in official compendia, but its strength is different from official standards, or the purity or quality is lower than the <u>official standards</u>.

■ It contains a drug <u>not</u> recognized in official compendia, but its strength is different from that listed on the label, or the purity or quality is lower than that listed on the <u>label</u>.

The official monographs of the United States Pharmacopoeia (USP) are used to make sure that the drug meets the requirements of the USP Chapter for the compound's identity, strength, quality and purity.[7]

Causes of Drug Misbranding:

- If there is a <u>lack of required information</u> on the package and in the labeling (weight, count, warnings, use in specific groups, unsafe dosages, methods of use, treatment duration).

- If there is any <u>false</u> or <u>misleading</u> product information, such as imitating the properties of another drug, or promising false cures.

- If there is a lack of special precautions needed to prevent decomposition that must be specified on the packaging, such as "keep in original container" or "protect from humidity and light".

- If there is information that is illegible (cannot be read).

- If the packaging does not contain the proprietary (branded) or established common name (as recognized by USP or Homeopathic Pharmacopoeia).

- If the ingredients differ from the standard of strength, quality, or purity, as determined by the test laid in the USP monograph.

- If it does not contain the manufacturer and business location and packer or distributor.

- If there is improper packaging or improper or incomplete labeling of additives.

- If there is a deficiency in packaging according to the requirements of the Poison Prevention Packaging Act (described further).

Example #1

A packet labeled *Ortho Tri-Cyclen* contains ethinyl estradiol and norgestimate. Each blue tablet contains 0.25 mg norgestimate and 0.035 mg ethinyl estradiol. Each green tablet contains inert ingredients. The *Ortho Tri-Cyclen* is dispensed to a patient without a patient package insert.

A patient package insert must be dispensed with estrogen-containing products. This drug is misbranded.

Example #2

A bottle is labeled to contain levothyroxine 100 mcg per tablet. The bottle is found to contain particulate contaminants in the tablets.

The purity of the drug is compromised. The drug is adulterated.

---

7 USP and the National Formulary (NF) used to be separate organizations, and have since merged. The designation USP-NF is seen as a reference in some of the USP sources.

DURHAM-HUMPHREY AMENDMENT OF 1951

The Durham-Humphrey Amendment was sponsored by two pharmacist-politicians, Congressman Carl Durham, a pharmacist from North Carolina, and Senator Hubert H. Humphrey, a pharmacist from South Dakota, who later became the 38th Vice President of the United States.

Hubert Humphrey

Carl Durham

This was the first time that a clear distinction was made between <u>OTC</u> and <u>prescription</u> drugs. The amendment classified the three conditions that would make a drug available only by prescription:

- Drugs that are habit-forming.

- Drugs considered unsafe for use except under expert supervision due to toxicity concerns.

- Drugs limited to prescription use only under a manufacturer's new drug application.

Another term used for prescription drugs are <u>legend</u> drugs. The term "legend" comes from the original legend required by the amendment to be placed on prescription drugs: "Caution: Federal law prohibits dispensing without a prescription." The requirement for this legend has since been simplified to "<u>Rx Only</u>" and is discussed further under the FDA Modernization Act of 1997.

OTC drugs were required to contain <u>adequate directions for use</u> in the "Drug Facts Label". The labeling must include safety in pregnancy and breast feeding, the calcium, sodium, magnesium and potassium content, and the product's U.S. contact information to report adverse events. Unit-dose labeling requirements were established, and are discussed further in the pharmacy practice section. The unit-dose container is common in the hospital setting as it improves efficiency and safety. The container has a barcode that can be scanned and matched to the patient's wristband, which enables the nurse to confirm that the correct medication will be administered to the correct patient. Additionally, the unit-dose container permits the drug to be placed in an automated dispensing system (ADS). The ADS has replaced the individual cassettes in many hospital settings. The cassettes were previously used to hold an individual patient's medications, and required considerable staff time to fill and replenish.

KEFAUVER-HARRIS AMENDMENT OF 1962

In 1961, an Australian obstetrician reported an increase of severe malformations in children born to mothers using thalidomide, which was marketed as "the first safe sleeping pill" for use in pregnancy. It was also used for nausea during pregnancy. Although thalidomide was approved and was heavily marketed in Western Europe, the approval in the U.S. was blocked by a young pharmacologist, Dr. Frances Oldham Kelsey, who had just started working at the FDA. She had concerns about the drug's safety and refused to approve the drug. Thalidomide is marketed in the U.S. today as *Thalomid* (along with related compounds) for cancer and complications of Hansen's disease, with a risk evaluation mitigation strategy to ensure safe use.

In response to this near catastrophe event, Congress passed the Kefauver-Harris Amendment (also known as the Drug Efficacy Amendment), which implemented the following changes:

- Manufacturers must prove that a drug is <u>both safe and effective</u> before it can be FDA-approved. Previously, drugs only had to be proven safe before it could be marketed. Evidence of effectiveness must be based on adequate and well-controlled clinical studies conducted by qualified experts.

- After the drug is on the market, manufacturers must continue to <u>report serious side effects</u> to the FDA.

- Individuals must give their <u>informed consent</u> when they are study subjects of a clinical trial. This means that the individual has a right to know what to expect, including all the risks and possible benefits, and must agree to participate.

- The FDA had to conduct a <u>retrospective evaluation</u> of the <u>effectiveness</u> of drugs approved between 1938 and 1962.

- Allowed the FDA to establish <u>Current Good Manufacturing Practices</u> (CGMPs) for drug manufacturing and to perform inspections.

  - Adherence to the CGMP regulations assures the identity, strength, quality, and purity of drug products by requiring drug manufacturers to establish quality management systems, obtain quality raw materials, establish operating procedures, detect and investigate drug quality deviations, and maintain reliable testing laboratories. CGMPs help prevent contamination, mix-ups, deviations, failures, and errors.

- The FDA was given oversight to regulate the <u>advertising of prescription drugs</u>. The Federal Trade Commission continues to regulate advertising of OTC drugs.

CONTROLLED SUBSTANCES ACT OF 1970

The Controlled Substances Act (CSA), also known as the Comprehensive Drug Abuse Prevention and Control Act, establishes the regulations surrounding controlled substances which all manufacturers, importers, exporters, distributors, researchers, hospitals, pharmacies, prescribers, and pharmacists must follow. Controlled substances are drugs that have the potential for <u>addiction and abuse</u> and thus require stricter regulation and control. This act established a <u>closed system</u> of the manufacturing, distribution, and dispensing of drugs with the purpose of <u>reducing drug diversion</u>.

This act is discussed in detail in the Controlled Substances section.

POISON PREVENTION AND PACKAGING ACT OF 1970

Before the implementation of the Poison Prevention and Packaging Act (PPPA), accidental poisoning was the top cause of injury in children less than 5 years old. There was literally no standard way to protect children from common dangerous substances, including drugs and dangerous household substances. The PPPA is enforced by the Consumer Product Safety Commission. It requires a number of household substances and drugs to be packaged in child-resistant (C-R) packaging. The packaging must be significantly difficult for children under 5 years of age to open within a reasonable time, and not difficult for normal adults to use properly. Child resistant packaging is discussed further in the Pharmacy Practice section.

DRUG LISTING ACT OF 1972

The Drug Listing Act of 1972 amended the FDCA to require drug establishments that are engaged in the manufacturing, preparation, propagation, compounding, or processing of a drug to register all of their drugs with the FDA. Each individual listed drug was required to have a unique national drug code (NDC) number.

The NDC is the product identifier that is present on OTC and prescription drug packages and inserts. The NDC is a 10 or 11 digit code with three segments:

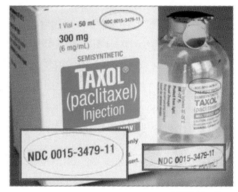

NDC Numbers

- The first is the labeler code, and is 4 or 5 digits. A labeler is any firm that manufactures, repacks or distributes a drug product. This segment is assigned by the FDA.

- The second is the product code and identifies the strength, dosage and formulation and is 3 or 4 digits. This number is determined by the labeler.

- The third is the package code and identifies the package size and type and is 1 or 2 digits. This number is determined by the labeler.

FEDERAL ANTI-TAMPERING ACT OF 1982

In 1982, seven people died after ingesting adulterated drugs in the Chicago metropolitan area. The victims had ingested over-the-counter *Tylenol* capsules that had been laced with potassium cyanide.

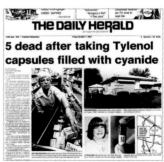

Chicago newspaper reporting on tainted Tylenol

In response to this tragedy, the Federal Anti-Tampering Act was passed and made it a federal crime to tamper with OTC products, and required tamper-resistant features on OTC medications. The label of the package must indicate the tamper-resistant features. Certain products are exempt from using tamper-resistant features in the packaging: skin products, insulin, lozenges and tooth cleaning powder (dentifrice).

ORPHAN DRUG ACT OF 1983

In response to a major public campaign by people with rare diseases and their supporters, the Orphan Drug Act was approved in 1983. Before this act, there was little motivation for pharmaceutical manufacturers to invest in drugs that would treat a relatively small number of people due to the limited potential return on the major investment required to get a drug to market. To get around this dilemma, the act authorized providing incentives to manufacturers to develop orphan drugs, including a tax credit for 50% of the clinical testing costs. Drugs are also given a 7-year period of exclusivity. Orphan drugs are developed under the FDA's Office of Orphan Products Development (OOPD). Drugs eligible for inclusion in this program include products that will treat diseases that affect less than 200,000 people in the United States, or for products with no reasonable expectation that the cost of research and development will be recovered by the sales revenue.

HATCH-WAXMAN ACT (DRUG PRICE COMPETITION AND PATENT TERM RESTORATION ACT) OF 1984

Previously, generic drugs were required to go through the same lengthly and costly FDA-approval process as new drugs. Congress passed the Hatch-Waxman Act (also referred to as the Drug Price Competition and Patent Term Restoration Act of 1984), to streamline generic drug approvals and to grant patent protection to drug innovators (the manufacturer that made the brand name drug). The purpose of the legislation was to increase the availability of generics and cut costs for the patient and the healthcare system.

Provisions in the legislation have made it possible for generic drug companies to file one of two abbreviated applications for generic drug approval: the Abbreviated New Drug Application (ANDA), or the 505(b)(2) application, which is referred to as a paper NDA. Under an ANDA, a generic drug company must provide study data to establish that the generic drug has the same active ingredient, route of administration, dosage form, and strength as the branded drug, and is bioequivalent to the branded drug. The inactive ingredients (coloring, excipients, binders) can be different. The generic drug manufacturer no longer had to conduct clinical trials to establish safety and efficacy. The paper NDA, allows the generic drug manufacturer to submit evidence of previously published reports of investigations of safety and effectiveness.

INACTIVE INGREDIENTS

Inactive ingredients are also called inert (which means chemically inactive) or excipients. Examples include fillers, extenders, diluents, wetting agents (surfactants), solvents, emulsifiers, preservatives, flavors and sweeteners, absorption enhancers, sustained-release matrices, and coloring agents.

The FDA defines an inactive ingredient as any component of a drug other than the active ingredient. Inactive ingredients do not affect the therapeutic action of the drug either by increasing or decreasing the effect.

Inactive ingredients are not always inert. For example, phenylalanine is a common sweetener, but can have a severe effect and must be avoided in patients with phenylketonuria, and the lipid emulsion that is used to deliver propofol can increase triglycerides in anyone. Inactive ingredients are listed in the CDER Ingredient Dictionary, which is part of the Orange Book.

Pharmacists check for inactive ingredients that can be harmful to certain patients, and there are many, including starch (with gluten-sensitivity), sulfites (with sulfite sensitivity) and soya lecithin (with peanut/soy allergy).

The legislation also provided patent protection to the company that created the brand name drug by granting up to 5 years of <u>patent exclusivity</u> to make up for the effort the company spent conducting clinical trials to establish safety and efficacy. During this period of patent exclusivity, no generic versions can be approved.

PRESCRIPTION DRUG MARKETING ACT OF 1987

The Prescription Drug Marketing Act (PDMA) was enacted to reduce public health risks from adulterated, misbranded, counterfeit or expired drugs. The law prohibits reimportation: prescription drug products manufactured in the U.S. and subsequently exported to a foreign country cannot be reimported back into the U.S, except by the product's manufacturer. The sale of drug samples was prohibited. Drug samples are meant to be provided by the prescriber to the patient at no cost. The sale of drug coupons was prohibited. Drug coupons are either given to prescribers to provide to patients at no cost, or are given to consumers by the manufacturer in some type of product promotion, such as an advertisement. Patients cannot buy drugs in other countries and bring them into the U.S., except under either of these conditions:

- The quantity is for a ≤ 90-day supply, and is for the <u>patient</u> (cannot be resold).

- An <u>effective treatment is not available in the U.S.</u>, the <u>condition is serious</u>, and the drug being imported has <u>no unreasonable risk</u>.

The patient may need to affirm the above in writing. Baggage is not supposed to be searched by law enforcement without a reasonable suspicion of the contents posing a risk to other travelers.

PDMA requires wholesalers to be state-licensed and meet uniform standards. It blocked hospitals from reselling drugs as a normal part of business by placing strict limits on the percentage of drugs that hospital pharmacies can resell. A hospital that is large or is part of a chain, or a hospital that has government or other non-profit status, may be able to obtain drugs at a lower cost than other hospitals. In past years, it was a routine part of business at some hospitals to resell drugs that were obtained at a lower cost to other hospitals for a profit. Currently, selling drugs to another hospital (that is not part of the same hospital group) is only permitted in order to help the other hospital manage a drug shortage.

OMNIBUS BUDGET RECONCILIATION ACT OF 1990

Concerns about improper medication use and inefficient use of federal dollars spent on healthcare led to the Omnibus Budget Reconciliation Act (OBRA). OBRA requires the pharmacists to perform a <u>prospective drug utilization review</u> and <u>counseling</u> for all <u>Medicaid beneficiaries</u> before dispensing the prescription to the patient. Most states have expanded counseling requirements for all patients. As a result, all patients should receive counseling on their medications. Counseling requirements are reviewed in the pharmacy practice section. States were also required to perform a <u>retrospective drug utilization review</u>.

DIETARY SUPPLEMENT HEALTH AND EDUCATION ACT OF 1994

The Dietary Supplement Health and Education Act (DSHEA) defined dietary supplements as food products. Prior to the signing of the DSHEA, dietary supplements were regulated in the same manner as drugs. <u>Adulteration and misbranding remain prohibited</u>, but otherwise dietary supplements are regulated quite differently. If the product includes a new dietary ingredient, the FDA will require a pre-market review for safety data. This is the only time a pre-market review is required. Otherwise, the company does not need to provide the FDA with safety and efficacy data and <u>FDA approval is not needed</u> prior to the release of the product and any related marketing material. The product must include a disclaimer that the FDA has not evaluated the claim and must have supporting research to back up any claims made in advertising or in the package labeling.

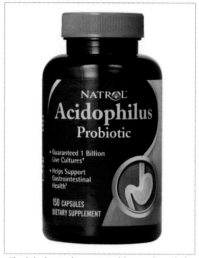

The label uses the acceptable wording "helps support gastrointestinal health" and does not claim to prevent, treat or cure an illness.

The key differentiating factor between a drug and a dietary supplement is the <u>health claim</u> of the product. When a claim is made that the product cures, prevents, corrects or treats a disease or condition the product is considered a drug. In contrast, the manufacturer of a dietary supplement is permitted to claim that a supplement addresses a <u>nutrient deficiency, supports health or is linked to body functions</u>. Naming a dietary supplement CarpalHealth or CircuCure implies that it can treat carpal tunnel or improve your circulation; these are disease claims and are not acceptable for dietary supplements. "Supports intestinal health" is acceptable but "treats gastrointestinal infection" is not. "Relax and sleep" is acceptable but "cures insomnia" is not.

Information that must be on a dietary supplement label includes a descriptive name of the product, the wording "supplement" or "dietary supplement", the name and address of the manufacturer, packer or distributor, a complete list of ingredients and the net contents, which is the amount in the container. Each dietary supplement (with the exception of some small volume products or those produced by eligible small businesses) must include the "Supplement Facts" box on the label.

FDA MODERNIZATION ACT OF 1997

The FDA Modernization Act (FDAMA) brought the FDA into the 21st century. It required the establishment of a registry for clinical trials (available at clinicaltrials.gov), approved labeling changes for foods and drugs, enabled the manufacturer to discuss off-label drug use (when requested), and extended an amendment passed previously in 1992 (the Prescription Drug User Fee Act, or PDUFA) that permits the FDA to charge a manufacturer fees to expedite the drug review process.

FDAMA made a special exemption for compounding pharmacists to continue preparation of individualized drug products not otherwise available.

Without accurate labeling, a drug is misbranded. Previously, under the Durham-Humphrey Amendment, all prescription (i.e., legend) drugs required a label that included the statement "Caution: Federal law prohibits dispensing without a prescription." Under FDAMA the wording was simplified to "Rx only."

The FDAMA regulations permitting fast-track approval updated previous regulations that had been initiated in the 1980s. At this time, the human immunodeficiency virus (HIV) epidemic led to a public clamor for access to investigational drugs. Regulations were developed to accelerate approval for high-priority medications. The FDA now has four programs to help speed the development and review of new drugs that may alleviate or treat unmet medical needs in serious or life-threatening conditions: fast track designation, breakthrough therapy designation, accelerated approval, and priority review designation.

The FDA makes a primary judgment for faster approval based on whether the drug's benefit can justify the risk and defines a "surrogate endpoint" that is likely to predict a clinical benefit. If a patient is terminal and there is no appropriate treatment available, it may be worthwhile using an investigational drug. Patients with terminal illness are often desperate to get enrolled in an expedited trial. Many critics complain that the approval processes are still too cumbersome and slow; yet, the FDA does not wish to cause harm when it is attempting to provide benefit.

THE DRUG ADDICTION TREATMENT ACT OF 2000

Opioid abuse and dependence is widespread in the United States. Prior to the Drug Addiction Treatment Act of 2000 (DATA 2000), the primary treatment was methadone, which was available only through a DEA-registered opioid treatment program. These are not widely available and can stigmatize those seeking care. DATA 2000 permits physicians to prescribe and dispense controlled substances in an office-based setting to treat opioid dependence. In 2016, the Comprehensive Addiction and Recovery Act (CARA) allowed nurse practitioners and physician assistants to treat patients for opioid dependence as well. This is described further under opioid treatment programs (OTP).

FDA AMENDMENTS ACT OF 2007

The FDA Amendments Act (FDAAA) gave new authority to the FDA to enhance drug safety. The Risk Evaluation and Mitigation Strategy (REMS) program was part of this legislation. A drug in which the FDA requires a REMS program will require more involvement from the manufacturer, distributor, prescriber, pharmacist, and/or patient to ensure that the benefits of the drug or biologic outweigh the risks. These include various types of education and monitoring.

AFFORDABLE CARE ACT OF 2010

The Affordable Care Act (ACA), also known as "Obamacare", includes many provisions that are important to pharmacists. The American Pharmacists Association (APhA) has identified several areas that have a large impact on the profession of pharmacy:

- CMS Innovation Centers (CMSIC)

- Essential Health Benefits

- Medical Loss Ratio

- Integrated Care Models

- Transitional Care Models

- Improvements to Medicare Part D Medication Therapy Management (MTM)

Questions on this Act are unlikely to be included on the MPJE since many provisions are likely to be clarified or changed. If information on the Act is required, these will be posted as an update to the MPJE course on the RxPrep website.

THE BIOLOGICS PRICE COMPETITION AND INNOVATION ACT OF 2010

Biologics are derived from living organisms (such as animals, microorganisms and yeast) and includes: vaccines, insulin, human growth hormone, erythropoietin, interferons, and others. Most of the specialty products are biologics. Conventional drugs (such as aspirin and lisinopril) are small and chemically-derived. Biologics are large and have a complex manufacturing process.

Only living organisms reproduce with this degree of complexity and there is some degree of variability even among the same biologic product. True "generics" for biologics are not possible according to the conventional definition, therefore the term "biosimilars" is used instead. The cost of a biosimilar approval is ~20-35% lower than the reference biologic, which is not the degree of cost savings expected with conventional drug generic approval (~75% cost savings), but considering the high cost of the original biologic, the savings can still be substantial.

The FDA was slow in developing a biosimilar approval process. In Europe, biosimilars have been used since 2003 and are usually approved a few years after the reference biologic product. In the past, the FDA approved a few biosimilars under the ANDA pathway, but these were not rated as therapeutically equivalent.

The Biologics Price Competition and Innovation (BPCI) Act was passed as part of the ACA and created an abbreviated licensure pathway for biological products that are demonstrated to be biosimilar to or interchangeable with an FDA-approved biological product. The legislation permits licensing to be awarded based on less than a full complement of product-specific preclinical and clinical data. The biosimilar must have the same mechanism of action, route of administration, dosage form and strength as the reference product, and will only be approved for the indications of the reference biologic. In 2015, filgrastim-sndz (*Zarxio*), a leukocyte growth factor, became the first biosimilar approved in the United States. These drugs are now listed in the FDA's *Lists of Licensed Biological Products with Reference Product Exclusivity and Biosimilarity or Interchangeability Evaluations,* commonly known as the *Purple Book.*

DRUG QUALITY AND SECURITY ACT OF 2013

The tragedy at the New England Compounding Center led Congress to pass the Drug Quality and Security Act (DQSA) as an amendment to the FDCA. The DQSA consists of the Compounding Quality Act and the Drug Quality and Security Act.

The <u>Compounding Quality Act</u>, gave the FDA increased authority to regulate compounding. The law makes a distinction between traditional compounders and "outsourcing facilities". If a facility compounds sterile drugs for humans, they can register as an outsourcing facility under 503B. Drugs compounded by an outsourcing facility are exempt from the FDA new drug approval process and certain labeling requirements, but need to comply with CGMP requirements, report adverse events, and provide the FDA with certain information about the products they compound.

To prevent counterfeit drugs from entering the market, the <u>Drug Supply Chain Security Act</u> establishes requirements to document the transactions of prescription drug products through the pharmaceutical supply distribution chain. Documentation must include transaction information, transaction history, and transaction statements.

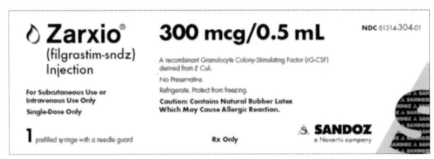

The package label for Zarxio, the first drug approved as a biosimilar in the U.S.

PREGNANCY AND NURSING LABELING FINAL RULE 2014

The drug labeling information requirements for pregnancy and nursing were changed in 2014. The previous Pregnancy Categories (A, B, C, D and X) will no longer be used and the information will be placed into new categories designed to provide more useful information of the health risks. The new requirements will be in package inserts by 2020. Drugs approved since June 30, 2001 will be required to use the new labeling requirements (see the figure). If the drug was approved prior to this date, the only change required in the labeling is to remove the letter category, and keep the previous information (the categories on the left of the graphic) the same.

The new information is placed into <u>three categories</u>:

- <u>Pregnancy</u>: Labor and delivery guidelines now fall under this category, which includes information for pregnancy exposure registries. The registries track data on the effects of certain medications on pregnant and breastfeeding women.

- <u>Lactation</u>: Previously labeled "Nursing Mothers," this category provides information such as how much drug is secreted through breast milk and the potential effects on a breastfed infant.

- <u>Females and Males of Reproductive Potential</u>: This is a new category that includes information on how a certain medication might affect pregnancy testing, contraception, and infertility

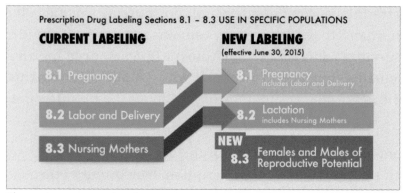

Changes to pregnancy categories.

THE COMPREHENSIVE ADDICTION AND RECOVERY ACT OF 2016

The Comprehensive Addiction and Recovery Act (CARA) is an amendment to the Controlled Substances Act. <u>CARA</u> authorizes funding and regulatory help in response to the <u>opioid epidemic</u> Large amounts of unused opioids are a key contributor to the opioid crisis. Most surgery patients report that they have unused opioids that had been indicated for post-surgical recovery. <u>The opioids find their way into the hands of others, including younger family members.</u>

CARA permits pharmacists to <u>partially fill schedule II drugs at the request of the patient or prescriber</u>. Previously, schedule II prescriptions could only be partially filled if the pharmacy was unable to dispense the full quantity. Any remaining opioids <u>must be filled within 30 days from the date the prescription was issued</u> (i.e., written). Previous law regarding schedules III-V still apply (i.e., partial fills are permitted for schedules III-V for up to six months from the issue date).

THREE | PHARMACY
OPERATIONS

CHAPTER CONTENTS

Licensure, Registration and Certifications 34
    Pharmacist 34
    Continuing Pharmacy Education 36
    Pharmacist Intern 40
    Pharmacy Technician 42
    Controlled Substance Registrants 44
Disciplinary Actions Against Pharmacy Staff 46
Recovery Programs for Drug and Alcohol Abuse or Psychological Illness 47
Renaming, Relocating, or Closing a Pharmacy 48
Inspection of a Pharmacy 48
Drug Supply Chain Integrity 49
Space and Equipment 49
Temporary Absence of the Pharmacist 50
Advertising and Signage 53
Pharmacy Security 54
Policies and Procedures 54
Libraries 54
Display of Licenses 55
Drug Storage in a Pharmacy Setting 55
    Controlled Substance Storage 55
    Investigational New Drug Storage 55
    Repackaged and Resold Drug Storage 55
    Drug Recalls 55
    Expired (Outdated) Drug 56
    Drug Samples 56
Drug Delivery 57
    Drug Delivery Through Mail or by a Pharmacy Employee 57
    Vacuum Tubes 58
    Drive-up Windows 58
Quality Assurance and Medication Error Reporting 59
Notification of Potential Terrorist Events 60
Reporting Physical Abuse 60
Treatment for Tuberculosis 60

THREE | PHARMACY OPERATIONS

LICENSURE, REGISTRATION AND CERTIFICATIONS

PHARMACIST

If a pharmacist would like to become licensed to practice pharmacy, the pharmacist must pass that state's version of the MPJE, except for a few jurisdictions that require an alternative law exam.[8] All states require the applicant to pass the NAPLEX. Most states permit transfer of the NAPLEX score to another state. In addition to the NAPLEX and the law exam, a few states require an interview with the state board, a compounding exam or some other type of practical exam.

Foreign-trained pharmacists must complete the Foreign Pharmacy Graduate Examination Committee (FPGEC) certification by passing the Foreign Pharmacy Graduate Equivalency Examination (FPGEE), and the Test of English as a Foreign Language (TOEFL). Once the FPGEC certification is obtained, the foreign-trained pharmacist will complete the state's intern hour requirements, and take the NAPLEX and the state-specific law exam.

Requirements for a pharmacist license vary by state, and are set by the state's Board of Pharmacy. Select states issue pharmacist licenses from other agencies, such as the Health Department or the Consumer Protection Department. In most states, the legal age to become licensed is at least 18 years old and one-third do not specify an age requirement. It is common to require a criminal history background check, which is sensible as the pharmacist has responsibility for drugs with abuse and diversion risk.

Name of agency issuing pharmacist licenses in your state: _____

Your state specific law exam if not MPJE: _____

List any other exam required for licensure: _____

How long a transferred NAPLEX score is valid for in your state: _____

Pharmacist License Renewal Periods

Pharmacists must maintain an active license to practice pharmacy. License renewal is usually every 1 – 3 years. Continuing pharmacy education (CPE) must be completed within the renewal cycle. If the license becomes inactive, the pharmacist will not be able to legally practice. The pharmacist may need to retake licensing exams to have their license reinstated.

STATE	PERIOD	SPECIFIC YEARS	DUE DATE
Alabama	Biennial	Even years	December 31
Alaska	Biennial	Even years	June 30
Arizona	Biennial		November 1
Arkansas	Biennial	Odd years	December 31
California	Biennial		Last day of birth month
Colorado	Biennial	Odd years	October 31
Connecticut	Biennial	Even years	January 31
Delaware	Biennial	Even years	September 30
District of Columbia	Biennial	Odd years	February 28 or 29
Florida	Biennial	Odd years	September 30
Georgia	Biennial	Even years	December 31
Guam	Biennial	Odd years	September 30
Hawaii	Biennial	Odd years	December 31
Idaho	Annual		Last day of birth month
Illinois	Biennial	Even years	March 31
Indiana	Biennial	Even years	June 30
Iowa	Biennial		June 30
Kansas	Biennial	Based on the date of original license	June 30
Kentucky	Annual		February 28
Louisiana	Annual		December 31
Maine	Annual		December 31
Maryland	Biennial		Last day of birth month
Massachusetts	Biennial	Even years	December 31
Michigan	Biennial		July 1
Minnesota	Annual		March 1
Mississippi	Annual		December 31
Missouri	Biennial	Even years	October 31
Montana	Annual		June 30
Nebraska	Biennial	Even years	January 1
Nevada	Biennial	Odd years	October 31
New Hampshire	Annual		December 31
New Jersey	Biennial	Odd years	April 30
New Mexico	Biennial		Last day of birth month
New York	Triennial	Birthday	Birthday month

STATE	PERIOD	SPECIFIC YEARS	DUE DATE
North Carolina	Annual		December 31
North Dakota	Annual		March 1
Ohio	Biennial	Odd years	September 15
Oklahoma	Annual		Last day of birth month
Oregon	Biennial	Odd years	June 30
Pennsylvania	Biennial	Even years	September 30
Puerto Rico	Triennial		Variable
Rhode Island	Annual		June 30
South Carolina	Annual		April 30
South Dakota	Annual		September 30
Tennessee	Biennial		Cyclical
Texas	Biennial		Last day of birth month
Utah	Biennial	Odd years	September 30
Vermont	Biennial	Odd years	July 31
Virginia	Annual		December 31
Washington	Annual		Birth date
West Virginia	Biennial		June 30
Wisconsin	Biennial	Even years	May 31
Wyoming	Annual		December 31

CONTINUING PHARMACY EDUCATION

Education in pharmacy does not stop at the point of graduation. Pharmacists must be current with new drugs and with the changes in existing drug labeling and treatment guidelines. If this knowledge is lacking, the pharmacist will not be able to adequately assess the drug treatment and will lack expertise in advising patients and other healthcare professionals. Keeping current is an essential part of the professional practice of a pharmacist.

The professional licensing agencies are granting a license that certifies a minimum skill level and therefore require a certain number of continuing pharmacy education (CPE) hours to be completed each license renewal cycle. If the pharmacist is involved with a certain area of patient care (immunizations, HIV, others) there may be requirements for CPE in the area of expertise. Pharmacists can participate in live or correspondence (mail/Internet) CPE. A certain number of hours may need to be completed by attending a live program. In a few states, the first license renewal cycle does not require CPE hours; the requirement is waived with the belief that the pharmacist is relatively current due to recent schooling, intern experience and preparation for the licensure exams.

Continuing Pharmacy Education Requirements*

STATE	REQUIREMENTS
Alabama	15 hrs/yr: 3 hrs live, Board-approved or ACPE-accredited
Alaska	30 hours/2 yrs, ACPE-accredited, any program approved by Alaska Pharmacists Association, 1 hour credit for CPR course that leads to certification by American Red Cross or American Heart Foundation
Arizona	30 hrs/2 yrs: 3 hrs law, ACPE-accredited or state CPE committee
Arkansas	30 hrs/2 yrs, 12 hrs ACPE-accredited, 2 hrs in immunization to retain competency, 3 hrs in senior care if applicable (nursing home pharmacist)
California	30 hrs/2 yrs, 2 hrs in Law and Ethics, Board-approved. Advanced practice pharmacists to complete additional 10 hrs
Colorado	24 hrs/2 yrs by 10/31 license renewal in odd-numbered yrs, ACPE-accredited
Connecticut	15 hrs/yr (Jan-Dec), 5 hrs live, 1 hr on pharmacy law or drug law, Board-approved or ACPE-accredited
Delaware	3- hrs/2 yrs, 2 hrs in medication safety/errors, 2 hrs in either distribution, dispensing, or delivery of controlled substance; or detection and recognition of symptoms, patterns of behavior, or other characteristics of impairment and dependency from abusive or illegal use of controlled substances. Newly licensed to complete CEU proportional to total number of CEU req'd for renwal. Board-approved, ACPE-accredited.
District of Columbia	40 hrs/2 yrs, 10 hrs live, 2 hrs on HIV training, 2 hrs in medication/dispensing errors, 2 hrs on cultural competency or specialized clinical training for patients who identify as LGBTQ
Florida	30 hrs/2 yrs, 10 hrs live, 2 hrs in medication errors, 5 hrs in risk management, up to 5 hrs can be volunteer work for underserved areas, Board-approved. 24 hrs for consultant pharmacist. 24 hrs for nuclear pharmacist. If initial license renewal is less than 12 months from initial licensure, no hours req'd. If initial license renewal is 12 months or more from initial licensure, then 15 hrs req'd. For initial renewal, 1 hr must include HIV/AIDS, Board-approved.
Georgia	30 hrs/2 yrs, licenses expire 12/31 of even yrs. If initial licensure occurs in first 6 months of 2 yr cycle (Jan-June), 30 hrs must be completed. If initial licensure occurs in the following 12 months (June-July), 15 hrs must be complete. If initial licensure occurs in last 6 months of 2 yr cycle, CE hrs are exempt. Board-approved, ACPE-accredited.
Guam	15 hrs/2 yrs, expires 9/30 of odd yrs. Board-approved.
Hawaii	30 hrs/2 yrs, 12/31 of odd yrs. If licensee has graduated from accredited pharmacy school w/i 1 yr of first license renewal, then no hrs req'd. If pharmacist administers vaccines for ages 14-17, or for HPV, Tdap, meningococcal, or flu vaccine to persons aged 11-17, they must complete training program during each renewal. Pharmacist prescribing/dispensing contraceptives to complete training every other renewal. Board-approved, ACPE-accredited.
Idaho	15 hrs/yr before last day of birth month, 12 hrs ACPE-accredited or CME-approved. 3 hrs max non-ACPE-acredited. 1 hr law, Board-approved. To administer immunizations, 1 hr related to vaccines, immunizations, ACPE-accredited.
Illinois	30 hrs/2 yrs, ACPE-accredited. 1st year exempt.
Indiana	30 hrs/2 yrs, 12/31 of odd yrs. 6 hrs of business or computer courses. 24 hrs of pharmacy practice. At least 15 hrs ACPE-accredited, all other hrs Board-approved. For those licensed during 2 yr period, 1.25 hrs of courses for each month or part of a month from date of licensure until end of 2 yr period. Newly licensed in last 6 months of 2 yr period are exempt.
Iowa	30 hrs/2 yrs on 6/30. First renewal exempt. 15 hrs ACPE-accredited. 2 hrs in law, ACPE-accredited. Remaining hrs can be gained through CME-accredited. Those currently enrolled in health-related grad studies may apply for exemption.
Kansas	30 hrs/2 yrs, board-approved or ACPE-accredited
Kentucky	30 hrs/2 yrs on 6/30. Board-approved or ACPE-accredited.
Louisiana	15 hrs/yr: 3 hrs live or 20 hrs total, ACPE-accredited

STATE	REQUIREMENTS
Maine	15 hrs/yr. 2 hrs in drug administration, Board-approved. Collaborative practice pharmacists must have 5 hrs completed in areas of practice in agreement. Newly licensed exempt.
Maryland	30 hrs/2 yrs. 2 hrs live, 1 hr med errors
Massachusetts	20 hrs/yr, 40 hrs total/renewal cycle every 2 yrs. Max 15 hrs/yr of home study. 5 hrs live/yr. 2 hrs law/yr. Any pharmacists engaged in the following activities must complete CE hrs: 1 hr/2 yrs in immunizations, 5 hrs/2 yrs in sterile compounding, 3 hrs/2 yrs in non-sterile compounding, 5 additional hrs/yr for collaborative practice agreement in areas related to agreement.
Michigan	30 hrs/2 yrs. Max 12 hrs/day. 10 hrs live. 1 hr in pain management. Newly licensed for less than a year, exempt. Newly licensed more than 1 yr, but less than 2 yrs, 15 hrs req'd.
Minnesota	30 hrs/2 yrs, 9/30 of even yrs. Board-approved, ACPE-accredited.
Mississippi	15 hrs/yr. 5 hrs in drug abuse, 2 hrs live.
Missouri	30 hrs/2 yrs, 10/31 of even yrs. Newly licensed in 12 months before renewal date is exempt. Board-approved or ACPE-accredited. Educational training may be approved for credit. Post-graduate study may be approved for credit.
Montana	15 hrs/yr: 5 hrs live or 20 hrs total, Board-approved or ACPE-accredited or Continuing Medicine Education (CME), 1st cycle exempt
Nebraska	30 hrs/2 yrs, 1/1 of even yrs. ACPE-accredited, Nebraska CPE, or other providers who meet Criteria for Quality of ACPE.
Nevada	30 hrs/2 yrs, 10/31 of odd yrs. 1 hr law. Can attend full day board meeting, which fulfills 1 hr law and 3 hrs CE. Can take posted *Pharmacist's Letter* for law CE
New Hampshire	15 hrs/yr: 5 hrs live, Board-approved, ACPE-accredited, or ACCME accredited
New Jersey	30 hrs/2 yrs. 3 hrs in law. 10 hrs live. 2 hrs in immunization, if approved to perform immunzations. If in collaborative practice agreement, 10 hrs in specialty area of agreement. Newly licensed are exempt. 10 hrs can be carried over into next renewal if taken in the last 6 months of current renewal and were not used in current renewal.
New Mexico	30 hrs/2 yrs: 10 hrs live, 2 hrs opioids/patient safety, 2 hrs pharmacy law, ACCME, ACPE-accredited
New York	45 hrs/3 yrs. Max 22 hrs by correspondence/non-live, 3 hrs med errors, ACPE-accredited. If participating in collaborative drug therapy management, 5 hrs in area of related practice.
North Carolina	15 hrs/yr, 5 hrs live
North Dakota	15 hrs/yr, ACPE-accredited. Hrs obtained prior to the 12 months of each renewal period can be used for past or current renewal, but not both.
Ohio	40 hrs/2 yrs. 2 hrs med errors, 2 hrs law. ACPE-accredited, Board-approved.
Oklahoma	15 hrs/yr: accredited CPE, recommend 3 hrs live
Oregon	15 hrs/yr. 1 hr of law, 1 hr of med errors, one-time 7 hrs of pain management (1 hr specific to Oregon, 6 hrs in general).
Pennsylvania	30 hrs/2 yrs, 2 hrs pain management, 2 hrs patient safety, 2 hrs injectable medications/biologics/immunizations if licensed in it. ACPE-accredited. 2 hrs in child abuse/reporting, Board-approved. Newly licensed exempt.
Puerto Rico	35 hrs/3 yrs. 15 hrs from home study, 3 hrs in infection control.
Rhode Island	15 hrs/yr, 5 hrs live. First year renewals exempt.
South Carolina	15 hrs/yr. 6 hrs live, 7.5 hrs drug/patient management, 1 hr controlled substances. All excess credits may be carried forward one year.
South Dakota	12 hrs/in previous 24 months to registration renewal
Tennessee	30 hrs/2 yrs. 15 hrs live, Board-approved, ACPE-accredited.
Texas	30 hrs/2 yrs, 1 hr law, 1 hr opiod abuse

STATE	REQUIREMENTS
Utah	30 hrs/2 yrs, 9/30 of odd yrs. 12 hrs live, 15 hrs drug/patient management, 1 hr law/ethics. ACPE-accredited or by pharmacy professional associations or divisions.
Vermont	30 hrs/2 yrs: 10 hrs live, 1st cycle exempt
Virginia	15 hrs/yr, 1st cycle exempt
Washington	15 hrs/yr. Expires on birth date. Pharmacist may claim .15 CEU for each hr of patient education training-cannot exceed 1.2 CEU. ACPE-accredited or Board-approved. If newly licensed less than 12 months after graduation from accredited school, pharmacist is exempt.
West Virginia	30 hrs/2 yrs: 3 hrs on drug diversion, 6 hrs live, 4 hrs immunization if immunizing pharmacist
Wisconsin	30 hrs/2 yrs, ACPE-accredited
Wyoming	12 hrs/yr, if inactive provide 5 yr CE prior to re-activation

*CPE	0.1 CEU = 1 hour of Continuing Pharmacy Education (CPE). Most states do not permit CPE hours in excess of the current period's requirements to be used for the next renewal cycle (carry over). If the state board permits carry-over it is noted in the table.
ACPE-accredited	The Accreditation Council for Pharmacy Education (ACPE) is the national agency for the accreditation of professional degree programs in pharmacy and for the providers of CPEs.
Board reviewed	The board or licensing agency can approve CPE programs; this may require submission and a fee.
1st year exempt	1st license renewal cycle post-graduation is exempt from CPE requirements.

Specialty Pharmacist

At the state level, the individual board of pharmacies may offer certain speciality pharmacist licenses. Examples include a <u>nuclear</u> pharmacist license, a <u>consultant</u> pharmacist license, or an <u>advanced practice pharmacist</u> license. If pharmacist specialists require specific registration in your state, list the specialist classifications, the requirements and the privileges that come with a classification:

_____

_____

Pharmacist Preceptor

The preceptor is a licensed pharmacist who mentors pharmacist interns during their college of pharmacy's introductory and advanced pharmacy practice experience, and when completing the intern hours required for licensure as a pharmacist.

Preceptors require state registration in about half of the states and in the other half all that is required is an active pharmacist license in good standing. A few states require the training site (i.e., the pharmacy) to register with the board. Most states have set a maximum number of interns that can be supervised by each pharmacist at one time.

Circle if your state requires preceptors to register with the state board. Yes / No

List any additional requirements in your state to become a preceptor:

_____

PHARMACIST INTERN

Pharmacist intern experience provides real-life pharmacy practice exposure. The common requirement is to complete 1500 practice hours, with some exceptions. Some states permit hours to be obtained partially or solely as part of the PharmD curriculum in an American College of Pharmacy Education (ACPE)-accredited program. Refer to the table on the hours required in each state and the duration in which the internship remains active.

Most states will require pharmacy students to register as pharmacist interns for this experiential learning. The term "experiential" refers to learning based on experience and observation, versus traditional classroom-style learning. The intern hours are most commonly completed in pharmacies or as part of the school rotation experience. Several states permit interns to obtain hours (which will count towards licensure) in research or industrial settings under the supervision of non-pharmacist professionals.

The intern is a pharmacist in training and can perform the duties of a licensed pharmacist at the discretion of, and under the supervision of, a pharmacist. There may be exceptions; for example, the intern may not be permitted to have a key to the pharmacy in California and interns are not allowed to administer vaccinations in New York. If the care that the intern is providing involves specialized training, such as administering immunizations, the supervising pharmacist must also be trained or they will not be competent to provide supervision.

A state may permit the intern to counsel, which must be under the supervision of a pharmacist. Pharmacists are responsible for the work of the intern and thus there are ratios restricting the number of interns (and technicians) that the pharmacist can supervise.

Does the state permit interns to provide counseling? Yes / No

Are there any limitations on the activities that an intern may conduct as compared to a pharmacist? _____

Provide the intern hours required in your state prior to sitting for the NAPLEX (see table):

_____

Provide the duration of an intern registration (see table): _____

If the board specifies the type of hours required, list them: _____

What is the ratio of interns for each pharmacist in a community setting: _____

What is the ratio of interns for each pharmacist in a hospital setting: _____

Are there permitted conditions in which the number of interns per pharmacist can increase? Yes / No

If yes, list the conditions under which this is permitted: _____

Does the state require the intern to submit a fingerprint card? Yes / No

Does the state require the intern to have a criminal background check? Yes / No

Pharmacist Intern Hour Requirements

STATE	HOURS REQUIRED
All states not listed	1500
Arkansas, South Dakota	2000
District of Columbia	1500 independent/1000 ACPE accredited
Florida	2080
Idaho, Ohio	None
Illinois	400
Kansas, Nevada, Utah, Vermont	1740
Maryland	1560 foreign/ 1000 ACPE-accredited
Michigan, Minnesota, Mississippi	1600
New Jersey, Oregon	1440
New York	1040
Tennessee	1700
Wyoming	1200

Intern License Expirations

STATE	INTERN LICENSE EXPIRATION
Alabama, Connecticut, Delaware, Florida, Hawaii, Minnesota, Virginia	Intern duration
Guam, Idaho, Illinois, Indiana, Maine, Michigan, New Hampshire, New Mexico, North Dakota, Ohio, Rhode Island (expires on 6/30), South Dakota, Washington, West Virginia, Wyoming (expires on 9/30)	1 year
District of Columbia, Iowa, Louisiana, Montana, Vermont	1 year post-graduation
Nebraska	15 months post-graduation
Colorado, Alaska, Maryland, Missouri, Nevada, New Jersey, Oregon	2 years
California	1-6 years
Georgia, Massachusetts, New York, Oklahoma, Utah	5 years
Mississippi, Texas	6 months post-graduation
Arizona, Kansas, Kentucky, Pennsylvania, South Carolina	6 years
North Carolina, Puerto Rico, Tennessee, Wisconsin	Not specified

PHARMACY TECHNICIAN

Pharmacy technicians have been assisting in the pharmacy throughout the history of the profession. Previously, training was done on the job for the type of help the pharmacist required. The first formal technician training programs were developed in hospitals by the American Society of Hospital Pharmacists (ASHP) in order to enable the technicians to perform accurate calculations and prepare sterile medications. Training is now required in most practice settings.

Technician Registration

Most states require registration with the state board for the primary purpose of having the applicant attest that they have not been convicted of a felony or misdemeanor and that they have not been involved in any criminal actions with controlled or non-controlled drugs. As part of registration, a criminal background check and/or drug screening may be required. It is common for states to require that the technicians be at least 18 years old, have a high school diploma or general equivalency degree (GED), and lack a criminal history.

Technician Licensure

A handful of states grant professional licenses to technicians.[9] Licensure is more involved than registration and will include requirements such as work experience, some type of examination, and education, such as a technician training program or graduation from a college of pharmacy.

Technician Certification

Currently, most technicians are not certified on a nationwide basis. This is changing as technicians are taking on more complex tasks to allow pharmacists to devote more time to patient care activities. In August of 2014, the NABP published the *Model State Pharmacy Act* with the goal of assisting the state boards by defining basic requirements for various issues concerning pharmacy practice.[10] This document included an important discussion on the expanding role of technicians, and the requirements for certification. All technicians can enter prescriptions into the computer and assist with drug storage, insurance claim processing and cashiering. Certification may allow the technician to be involved with limited patient care activities, which can include receiving new written or electronic prescriptions,[11] transferring prescriptions, and compounding. Technicians who are certified will need to complete continuing education hours in order to retain the certification.

The two primary certification exams are the Pharmacy Technician Certification Board's (PTCB) Pharmacy Technician Certification Examination and the National Healthcareer Association's (NHA) ExCPT Pharmacy Technician Certification Exam. The certified technicians may have a greater scope of practice compared to non-certified technicians.

---

9   Alaska, Arizona, California, Florida, Illinois, Indiana, Louisiana, Maine, New Mexico, Oregon, Rhode Island, Utah, and Wyoming
10   https://nabp.pharmacy/publications-reports/resource-documents/model-pharmacy-act-rules/ (accessed 2018 Jan 17).
11   Illinois, Idaho, Iowa, Louisiana, Massachusetts, Michigan, Missouri, New Hampshire, North Carolina, North Dakota, Puerto Rico, Rhode Island, South Carolina and Tennessee.

Over a dozen states have initiated "tech check tech" (TCT) programs where <u>one technician</u> <u>checks the work of another technician</u>, such as restocking automated dispensing cabinets.[12] TCT programs are expanding due to the increase in prescription volume and the increase in pharmacist responsibilities. The ASHP Pharmacy Practice Model Initiative Summit recommended that technicians should be more routinely involved with distributive functions that do not require clinical judgment.[13]

What is the minimum age in which a person can become a pharmacy technician in your state?

_____

Activities beyond those discussed above that are permitted for non-certified technicians in your state: _____

List any exams or certifications required for all technicians: _____

If your state has a basic level of technicians and higher level of technicians, list the higher level designation here and identify the training or examination required: _____

What is the ratio of technicians for each pharmacist in a community setting: _____

_____

What is the ratio of technicians for each pharmacist in a hospital setting:

_____

Are there permitted conditions in which the number of technicians per pharmacist can increase? If yes, list the conditions under which this is permitted:

_____

_____

_____

12   California, Colorado, Idaho, Kansas, Kentucky, Michigan, Montana, North Carolina, North Dakota, Oregon, South Carolina, Texas, Utah and Washington
13   https://www.ashp.org/news/2016/11/22/14/33/pharmacy_practice_model_summit_recommendations (accessed 2018 Jan 18).

CONTROLLED SUBSTANCE REGISTRANTS

DEA registration is required for the manufacture, distribution, research, prescribing and dispensing of controlled substances.

Individual persons or facilities will require DEA registration. For example, a physician will require a DEA number in order to be authorized to write prescriptions for controlled substances. The pharmacy or hospital will require DEA registration in order to receive, store and dispense the controlled substances. Individuals or facilities that have registered with the DEA are referred to as registrants.

Individuals and institutions (including prescribers, hospitals and pharmacies) submit the DEA Form 224 to apply for a DEA number. There are different registration forms for companies involved with the manufacture or distribution of drugs and for other types of organizations that require controlled substances.

The authority to manufacture, distribute, prescribe or dispense non-controlled drugs comes from the state in which the facility or practitioner is licensed. The state license is obtained first, before registering with the DEA.

DEA FORM #	PURPOSE
224	New Registration Form for Retail Pharmacies, Hospitals/Clinics, Practitioners, Teaching Institutions, or Mid-Level Practitioners
224a	Renewal Registration Form for Retail Pharmacies, Hospitals/Clinics, Practitioners, Teaching Institutions, or Mid-Level Practitioners
225	New Registration Form for Manufacturers, Distributors, Researchers, Analytical Laboratories, Importers, Exporters
225a	Renewal Registration Form for Manufacturers, Distributors, Researchers, Analytical Laboratories, Importers, Exporters
363	New Registration Form for Narcotic Treatment Programs
363a	Renewal Registration Form for Narcotic Treatment Programs

Application for Registration Under Controlled Substances Act of 1970
(New Applicants Only)

ON-LINE REGISTRATION CONSISTS OF SIX (6) SECTIONS. Please have the following information available **before** you begin the application:

Section 1. Personal/Business Information

If you are applying for an Individual Registration (Practitioner, MLP, Researcher) you are required to provide your Full Name, Address, Social Security Number, and Phone Number. If you are applying for a Business Registration, you are required to provide the Name of the Business, Address, Tax ID, and Phone Number.

Section 2. Activity

Business Activity and Drug Schedule information. **In addition** - Certain registrants for forms 225 and 510 will need to provide specific drug codes and/or chemical codes related to their operations.

Section 3. State License(s)

It is mandatory to provide State medical and/or controlled substance licenses/registrations. Failure to provide VALID and ACTIVE state licenses will be cause to declare the application as defective and it will be withdrawn **WITHOUT refund**.

Section 4. Background Information

Information pertaining to controlled substances in the applicant's background.

Section 5. Payment

Payment, via this on-line application, must be made with a Visa or MasterCard, American Express, or Discover. **Application fees are not refundable.**

Section 6. Confirmation

Applicants will confirm the entered information, make corrections if needed, and electronically submit the application and a submission confirmation will be presented. Applicants will be able to print copies for their records.

WARNING: 21 USC 843(d), states that any person who knowingly or intentionally furnishes false or fraudulent information in the application is subject to a term of imprisonment of not more than 4 years, and a fine under Title 18 of not more than $250,000, or both.

Select Your Business Category

Form 224
Practitioner (MD, DO, DDS, DMD, DVM, DPM)
Mid Level Practitioner (NP, PA, OD, etc.)
Pharmacy
Hospital/Clinic
Teaching Institution

Form 225
Manufacturer
Importer
Exporter
Distributor
Rev. Distributor
Researcher
Canine Handler
Analytical Lab

Form 510
Chemical Manufacturer
Chemical Importer
Chemical Exporter
Chemical Distributor

Form 363
Narcotic Treatment Clinics

Select One Business Activity

Applying for a registration with the wrong Business Category/Activity will cause either delay in processing your application or the withdrawal of your application. If you are not certain of your Business Category/Activity, please contact DEA Customer Service at 1-800-882-9539.

Please do not use your browser's BACK and FORWARD buttons while navigating this form.

> Begin

> -Cancel-

Online DEA Registration https://apps.deadiversion.usdoj.gov/webforms/jsp/regapps/common/newAppLogin.jsp

DISCIPLINARY ACTIONS AGAINST PHARMACY STAFF

ACTION	DESCRIPTIONS
Suspended	License is inactive; may be reinstated after conditions are met (e.g., completion of pharmacist recovery program, probation)
Revoked	License is taken away by the licensing agency
Reinstated	License that was taken away is given back, in active status
Surrendered	Individual agrees to voluntarily gives up licensure, often with compulsion in order to avoid penalties and/or criminal charges

In most states, the board of pharmacy has responsibility for initiating action against a pharmacist who is deemed unfit to practice for a limited period, or on a permanent basis. The board may have delegated this authority to a division within the board, such as the Board's Quality Assurance Committee. There are some jurisdictions where this responsibility rests with another agency. The most common causes of disciplinary action are <u>impairment, drug theft and drug diversion</u>.[14]

Since the board in each state is primarily concerned with the health of the public, they have instituted policies to prevent personnel from working in pharmacies who have been involved with drug diversion, including requirements for background criminal checks and/or a requirement for urine screening. Leniency may be extended to an individual with drug addiction if the licensee is willing to enroll in a rehabilitation program, which are described in the next section. Drug abuse and addiction can involve prescription drugs, illicit drugs and alcohol.

The board (or other designated regulatory agency that manages disciplinary actions) has the final authority over disciplinary proceedings, which can involve license probation, suspension or revocation. If the activity involves criminal actions, such as drug diversion or other types of theft, the matter will need to involve law enforcement. Pharmacies can lose the license to operate: for example, if a pharmacy is found to be operating as a "pill mill" where excessive and inappropriate opioid prescriptions are filled, the pharmacy may have the state license to operate (and the pharmacy's DEA registration) revoked.

---

14   Nebraska: Department of Health and Human Services, Division of Public Health; Guam: Board of Examiners for Pharmacy; New York: Board of Regents; Utah: Division of Occupational and Professional Licensing; Wisconsin: Pharmacy Examining Board.

RECOVERY PROGRAMS FOR DRUG AND ALCOHOL ABUSE OR PSYCHOLOGICAL ILLNESS

Addiction is an occupational hazard in pharmacy due to the stress involved with this type of work and the easy access to drugs. The drug abuse rate among pharmacists is thought to be about twice as large as the general population. Pharmacists who abuse drugs may falsely believe that their own clinical knowledge will somehow prevent them from developing dependence. This belief is inaccurate. Substance use among pharmacists can jeopardize the public health; compounding or dispensing errors resulting from the impairment can cause injury, including death. The goal of the board or other licensing agency, if no serious offense has been committed, is to assist the pharmacist in obtaining treatment and returning to practice.

The majority of the state programs are available for all licensed healthcare professionals. Physicians and nurses have similar abuse concerns, including high stress levels at work and easy access to drugs. The state board or regulatory agencies financially sponsor these programs. The only requirement for voluntary enrollment is a desire to seek help and maintain recovery. The enrollment may be involuntary when it is part of a disciplinary action.

> The purpose of a pharmacist recovery program is to develop a treatment plan, monitor participation and provide encouragement and support. In the quickest, most confidential and least stressful manner possible, the individual receives the proper help to face the problem, deal with it and, if possible, return to the profession as a contributing member.
>
> The goal is recovery and rehabilitation.
>
> Colleagues who refer coworkers for help remain confidential.

If a pharmacist is known to be impaired at work, it is likely a requirement of the other licensees at the pharmacy to report the suspected person to the state board, and possibly to law enforcement if theft has occurred. The board may elect to offer the licensee a path to treatment with or without license probation or suspension, depending on whether an incident, such as a dispensing error, was involved, and if the licensee is a repeat offender. If theft of a controlled substance was involved, the repercussions will be more severe and would likely include license revocation.

If a license has been revoked for drug abuse or any other threat to public safety, the pharmacist can apply to the state board or licensing agency for reinstatement, which may or may not be granted. The board has broad discretionary options to determine if the license should be reinstated. If the agency is convinced that the person involved is rehabilitated, reinstatement may be possible; if the agency views the person as a continued threat to public safety, it is likely to deny the reinstatement request.

My state provides an impaired pharmacist recovery program. Yes / No

Name the organization that operates the program: _____

List who can enroll in the state's program: _____

What are the enrollment conditions?_____

Can a pharmacist enroll themselves? _____

RENAMING, RELOCATING, OR CLOSING A PHARMACY

A change of business name, closure or relocation of a pharmacy will require notification to the state board within a set time limit, which will be short, such as "immediately" or "within 30 days". Many states require inspection of the new site prior to approving a relocation request. In some jurisdictions all that is required is a notification of the move to the state board, which is made by completing a change of address form.

The DEA will require a notice of change of the address of the registrant when scheduled drugs are moving location, such as with relocation. If the pharmacy is transferred to another owner, an inventory of the controlled substances must be taken on the day the drugs are moved, either before the day's shift has started, or at the end of the day. Schedule II drugs will require completion of a DEA Form 222 (or the electronic CSOS equivalent) when the drugs are changing location. The transfer of schedules III – V drugs must be documented in writing to show the drug name, dosage form, strength, quantity, transfer date, and the names, addresses, and DEA registration numbers of the parties involved in the transfer.

In my state, pharmacy closures must be reported to the state board within this number of days:

_____

INSPECTION OF A PHARMACY

State boards hire pharmacists (and in some states, non-pharmacists) to inspect pharmacies and make sure that the store is in accordance with federal and state laws and regulations. The list of the items inspected is long, and includes everything from recordkeeping requirements in accordance with the controlled substances act to the temperature of the refrigeration units. The pharmacy will be subject to minor or major infractions if the requirements are not met. Most states provide self assessment (or "self-inspection") forms for the pharmacist-in-charge to use to identify deficiencies and correct them, preferably prior to an announced or unannounced inspection. The completion of these forms may be required on a scheduled basis. The self-assessment/self-inspection form is useful for MPJE preparation since these forms include the items that the state board feels is important. There may be separate forms for the outpatient community pharmacy setting, inpatient setting and forms for pharmacies involved with sterile compounding.

The name of the inspection or assessment form/s used by the pharmacists in my state:

_____

If the form must be completed on a scheduled basis, list the time period: _____

Who is responsible for completing this form? _____

Is the form sent into the board or kept at the pharmacy? _____

How long must the pharmacy keep the form? _____

DRUG SUPPLY CHAIN INTEGRITY

The FDA requires that manufacturers, repackagers and pharmacies that are registered with the FDA as outsourcing facilities to follow <u>Current Good Manufacturing Practice</u> (CGMP) requirements. CGMPs are designed to ensure drug identity, strength, quality and purity. Examples of CGMPs include the requirement to use only quality raw materials and reliable testing procedures.

Prescription drugs must be purchased only from licensed drug distributors. The license must be current in each state/s in which the wholesaler operates.

There is an increasing prevalence of counterfeit, misbranded, adulterated, and diverted prescription drugs showing up in the United States. To prevent these drugs from entering the legitimate drug supply, the Drug Supply Chain Security Act was passed in 2013, which outlines steps to build a system to <u>track and trace</u> drugs as they are distributed within the United States.[15] This requirement applies to most <u>prescription</u> drugs intended for <u>human</u> use.

Pharmacies must be able to capture and maintain <u>transaction information</u> (TI), <u>transaction history</u> (TH), and a <u>transaction statement</u> (TS), in paper or electronic form, for each drug product received for <u>six years</u> from the date of the transaction. There are some situations that are exempt from this requirement, including: dispensing drugs to a patient, providing drugs to a practitioner for office use, and distributing samples.

SPACE AND EQUIPMENT

A facility that stores and distributes prescription drugs should be in accordance with the standards set by USP, which include requirements on the facility size, construction and storage space. There must be a separate (quarantined) storage area for counterfeit/adulterated/expired drugs. The space must be maintained in a clean and orderly condition, be free from rodent and vermin infestation, be in a commercial location, have restricted access, and include inventory controls to identify theft and diversion. Individual state boards of pharmacies can mandate requirements for additional specifications.[16]

If sterile medications are prepared, they must be prepared in a laminar flow hood and/or biological safety cabinet. Other equipment which may be required include a dose calibrator, an analytical balance, a lead-shielded drawing station (if involved with radiopharmaceuticals), assorted glassware, a microscope, a thermometer, refrigeration equipment, syringes, decontamination supplies, transport and packing material, and any other required supplies. Instruments must be calibrated at scheduled times and documentation on the calibration history should be available in the pharmacy.

The self assessment/inspection form may include space requirements that are specified by the state.

List any state-specific pharmacy space requirements: _____

---

15   https://www.fda.gov/Drugs/DrugSafety/DrugIntegrityandSupplyChainSecurity/DrugSupplyChainSecurityAct/ (accessed 2019 Jan 15).
16   USP Chapter 1079

TEMPORARY ABSENCE OF THE PHARMACIST

Fatigue resulting from continuous physical and mental activity can cause lapses in attention and lead to dispensing errors. Breaks are challenging when there is one pharmacist on duty; without a pharmacist present, dispensing new prescriptions and provided counseling is generally prohibited. Several of the states specify additional restrictions if one pharmacist is on duty alone.

STATE	RESTRICTIONS FOR TEMPORARY ABSENCE OF PHARMACIST
Alabama, California	If one pharmacist: may leave pharmacy open if controlled substances are secured. Only refills can be provided to patients (if they have been visibly checked by the pharmacist) and only if counseling is not required. Break is limited to 30 minutes if store will be without a pharmacist. The pharmacist can leave the store during the break. Technicians and interns can continue to work, and the pharmacist will check the work upon return. P&P required.
Arizona	Pharmacy personnel are allowed to 'close and secure' a pharmacy for a maximum of thirty minutes at mid-shift. Signs must be posted and phones should be programmed to advise that the pharmacy is closed and the time the pharmacy will reopen. 'Shut-downs' should be consistent to minimize confusion within the public and professional community
D.C.	If one pharmacist, the pharmacy must close during meal times and breaks.
Florida	Break is limited to 30 minutes if store will be without a pharmacist. If a sign is posted that the pharmacy is open at that time the pharmacist must remain on the premises and be available to counsel. If patient requests counseling and the pharmacist is not available, the pharmacist should contact the patient at the earliest possible time. Technicians can continue to work if the pharmacist remains on the premises and is available to respond to questions. The pharmacist will check the work upon return.
Georgia	The pharmacist can be absent a maximum of three hours daily, or up to one and a half hours at any one time. If the pharmacist is absent for less than five minutes, it is not considered an "absence". If a pharmacist is absence, the pharmacy shall be closed and locked, and a sign must be displayed that says "Pharmacy Department Closed" in letters at least 3" high.
Illinois	A single pharmacist working at least 7 hours may take two 15-minute break and one 30-minute meal period, in which a pharmacist is not required to work. If a pharmacist does not receive the required breaks, they will be paid 3 times the pharmacist's regular hourly rate of pay for each day that regular breaks are not provided. Pharmacists are limited to work no more than 8 hours for each workday. A clean and comfortable room shall be made available on the premises for pharmacists to enjoy their break, and an accurate record of break periods will be kept.
Iowa	A temporary absence of a pharmacist-in-charge is any time less than two hours. Only the PIC can designate pharmacy technicians or interns to perform technical or non-technical duties. The pharmacy must be secured, and the public must be notified of the temporary absence. No prescriptions may be dispensed until the pharmacist has returned. At the discretion of the pharmacist, during a break when the pharmacist is absent, a technician may be designated to dispense previously verified prescriptions that do not require counsel.
Louisiana	A single pharmacist can leave the pharmacy for a break and leave the pharmacy operating if at least one certified pharmacy technician or pharmacy intern remains present, the pharmacist is available for emergencies and the break does not exceed 30 minutes and for a total of 60 minutes in 12 hours. New prescriptions cannot be dispensed without the final pharmacist's check. A notice should be posted that states the pharmacist is on a break and the time the pharmacist will return. If the pharmacist does not find it acceptable to leave the pharmacy open and closes the pharmacy, a sign should be posted that the pharmacy is closed. An absence of less than 5 minutes (e.g., to use the restroom) does not apply, and no sign is needed.
Massachusetts	If one pharmacist: can leave pharmacy open if controlled substances are secured. Only refills can be provided to patients (if they have been visibly checked by the pharmacist) and only if counseling is not required. Break is limited to 30 minutes if store will be without a pharmacist. The pharmacist can leave the store during the break. Technicians can continue to work, and the pharmacist will check the work upon return. The pharmacy manager can develop a P&P to permit PTCB and/or board-certified technicians and interns to receive telephone prescriptions.

STATE	RESTRICTIONS FOR TEMPORARY ABSENCE OF PHARMACIST
Minnesota	If a single pharmacist is on break, the pharmacy may close, but it is not required. If the pharmacy remains open, the pharmacist must remain on the premises of the pharmacy, in case of emergencies. Pharmacists working longer than six hours per day are allowed a 30-minute uninterrupted break. Only prescriptions that have been certified by the pharmacist may be dispensed while the pharmacist is on a break. New or refill prescriptions that require counseling can only be dispensed when a pharmacist is on break if: the patient is told that the pharmacist is on a break and is offered the chance to wait until the pharmacist returns from break in order to receive counseling; a patient is offered a phone number to call if they decline to wait; after returning from a break the pharmacist should make a reasonable effort to contact any patients for counseling; and the pharmacist documents what counsel has been provided or why counsel was not provided with details on efforts to provide counseling. The pharmacy must also develop a list of drugs that may not be dispensed while a pharmacist is taking an allowed break without the patient receiving counsel. If there are two or more pharmacists, the pharmacists will stagger breaks, so that one pharmacist remains on duty at all times.
Mississippi	Periodic breaks are permitted to "relieve fatigue and mental and physical stress".
Montana	If one pharmacist: can leave pharmacy open if controlled substances are secured. Only refills can be provided to patients if they have been visibly checked by the pharmacist, and if counseling is not required. A sign displaying the scheduled break time/s must be prominently posted. Break is limited to 30 minutes. The pharmacist must remain on site during the break. Support personnel can continue to work. If more than one pharmacist is on the shift the breaks must be staggered. P&P required.
Nevada	If only a single pharmacist is on duty, the pharmacist may choose to remain on the premises or leave. If the pharmacist remains on the premises, they may not be interrupted or disturbed, unless the pharmacist agrees to such interruptions. If the pharmacist leaves the premises, they must close and secure the pharmacy, and post a visible sign for the public which states a time the pharmacist will return. Prescriptions may only be accepted while the pharmacist is on a break if the prescription is placed in a secure container or receptacle that ensures the prescription cannot be seen, if an authorized pharmacy employee accepts and secures the prescription outside the closed and secure premises of the pharmacy. The pharmacy may schedule a regular time during which a pharmacist may take a meal period.
New Hampshire	A single pharmacist may take a 30-minute rest break without closing the pharmacy, and pharmacy technicians, NH certified pharmacy technicians and pharmacy interns who have been authorized by the pharmacist may remain in the pharmacy, if the pharmacist reasonably believes that the prescription drugs will remain secure during the pharmacist's absence. Only pharmacy technicians and pharmacy interns authorized by the pharmacist on duty may continue to perform non-discretionary duties, but all duties shall be reviewed by the pharmacists upon returning from a rest break. While the pharmacist is on break, there shall be no dispensing or sale of new prescriptions, and counseling cannot be provided by pharmacy technicians and pharmacy interns. New written prescriptions presented in person can be accepted and processed by the pharmacy technician or intern, except for the final check, during the absence of a pharmacist. No new prescriptions can be dispensed or sold until the pharmacist is able to complete the final check. New prescriptions via telephone can be accepted by a NH certified pharmacy technician or intern, or when authorized by the pharmacist, the caller can either call back or leave a number at which they can be contacted. Refill prescriptions that have been previously filled and checked by the pharmacist may be picked up and the sale can proceed as normal. If the patient has questions, they shall be asked to wait for the pharmacist to return, or asked to leave a phone number for the pharmacist to reach them at a later time. Both telephone refill orders and in-person refill orders can be processed by a pharmacy technician or intern, but cannot be dispensed or sold until the pharmacist has completed a final check. Rest breaks should be scheduled as close to the same time each day, so that patients can become familiar. The pharmacist must remain on the premises during the rest break and be available for emergencies. A sign shall be posted in full view of patients whenever the pharmacist temporarily leaves the prescription department for a rest break with the time that the pharmacist will return. Pharmacists remain responsible for the operation and security of the pharmacy while taking a rest break; therefore, the pharmacist may close the pharmacy for security, or other reasons, during their absence. All pharmacy technicians, NH certified pharmacy technicians and interns shall leave the pharmacy if the pharmacist closes the pharmacy. A sign shall be posted in full view of the public with information on the pharmacists return.

STATE	RESTRICTIONS FOR TEMPORARY ABSENCE OF PHARMACIST
New Jersey	Break is limited to 30 minutes for a meal, and additional "restroom" breaks. The pharmacist must remain on site during the break. A sign must be posted that the pharmacist is on break but is available for emergencies and counseling. Support personnel can continue to work.
North Carolina	A pharmacist cannot work longer than a 12-hour shift per day. If working 6 continuous hours, a 30-minute and a 15-minute break must be provided.
Oregon	There must be appropriate opportunities for uninterrupted rest periods and meal breaks.
Pennsylvania	A single pharmacist may take a 30-minute break while the pharmacy remains open if the pharmacist remains on the premises and is accessible for emergencies. The pharmacy may continue to accept new written prescriptions, prepare prescriptions to be reviewed by the pharmacist before dispensing, and deliver medications that have already been prepared and verified by the pharmacist.
South Carolina	If a facility allows, pharmacists may take a 30-minute meal break only if the following condition are met: pharmacists must stay on the premises and attempt to schedule their break at the same time every day; pharmacist must be available for emergencies; a sign must be posted notifying the public. Pharmacy technicians may perform the following duties while a pharmacist is on a break: prepare prescriptions which must be checked by the pharmacist upon return from a break; dispense prescriptions to patients that have already been prepared and verified by the pharmacist; receive and prepare prescriptions, which must be checked by the pharmacist. All prescriptions must be checked by the pharmacist before being dispensed to the patient. If a patient requests counsel, the pharmacist must call the patient within a reasonable timeframe to review any counseling.
Tennessee	There can be one absence of a pharmacist for a max of 1 hour/day. A sign with "Pharmacist not on duty" must be posted. No medication can be dispensed. The prescription area must be closed off by a floor to ceiling barrier.
Texas	A single pharmacist may leave the prescription department for short periods of time without closing the prescription department and removing all personnel if all of these conditions are met: one pharmacy technician remains in the prescription department; the pharmacist remains on-site and is immediately available; the pharmacist reasonably believes the prescription department will remain secure during their absence; a notice is posted that declares the pharmacist is on break and the time the pharmacist will return. Pharmacy technicians may begin processing prescription drug orders or refills brought in during the pharmacist's absence, but may not deliver any prescription drug orders or refills until the pharmacist verifies the prescription. While the pharmacist is absent, only a pharmacy technician who has completed the pharmacy training program may complete the following tasks, provided a pharmacy verifies the accuracy prior to delivery of the prescription: initiating and receiving refill authorization requests; entering prescription data into a data processing system; taking a stock bottle from the shelf for a prescription; preparing and packaging prescription drug orders; affixing prescription labels and auxiliary labels to the prescription container; prepackaging and labeling prepackaged drugs. Once the pharmacist has returned to the prescription department, they shall conduct a drug regimen review, and verify the accuracy of all acts, tasks, and functions performed by the pharmacy technicians. A previously verified drug prescription can be delivered by an agent of the pharmacist if a record of delivery is maintained containing the following: date of the delivery; unique identification number of the prescription drug order; patient's name; patient's phone number or the phone number of the person picking up the prescription; and signature of the person picking up the prescription. When a pharmacist is absent, a pharmacist intern shall be considered a pharmacy technician. If there are two or more Pharmacists on duty, the pharmacists shall stagger their breaks so that there is always one pharmacist on duty.
Vermont	If one pharmacist: can leave pharmacy open if controlled substances are secured. A break is required if shift is more than 8 hours. The break time should be consistent and for a maximum of 30 minutes. Only refills can be provided to patients, if they have been visibly checked by the pharmacist, and only if counseling is not required. During the break, refills (but not new prescriptions) can be taken over the phone. Written prescriptions can be taken. A sign displaying the break time/s must be posted. The pharmacist must remain on site during the break. If more than one pharmacist is on the shift, the breaks must be staggered. P&P required.
Virginia	A pharmacist cannot be required to work longer than 12 continuous hours in any work day and shall be allowed at least six hours of off-time between consecutive shifts. Any pharmacist that work longer than six hours is allowed to take a 30-minute break.

STATE	RESTRICTIONS FOR TEMPORARY ABSENCE OF PHARMACIST
Washington	If a pharmacist is absent, the pharmacy must be closed and access limited to persons authorized by the pharmacist. Written prescription orders and refill requests must be deposited into a mail slot or drop box if the pharmacist is absent.
West Virginia	A single pharmacist may take a thirty minute break during any contiguous eight hour shift. The pharmacist may leave the pharmacy area, but may not leave the building. During a pharmacist's break, a pharmacy technician may continue to prepare prescriptions; however, prescriptions cannot be delivered until verified by the pharmacist, and if required, counseling has been provided. If a pharmacy permits indirect supervision of a pharmacy technician during a pharmacist's break, there should be either an interactive voice response system or voice mail system installed on the pharmacy phone line to receive new prescription orders and refill authorizations. In the event of an emergency, protocols shall be established for when a pharmacy technician should interrupt a pharmacist's break

Permissible pharmacist breaks and maximum durations in my state:_____

_____

Must a sign be posted that the pharmacist is not on duty? Yes / No

Activities that are restricted during the absence of a pharmacist: _____

_____

ADVERTISING AND SIGNAGE

The state board may have requirements and restrictions on advertising and signage. Some pharmacies advertise prescription drug prices to the public, such as a $4 or $10 generic drug list. This is allowed by the FDA and is considered to be "reminder advertising." Some state boards may require pharmacies to post a public notice to alert patients about the pharmacy's business hours, when a pharmacist on duty is temporarily away, the right to counseling, or the availability of interpreter services for patients with limited English proficiency.

Signage indicating radiation is present due to the presence of radiopharmaceuticals.

NABP recommends that three items be displayed in the pharmacy, which may have been adopted by your state:

- If the pharmacy is involved with radiopharmaceuticals, radiation caution signs should be posted throughout the restricted area.

- Biohazard caution signs should be properly used and posted throughout the appropriate area/s.

- Appropriate notices to employees are posted.

List if your state has advertising limitations or signage requirements. _____

_____

_____

PHARMACY SECURITY

All pharmacists on duty are responsible for the security of the pharmacy, including effective control against theft and diversion. The space must be secured by a physical and/or electronic barrier which can be locked and, preferably, be able to identify entry at all times. Access to non-pharmacy personnel should be kept to a minimum and any entry of non-pharmacy staff will be at the discretion of the pharmacist. Security systems should include protection against outside and inside theft, including theft of electronic information and patient records. Safe practices to reduce risk and respond safely during a robbery are discussed in the pharmacy practice section.

To maintain the security and confidentiality of patient records, the computer system must have safeguards for entry. The system must be backed up and the prescription order information should be available quickly; the NABP recommends a 2-hour time period to retrieve back-up prescription data. An auxiliary system must be used to store refill information. When the computer system has been down (i.e., not operable) and comes back up and operable, all prescription information that has been manually recorded during this time should be entered promptly.[17] In the event that the prescription information is permanently lost, the board of pharmacy should be notified.

POLICIES AND PROCEDURES

The majority of states require every pharmacy to have a current policy and procedures (P&P) manual. A policy is a course of action for a specific activity and the procedure (written into the policy) includes the steps involved that must be carried out by the staff. It's a "what to do" for the various expected and unexpected events that occur in a pharmacy. P&Ps help keep the pharmacy running efficiently. The manual can protect the pharmacy in case of litigation and may be required for state or insurance company reimbursement.

Select states will require pharmacists to prepare P&Ps for all pharmacy operations and others identify the types of P&Ps required. All P&Ps must conform to federal and state laws and regulations.

LIBRARIES

A pharmacist should keep a current copy of the state laws and regulations, USP reference chapters, reference texts specific to the type of work performed (for example, radiopharmaceutical reference sources if involved in nuclear pharmacy), and current drug information resources. Every state permits the use of electronic reference materials, with a few state-specific requirements.[18]

---

17   The NABP, in the Model Act, recommends that all information recorded manually during a lapse in the computer system should be entered within 96 hours from the time the system is back up and operable.

18   South Dakota permits maintaining reference materials as print or electronic. Maryland permits electronic resources to be used as supplements to the printed versions, and only if the site is created by a reputable medical publisher that is recognized as a standard for that type of information. Massachusetts permits electronic resources if they are updated at least quarterly. Guam and South Carolina do not address the issue of electronic reference sources.

DISPLAY OF LICENSES

All facilities must publicly display or have readily available all licenses of the licensed personnel.

Does your state require licenses to be displayed in public view? Yes / No

DRUG STORAGE IN A PHARMACY SETTING

CONTROLLED SUBSTANCE STORAGE

The DEA requires that controlled substances be kept in a securely <u>locked cabinet</u> of "substantial construction". This means that the cabinet should not be easy to break apart in order to access the contents. Another option that is acceptable is to partially conceal the controlled drugs by <u>dispersing them throughout the stock of non-controlled drugs</u>. For example, Ambien could be placed on the shelf in alphabetical order with the other drugs beginning with the letter A.

INVESTIGATIONAL NEW DRUG STORAGE

Investigational drugs must be stored in a location that has limited access and in accordance with instructions from the supplier, including any required storage conditions. This means that the drugs must be "quarantined" (separated) from other drug stock. Documentation should be maintained for each transport, handling and receipt of the study drugs. Any breach in practice must be reported to the investigator.

REPACKAGED AND RESOLD DRUG STORAGE

The FDA defines repackaging as the "act of taking a finished drug product from the container in which it was distributed by the original manufacturer and placing it into a different container without further manipulation of the drug". Pharmacies repackage drugs in both hospital and community settings in order to meet the needs for unit-dose dispensing, to prepare smaller doses of medications that are not commercially available, and to repackage a large container into smaller sizes for dispensing purposes. On occasion, a pharmacy may repackage smaller containers into larger containers to manage a shortage.

If the drug being repackaged is an FDA-approved drug, the repackaged drug is assigned a beyond use date (BUD) that will be in accordance with the dates provided in the USP guidance. These are discussed in the pharmacy practice section. If the expiration date on the original (larger) container that was repackaged is a shorter time period than the BUD recommendation in the USP, the shorter time period from the original container must be used.

DRUG RECALLS

The actions on getting the recalled drug back should correlate with the severity of the recall. If the recall involved specific batches or lot numbers, the pharmacist will need to have the stock checked and pull the recalled drug. It is often the person responsible for drug purchases that identifies the lots involved and the locations of the recalled drug.

Pharmacies must be positioned to received notification of recalls from multiple sources, which includes the FDA, federal, state or local law enforcement, and manufacturers or repackagers. If there are multiple locations in a central facility, the pharmacists involved with the recall will need to identify where the drug is located, and <u>remove it from all patient care areas and storage locations</u>, including in ADCs. If patients have received the drug, it may be necessary to send urgent mailings with the envelope stamped "drug recall" and marked "urgent" in bold red letters. If the drug has been taken by the patient, the prescriber will be involved with any corrective action. The pharmacy staff may be asked to identify alternative treatments.

When the recalled drug is returned to the pharmacy, it is quarantined (separated) from other drugs prior to being returned or destroyed. Drugs that are quarantined for any reason (recalls, adulteration, expiration) must be labeled appropriately and placed in separate containers. Otherwise, they may be sent to the wrong location, or accidentally dispensed.

A P&P describing the procedure for managing drug recalls is required and will include providing written documentation on the disposition of the drugs. The documentation must be kept for the state's required period, which will be 2 or more years.

Recalls are carried out by the manufacturer. Recalls may be initiated by FDA request, by an FDA order under statutory authority or at the company's own initiative.

CLASS	DESCRIPTION
Class I Recall	A situation in which there is a reasonable probability that the use or exposure will cause serious adverse health consequences or death. For example, a morphine tablet manufactured with ten times the amount of active ingredient.
Class II Recall	A situation in which use or exposure can cause temporary or reversible adverse health consequences or where the probability of harm is remote. For example, ketorolac injections have been recalled in 2010 and 2015 due to the possibility of particles in the vials.
Class III Recall	A situation in which use of or exposure is not likely to cause adverse health consequences. For example, the coloring on tablets may have been applied inconsistently.

EXPIRED (OUTDATED) DRUGS

Expiration dates are estimated in a conservative manner using FDA-mandated stability testing. The manufacturer will not make recommendations regarding product use beyond the expiration date, based on legal and liability concerns, and pharmacies must follow the same procedure because the FDCA prohibits the sale of expired prescription and non-prescription drugs.

Expiration date requirements extend to donated drugs provided to charities or non-profit medical clinics, and to drug samples. It is not acceptable to dispense or send out any expired drugs, even if they are provided at no cost. If drugs are provided to charitable or non-profit organizations, the charity or non-profit must agree to send to disposal or return any drugs that become expired while in their possession. Drugs that have become expired must be quarantined from the rest of the drug stock in labeled containers prior to return or disposal.

DRUG SAMPLES

Retail pharmacies cannot receive drug samples.

DRUG DELIVERY

DRUG DELIVERY THROUGH THE MAIL OR BY A PHARMACY EMPLOYEE

There are few limitations imposed by states on drug delivery services besides the need to provide a toll-free phone number (with stated hours) for the patient or their agent to use if they wish to receive counseling or have drug-related questions. Patients on chronic medications who make multiple trips to the community pharmacy may find home delivery more convenient, especially when the patient has difficulty with movement or transportation.

It is permissible according to federal law to mail scheduled and non-scheduled drugs; the outer packaging cannot indicate the contents.

There are several large companies that deliver medication through the mail in many states, such as *Express Scripts*. There are smaller companies that work with different insurance plans to deliver medications in daily or weekly dose packs for patients that need help with adherence, which is discussed further.

Under federal law, it is acceptable to deliver controlled substances through the U.S. Postal Service (USPS). Federal law does not address other common carriers, such as FedEx. There are no restrictions on the use of common carriers stated under federal law. The carrier, in some cases, may have set their own limitations.

When sending drugs by mail delivery, the <u>outside</u> packaging <u>should not contain any identifiable marks</u> that could be used to indicate the contents. The <u>inner labeling</u> must have the <u>required information</u> in accordance with federal and state labeling requirements. The restrictions for safe packaging imposed by the Poison Prevention Packaging Act apply to the containers inside the package.

If a pharmacy employee has attempted delivery to a patient's work or residence and the patient refused delivery or the employee was not able to find the location, the drug can be returned to stock if it has not left the control of the pharmacy, which means that the contents must have remained in the manufacturer's original, sealed, and tamper-evident bulk, unit-of-use, or unit-dose packaging or the dispensing pharmacy's original packaging, and was returned to the pharmacy within the same day as the unsuccessful delivery attempt.

If your state has set limitations on medication delivery (by couriers, pharmacy employees, or by kiosk dispensing) list the limitations here: _____

_____

VACUUM TUBES

Vacuum or pneumatic tubes are used for drug delivery in many hospitals. Tube delivery systems vary in the shape and size of the tube and in the transport force and speed. In any setting, limitations on the use of vacuum tubes for this purpose can be due to hazards created by the drug itself or drug decomposition that can occur during the delivery process. Drugs that are not safe to deliver by tube at any time include:

Preparing pneumatic tubes used for drug delivery.

- Hazardous compounds, including chemotherapy.

- Combustible products, including some gels and sprays.

- Protein products, which can become damaged from agitation (such as insulin and immunoglobulins).

Each facility will need to develop guidelines in a P&P that will include a list of drugs that should not be delivered by this method. If a specific drug is not mentioned, and there is a lack of guidance on whether a drug can be delivered safely by this method, it will be left to the pharmacist's judgment to decide whether the tube delivery is acceptable. If there is doubt for a particular drug, the tube delivery should not be used.

DRIVE-UP WINDOWS

Pharmacies with drive-up (also known as drive-through) windows are convenient for patients to pick up medications. However, there are limitations with dispensing drugs through a window, including difficulty providing confidential counseling, the inability to open a container to discuss the contents, and the inability to provide a demonstration of the use of non-oral medications, such as inhalers.

A pharmacist assisting a patient at a drive-up window.

The window imposes a barrier to the pharmacist's ability to assess the patient for "red flags" of drug diversion. A few state boards have issued limitations on the use of drive-up windows. For example, Delaware permits schedule II prescriptions to be dropped off at a drive-up window, but requires the filled prescription to be picked up inside the pharmacy.

If your state has issued limitations on drive-up windows list them here: _____

_____

QUALITY ASSURANCE AND MEDICATION ERROR REPORTING

The most common error made by pharmacists is giving the <u>wrong drug to a patient</u>. Most boards of pharmacy require pharmacies to maintain a Continuous Quality Improvement (CQI) program. When medication error occurs, an investigation (called a <u>root cause analysis</u>) should be performed.

The CQI program should include:

- Designated individuals responsible for the program, including implementation, maintenance and monitoring.

- A set time frame under which the CQI is initiated after the medication error has occurred. NABP recommends that the investigation be initiated within 3 days and individual state boards may have a more stringent requirement of 1 or 2 days.

- Formulation of a plan to amend the pharmacy system and workflow to avoid a repeat of the same or similar type of medication error, based on the data provided by the CQI.

- Any required changes in the pharmacy systems and workflow processes.

- Education to the staff, performed on a continual basis, on safe practices. Lessons learned from the CQI must be passed on to the rest of the pharmacy team.

NABP recommends that each pharmacy conduct a self-audit at least quarterly to determine if medication errors have decreased and a survey of the customers (or a sampling of the customers) at least annually to help determine patient perception of the pharmacy's quality.

NOTIFICATION OF POTENTIAL TERRORIST EVENTS

Pharmacists were involved in New York City in the management of patients injured or exposed to chemicals in the wake of the September, 2001 attacks. Since that time, the American Pharmacists Association (APhA) has developed recommendations for pharmacists to respond in the case of a terrorist event. This includes developing an alert system to notify staff and patients of such an event, plans to move affected persons to safety and to notify pharmacists who may be involved as first responders or as members of medical teams. Pharmacies may have to relocate temporarily or may need to supply medication to patients who are not their usual customers, but are unable to enter or reach their originating pharmacy. The pharmacy's terrorist attack response plan should be included in the P&P manual. Emergency dispensing requirements are described further.

Disease outbreaks could be possibly related to bioterrorism. All 50 states and Washington, D.C., can send reports to the National Electronic Disease Surveillance System (NNDSS).[19] This system connects healthcare facilities to public health departments and those health departments to the Centers for Disease Control and Prevention (CDC). NNDSS is used to monitor, control, and prevent disease.

REPORTING PHYSICAL ABUSE

Pharmacists are mandatory reporters of child abuse and neglect.[20] Mandatory reporters have regular contact with vulnerable people such as children, disabled persons, and senior citizens, and are therefore legally required to report suspected or observed abuse to an appropriate agency, such as social services, law enforcement, or the state's toll-free reporting hotline. Reports provided to the hotline may be made anonymously. A report should be made when the pharmacist, acting in his or her official capacity, suspects or has reason to believe that a child is a victim of abuse or neglect.

Many individual states have enacted legislation to require mandatory reporting of suspected elder abuse as well.

TREATMENT FOR TUBERCULOSIS

The World Health Organization has declared tuberculosis (TB) a global health emergency. About 10% of latent infections progress to active disease which, if left untreated, kills about half of those infected. The longer it goes without treatment or if medications are not taken as prescribed, the more difficult it is to treat, and the more deadly it becomes.

Many states require healthcare providers to report suspected or confirmed cases of TB to a designated authority (i.e., the state's public health department). The CDC recommends that the report should be made within 24 hours. Some states require healthcare providers to report patients who are noncompliant with their TB regimen.[21]

---

19   https://wwwwn.cdc.gov/nndss/ (accessed 2018 Jan 25).
20   42 U.S.C. § 13031
21   https://www.cdc.gov/tb/programs/laws/menu/caseid.htm (accessed 2018 Jan 25).

Treatment of active disease is long-term (6 months to 2 years, depending on the level of resistance), which can result in adverse consequences, including hepatic and ocular damage. The adverse effect of neuropathy from isoniazid use can be alleviated with pyridoxine (vitamin B6). There is a high risk of drug interactions due to the strong inducing effect of the common agent rifampin, and more modest interactions with other drugs in the regimen. TB drugs have to be taken in a consistent manner (such as without food, daily, or 2-3 times weekly) in order to be effective. The pill burden is high, which makes adherence challenging. Yet, adherence is essential due to multidrug resistance and the health consequences from inadequate treatment.

In select pharmacies, the pharmacists participate in directly observed treatment (DOT) in which patients come to the pharmacy two or three times weekly to take their medication in front of the pharmacist. The patient may be encouraged to attend with an incentive, such as a small amount of money. In Indiana, a successful DOT program resulted in a decline in the rate of TB and reduced the incidence of drug resistant cases. DOT is now the standard of care for tuberculosis

Directly observed therapy (DOT)

treatment in the state. Pharmacies are located in the community and provide an ideal location for DOT administration. Several states with high disease incidence currently have pharmacists participating in observing DOT.

FOUR

PHARMACY
PRACTICE

CHAPTER CONTENTS

Fundamental Responsibilities of the Pharmacy Staff..**64**

The Pharmacist 64

Collaborative Practice Agreement 65

The Pharmacist-in-Charge 65

The Pharmacist Intern 66

The Pharmacy Technician...67

The Pharmacy Clerk 68

Requirements for Valid Prescriptions **68**

Written, Oral, Electronic, and Faxed Prescriptions 68

Healthcare Providers Authorized to Prescribe Medications 69

Valid Prescriber/Patient Relationship 69

Self Prescribing and Prescribing for Family Members...69

Prescriptions from Retired or Deceased Prescribers...70

Prescriptions from Other States or Territories 70

Prescriptions from Foreign Countries..71

Off-Label Promotion by Manufacturers 71

Off-Label Prescribing..71

Correcting Errors and Omissions on Prescriptions....................................**71**

Prescription Refills...**72**

Emergency Refills without the Prescriber's Authorization.......................**72**

Prescription Transfers...**73**

Information Required on Multiple Unit (Multiple Dose) Prescription Labels **74**

Formatting Standards for Multiple Unit (Multiple Dose) Prescription Labels **74**

Expiration Dates versus Beyond Use Dates..**76**

Child-Resistant Packaging **76**

Drugs That Require C-R Packaging...77

Drugs That Do Not Require C-R Packaging...77

Single Dose (Unit-Dose) Prescription Labels..**79**

Unit Dose Beyond Use Date...**80**

Customized Patient Packaging for Adherence...**80**

Drug Utilization Reviews....................................82

Written Material that is Included as Part of the Package Labeling 84

   Consumer Medication Information....................84

   Patient Package Inserts....................................84

   Medication Guides 84

   Risk Evaluation and Mitigation Strategy 85

   Examples of REMS Requirements 86

Patient Identification Prior to Dispensing or Administering Prescription Drugs 86

Patient Counseling...87

   Counseling Face-to-Face...................................87

   Counseling When the Patient is Not Present....88

   Counseling the Limited-English Proficient Patient 88

   Exemptions for Patient Counseling....................88

   Counseling Requirements by State 89

Health Insurance Portability and Accountability Act 90

   The Notice of Privacy Practices.........................92

Drug Substitution or Selection..........................93

   Generic Drug Substitution.................................93

   Using the Orange Book......................................93

   Narrow Therapeutic Index Drug Substitution...94

   Biologics and Biosimilars...................................95

   Pharmacy & Therapeutics Committee..............95

   Drug Formularies...95

   Therapeutic Interchange 96

Pharmacy Compounding....................................97

   Traditional Compounding and Section 503A....97

   Outsourcing Facilities and Section 503B 98

   Compounding Versus Manufacturing................98

   Non-Sterile Compounding.................................99

   Sterile Compounding 99

   Master Formulation Record 100

   The Compounding Record or Log Book 100

   Compounded Product Labels 101

   Staff Training Requirements for Compounding 101

   Beyond Use Dating and Expiration Dates for Compounded Products....................................101

   Handling Hazardous Drugs 102

Dispensing Under Special Circumstances......103

   Conscience or Moral Clauses...........................103

   Requirements for Death with Dignity 103

   Medication Provisions During Declaration of Disaster or Emergency....................................104

   Telepharmacy 105

Vaccine Administration....................................105

Return, Disposal, or Reuse of Medications....106

   Returning or Disposing Prescription Medication to the Supplier 106

   Returns from the Pharmacy Will Call (Pick Up) Area 106

   Charitable Programs 107

   Drug Donations to Cancer or Other Repository Programs 107

   Patients Returning Previously Dispensed Medications to the Pharmacy 107

   Disposal of Prescription Medication by the Ultimate User 108

Manufacturer Drug Samples Given to Prescribers to Provide to Patients..................109

Resale of Discounted Prescription Drugs.......109

Prescription Medication Loss or Theft 110

Recordkeeping of Prescription Medication ...111

Maintaining Pedigrees to Ensure the Quality of Drugs..111

FOUR | PHARMACY
PRACTICE

This section reviews federal law for dispensing prescriptions and primarily covers non-controlled substances. The laws and regulations for controlled substances are more stringent and are reviewed in the next section.

FUNDAMENTAL RESPONSIBILITIES OF THE PHARMACY STAFF

THE PHARMACIST

The pharmacist is responsible for supervising the daily operations of the pharmacy to ensure that all activities in the pharmacy are performed safely, in compliance with the law, and without risk of harm to patients.

The traditional role of a pharmacist is the safe and proper dispensing of medications. When a pharmacist signs off on a prescription container or an IV bag, the pharmacist is confirming that the dispensed medication matches the prescription and the safety risks have been evaluated, including allergies, contraindications and warnings, adverse events, and drug interactions. For compounded preparations, the quality of the product is the legal responsibility of the pharmacist, not the technician who prepared the product, since the pharmacist is responsible for supervising the staff. The pharmacist's designation on the compounded product indicates that the pharmacist has verified that the compounded product was made correctly. The technician can still face consequences for careless work or legal action if any illegal activities (such as theft) have taken place.

Pharmacists have the discretion to decide on the best course of action for a patient, based on his or her professional judgment. This includes decisions on whether to fill a prescription when the prescriber cannot be reached, or whether a prescription should be filled at all.

Provider status for pharmacists had been approved on a state-by-state basis. This status enables pharmacists to receive compensation for the clinical services they provide.

My state permits pharmacists to perform clinical activities, which include: _____

_____

To perform clinical requirements these conditions should be met: _____

_____

My state has an advanced practice pharmacist designation. Yes / No

If yes, list the requirements for this designation and the tasks permitted: _____

_____

_____

COLLABORATIVE PRACTICE AGREEMENT

A <u>collaborative practice agreement</u> (CPA) is a formal relationship between a pharmacist and another healthcare provider or provider group, in which the healthcare provider makes a diagnosis, supervises the patient care, and refers patients to the pharmacist to manage drug therapy, which is a form of prescriptive authority. A CPA can be called a <u>collaborative drug therapy management</u> (CDTM). The CPA can allow the pharmacist to <u>initiate, modify, and/or monitor drug therapy</u>. Nearly all states permit some type of pharmacist prescriptive authority, whether in a CPA, with provider status (see above) or directly for select medications.

My state allows pharmacists to enter into a CPA. Yes / No

My state requires the CPA to be submitted to the board of pharmacy. Yes / No

My state requires the CPA to be renewed within this time period: _____

My state allows pharmacists in a CPA to manage the following disease states: _____

_____

My state allows the pharmacists to perform the following actions under a CPA (e.g., initiate, modify, monitor medications):_____

_____

THE PHARMACIST-IN-CHARGE

A pharmacy must have a pharmacist-in-charge (PIC) that is responsible for the daily operations of the pharmacy. The state board considers the PIC to be the primary person responsible for legal operation of the pharmacy, and will turn to the PIC in the event of a pharmacy inspection. The daily responsibilities for staff pharmacists and the PIC can overlap, but the PIC has the final responsibility. The PIC needs to ensure that the pharmacy is compliant with federal and state law. The PIC's license can be jeopardized (warnings, suspension or revocation) if inappropriate or illegal actions occur at the PIC's pharmacy, including a lack of counseling, manufacturing posing as compounding, drug diversion, or improper staff ratios.

Although the purpose of having a PIC is to make sure the store is operating legally, this does not diminish the legal responsibility of the individual staff pharmacists. However, if a store is found to be missing a substantial amount of a controlled substance over a period of time, if records are not being stored properly, or if controlled substance inventories are not performed when required, it is the PIC who will answer to the board.

State boards can have additional regulations regarding the PIC, such as:

- Limiting the number of pharmacies for which the PIC is responsible for supervising.

- Setting a maximum physical distance permissible between pharmacies if the PIC is responsible for more than one location.

- Requiring a minimum number of hours that a PIC must be present at the pharmacy.

- Requiring a pharmacist to complete a minimum number of years of experience as a staff pharmacist in order to be eligible to become a PIC.

My state permits a PIC to be in charge of more than one pharmacy: Yes / No

If yes, list the number of stores a PIC can manage: _____

List the minimum number of hours the PIC must be present at the pharmacy: _____

THE PHARMACIST INTERN

A pharmacist intern is training to become a pharmacist and can perform all functions of a pharmacist at the discretion of and under the supervision of a pharmacist, with a few state-specific exceptions. Your state may have set limitations, such as prohibiting the intern from having a key to the pharmacy, prohibiting interns from administering vaccines, or prohibiting interns from transferring controlled substance prescriptions.

Any activities performed by the intern must be known by the pharmacist in order for the pharmacist to provide adequate supervision.

For example, a pharmacist that supervises an intern providing immunizations must be trained in immunizations themselves [i.e., both the pharmacist (supervising) and the intern (immunizing) must be trained in immunizations].

In most states, only the pharmacist and the pharmacist intern can take new prescriptions over the phone (with only a few exceptions). The ratio of the number of interns that can be supervised by one pharmacist varies by state. Some states allow pharmacies to have more pharmacist interns present than the legal limit as long as the intern is only performing technician or clerk functions.

List your state restrictions and ratios:

Intern restrictions (versus what a pharmacist can perform): _____

_____

Ratio in hospital setting: 1 pharmacist to _____ intern/s.

Ratio in community setting: 1 pharmacist to _____ intern/s.

My state allows additional pharmacist interns present at any given time as long as the intern is only performing technician or clerk functions. Yes / No

If yes, does the intern's name badge need to be removed or replaced if they are performing technician or clerk functions? (The badge states the individual's name and classification). Yes / No

THE PHARMACY TECHNICIAN

Pharmacy technicians, unless they have specialized training or advanced certification, perform <u>non-discretionary</u> tasks in the pharmacy. Technicians are licensed staff (only clerks are non-licensed), which means they have to meet legal requirements set by the board of pharmacy.

Technicians are the primary staff who receive and fill prescriptions, in both community and hospital settings. They perform all or most of the compounding and IV medication preparation. Hospital technicians stock medications in automated dispensing cabinets, individual patient casettes and emergency "crash carts". The pharmacist must approve all work performed by technicians.

In some pharmacies, such as small independent pharmacies, technicians fulfill clerk responsibilities, including interfacing with both the patient and insurance companies. Pharmacy technicians are permitted (with some state exceptions) to perform the following tasks while under the direct supervision of a pharmacist:

- Enter prescriptions into the pharmacy computer.

- Package prescriptions, which include removing drugs from stock, counting drugs, placing drugs into containers, and labeling the container.

- Call prescribers for refill authorizations.

- Compound medications.

- Transfer prescriptions.

- Permit one technician to check the work of other technicians (rather than having the pharmacist check the technician's work) in a Tech Check Tech (TCT) arrangement.

- A handful of states permit technicians to accept called-in prescriptions from a prescriber's office in a hospital and/or community pharmacy.

My state permits technicians to accept new prescriptions over the phone. Yes / No

List the practice site and other requirements in your state for the technicians (such as training required or certification) and setting type if Tech Check Tech is permitted.

_____

Most states have a ratio of how many pharmacy technicians can be supervised for each pharmacist on duty. This varies from one pharmacist for each two technicians, to any number that the pharmacist feels they are reasonably able to supervise, which is always at the pharmacist's discretion.

Ratio in hospital setting: 1 pharmacist to _____ technician/s.

Ratio in community setting: 1 pharmacist to _____ technician/s.

Is there an exception in the state law that permits additional technician/s to be present in the pharmacy at any given time, such as having the technician perform some type of repetitive task (e.g., multiple doses and medications for one patient packaged into a blister card, which is called adherence packaging)?

_____

THE PHARMACY CLERK

Clerks are non-licensed personnel with no specific training required. The clerk is often the person accepting prescriptions at the "drop off" window, verifying the patient's insurance coverage, and completing the transaction at the point of sale or the "pick up" window. The clerk is permitted to type prescriptions into the pharmacy computer and the pharmacist will verify that it matches to the actual prescription. Depending on state law, clerks can request and receive refills. A clerk cannot pull medications from the shelves or package prescriptions.

My state permits clerks to request and receive refills. Yes / No

Clerks cannot be subject to license suspension or revocation since clerks do not have a license issued by the board. The pharmacist supervising the clerk is responsible for ensuring that the work meets the requirements of federal and state law. There are no maximum limits on the number of clerks allowed in the pharmacy at one time. There can be as many clerks as the pharmacist feels they can supervise, which will always be at the pharmacist's discretion.

REQUIREMENTS FOR VALID PRESCRIPTIONS

WRITTEN, ORAL, ELECTRONIC, AND FAXED PRESCRIPTIONS

The Durham-Humphrey Amendment of 1951 authorized dispensing of medications pursuant to a valid written prescription, or an oral prescription, which is immediately reduced to writing (i.e., is written on a prescription form). With the advent of technology, states passed their own laws that permit faxed, and subsequently, electronic prescriptions.

A prescription should minimally contain the following:[22] patient information (full name, date of birth, and street address), prescriber's information (name, license designation, address), drug information (name, strength, dosage form, and quantity), directions for use, refills, issue date, and the prescriber's signature.

Tamper-Resistant Security Forms for Medicaid Beneficiaries

In order for <u>outpatient</u> drugs to be paid for under the <u>federal Medicaid program</u>, all <u>written</u> prescriptions must be on <u>tamper-resistant security forms</u> that contain at least <u>three</u> tamper-resistant security features. This does not apply to electronic, oral, or faxed prescriptions. The CMS-required security features must include at least one feature from each of the following categories:

_____

22 https://nabp.pharmacy/publications-reports/resource-documents/model-pharmacy-act-rules/ (accessed 2019 Jan 15).

- **Prevents duplication** (e.g., the word "VOID" appears when photocopied or faxed (thermochromic ink changes to a visible color when heated from a copy machine or fax).

- **Prevents the erasure or modification** of the written information (e.g., with quantity check boxes, refill indicators, or with chemically reactive paper that changes color when an eraser is applied to the paper).

- **Prevents the use of counterfeit forms** (e.g., with pre-printed serial numbers or watermarks).

HEALTHCARE PROVIDERS AUTHORIZED TO PRESCRIBE MEDICATIONS

Healthcare practitioners who are licensed by law to prescribe medications can include physicians (MD, DO), dentists, podiatrists, veterinarians, nurse practitioners, pharmacists, optometrists, and naturopathic doctors. Independent and collaborative prescribing authority varies greatly by state. Before dispensing a medication, the pharmacist must make a good faith effort to determine that the prescription is valid, which includes having been written by a valid prescriber.

Physicians have unlimited, independent prescribing authority in all states. All other prescribers can only prescribe within their scope of practice and/or under a physician directed protocol. For example, a naturopathic doctor would be limited to natural drugs (and possibly epinephrine due to anaphylaxis risk), a dentist can prescribe medications related to the oral cavity and dental procedures, and an optometrist can prescribe medications related to ocular conditions. In contrast, an ophthalmologist (a physician who specializes in ocular conditions) can prescribe outside of the specialty.

VALID PRESCRIBER/PATIENT RELATIONSHIP

In order to fill a prescription, a prescriber/patient relationship should exist. The NABP recommends that each of these conditions should be met for the prescription to be considered valid:[23]

1. A patient has a medical complaint.

2. A medical history has been taken.

3. A face-to-face physical examination adequate to establish the medical complaint has been performed by the prescribing practitioner or through a telemedicine practice approved by the appropriate practitioner board.

4. A logical connection exists between the medical complaint, medical history, the physical examination and the drug prescribed.

SELF PRESCRIBING AND PRESCRIBING FOR FAMILY MEMBERS

Although not specifically addressed by the DEA, the American Medical Association (AMA) recommends against physicians treating oneself or immediate family members. There are ethical limitations involved with self-treatment and with the treatment of family members: the prescribers may not be able to objectively and adequately interview, examine, order diagnostic

---

23   https://nabp.pharmacy/publications-reports/resource-documents/model-pharmacy-act-rules/ (accessed 2019 Jan 15).

tests or drugs or counsel themselves or their family members due to personal relationships. There is also the potential for drug diversion.

Treating oneself or immediate family members can be prohibited by the state medical board in which the prescriber is licensed. Some states limit this type of prescribing to medical emergencies or for short-term, minor issues. Some states prohibit physicians from prescribing certain categories of drugs to oneself or to family members, such as schedule II drugs or all controlled drugs. Additionally, insurance companies may not provide coverage for treatment of oneself or known relatives. Federal law requires that all prescription medications be prescribed only in the context of a valid prescriber-patient relationship, which should include a written record of the encounter, such as a chart note. The same limitations on physicians that are set by the states and insurance companies commonly extend to the mid-level practitioners. In states that do not limit or have partial limitations on this type of prescribing, the pharmacist will need to make a judgment call on whether or not to fill such a prescription.

My state board sets limits on prescribing controlled drugs to oneself or family members. Yes / No

If yes, state the limitations: _____

_____

My state board sets limits on prescribing non-controlled drugs to oneself or family members. Yes / No

If yes, state the limitations: _____

_____

PRESCRIPTIONS FROM RETIRED OR DECEASED PRESCRIBERS

Federal law does not specify whether a prescription remains valid after it is discovered that the prescriber has become retired or deceased. In some states, the prescription will be invalid under state law. In other states, there is a lack of guidance on the matter, therefore it would not be against the law to refill prescriptions from retired or deceased prescribers. If there is no guidance from the state, then by default the pharmacist may use his or her discretion when deciding to fill or refill a prescription written by a retired or deceased prescriber.

If the prescriber is no longer practicing, the pharmacist should encourage the patient to look for a new prescriber as soon as possible and not to wait until the prescription is expired or the refills are exhausted. If another prescriber takes over the deceased prescriber's practice, the patient may be able to obtain a new prescription from the prescriber who took over the practice.

My state does not permit new prescriptions or refills to be filled if the prescriber is known to have become deceased. Yes / No

PRESCRIPTIONS FROM OTHER STATES OR TERRITORIES

In most cases, a prescription written by an out-of-state prescriber in a different U.S. state or territory is valid if a true prescriber/patient relationship is present. States can have specific

rules for out-of-state prescription, such as requiring the out-of-state prescription to meet the requirements for in-state prescriptions or only allowing non-controlled substances to be filled for out-of-state prescriptions. Hawaii, Puerto Rico, and Guam do not permit pharmacists to fill out of state prescriptions for controlled substances.

PRESCRIPTIONS FROM FOREIGN COUNTRIES

Except for a couple of states that permit the practice, a pharmacist may not fill prescriptions from other countries. States that share a border with Canada or Mexico are more likely to allow filling prescriptions from these foreign countries.

OFF-LABEL PROMOTION BY MANUFACTURERS

The drug manufacturer and their drug representatives cannot initiate conversations with other healthcare providers regarding off-label use for one of their drugs. The manufacturer and their representatives may discuss off-label use if a healthcare practitioner has voluntarily, on their own initiative, requested the information.

OFF-LABEL PRESCRIBING

Off-label use means that the drug will be used for a purpose for which the drug is not indicated. Indicated uses have been approved by the FDA, and will be listed in the package insert. Off-label use also includes using the drug for the indicated condition, but in a different patient population. If a drug has been FDA approved for at least one indication, prescribers are legally allowed to prescribe it for any other reason they feel is both safe and effective for the patient's health condition. Off-label prescribing is common and is often beneficial. There may be medical literature to support the off-label use, and the use may even be included in clinical guidelines. Occasionally, the off-label use is inappropriate and unsafe.

Pharmacists are legally permitted to fill prescriptions for off-label indications. The pharmacist must use his or her professional judgment when filling off-label prescriptions. Prior to filling a prescription for an unfamiliar off-label use, the pharmacist should attempt to find out if the drug has been studied for that purpose, if it is likely to be efficacious, and if it appears safe for the patient. The pharmacist can research the use and/or request supporting literature from the prescriber.

CORRECTING ERRORS AND OMISSIONS ON PRESCRIPTIONS

An omission is a type of error in which required information on a prescription has been left out, such as the number of tablets required. Errors on a prescription for non-controlled drugs can be revised by the pharmacist if the error is minor, such as misspelling the drug name. If the error is not minor, the pharmacist should consult with the prescriber, and document the discussion, including the agreed change/s. Alternatively, after verification with the prescriber, the prescription can be re-written as an oral prescription. In some cases, the original prescription will be voided and the prescriber will resend another prescription by fax or electronic transmission.

Correcting errors and omissions on prescriptions for controlled substances is stricter and is discussed in the controlled substances section.

PRESCRIPTION REFILLS

Refills of prescriptions are permitted as long as the refills were authorized orally or in writing by the prescriber. The majority of states allow prescriptions to be refilled up to 1 year from the original issue date. Wyoming and South Carolina allow prescriptions to be refilled for up to 2 years and a handful of states (including Georgia and New York) do not specify a time limit. This will depend on the pharmacist's judgment or individual store policy. Refills for schedules III and IV have shorter time limits (6 months) in which refills are permitted relative to non-controlled drugs, and some states have limits on the number of total day supply the refills can provide.

Schedule V refills are either handled the same way as schedules III and IV refills, or with the same requirements for non-controlled refills depending on the individual state. Federal law prohibits refills of schedule II drugs. Refilling controlled substances are further discussed in the Controlled Substances chapter.

In my state, refills of non-controlled prescriptions must be filled within this time period from the issue date: _____

In my state, refills on schedules III and IV prescriptions must be filled within this time period from the issue date: _____

My state specifies a day's supply maximum for schedules III and IV. Yes / No.

If specified, list the maximum day's supply: _____

My state treats refills on schedule V prescriptions differently than refills for non-controlled medications. Yes / No.

If schedule V refills are handled differently, list the difference/s:

_____

_____

EMERGENCY REFILLS WITHOUT THE PRESCRIBER'S AUTHORIZATION

Some states allow emergency refills without the prescriber's authorization if the prescriber is unavailable to authorize the refill and, if in the pharmacist's professional judgment, failure to refill the prescription might interrupt the patient's ongoing care and have a significant adverse effect on the patient's well-being. The pharmacist must have made a reasonable effort to contact the prescriber. The pharmacist must use caution that the emergency filling was medically necessary.

Limitations on emergency filling will vary from state-to-state. Some states allow emergency refills for non-scheduled drugs and schedule III – V drugs. Other states only allow emergency refilling of non-scheduled drugs. Schedule II drugs are prohibited from having refills. The emergency days' supply to be dispensed varies by state; this is typically 72 hours but can be up to a one-month supply. The emergency refill must be properly documented and an original prescription for the emergency filling must be obtained in a timely manner. Federal law prohibits refills on schedule

II drugs and emergency fills of schedule II medications must have at least the prescriber's oral authorization. This is discussed further in the Controlled Substances section.

My state allows emergency filling of non-controlled drugs without the prescriber's authorization. Yes / No

My state allows emergency filling of schedule III-V drugs without the prescriber's authorization. Yes / No

My state allows an emergency supply of medication for this amount of days: _____

If your state has additional restrictions on emergency filling, and states a time period in which to receive the prescription from the prescriber, list the restrictions/time limit: _____

_____

_____

PRESCRIPTION TRANSFERS

There are no federal limitations on the transfer of non-controlled prescriptions and, unless limited by state law, a pharmacist can transfer the prescription as long as there are refills remaining. The transfer must be directly communicated between two pharmacists (or certified pharmacy technicians, in states that permit this practice).

The pharmacist or certified pharmacy technician who transfers the prescription to another pharmacy must write or stamp "void" on the face of the prescription (front side). The name and address of the pharmacy to which the prescription is transferred to, the name of the pharmacist receiving the prescription, and the transfer date is written on the back of the prescription.

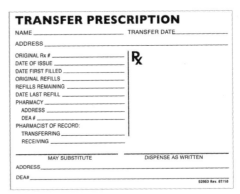

The pharmacist at the store receiving the transferred prescription will use a blank form to record the information.

The pharmacist or certified pharmacy technician that receives the prescription reduces it to writing and writes "transfer" on the face of the prescription, along with the information that is required for a prescription. Many pharmacies have transfer forms that have "transfer" preprinted on the top.

INFORMATION REQUIRED ON MULTIPLE UNIT (MULTIPLE DOSE) PRESCRIPTION LABELS

Multiple unit containers are the typical prescription containers dispensed to patients in the outpatient and community settings. These are usually given as a 30 or 90-day supply. The Durham-Humphrey Amendment exempts dispensing pharmacists from meeting most of the requirements that manufacturers must meet for container labeling except:

Requirements from the Durham-Humphrey Amendment

- The label must not be false or misleading
- The drug dispensed must not be an imitation drug
- The drug must not be sold under the name of another drug
- The packaging and labeling must conform to the official compendia standards
- If the drug is susceptible to deterioration, it must be packaged and labeled appropriately

Federal law requires the following information on the dispensed prescription label:

- Name and address of dispenser
- Serial or prescription number
- Date of filling
- Prescriber's name
- Patient's name
- Directions for use
- Cautionary statements

Some states require additional information on the prescription label such as:

- Date of initial fill
- Name of the dispensing pharmacist
- Business hours
- Pharmacy phone number
- Expiration date of drug
- Drug name and strength
- Address of patient
- Name of the manufacturer or distributor
- Lot or control number
- Physical description of drug (e.g., oblong ivory tablet 73 00 logo)
- Refills remaining

FORMATTING STANDARDS FOR MULTIPLE UNIT (MULTIPLE DOSE) PRESCRIPTION LABELS

The USP Chapter that covers standards for prescription container labeling (USP Chapter 17) is the official standard for prescription format, appearance, content and language instructions. The goal of standardizing container labels is to promote patient understanding of medication usage, increase adherence, and reduce medication errors. The USP standards do not apply to inpatient medications since they are labeled for administration by a healthcare professional, such as a nurse.

The content of the prescription container label is often the only drug information the patient will read. It must be large enough to read, simple to understand, and include the proper auxiliary labels. The label should only include the most important information needed for safe and effective use; excessive information can cause important details to be overlooked.

The prescription directions should follow a standard format so the patient is accustomed to finding the same information in the same location on each prescription. The text should be written in a horizontal direction only. For added emphasis, the label can highlight critical information in bold typeface or color, or use white space to set off the items listed. In an offset area designed to draw the patient's focus to key content (e.g., the gray box in the label), the most important information, including the instructions on when to take the medication, should be placed inside the offset area.

Critical Items on a Prescription

The following critical items should be prominently displayed in a large font size (e.g., 12-point Times Roman or 11-point Arial):

1. Patient name

2. Drug name (brand and generic) and the drug strength

3. Clear and simple directions for use

```
JOHNSON, JUDITH                          Rx# 06197 1234567
                                         DATE FILLED: 08/31/2010
                                         ORIG RX DATE: 02/24/2010
VERAPAMIL ER 240 MG tablet               RPH: KPT
Ivax Pharmaceutical                      Store DEA# BT5555555

                                         Judith Johnson
Take 1 tablet in the morning, and        5873 EVERGREEN AVE
take 1 tablet in the evening             DAVIS, CA 95615
                                         (555) 555-7889

Treats high blood pressure               CAUTION: Federal law PROHIBITS
                                         the transfer of this drug to any
                                         person other than the patient for
                                         whom it was prescribed.

Prescriber: Roger Brown MD   Quantity: 60      VICTOR'S PHARMACY
Oblong ivory tablet 73  00 logo          1625 N. Market Blvd., Sacramento, CA 95834
Refills remaining: 3   Expires: 05/30/2011     (555) 555-9810
```

https://www.pharmacy.ca.gov/publications/10_sep_script.pdf

Non-Critical Information

Non-critical information should not distract from the critical information, and should be placed at the bottom of the label or in another less-prominent location. If the indication for the drug has been included on the prescription, it should be included on the prescription label, unless the patient desires otherwise.

Critical Items on a Prescription

Directions for use should be clear and easy to interpret. Time periods should be specified and numbers should be used instead of alphabets, when appropriate. For example, rather than "Take two tablets twice daily" the label should read "Take 2 tablets in the morning and 2 tablets in the evening." Avoid hourly intervals (such as "every 8 hours") since this requires the patient to count. In general, specifying an exact time should be avoided except if required for drugs that must be taken at exact times (e.g., tacrolimus for a transplant patient is usually given at set times, 12 hours apart). Specifying an exact time can be too restrictive for patients who are busy with work, school, or other responsibilities. Jargon or Latin terminology should not be used. When possible, directions for use should be in the patient's preferred language, if not English.

Auxiliary labels should be evidence-based and written in simple language for key warnings. They should be placed in a standard place on the label and should be provided for each and every prescription as needed, and not at the discretion of the pharmacist. See the dispensing controlled substances section for more information on the labeling for scheduled drugs.

My state requires tablet identification (the description, such as number, shape and color) on the container label. Yes / No

My state requires the pharmacy to include their phone number on the container label. Yes / No

My state requires the ability to provide patients with visual impairment a larger container label type size. Yes / No

My state requires that the critical information on a container label be printed in at least 12-point san serif type for all patients. Yes / No

My state requires critical information on the label to be bolded or printed in colored ink (circle if either bold or colored ink is specified). Yes / No

EXPIRATION DATES VERSUS BEYOND USE DATES

The expiration date listed on the manufacturer's drug container identifies the time during which the prescription drug will still meet the requirements of the USP monograph, as long as it is kept in appropriate storage conditions in the original sealed container. The expiration date will usually be notated with a month and year, and the drug is acceptable to use until the end of the month in which it expires. For example, if the expiration date is 3/2019, then the last date of use should be March 31, 2019.

The pharmacist must determine a suitable beyond use date at which the patient should no longer use the medication. This date should be indicated on the prescription container. Depending on state law, the beyond use date may or may not be the same as the manufacturer's expiration date. The beyond use date is never greater than the manufacturer's expiration date. The instructions for compounded or reconstituted preparations will provide the recommended beyond use date. For example, the beyond use date for reconstituted *Augmentin* suspension is 10 days.

Unless otherwise specified in the individual monograph (such as with an *Augmentin* suspension) or in the absence of stability data to the contrary, the beyond use date for a multiple unit container is no later than either of the following:[24]

- The <u>expiration date</u> on the <u>manufacturer's container</u>, or
- <u>One year</u> from the <u>date the drug is dispensed</u>, whichever is earlier

If the pharmacy receives a drug container of any type, such as a bottle of 1000 tablets of acetaminophen, <u>without an expiration date</u> on the container, the container is <u>misbranded</u>, and should not be dispensed. It can be considered similar to expired drugs, which cannot be used or dispensed.

CHILD-RESISTANT PACKAGING

Prior to implementation of the Poison Prevention Packaging Act (PPPA) in 1970, accidental poisoning was the leading cause of injury in young children. At that time, there was no standard way to protect children from ingesting common dangerous substances, including drugs and household cleaners. The PPPA required the use of child-resistant (C-R) containers for most over-the-counter drugs, prescription drugs, and dangerous household chemicals. Child-resistant containers are designed to prevent 80% of children less than 5 years of age from opening the container, and at the same time permitting at least 90% of adults to open the container.

The PPPA mandates that a <u>new plastic container and closure</u> (e.g., a plastic cap) must be used for <u>each prescription dispensed</u>. This requirement is meant to avoid damage to the seal from

"wear and tear", which can reduce the C-R effectiveness. If a glass container is used, only the top closure needs to be replaced. Reversible containers (child-resistant when turning the closure one direction, but not child-resistant in the other direction) are permitted if dispensed in the child-resistant mode, but are not recommended.

The patient or the prescriber can request that the pharmacy package the prescription drugs in an "easy open", non-child-resistant container. The prescriber can waive the use of a child-resistant container for a single prescription at a time. The patient can provide a blanket waiver for all prescriptions. The pharmacist should document the waiver request with the patient's signature.

Child-resistant packaging is not required for drugs administered by a healthcare provider.

For the benefit of elderly and handicapped patients who might have difficulty opening C-R containers, the PPPA allows manufacturers to package one size of OTC drugs in a non-C-R (easy open) container as long as the same product is also available in a C-R container. The package must have the warning "This package is for households without young children" or "Package Not Child-Resistant."

DRUGS THAT REQUIRE C-R PACKAGING

- All oral prescription drugs

- Liquid anesthetics such as lidocaine and dibucaine (*Nupercainal*), OTC NSAIDs, including salicylates

- Any OTC iron supplement, multivitamin/mineral with iron and natural products with iron

- Loperamide (*Imodium*)

- Minoxidil (*Rogaine*)

- Prescription drugs that were converted to OTC

- Mouthwash, including fluoride-containing mouth rinses

- Oral and non-oral investigational drugs for outpatient use, with an exception for drugs packaged in unit-dose if there is data that the amount being used would not cause harm to a young child if ingested; these are for patients who are enrolled in a clinical drug trial

DRUGS THAT DO NOT REQUIRE C-R PACKAGING

- Sublingual dosage forms of nitroglycerin

- Sublingual and chewable forms of isosorbide dinitrate in dosage strengths of 10 milligrams or less

- Erythromycin ethylsuccinate (EES) granules and oral suspensions that do not exceed eight grams

- Cyclically administered oral contraceptives in manufacturer (memory-aid) packages that rely solely upon the activity of one or more progestogen or estrogen substances (i.e., birth control packets)

- Anhydrous cholestyramine in powder form

- All unit-dose forms of potassium supplements, including individually-wrapped effervescent tablets, unit-dose vials of liquid potassium, and powdered potassium in unit-dose packets, that contain no more than 50 mEqs of potassium per package

- Sodium fluoride preparations, including liquid and tablet forms, that contain no more than 110 milligrams of sodium fluoride (the equivalent of 50 mg of elemental fluoride) per package or no more than a concentration of 0.5 percent elemental fluoride on a weight-to-volume basis for liquids or a weight-to-weight basis for non-liquids that contain no other substances

- Betamethasone tablets packaged in manufacturers' dispenser packages, that contain no more than 12.6 milligrams betamethasone

- Pancrelipase preparations in tablet, capsule, or powder form that contain no other substances

- Prednisone in tablet form, when dispensed in packages that contain no more than 105 mg of the drug, and contain no other substances

- Mebendazole in tablet form in packages that contain no more than 600 mg of the drug, and contain no other substances

- Methylprednisolone in tablet form in packages that contain no more than 84 mg of the drug and contain no other substances

- Colestipol in powder form in packages that contain no more than 5 grams of the drug and contain no other substances

- Erythromycin ethylsuccinate tablets in packages that contain no more than the equivalent of 16 grams erythromycin

- Conjugated Estrogens Tablets, USP, when dispensed in mnemonic (memory-aid) packages that contain no more than 32 mg of the drug and contain no other substances

- Norethindrone Acetate Tablets, USP, when dispensed in mnemonic packages that contain no more than 50 mg of the drug and contain no other substances

- Medroxyprogesterone acetate tablets

- Sacrosidase (sucrase) preparations in a solution of glycerol and water

- Hormone Replacement Therapy Products that rely solely upon the activity of one or more progestogen or estrogen substances

- Colesevelam hydrochloride in powder form in packages that contain no more than 3.75 grams of the drug

- Sevelamer carbonate in powder form in packages that contain no more than 2.4 grams of the drug

Electronic cigarettes (e-cigs) may require C-R packaging in the near future. There has been an increase in emergency room visits and poison control center phone calls after young children had accidently ingested electronic cigarettes due primarily to the presence of flavorings (e.g., apple, mango, strawberry).

SINGLE DOSE (UNIT-DOSE) PRESCRIPTION LABELS

Drugs packaged as unit-doses are convenient for hospitals and skilled nursing facilities because they reduce drug diversion, drug waste, and medication errors. The unit-dose container is a non-reusable container designed to hold a quantity of a drug intended for direct, oral administration as a single dose. Unit-dose packaging can be performed by the drug company or prepared from multiple dose containers in the pharmacy.

Unit dose packages prepared in a hospital pharmacy, from multiple dose containers.

A benefit of unit-dose packaging is that if the drug is not used and the container is intact, the drug can be returned to pharmacy stock and re-dispensed. Pharmacies repackage drug from multiple dose containers into unit-dose packaging for administration to patients in facilities such as hospitals on a routine basis; it is important to know the requirements for the unit-dose label listed below in order to repackage the drug.

Unit-dose Packaging with Barcoding Reduces Medication Errors

Unit-dose packaging reduces medication errors. Before administering the drug, the nurse scans the barcode on the patient's wristband and the barcode on the unit-dose package. If that drug and dose was not entered into that patient's medication list by a pharmacist, an alert will sound, preventing the nurse from administering the wrong drug or dose to the patient.

The unit-dose is commonly placed into automated dispensing cabinets (ADC) rather than into patient-specific cassette—thus, the label will not require information such as the patient's name, prescriber's name, dispensing date, or prescription number. Since the size of the unit-dose packaging is too small to accommodate all the mandatory information on a typical label, only the following information is required:

- The drug name

- The quantity of the active ingredient

- The beyond use date

- The lot number

- The name of the manufacturer, packager, or distributor

- Any required cautionary statements

UNIT-DOSE BEYOND USE DATE

According to the USP/NF standards, the beyond use date for unit-dose containers is no later than either of the following:

- <u>One year</u> from the <u>date the drug has been repackaged</u>, or

- The <u>expiration date</u> on the <u>manufacturer's container</u>, whichever is earlier

CUSTOMIZED PATIENT PACKAGING FOR ADHERENCE

USP has published guidance on customized patient medication packages ("med paks"), which is found in USP 661. Instead of dispensing two or more prescribed drugs in separate containers, a pharmacist can prepare a customized med pak, with the consent of either the patient, the patient's caregiver, or the prescriber. The med pak has a series of containers, or compartments, and each compartment holds multiple doses of solid, oral drugs. Med paks make it easier to provide medications for patients on multiple doses, and are useful for increasing adherence in patients on a complicated medication regimen.

The med pak label must contain the following:

- The name of the patient

- A serial/prescription number for the med pak itself, and a separate serial/prescription number for each drug in the med pak

- The name, strength, physical description, and total quantity of each drug

- The direction for use and required cautionary statements for each drug

- Required storage instructions

- The name of the prescriber for each drug

- The date of preparation of the med pak and the beyond use date assigned to the med pak, which shall be no later than 60 days from the date that the med pak was prepared

- The name, address, and telephone number of the pharmacy, and the pharmacy's DEA registration number, if controlled substance/s are included in the med pak

- Any other information, statements, or warnings required for any of the drugs

- If the patient med pak allows for the removal or separation of the intact containers, each individual container shall bear a label identifying each of the drugs inside

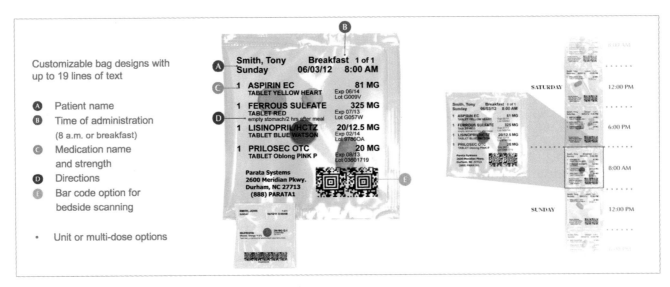

Customizable bag designs with up to 19 lines of text

Ⓐ Patient name

Ⓑ Time of administration
(8 a.m. or breakfast)

Ⓒ Medication name
and strength

Ⓓ Directions

Ⓔ Bar code option for
bedside scanning

• Unit or multi-dose options

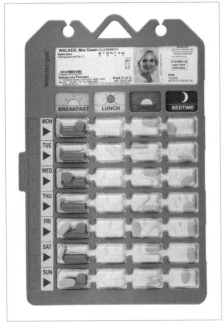

The weekly medication doses can be prepared for facility patients, or those living at home that require this assistance to help with adherence or dexterity issues.

If a drug has a patient package insert (PPI), it should be sent with the med pak. Alternatively, all the required information can be combined into a single educational insert and sent with the med pak.

In the absence of more stringent packaging requirements for any of the drugs, each container of the patient med pak shall comply with the moisture permeation requirements for a Class B single-unit or unit-dose container. Each container must be designed so that it shows evidence of having been opened or is not re-sealable.[25]

In addition to any individual prescription filing requirements, a record of each patient med pak shall be made and filed. Each record should contain:

- The name and address of the patient

- The serial number of the prescription order for each of the drugs

- The name of the manufacturer or labeler and lot number for each of the drugs

- Information identifying or describing the design, characteristics, or specifications of the patient med pak sufficient to allow subsequent preparation of an identical med pak

- The date of preparation of the patient med pak and the beyond use date that was assigned

- Any special labeling instructions

- The name or initials of the pharmacist who prepared the med pak

DRUG UTILIZATION REVIEWS

OBRA requires each state to have a drug utilization review (DUR) program in order to be reimbursed for Medicaid services. There are two types of drug utilization reviews required:

- A prospective drug utilization review: this is the evaluation of a patient's drug therapy prior to dispensing (performed by the dispensing pharmacist)

- A retrospective drug utilization review: a review of drug therapy after medication dispensing (performed by the state)

Pharmacists must perform a prospective DUR for individual Medicaid patients prior to dispensing a new prescription or refill. Most of the states have extended this requirement to include all patients. The purpose of performing a prospective DUR is to look for the following errors:

- A therapeutic duplication

- Incorrect dosing

- Incorrect treatment duration

- Contraindications to the drug

- Interactions between the drug, a disease state, or a patient allergy

- Abuse or misuse

Although pharmacy software is designed to identify drug interactions, some systems are better than others, and with all systems, the pharmacist will need to use his or her professional judgment regarding the severity of an interaction. The software can be incorrect or incomplete, with certain types of interactions missing (e.g., P-gp interactions). The pharmacist may decide to override a minor warning, if the benefits of using the drug outweigh the risks. The pharmacist may need to recommend a dose adjustment due to an interaction. Patients may be receiving medications from more than one source, which may not show up as an interaction in the software but should

be present in the medication profile if all of the drugs the patient is using have been entered. This information must be entered manually, because not all of the drugs are obtained from one pharmacy. It is common to take OTC medications and natural products, and patients can go to other pharmacies to take advantage of a less expensive generic drug cost at a different store, or they may have had a prescription transferred to take advantage of a promotional discount coupon. They may be getting some of their drugs at the veterans administration, they may be getting drugs under a patient assistance plan directly from the manufacturer, or they may be getting free drug samples from a prescriber.

The pharmacy must make a reasonable effort to update the patient profile information each time a medication is dispensed. This is why a technician or clerk at the drop off window asks the patient if there have been any changes or updates to the medications. The patient may refuse to provide any or all of the required profile information, and if so, the pharmacy staff should document the refusal. The information required in a patient profile includes:

- Patient's name, address, telephone number

- Date of birth

- Gender

- Disease state information, drug allergies or intolerances, adverse drug reactions

- Comprehensive list of medications or devices previously dispensed

- Any relevant pharmacist comments

If an issue is present, the pharmacist must manage it according to his or her professional judgment. This will involve either contacting the prescriber for notification or clarification, and/or discussing the concern and any management necessary with the patient or caregiver.

OBRA requires the individual states to perform a system-wide retrospective DUR to analyze physician prescribing habits and assess appropriate use of certain drugs. This type of DUR is discussed in the RxPrep Course Book.

My state requires that a patient profile be kept in the pharmacy for all patients. Yes / No

My state requires that the patient profile be kept for this time period after the last fill: _____

My state does not require patient profiles be kept for dispensing that is likely to be a one-time fill (such as a patient visiting the area who is on vacation who comes to the pharmacy with an antibiotic prescription). Yes / No

If your state requires that the patient profile include information in addition to the items listed above, list them here:

_____

WRITTEN MATERIAL THAT IS INCLUDED AS PART OF THE PACKAGE LABELING

All information provided by the manufacturer for distribution with the drug, even if it is not physically affixed to the product, is considered part of the labeling. The drug's labeling includes:

- The drug container, such as a plastic container or bottle

- Consumer Medication Information (CMI) — not approved by the FDA

- Patient Package Inserts (PPI) — approved by the FDA

- Medication Guides (MedGuides) — approved by the FDA

- Any paperwork required as part of a REMS; see following REMS description

CONSUMER MEDICATION INFORMATION

The FDA mandates that useful written patient information be provided to patients with each new prescription. The consumer medication information handouts (CMIs) are the paper leaflets of drug information that are put inside the bag, or stapled to the outside.

- The information should be simplified for patients to understand and should reflect the FDA-approved package insert.

- They should explain how to use the drug and what to expect.

- These are not reviewed or approved by the FDA.

PATIENT PACKAGE INSERTS

In the late 1960s, the FDA required that all estrogen-containing drugs be dispensed with the FDA-approved PPI in order for the patient to be fully informed of the benefits and risks involved with the use of these drugs. Oral contraceptives for birth control were first available in 1960 and, after just 5 years, 6.5 million women were using "the pill". Initially, the estrogen content was much higher than the pills in use today. Consequently, there was a higher incidence of clotting. The FDA required the PPIs due to the lack of awareness of this risk.

The PPI must be given each time the drug is dispensed in the outpatient setting, with both the initial fill and with refills. If the PPI is not provided, it is considered misbranding. In an institutional setting such as a hospital or long-term care facility, the PPI must be provided to the patient prior to the administration of the first dose and every 30 days thereafter.

Some of the more recent drugs come with a PPI. These are voluntarily provided by the manufacturer if they feel there is important information that the patient should know about the drug. The PPIs require FDA approval.

MEDICATION GUIDES

Medication Guides (MedGuides) are FDA-approved patient handouts that come with many prescription medicines that may have a serious and significant health concern.

The FDA requires that MedGuides be issued with drugs or biologics that require certain information to prevent serious adverse events, if the patient needs to know about serious side effects or adverse events, or if adherence to specific instructions is essential to effectiveness. The manufacturer must supply the MedGuides to the dispenser by providing the physical handouts or the electronic file so the pharmacy can print them out for the patient.

Drugs that require MedGuides include all antidepressants, antipsychotics, anticonvulsants, most antiarrythmics, NSAIDs, and many others. There are over 300 medications which require MedGuides. The list can be found on the FDA website.

The MedGuide must be given when:

- A drug is dispensed in the <u>outpatient</u> setting, and the drug will be used by the patient without the supervision of a healthcare provider, with each <u>new fill</u> and <u>refills</u>

- The <u>first time</u> the drug is being dispensed to a healthcare provider for <u>administration</u> to a patient in an <u>outpatient</u> setting

- When the patient or their caregiver <u>asks for it</u>

- If the MedGuide has been <u>revised</u>

- If the drug is subject to a <u>Risk Evaluation and Mitigation Strategy</u> (REMS) that requires a MedGuide

RISK EVALUATION AND MITIGATION STRATEGY

In 2007, with the enactment of the FDAAA, the FDA was given new authority to improve drug safety. One of the provisions of this act is the use of risk evaluation and mitigation strategy (REMS) that the FDA could require if a drug or biological had risks that may outweigh the benefits. The risk/benefit for any drug should always be established between the healthcare provider and the patient. If a REMS exists for a drug or drug class, the risks are considered serious and the FDA uses the REMS requirements to make sure that the risks are known and are managed adequately.

There are four parts to a REMS program:

1. Communication plans
2. Elements to assure safe use
3. Implementation systems
4. MedGuides

Key Points:

- A REMS may be required for a new drug or when safety issues arise with an existing drug.

- A REMS can be applied to an individual drug or to a drug class, such as the REMS required with long-acting opioids.

- The manufacturer (which the FDA refers to as the drug's sponsor) has to develop the REMS, and the FDA reviews it and approves it, when it is acceptable.

- Since the safety issues are different, the REMS are different, and the components will depend on the risks associated with that drug or drug class.

- The requirements include some combination of prescribing, shipping and dispensing safety requirements.

EXAMPLES OF REMS REQUIREMENTS

DRUG	PRIMARY RISK	REMS REQUIREMENTS TO ↓ RISK
Clozapine	Severe neutropenia	Monitor absolute neutrophil count (ANC). ANC must be ≥ 1500/μL to start and ≥ 1000/μL to continue treatment (i.e., dispense refills). Educate provider and patient.
Isotretinoin	Severe birth defects (teratogenicity)	Prescribers, patients and pharmacies must enroll in the iPLEDGE program. Prevent fetal exposure. Requires a negative pregnancy test prior to dispensing. Dispense with MedGuide. Educate provider and patient.
Extended-Release, Long-Acting (ER/LA), and Immediate-Release (IR) opioid analgesics	Overdose and death	Educate providers about treating and monitoring pain by completing REMS-compliant training and taking knowledge assessment. Dispense with MedGuide. Educate provider and patients on safe use, risks, storage and disposal.

PATIENT IDENTIFICATION PRIOR TO DISPENSING OR ADMINISTERING PRESCRIPTION DRUGS

Some states require the pharmacy staff to verify the patient's identity in order to prevent drug diversion and reduce medication errors. There is presently no federal law requiring patients to provide identification prior to receiving prescriptions. In the community setting, the most commonly used identifiers are the patient's name and date of birth. If the patient has a common name, the home address can be requested for additional verification. Some states require patient identification for all prescriptions in the community setting while other states require identification only for controlled substances.

Is patient identification required in your state in order to dispense all drugs in the community pharmacy setting? Yes / No

Is patient identification required in your state for controlled substance dispensing only? Yes / No

In order to reduce errors, institutional settings certified by The Joint Commission require healthcare providers to verify two patient identifiers prior to administering a drug or performing a procedure.[26] The identifiers must be patient-specific, therefore identifiers that can be used for many patients are not acceptable (such as the prescriber's name, or the patient's city or zip code). In an institution setting such as a hospital, the medical record number (usually located on the patient's wrist band) and the patient's name or date of birth are commonly used.

26 The Joint Commission's National Patient Safety Goal NPSG 01.01.01.

86

PATIENT COUNSELING

Pursuant to OBRA 90, pharmacists must offer <u>oral consultation</u> before dispensing prescriptions to <u>Medicaid</u> patients. The majority of states have made the offer to counsel a mandatory requirement for all patients. Some state laws only mandate the offer to counsel for new prescriptions, while other states mandate the offer to counsel for refills as well. Although the offer to counsel must be made, the patient or patient's caregiver may refuse counseling.

COUNSELING FACE-TO-FACE

The pharmacist provides patient counseling in an area suitable for <u>confidential</u> patient consultation to protect the <u>patient's privacy</u>, including the protected health information. Depending on individual state requirements, the offer for patient consultation may be initiated by the pharmacist or by other pharmacy personnel. For example, some states allow any personnel to ask the patient "would you like to be counseled by the pharmacist?" whereas other states mandate that the pharmacist must personally ask the patient if he or she would like to be counseled. In all states, the pharmacist must provide the actual counseling. It is up to the pharmacist's judgment to decide which information should be discussed with the patient during counseling. Due to time limitations, pharmacists may discuss select information.

Patient counseling can include:

- Name and description of drug

- Route of administration

- Dosage form

- Dose

- Duration of therapy

- How to prepare drug for administration

- Techniques for self-monitoring

- Common and/or severe adverse drug reactions or interactions

- What to do if a dose is missed

- Prescription refill information

- Importance of compliance

- Storage

COUNSELING WHEN THE PATIENT IS NOT PRESENT

Many states still require an "offer" of counseling when prescriptions are delivered to home or work, or sent through the mail or by a delivery service. An acceptable method is to provide the pharmacy business hours and a toll-free phone number on the printed drug information or container label. Some states require mail-order pharmacies to be open for a minimum number of hours and days per week to receive patient calls.

My state requires the pharmacy's hours and a toll-free number to be listed on the prescription container labeling. Yes / No

My state requires mail-order pharmacies to be open for a defined number of days and hours per week. Yes / No

List any other counseling requirements for medications delivered to the patient or sent by mail:

_____

_____

_____

COUNSELING THE LIMITED-ENGLISH PROFICIENT PATIENT

Depending on local and regional demographics, pharmacies may interact with patients with limited grasp of the English language. The largest number of limited-English proficient (LEP) patients who speak Spanish, Chinese, Korean, Vietnamese, or Tagalog are located in New York, California, Texas and Florida. All patients in the United States need to know how to safely use their medication. In states with large immigrant populations, the state board may have specific protocols and requirements for communicating with LEP patients. This may include the use of a language translator to assist with patient counseling.

My state does/does not require pharmacies to provide translation services to LEP patients.

If yes, list the acceptable methods, if specified: _____

_____

EXEMPTIONS FOR PATIENT COUNSELING

Many states will not require pharmacists to counsel on patients receiving institutional care, such as in a hospital. It is presumed that the healthcare provider taking care of the patient will provide any necessary drug information. Some hospitals will send pharmacists to the floor to review the drugs being given or to provide counseling when the patient is ready to be discharged, which is called "discharge counseling".

Another exception to providing patient counseling is when the patient or caregiver has been offered counseling, and the offer has been refused.

COUNSELING REQUIREMENTS BY STATE

A summary of counseling requirements is provided by CMS' Position Paper on Patient Counseling Requirements. In different states, different personnel are permitted to make the offer to counsel. The required content of the counseling is reviewed in the Pharmacy Practice section.[27]

STATE	REQUIRE ORAL COUNSELING IN CERTAIN SITUATIONS OR AN "OFFER TO COUNSEL"	DOC. OF "OFFER TO COUNSEL" REQ'D BY STATE	DOC. OF PATIENT'S REFUSAL FOR COUNSELING	COUNSEL NEW RX AND REFILLS	PROCESS FOR COUNSELING WHEN PATIENT IS NOT IN THE PHARMACY	DISCUSS WITH PATIENT PRIOR TO GENERIC SUBSTITUTION	REQUIRE DIST. OF WRITTEN MATERIALS
Alabama	Y	Y	N	Y	Y	N	Y
Alaska	Y	N	N	Y	Y	Y	N
Arizona	Y	Y	Y	N	Y	Y	Y
Arkansas	Y	N	N	N	Y	Y	N
California	Y	Y	N	N	Y	Y	Y
Colorado	Y	Y	Y	N	N	Y	Y
Connecticut	Y	Y	Y	Y	N	Y	N
Delaware	Y	Y	Y	N	Y	Y	Y
District of Columbia	Y	Y	Y	N	Y	N	Y
Florida	Y	Y	N	Y	Y	Y	Y
Georgia	Y	N	N	N	Y	N	N
Hawaii	N	Y	N	N	N	Y	Y
Idaho	Y	Y	N	Y	N	N	Y
Illinois	Y	Y	Y	Y	N	N	N
Indiana	Y	Y	Y	Y	N	N	Y
Iowa	Y	Y	Y	N	N	N	N
Kansas	Y	Y	N	N	N	Y	N
Kentucky	Y	Y	Y	N	N	N	Y
Louisiana	N	N	N	N	N	N	N
Maine	Y	Y	Y	N	N	Y	Y
Maryland	Y	N	N	N	N	Y	Y
Massachusetts	Y	Y	Y	N	Y	N	Y
Michigan	Y	Y	N	N	Y	Y	N
Minnesota	Y	Y	N	N	Y	Y	Y
Mississippi	Y	Y	N	Y	Y	Y	N
Missouri	Y	N	N	Y	Y	N	Y
Montana	Y	Y	Y	N	N	N	N
Nebraska	Y	Y	Y	Y	N	Y	N
Nevada	Y	Y	Y	N	Y	Y	Y

27   https://nabplaw.pharmacy/site/ (accessed 2019 January 15).

STATE	REQUIRE ORAL COUNSELING IN CERTAIN SITUATIONS OR AN "OFFER TO COUNSEL"	DOC. OF "OFFER TO COUNSEL" REQ'D BY STATE	DOC. OF PATIENT'S REFUSAL FOR COUNSELING	COUNSEL NEW RX AND REFILLS	PROCESS FOR COUNSELING WHEN PATIENT IS NOT IN THE PHARMACY	DISCUSS WITH PATIENT PRIOR TO GENERIC SUBSTITUTION	REQUIRE DIST. OF WRITTEN MATERIALS
New Hampshire	Y	Y	Y	N	Y	Y	Y
New Jersey	Y	Y	Y	N	Y	N	N
New Mexico	Y	Y	N	N	Y	N	Y
New York	Y	Y	Y	N	Y	Y	Y
North Carolina	Y	Y	N	N	Y	N	N
North Dakota	Y	N	N	Y	Y	Y	Y
Ohio	Y	Y	Y	Y	Y	N	N
Oklahoma	Y	Y	Y	N	Y	N	N
Oregon	Y	N	Y	N	Y	Y	N
Pennsylvania	Y	Y	Y	N	Y	Y	Y
Rhode Island	Y	Y	Y	N	N	Y	N
South Carolina	Y	Y	N	N	N	Y	N
South Dakota	Y	N	Y	N	Y	N	Y
Tennessee	Y	Y	N	N	Y	N	N
Texas	Y	Y	Y	N	Y	Y	Y
Utah	Y	Y	Y	Y	Y	Y	N
Vermont	Y	Y	Y	Y	N	Y	N
Virginia	Y	Y	Y	N	Y	Y	Y
Washington	Y	Y	Y	Y	Y	N	Y
West Virginia	Y	Y	Y	N	N	Y	N
Wisconsin	Y	Y	Y	N	N	Y	N
Wyoming	Y	Y	Y	N	N	N	N
Total number of states with requirement	48	42	30	15	33	30	26

HEALTH INSURANCE PORTABILITY AND ACCOUNTABILITY ACT

The Health Insurance Portability and Accountability Act (HIPAA) protects the privacy of the patient's health information, outlines how it can be shared, and provides the patient the right to access their own information. HIPAA also involves insurance portability, which allows individuals to keep their insurance if transitioning from one job to another.

Pharmacists are more concerned with protecting the privacy of the patient health information. All healthcare professionals who have access to confidential patient information must have documented HIPAA training. Violation of HIPAA, either inadvertently or deliberately, can result in fines and imprisonment. An individual at each facility must be designated to enforce the privacy policy.

Examples of privacy abuse include:

- Labels with identifiers sent to shredding (recycling) company

- Pharmacy employees snooping around in celebrity patient records

- Pictures or information about patients posted on social media sites

The information covered under HIPAA is called protected health information (PHI) and includes private information in <u>electronic, verbal, or written form</u>. According to HIPAA, PHI includes:

- The patient's past, present, or future <u>physical or mental health or condition</u> (e.g., the medical record)

- The <u>healthcare</u> provided to the patient (e.g., laboratory tests, surgery)

- The past, present, or future <u>payment</u> for providing healthcare to the patient, which can identify the patient (e.g., hospital bills)

Protected health information includes many common identifiers, such as the name, address, birth date and social security number when they can be associated with the health information listed above. If the identifying information is not related to health information, then it is not considered PHI. For example, names, residential addresses, or phone numbers listed in a public directory such as a phone book would not be PHI because there is no health data associated with it.

The healthcare facility or pharmacy must ensure that any patient information is secure and not available to viewers who do not require the access. Healthcare providers must be mindful of the following:

- Avoid discussing patient care in elevators

- Shred all documents prior to disposal

- Cover patient identifiers on prescription bottles and bags prior and during dispensing

- Close patient records on computer screens when not in use and logout of the system

<u>Incidental disclosures are not a violation</u>, such as calling out a patient's name in a waiting room, discussing a patient's care during medical rounds, or using patient sign-in sheets in waiting rooms.

The "<u>minimum necessary</u>" information required for the job is what should be shared. This becomes an issue for pharmacists when the insurer may not wish to pay without additional information, which the pharmacist may not think is required. Minimum necessary is also designed to encourage the pharmacy or practice site to evaluate who should be accessing patient records. If support staff do not need patient medical records to do their jobs, they should not have access. A pharmacy student accessing a relative's medical records at a hospital during their intern experience (when they are not involved with the relative's medical care at the facility) would constitute a privacy violation.

It is permissible to share PHI with:

- The patient

- <u>Other healthcare providers</u> providing care to the patient

- Persons requiring the information for <u>treatment, payment, or operational</u> purposes

- Others, when authorized by the patient

- A limited data set can be provided for research, public health or institutional operations

- <u>Law enforcement</u>, the DEA, the FDA, medical board inspectors, pharmacy board inspectors (for a public health purpose or drug abuse concern)

Pharmacists may leave voicemails regarding medications on patients' home machines, discuss care with patients' family members or caregivers, and provide written material. Prescriptions can be picked up by family or friends unless the pharmacist has reason to believe that this would be against the wishes of the patient.

If the release of patient health information is not for purposes of treatment, payment, or operations, the pharmacist must receive the <u>patient's written authorization</u>. This authorization must include whom the information will be shared with, the purpose, the expiration date, and the patient's signature. If the patient is requesting the release, a written authorization is not necessary according to HIPAA, but some facilities will require it.

THE NOTICE OF PRIVACY PRACTICES

HIPAA requires a site-specific notice on the policies in place to protect patient information and to whom the information can be shared. This should be in simple language, and state the patient's rights to their own information and be specific that any release beyond that which is stated in the policy will require the patient's approval. It should list the contact for Department of Health & Human Services if the patient wishes to file a complaint, along with the contact for a person within the pharmacy if the patient wishes to discuss privacy concerns.

The <u>privacy notice</u> must be given to the patient on the <u>first day</u> that service is provided. The pharmacy must make a good faith effort to obtain the patient's <u>written acknowledgment </u>of the receipt of the notice. A covered entity must promptly revise and distribute its notice whenever there are changes to any of its privacy practices. The pharmacy <u>can still provide services if the patient refuses to sign</u>. This written acknowledgment must be separate from other signatures. This means that one signature cannot be used to both acknowledge receipt of the HIPAA privacy notice, and to acknowledge another item, such as refusing the right to counsel. The signature for HIPAA must be separate. The HIPAA privacy notice should also be placed in a prominent location within the pharmacy and on the pharmacy's website. The patient has a right to request all of their privacy disclosures for the past 6 years; thus, the HIPAA signed privacy disclosure forms must be kept for <u>6 years</u>.

DRUG SUBSTITUTION OR SELECTION

GENERIC DRUG SUBSTITUTION

Every state has a generic drug substitution law, which permits or mandates the pharmacist to substitute a brand name drug with a generic drug. The purpose is to provide the patient with a lower cost drug, while still providing the same therapeutic benefit. Drug substitution laws vary by state. Most state laws permit pharmacists to substitute generic, therapeutically-equivalent drugs for the branded drug using the FDA's *Orange Book: Approved Drug Products with Therapeutic Equivalence Evaluations*, unless the prescriber and/or patient has requested otherwise. Not all states reference the *Orange Book*; for example, in Georgia, "A pharmacist may substitute a drug with the same generic name in the same strength, quantity, dose, and dosage form as the prescribed brand name drug product which is, in the pharmacist's reasonable professional opinion, pharmaceutically equivalent."[28]

When a prescriber writes the brand name of a drug on a prescription, the pharmacist may substitute with a generic as long as the prescriber has not indicated otherwise. If the prescriber writes or checks off a box with his/her initials that states DO NOT SUBSTITUTE, no substitution can be made. Some state laws permit the pharmacist to decide whether or not to make a generic substitution; this is called a permissive drug product selection law. Other states make it mandatory to make a generic substitution unless the patient or prescriber has noted otherwise; this is called a mandatory drug product selection law.

It is considered misbranding if the pharmacist labeled a generic drug as the brand drug, or vice versa. This practice may be done because the pharmacist is attempting to increase profits by billing insurance for the more expensive brand name drug but dispensing a lower cost generic drug.

My state permits generic substitution according to the *Orange Book*, unless certain action/s have been taken by the prescriber and/or patient. Yes / No

If yes, list the actions that must be taken to prevent generic interchange: _____

My state permits generic substitution according to requirements other than the *Orange Book*. Yes / No

If yes, list the requirements and the actions a prescriber and/or patient can take to block the substitution: _____

USING THE ORANGE BOOK

The Food and Drug Administration publishes and frequently updates the *Approved Drug Products with Therapeutic Equivalence Evaluations* (commonly known as the *Orange Book*), which serves as a guide for therapeutically equivalent drugs. If a drug is listed as a generic equivalent in the *Orange Book*, it means that the generic has demonstrated pharmaceutical equivalence and bioequivalence.

28 *Georgia Code, Title 26, Chapter 4, Article 5, 2014*

AB-Rated Drugs are Therapeutically Equivalent and Can Be Interchanged

The *Orange Book* uses a two-letter code system. Drugs that have the AB code are therapeutically equivalent to an individual brand name drug, which is called the <u>reference listed drug</u> (RLD). Most states permit brand drugs to be interchanged with AB-generics as a cost-savings measure.

In some instances, (e.g., levothyroxine) a number is added to the end of the two letters to make a 3-character code (AB1, AB2, AB3, etc.) Three-character codes are assigned when more than one

RLD of the same strength has been designated under the same heading. With levothyroxine, a generic dosage that has a 3-character code can be used to substitute for 3 different branded drugs with the same dose.

The Electronic *Orange Book* (EOB) can be accessed on the FDA website at http://www.accessdata.fda.gov/scripts/cder/ob/default.cfm.

N021402	AB1,AB2	No	LEVOTHYROXINE SODIUM	TABLET; ORAL	0.025MG **See current Annual Edition, 1.8 Description of Special Situations, Levothyroxine Sodium	SYNTHROID	ABBVIE INC
N021402	AB1,AB2	Yes	LEVOTHYROXINE SODIUM	TABLET; ORAL	0.3MG **See current Annual Edition, 1.8 Description of Special Situations, Levothyroxine Sodium	SYNTHROID	ABBVIE INC
N021210	AB1,AB2,AB3	No	LEVOTHYROXINE SODIUM	TABLET; ORAL	0.025MG **See current Annual Edition, 1.8 Description of Special Situations, Levothyroxine Sodium	UNITHROID	JEROME STEVENS PHARMACEUTICALS INC
N021210	AB1,AB2,AB3	No	LEVOTHYROXINE SODIUM	TABLET; ORAL	0.05MG **See current Annual Edition, 1.8 Description of Special Situations, Levothyroxine Sodium	UNITHROID	JEROME STEVENS PHARMACEUTICALS INC

Orange book listing for some of the levothyroxine oral tablets.

NARROW THERAPEUTIC INDEX DRUG SUBSTITUTION

Narrow therapeutic index (NTI) drugs are defined as drugs where small differences in dose or blood concentration could cause treatment failure or toxicity. NTI drugs have very small differences between the subtherapeutic dose, the therapeutic dose, and the toxic dose. Even small differences in bioavailability between generic drugs can cause a significant difference in serum drug concentration. Examples of NTI drugs include lithium, digoxin and warfarin. Each of these drugs requires close monitoring.

Several states (Florida, Idaho, Kentucky, Maine, Minnesota, North Carolina, Pennsylvania, Rhode Island and Hawaii) do not permit substitution of NTI drugs and will define an NTI list that could include a few or up to a dozen different NTI drugs. This is commonly referred to as a <u>negative formulary</u>. In these states, the NTI drug must be dispensed with the same formulation from the same manufacturer as was previously filled to provide therapeutic consistency for the patient, unless the prescriber and/or the patient have been notified and consents to the change.

My state permits substitution of NTI drugs unless this action/s has been taken by the prescriber and/or patient. Yes / No

My state does not routinely permit the pharmacist to substitute an NTI drug. Yes / No

NTI drugs that cannot be substituted in my state include: _____

BIOLOGICS AND BIOSIMILARS

Biologics are discussed under the Biologics Price Competition and Innovation Act (BPCI) of 2000. Biologics are manufactured from living organisms by programming cell lines to produce the desired therapeutic substances. They are complex, large molecules. True generics for biologics are not possible according to the conventional definition, therefore the term biosimilar is used instead. Common biologics in use today include human growth hormone, injectable treatments for arthritis and psoriasis, among others. The first biosimilar was approved in 2014.

PHARMACY & THERAPEUTICS COMMITTEE

Formulary members who serve on the P&T committee

The P&T committee is responsible for all aspects of drug use in a healthcare system, which could be a small hospital or a large PBM. The P&T members would include physicians, pharmacists, nurse/s, administrator/s, quality improvement manager/s and the medication safety officer. The primary responsibilities of the P&T committee are to create and update the formulary (a continual process as drugs change), conduct medication (or drug) use evaluation (MUE/DUE), have responsibility for adverse drug event monitoring and reporting, and conduct medication error safety initiatives (which will involve the medication safety officer) and develop the clinical care plans and protocols. This includes the development of protocols to guide the use of high-alert drugs, which have a high risk of causing patient harm when used incorrectly.

Hospital pharmacists rely on guidance from the American Society of Hospital Pharmacists (ASHP), the Joint Commission, the Institute of Safe Medication Practices (ISMP) and select professional organizations for best practices in hospitals, such as high-alert drug protocol development, management of blood products, quality assurance for sterile compounding, therapeutic interchange, and many other areas related to the practice of hospital pharmacy.

DRUG FORMULARIES

A formulary is a preferred drug list that a hospital or other institution, healthcare plan, or pharmacy benefit manager (PBM) has chosen for their patients or members. The formulary should include the <u>safest</u> and <u>most effective</u> drugs according to current clinical guidelines/practices, while taking <u>cost</u> into consideration. When similar drugs exist in a class, a competitive bidding process is used. For example, if a P&T committee wishes to select a prostaglandin analogue for glaucoma, and there are five equally safe and effective agents on the market, the committee is likely to choose the least expensive option.

Healthcare plans have formularies to outline which drugs will be covered in the outpatient or retail setting. Patients can refer to these formularies to be aware of different tiers and copays. The typical formulary for outpatient use has 3, 4, or 5 tiers. The lower tier level has a lower copay. A copay is the out-of-pocket expense that the patient is responsible for in order to receive services such as doctors visits and prescription drugs. Specialty drugs, including the biologics, will be placed on a high tier (such as tier 4 or 5) and may require prior authorization from the insurance plan in order to permit the patient to obtain the drug using the insurance coverage.

An example of formulary drug tiers for outpatient prescription medications:

TIER	TIER NAME	COST TO PATIENT (COPAY)
1	Generic drugs	$5 per prescription
2	Preferred brand drugs	$15 per prescription
3	Non-preferred brand drugs	$25 per prescription
4	Specialty drugs	10% copay, up to $250 maximum per prescription

If a drug has a history of unsafe use, it may be withdrawn from the formulary. If there are sound-alike, look-alike drugs, the P&T committee may remove one of them to avoid mix-ups. If multiple drugs have similar risk-benefit profiles, it is likely the least expensive drug will be included and the pricier drug will be excluded. Or, if one agent has safety risks but is effective in refractory cases, it can be given restricted-use status and can be used only if the patient has failed the first-line agents.

THERAPEUTIC INTERCHANGE

Therapeutic interchange is the dispensing of medications by pharmacists that are chemically different, but therapeutically similar, to the medication prescribed. The drug that is substituted is usually in the same pharmacological/therapeutic class. Most hospitals, nursing facilities and other healthcare institutions have therapeutic interchange protocols as a cost-effective strategy: a new and more expensive drug can be interchanged with an older, less costly drug that provides a similar therapeutic benefit. Therapeutic interchange has become much more common in recent years because of many drugs in the same therapeutic class. The P&T committee will determine which drugs should be included in the institution's therapeutic interchange protocol.

The pharmacist who substitutes one drug for another does not need to discuss the change with a physician as long as the substitution is established in the institution's therapeutic interchange protocol. For example, if rosuvastatin (*Crestor*) is not on the formulary but the generic atorvastatin and simvastatin are on the formulary, the hospital pharmacist will choose the therapeutically equivalent dose of a formulary drug when *Crestor* is ordered by the physician. The agents most commonly included on therapeutic interchange programs are antacids, H2-blockers, hypnotics, ACE inhibitors, angiotensin receptor blockers, proton pump inhibitors, potassium supplements, quinolones, first, second and third-generation cephalosporins, statins, insulins, topical steroids and laxatives and stool softeners.

Example of therapeutic equivalence: For all other PPIs, use pantoprazole 40 mg.

Example of IV to PO (can be written as IV:PO) conversion: For levofloxacin IV to treat a mild-moderate infection in a patient consuming a normal diet (not NPO), use the same dose of oral levofloxacin (e.g., 500 or 250 mg).

Therapeutic interchange can also be used in ambulatory practice settings as long as the two basic requirements exist: the presence of a functioning formulary system and a P&T committee.

PHARMACY COMPOUNDING

TRADITIONAL COMPOUNDING AND SECTION 503A

In November 2013, under section 503A of the Drug Quality and Security Act (DQSA), drug products prepared using traditional compounding methods were given three exemptions from requirements that apply to prescription drugs:

- Compliance with current good manufacturing practices (CGMP)

- Labeling with adequate directions for use

- The need to obtain FDA approval for the new drug product

Traditional compounding must be performed by a licensed pharmacist (or in some cases, by a physician), and be based on a prescription that has been written for an individual patient. Traditional compounding enables the pharmacist to prepare a drug formulation to fit the unique needs of an individual patient. There are valid reasons why this type of compounding may be required:

- If a drug exists only in a tablet or capsule and the patient has difficulty swallowing hard formulations

- In shortages; for example, if a drug typically comes in a suspension for children's use but only the capsule formulation is available, a pharmacist may compound the capsule contents into a suspension[29]

- To create a dose or concentration that is not commercially available

- To add flavoring for palatability

- To exclude inactive ingredients (excipients) that an individual patient has an allergy or sensitivity to, such as wheat, lactose or a certain preservative

Section 503A also permits the pharmacist to prepare small batches of a compounded preparation in advance if the dispensing history of the store supports the need. The primary reason for this allowance is convenience; it takes time to set up ingredients and equipment, prepare the product, document the preparation, and clean the area. If a pharmacist in a medical building prepares 3-4 prescriptions of the same strength of a progesterone cream each day, the pharmacy can prepare a few days' worth of the cream so it is ready when the prescriptions are received. Federal law does not define an exact amount of compounded drug that can be prepared in advance, but some states define a set number of days (such as 3 days). These preparations will need to be labeled with the appropriate beyond use date (BUD).

---

29 For example, in the 2009-2010 H1N1 influenza pandemic, there was a shortage of liquid Tamiflu. Pharmacists in almost every state were able to compound the capsules into flavored suspensions in order to fill prescriptions written for young children.

OUTSOURCING FACILITIES AND SECTION 503B

In 2012, a fungal meningitis outbreak due to contaminated methylprednisolone injections prepared at the infamous New England Compounding Center (NECC) led to over 700 fungal infections and 64 deaths nationwide.[30] NECC prepared vials of methylprednisolone injections in bulk in order to capitalize on a drug shortage and distributed the drug across state lines. The vials were contaminated due to unsanitary conditions and lack of aseptic technique. Pharmacists involved have been charged with murder, racketeering, and mail fraud due to the gross negligence involved with these preparations. This highly publicized public health crisis led to stricter compounding regulations nationwide.

Shortly after the NECC meningitis outbreak, the federal Food, Drug, and Cosmetic act was amended to add section 503B. This legislation permits specially licensed compounding facilities to operate as an "outsourcing facility" in order to prepare medications in bulk and without a prescription written for an individual patient as long as the facility met certain requirements. This is especially important in the event of drug shortages. To register as an outsourcing facility under 503B, the facility needs to be compounding sterile drugs for humans.

Facilities can operate as an outsourcing facility if the following requirements are met:

- The drugs must be compounded in compliance with current good manufacturing practices

- The facility is licensed as an outsourcing facility by the FDA.

- The facility is subject to inspection by the FDA.

- The preparations must be made by or under the supervision of a licensed pharmacist.

- The facility must meet certain labeling requirements, drug reporting requirements, and adverse event reporting requirements.

COMPOUNDING VERSUS MANUFACTURING

Manufacturing involves the development and production of licensed drugs, which are produced in bulk for groups of patients rather than for an individual patient. Outsourcing facility pharmacies can bulk-compound—this is an explicit exception provided under 503B.

- Manufacturing and outsourcing facilities[31] are regulated by the FDA; traditional compounding is regulated by state boards

- Manufacturing requires CGMPs; compounding does not, unless it is an outsourcing facility

- Manufacturing does not require a prescription; traditional compounding is done by prescription for a specific patient

- Manufactured drugs have NDC numbers; compounded drugs do not

- Outsourcing facilities require a separate license, must register with the FDA, but are not registered as drug manufacturers, and the agency does not approve their prescriptions before marketing, nor automatically receive adverse events reports

30 https://www.cdc.gov/hai/outbreaks/meningitis.html (accessed 2019 Jan 15).
31 http://www.fda.gov/downloads/drugs/guidancecomplianceregulatoryinformation/guidances/ucm377051.pdf (accessed 2019 Jan 15).

My state has additional requirements for compounding that go beyond federal requirements.
Yes / No

If yes, list the additional compounding requirements: _____

_____

My state permits drugs that were compounded in another state to be sent to patients in my state.
Yes / No

If yes, list the requirements that must be met (such as any required inspections, required permits
and fees): _____

_____

NON-STERILE COMPOUNDING

Community pharmacies regularly perform non-sterile compounding on a routine basis. Some
states define mixing water with powder for a suspension as compounding. Other states do not
refer to this process as compounding; it is simply referred to as reconstitution. The non-sterile
compounding chapter in the RxPrep Course book describes commonly used compounding
equipment (balances, spatulas, etc.), preparations (suspensions, emulsions, etc.) and terminology
(levigation, trituration, etc.).

The compounding master formula, record log and label requirements are provided in detail in
USP Chapter 795.

STERILE COMPOUNDING

The most common type of sterile compounding is preparing IV medications in a hospital setting.
If the medication is not prepared in an aseptic manner and becomes contaminated, the pathogen
(which will be injected directly into the patient's blood stream) could cause infection. This is
what caused the large number of infections and fatalities with the NECC fiasco.

Sterile compounding is required for injections, inhalations, wound and cavity irrigation baths,
eye drops and eye ointments. Water used in a sterile preparation must be sterile water for
injection, or bacteriostatic water for injection. Sterile compounding requires personnel trained
and evaluated at least annually for competency in aseptic techniques, environmental control,
quality assurance testing and end-product evaluation and sterility testing. If the product is an
injectable, the certified sterile compounding environment must be either an ISO class 5 (class
100) laminar air flow hood within an ISO class 7 (class 10,000) clean room (with positive air
pressure differential relative to adjacent areas) or an ISO class 5 (class 100) clean room with
positive air pressure differential relative to adjacent areas or a barrier isolator that provides an
ISO class 5 (class 100) environment.

Clean room garb (low-shedding coverall, head cover, face mask and shoe covers) is required and
should be put on and taken off outside the designated area. Hand, finger and wrist jewelry is not
allowed. Head and facial hair have to be out of the way (tied up) and covered. Cytotoxic agents
require specialized gowns, gloves, masks and product labeling.

MASTER FORMULATION RECORD

The formulation record is the formula or "recipe" book that the pharmacy uses to prepare compounded products. This is the "how-to" instructions for the compounded products made at that pharmacy. Some of the formulas may be based on the store's past experience and others will come from professional compounding compendia.

The formulation record must be complete enough to enable any competent staff member to follow the instructions and replicate the product. The formulation record should include:

- The official or assigned name, strength, and dosage form of the preparation

- The calculations needed to determine and verify the quantities of the components and the doses of the active pharmaceutical ingredients (APIs)

- A description of all ingredients and their quantities

- Compatibility, stability and storage information, including references when available

- Equipment needed to prepare the preparation

- Appropriate mixing instructions that should include:

    ❏ Order of mixing

    ❏ Mixing temperatures or other environmental controls

    ❏ Duration of mixing

THE COMPOUNDING RECORD OR LOG BOOK

The compounding record book is used to document individual products prepared and should include:

- Official or assigned name

- Strength and dosage of the preparation

- Master Formulation Record reference for the preparation

- Names and quantities of all components

- Sources, lot numbers, and expiration dates of all components

- Total quantity compounded

- Name of the person who prepared the preparation

- Name of the person who performed the quality control procedures

- Name of the compounding pharmacist who approved the preparation

- Date of preparation

- Assigned control or prescription number

- Assigned BUD

- Duplicate container label that is placed in the log book

- Description of final preparation

- Results of quality control procedures (e.g., weight range of filled capsules, pH of aqueous liquids)

- Documentation of any quality control issues and any adverse reactions or preparation problems reported by the patient or caregiver

COMPOUNDED PRODUCT LABELS

The label on the container must include:

- Generic name

- Quantity or concentration of each active ingredient (for capsules include the mcg or mg/capsule)

- Beyond use date

- Storage conditions

- The prescription or control number, whichever is applicable

- Container used in dispensing

- Any required auxiliary labels (such as "Shake Well" for emulsions and suspensions, "Keep Refrigerated", "External Use Only")

- The label should include the statement or similar "This is a compounded preparation"

- Packaging and storage requirements

STAFF TRAINING REQUIREMENTS FOR COMPOUNDING

All staff require on-going, periodic training for the type of compounding conducted. The staff need to be evaluated at least <u>annually</u>. During the training session, the steps are demonstrated to the staff that will be making preparations. The staff must be able to demonstrate the steps back, without instruction. All training and evaluation results must be documented. Steps in the training procedure should include: hand hygiene, garbing, sanitization of compounding areas, proper aseptic technique, labeling, and recordkeeping.

The compounding pharmacist who has signed off on the product is responsible for the finished preparation.

BEYOND USE DATING AND EXPIRATION DATES FOR COMPOUNDED PRODUCTS

The USP emphasizes that beyond use date (BUD) should be applied conservatively. If an expiration date of any of the active pharmaceutical ingredients (API) is sooner than the BUD, the earlier expiration date is used. If drug-specific stability data is available, it should be used to make the BUD determination.

The storage must be considered; products kept in a refrigerator will usually be stable for longer periods than products left at room temperature since heat speeds up chemical reactions that can degrade the substance. The container can be chosen to block out light and moisture. Light and humidity exposure contributes to degradation. Preservatives may be required to block microbial contamination. The preservatives are required in sterile formulations that contain more than one dose. The BUDs for non-sterile and compounded sterile preparations (CSPs), in the absence of stability studies, are listed below.

NON-STERILE FORMULATION	BEYOND USE DATE
Nonaqueous Formulations	The BUD is not later than the time remaining until the earliest expiration date of any API or 6 months, whichever is earlier.
Water-Containing Oral Formulations	The BUD is not later than 14 days when stored at controlled cold temperatures.
Water-Containing Topical/Dermal and Mucosal Liquid and Semisolid Formulations	The BUD is not later than 30 days.

CSP RISK LEVEL	BUD ROOM TEMP	BUD FRIDGE TEMP	BUD FREEZER TEMP
Low	48 hours	14 days	45 days
Low non-HD Low/medium HD < 12-hr BUD	12 hours	12 hours	N/A
Medium	30 hours	9 days	45 days
High	24 hours	3 days	45 days
Immediate-use	1 hour	N/A	N/A

HANDLING HAZARDOUS DRUGS

The National Institute for Occupational Safety and Health (NIOSH) issues a list of hazardous drugs (HDs) that require special precautions in order to prevent work-related injury and illness. HDs can cause harm to healthcare staff who handle them, including pharmacists, technicians, nurses and cleaning staff. Common HDs include antineoplastics (chemotherapy drugs), pregnancy category X drugs, hormones, and transplant drugs. The standard for handling drugs on the NIOSH list are set by the U.S. Pharmacopeia (USP), in Chapter 800.[32] The standards were recently published. Many states are in the process of integrating all or part of USP 800 into their regulations.

Minimally, a pharmacy or other setting handling HDs must have the following:

- Engineering controls, such as closed system transfer devices and negative pressure ventilated cabinets (e.g., biological safety cabinets). The hoods vent the drug's toxic fumes to the outside (away from the staff standing at the hood).

- Personal protective equipment (e.g., protective gown, respiratory protection, goggles, chemotherapy gloves). HDs will require either single or double gloves when handling.

---

32 https://www.usp.org/sites/default/files/usp/document/our-work/healthcare-quality-safety/general-chapter-800.pdf (accessed 2019 Jan 15).

- Safe work practices, <u>spill kits</u>, and disposal requirements.

For more information, refer to the RxPrep Course Book, Handling Hazardous Drugs chapter.

DISPENSING UNDER SPECIAL CIRCUMSTANCES

CONSCIENCE OR MORAL CLAUSES

The pharmacist's right to refuse dispensing certain medications based on the pharmacist's religious or moral beliefs has been a controversial issue. The medications involved usually are <u>emergency contraception</u>, oral contraceptives, abortion pills, erectile dysfunction drugs, and medications used for physician-assisted suicide. Some states have issued refusal or conscience clauses allowing pharmacists to refuse dispensing prescriptions based on personal values.[33]

A handful of states (Colorado, Florida, Illinois, Maine and Tennessee), there are broad refusal clauses in state legislation that apply to all healthcare providers. In some states, including California, a pharmacist must dispense the prescription, unless the employer was informed of the objection ahead of time and another pharmacist can provide the medication in a timely manner. In other states, such as New Jersey, refusal is prohibited on moral, religious or ethical grounds, in all circumstances.

Most of the debate revolves around a pharmacist dispensing emergency contraception. Emergency contraception is used to prevent a pregnancy, not terminate a pregnancy. A handful of states (Arizona, Arkansas, Georgia, Idaho, Mississippi, and South Dakota) have passed laws specifically allowing a pharmacist to refuse to dispense emergency contraception drugs.

If your state has enacted legislation concerning pharmacist conscience clauses, list the drugs involved and alternate methods, if stipulated, to provide the patients with the medication:

REQUIREMENTS FOR DEATH WITH DIGNITY

Death with dignity is another controversial issue as it goes against many healthcare providers' oath to do no harm. Currently, the states of California, Colorado, Oregon, Vermont, Washington, and Washington D.C. have Death with Dignity laws, which allow <u>mentally competent, terminally ill adult state residents</u> to voluntarily request for physician-assisted death and receive a prescription medication to end their life in a quick and painless manner.[34] Typically, controlled substances (i.e., <u>secobarbital, pentobarbital</u>) are prescribed for this purpose.

To be eligible, the patient must meet the following requirements:

- 18 years of age or older

- A resident of a state permitting physician-assisted death

- Capable of making and communicating healthcare decisions for him/herself

---

33   http://www.ncsl.org/research/health/pharmacist-conscience-clauses-laws-and-information.aspx (accessed 2019 Jan 15).
34   https://www.deathwithdignity.org/learn/healthcare-providers/ (accessed 2019 Jan 15).

- Diagnosed with a terminal illness that will lead to death within 6 months

- Two physicians must determine whether the above criteria have been met

Timeline it takes for a patient to receive medication:

- Patient makes first oral request to the physician

- After at least 15 days from the initial request, the patient makes a second oral request to the physician

- Patient makes a written request to the physician

- After at least 48 hours from the written request, the patient may pick up the prescribed medications from the pharmacy

MEDICATION PROVISIONS DURING DECLARATION OF DISASTER OR EMERGENCY

The Emergency Prescription Assistance Program (EPAP) is a federal program managed by the Department of Health and Human Services, which provides a way for pharmacies to process claims for prescription medications and limited durable medical equipment (DME) provided to uninsured individuals from a disaster area declared by the U.S. President.[35] Claims for individuals with health insurance are not eligible for payment under the EPAP. Claims will be processed for a specific period of time to be determined under the EPAP activation.

Eligible individuals may be provided essential pharmaceutical and DME written prescription assistance limited to a 30-day supply for a medication to treat an acute condition, to replace maintenance prescription drugs or medical equipment lost as a direct result of a disaster event or as a secondary result of loss or damage caused while in transit from the emergency site to the designated shelter facility, at no cost to the patient. Enrolled pharmacies must check for other forms of health insurance coverage at the point of sale to determine eligibility.

In order to receive prescription medications and/or DME, eligible individuals must have one of the following:

- New prescription from a licensed healthcare practitioner

- Current prescription bottle

- Prescription called in by a licensed healthcare practitioner

- Proof of an existing prescription

Enrolled pharmacies must dispense the generic form of medication unless otherwise indicated as Brand Medically Necessary (BMN) or Dispense as Written (DAW) by the licensed healthcare provider.

35   http://www.phe.gov/Preparedness/planning/epap/Pages/pharmacies.aspx (accessed 2019 Jan 18).

TELEPHARMACY

States that have patients in remote, rural areas have enacted regulations for telemedicine and telepharmacy to help improve healthcare delivery to underserved communities. These regulations allow the practice of virtual pharmacy using remote order verification, automated dispensing systems (ADS), videoconferencing, telephones, and the Internet. Telepharmacy provides pharmacists with a means to verify prescriptions, perform drug utilization reviews, and counsel patients remotely. State laws usually require remote telepharmacy sites to have a pharmacy license in order to receive third party reimbursement.

Patients bring prescriptions to the remote sites, which are staffed by pharmacy technicians or nurses. The central pharmacist supervises the workflow over a teleconferencing system (in real-time) and verifies prescriptions transmitted from the rural site. The prescription label and prepackaged medication are then dispensed from the ADS at the remote site. The pharmacy technician scans the barcode, attaches the label, and dispenses the medication to the patient. Finally, the pharmacist at the central location counsels the patient through a real-time video.

VACCINE ADMINISTRATION

Pharmacists play an important role in disease prevention by advocating and administering immunizations. The pharmacist's authority to administer vaccines is determined by each state's laws and regulations governing pharmacy practice. All 50 states permit some type of vaccine administration by pharmacists as part of their scope of pharmacy practice.

Vaccine administration may occur pursuant to individual prescription orders or through standing orders or protocols. The Centers for Disease Control (CDC) Advisory Committee on Immunization Practices (ACIP) encourages pharmacists and other healthcare providers to establish standing order programs in long-term care facilities, home healthcare agencies, hospitals, clinics, workplaces, and managed care organizations. In year 2002, the Centers for Medicare and Medicaid Services (CMS) no longer requires a physician order for influenza or pneumococcal immunizations administered in participating hospitals, long-term care facilities, or home healthcare agencies.[36] State-specific protocols or standing-order programs can be developed with state pharmacy associations, boards of pharmacy, and health departments.

Most states will require pharmacists to complete formal training before administering vaccines. Training can include:

■ The epidemiology of and patient populations at risk for vaccine-preventable diseases

■ Public health goals for immunization (e.g., local, regional, state, and federal goals)

■ Vaccine safety (e.g., risk–benefit analysis)

36 "Medicare and Medicaid Programs; Conditions of Participation: Immunization Standards for Hospitals, Long-Term Care Facilities, and Home Health Agencies; Final Rule with Comment Period," 67 Federal Register 191 (2 October 2002), pp. 61808-61814.

- Screening for contraindications and precautions of vaccination

- Vaccine stability, transportation and storage requirements

- Immunologic drug interactions

- Vaccine dosing, including interpreting recommended immunization schedules and patient immunization records, and determining proper dosing intervals and the feasibility of simultaneous administration of multiple vaccines

- Proper dose preparation and injection techniques

- Signs and symptoms of adverse reactions to vaccines, adverse reaction reporting, and emergency procedures, such as basic and advanced cardiac life support (BCLS and ACLS)

- Documentation

- Reporting to the primary care provider or local health department and the vaccine registry

- Billing

RETURN, DISPOSAL, OR REUSE OF MEDICATIONS

RETURNING OR DISPOSING PRESCRIPTION MEDICATION TO THE SUPPLIER

The FDA permits pharmacies to return prescription drugs to wholesalers and manufacturers as long as there is proper recordkeeping. Prescription drugs that are outdated, damaged, deteriorated, misbranded, or adulterated must be physically separated from other prescription drugs until they are destroyed or returned to the supplier.[37]

Opened prescription drug containers must be identified as opened (this is often done in the pharmacy by marking an "X" on the container), and kept physically separated from the un-opened containers if they are sent to be destroyed or are returned to the supplier.

If the storage conditions under which a prescription drug has been returned cast any doubt on the drug's safety, identity, strength, quality, or purity, then the drug should be returned to the wholesaler or manufacturer, or sent to disposal, unless the contents can be tested and the quality has been confirmed.

RETURNS FROM THE PHARMACY WILL CALL (PICK UP) AREA

If a patient has not picked up filled medication (which has not left the pharmacy premise), the unclaimed medication can be returned to stock, provided that there is an expiration date on the label. The returned medication can be combined with a stock bottle only if they have the same lot number.

Many states or companies have implemented their own policies on unclaimed medications, such as requiring courtesy calls if medication is unclaimed and a time duration before the medication can be returned to stock.

---

37   21 CFR 205.50

My state requires a courtesy call if a patient has not picked up their medication within a given time frame. Yes / No

If yes, specify the time frame: _____

My state does not permit medications to be returned to the shelf until this amount of time has passed: _____

CHARITABLE PROGRAMS

Commonly, states permit prescription drugs in single use or sealed packaging from state programs, nursing homes and medical facilities to be provided to low-income residents who cannot afford their drugs. This helps offset the costs of providing healthcare to uninsured patients in emergency rooms and clinics. The laws include some restrictions to secure the drug integrity, including:[38]

- Drugs must be in the original, unopened, sealed, and tamper-evident unit-dose packaging

- Drugs must not be expired

- The expiration date must be visible and at least 6 months from the donation date (in most states)

- Controlled substances cannot be donated—these are excluded (in most states)

- A state-licensed pharmacist or pharmacy is part of the verification and distribution process

- The patient receiving the donated drugs requires a valid prescription

DRUG DONATIONS TO CANCER OR OTHER REPOSITORY PROGRAMS

A handful of states (Colorado, Florida, Kentucky, Michigan, Minnesota, Montana, Nebraska, Nevada, Ohio, Pennsylvania, Utah, Washington, and Wisconsin) have enacted programs specifically for accepting and distributing unused cancer-related prescription drugs.

PATIENTS RETURNING PREVIOUSLY DISPENSED MEDICATIONS TO THE PHARMACY

On occasion, patients come back to the pharmacy asking to return prescription medications. This can be due to a variety of reasons: the dose may have changed, the course of treatment has been completed, or the patient simply has too much of the drug. The FDA compliance policy guide recommends that a pharmacist should not accept returned drugs from patients and return it to the pharmacy shelves (or pharmacy stock) after it has left the pharmacy premises.[39] This is because the pharmacist would no longer have any assurance of the strength, quality, purity or identity of the drugs. Many state boards of pharmacy have regulations prohibiting this practice. The pharmacist dispensing a drug is legally responsible for the adulteration that may be present if the returned drugs are combined with the pharmacy stock and subsequently re-dispensed to other patients.

38   http://www.ncsl.org/research/health/state-prescription-drug-return-reuse-and-recycling.aspx (accessed 2019 Jan 15).
39   http://www.fda.gov/ICECI/ComplianceManuals/CompliancePolicyGuidanceManual/ucm074399.htm (accessed 2019 Jan 15).

DISPOSAL OF PRESCRIPTION MEDICATION BY THE ULTIMATE USER

Community-based drug "take-back" programs are good options for patients to dispose of prescription medications. The take-back program offered by the DEA was temporarily discontinued but has now been restarted.[40] Patients should check on the DEA's website or contact their city or county government's household trash and recycling service to see if a local take-back program is available.

There are also new rules that allow authorized facilities, such as pharmacies, to collect unused and unwanted prescription drugs, including controlled substances. Previously, controlled substances could only be returned to a location with law enforcement present. A facility that is willing to collect unused drugs will need to apply for a permit.

Patients should follow any specific disposal instructions on the prescription drug labeling or patient information that accompanies the drug. Drugs should not be flushed down the sink or toilet unless instructed by the prescription labeling.

If no disposal instructions are given on the prescription drug labeling and no local take-back program is available, patients should dispose of drugs in the household trash following these steps:

- Remove the drugs from their original containers and mix them with an undesirable substance, such as kitty litter or used coffee grounds (this makes the drug less appealing to children and pets, and unrecognizable to people who may intentionally go through the trash seeking drugs)

- Place the mixture in a sealable bag, empty can, or other container, then discard in the trash

Some drugs are especially harmful if taken by someone other than the person for whom the medication was prescribed, and some of the medications that have the highest risk will include specific disposal instructions on the labeling. This may include instructions to immediately flush unused medication or used medication patches down the toilet. For example, too much fentanyl can cause severe respiratory depression and lead to death. Leftover and used fentanyl patches should be flushed down the toilet.

It is not acceptable practice to flush drugs down the toilet except where the risk is high. See the dispensing controlled substances section of this manual for more information on disposal of controlled substances.

40   http://www.deadiversion.usdoj.gov/drug_disposal/takeback/ (accessed 2019 Jan 15).

MANUFACTURER DRUG SAMPLES GIVEN TO PRESCRIBERS TO PROVIDE TO PATIENTS

The practice of drug company sales representatives providing drug samples to prescribers in order to push sales for their drugs has caused significant issues for safe drug delivery for many years. They also help steer use toward expensive brand drugs when less expensive generic alternatives may be available. The drug samples that are given to prescribers can become expired, adulterated, misbranded, or diverted, since they may not have been kept in proper storage requirements and may have been repackaged or relabeled.

The Prescription Drug Marketing Act (PDMA) regulated manufacturer activities to prevent drug diversion, adulteration, misbranding, and included restrictions on distributing drug samples. Samples can only be given to prescribers or to a hospital pharmacy or other healthcare entity at the written request of the prescriber. A "healthcare entity" is defined to specifically exclude retail pharmacies.

Sample drugs must be stored separately from other drug inventory. Many states require the prescriber's office to maintain receipts of samples received. Drug samples are different from "starter packs," and from drugs that are provided free of charge, or at a reduced price, pursuant to an indigent patient program.

RESALE OF DISCOUNTED PRESCRIPTION DRUGS

Many hospitals and health maintenance organizations are able to purchase drugs at a discounted rate due to competitive bidding and nonprofit status. In the past, additional drug was ordered or excess drug inventory was found to be present, and was resold. The institution made money by selling the drugs to community pharmacies or other healthcare facilities at a profit.

The resale of prescription drugs was prohibited by PDMA, with these exceptions:

- Sales or purchases to other facilities within the same organization

- Sales to nonprofit affiliates

- For emergency reasons

PRESCRIPTION MEDICATION LOSS OR THEFT

In the event of a robbery, the pharmacy staff should not resist, either verbally or physically. The staff should never try to apprehend or restrain the robber. Robbers are often armed. The staff members should take notice of the appearance of the robber in order to provide a description to law enforcement later. The pharmacy staff should sound the alarm and call the police when it is safe to do so. Doors should be locked immediately to prevent re-entry.

Theft or loss of controlled substances must be documented on a DEA Form 106. See the dispensing controlled substances section of this manual for more information on reporting loss or theft of controlled substances. The DEA recommends the following measures to be aware of and reduce the risk of theft:[41, 42]

- Maintain an inventory of controlled substances

- Monitor staff for changes in behavior or mood

- Contact law enforcement if theft is suspected

- Perform criminal background checks for all pharmacy staff

- Give alarm codes for all personnel

- Limit issuance of pharmacy keys

- Change locks, alarm codes, and safe combinations periodically

- Ensure lighting is adequate in the pharmacy area at all times

- Place opioids out of sight

- Have obvious surveillance or cameras in plain sight

- Install duress alarms

- Have adequate, physical barriers to prevent unsolicited entrance behind the pharmacy counter

- Install steel window curtains and doors

41   https://www.deadiversion.usdoj.gov/pubs/brochures/pharmtheft.pdf (accessed 2019 Jan 18).
42   https://www.deadiversion.usdoj.gov/mtgs/pharm_awareness/conf_2013/march_2013/browning.pdf (accessed 2019 Jan 18).

RECORDKEEPING OF PRESCRIPTION MEDICATION

Most states mandate that prescription records must be maintained for at least two years. Some states may have stricter requirements; the longest is Arizona, which requires prescription records be kept for 7 years.

My state requires prescriptions records to be kept for this number of years: _____

MAINTAINING PEDIGREES TO ENSURE THE QUALITY OF DRUGS

There is an increasing prevalence of counterfeit, misbranded, adulterated, and diverted prescription drugs showing up in the United States. To prevent these drugs from entering the legitimate drug supply, the Drug Supply Chain Security Act was passed in 2013, which outlines steps to build a system to track and trace drugs as they are distributed within the United States.[43] This requirement applies to prescription drugs intended for human use. Many products are exempt, including: over-the-counter drugs, medical devices, active pharmaceutical ingredients, veterinary drugs, blood products for transfusion, radioactive drugs, imaging drugs, certain intravenous products, certain medical gases (e.g., oxygen), homeopathic drugs and compounded preparations.

Manufacturers, wholesale distributors, pharmacies and repackagers (collectively referred to as "trading partners") are required to provide the subsequent purchaser with product tracing information when engaging in transactions involving certain prescription drugs. This means that anytime the drug is moved from one place to another, paperwork must follow.

Pharmacies must be able to capture and maintain transaction information (TI), transaction history (TH), and a transaction statement (TS), in paper or electronic form, for each drug product received for six years from the date of the transaction. There are some situations that are exempt from this requirement, including: dispensing drugs to a patient, providing drugs to a practitioner for office use, and distributing samples.

---

43   https://www.fda.gov/Drugs/DrugSafety/DrugIntegrityandSupplyChainSecurity/DrugSupplyChainSecurityAct/ (accessed 2019 Jan 15).

FIVE | CONTROLLED
SUBSTANCES

CHAPTER CONTENTS

Laws, Rules, and Regulations 114
Controlled Substances Act 114
Classification of Controlled Substances.. 115
Federal Controlled Substance Schedules 116
Drugs Scheduled Differently than the DEA 118
Maximum Limits and Set Opioid Amounts 121
Ordering Controlled Substances 121
DEA Form 222 121
Requesting DEA Form 222... 122
Ordering Schedule II Drugs with DEA Form 222 122
Cancelling or Voiding DEA Form 222... 124
Lost or Stolen DEA Form 222 125
Electronic Controlled Substance Ordering System 126
Ordering Controlled Substances with CSOS 127
Cancelling or Voiding Electronic Orders 127
Theft or Loss of Controlled Substance Orders 128
Granting the Power of Attorney 128
Ordering Schedule III – V Drugs 130
Prescribing and Filling Controlled Substances 130
Healthcare Providers Authorized to Prescribe Controlled Substances 130
Prescribing Controlled Substances for Oneself or Immediate Family Members 131
Checking the Validity of a DEA Number.. 131
Validity of Prescriptions for Controlled Substances.. 133
Written Prescriptions for Controlled Substances 133
Oral (Phone) Prescriptions for Controlled Substances 135
Faxed Prescriptions for Controlled Substances... 135
Electronic Prescriptions for Controlled Substances 136
Multiple Prescriptions for Schedule II Drugs... 137
Pre-signing and Post-signing Prescriptions for Controlled Substances....................... 138
Errors or Omissions on a Controlled Substance Prescription 139
The Prescriber's and Pharmacist's Corresponding Responsibility............................ 140
Recognizing Red Flags to Prevent Drug Diversion... 140
Prescription Drug Monitoring Programs 141

Refills of Controlled Substances 142
Controlled Substances Eligible for Refills 142
Paper Recordkeeping Requirements for
Refills of Schedule III – IV Drugs...................... 142
Electronic Recordkeeping Requirements for
Refills of Schedule III – IV Drugs...................... 142
Processing Schedule III – IV Refills When the
Computer System is Down 143

Partial Filling of Controlled Substances 144
Partial Fills of Schedule III – V Prescriptions.... 144
Partial Fills of Schedule II Prescriptions 145

**Emergency Refilling/Filling of
Controlled Substances** 146
Emergency Refilling of Schedule III – V Drugs
without Prescriber's Authorization................... 146
Emergency Filling of Schedule II Drugs 147

**Label Requirements for
Controlled Substances** 148
Labeling Requirements for All Controlled
Substances 148
DEA-Required Warning Statement on Label ... 148
Additional Label Requirement for Central
Fill Pharmacies 148
Exemptions to Labeling Requirements............ 148

**Transferring Controlled Substance
Prescriptions** 149
Transferring Schedule III – V Prescriptions...... 149
Transferring Schedule II Prescriptions............. 150

**Patient Identification Prior to Dispensing
Controlled Substances** 150

**Dispensing Non-Prescription
Controlled Substances** 151

**Delivering Controlled Substances
to Patients** 152

**Compounding or Repackaging
Controlled Substances** 152

**Dispensing Controlled Substances in Long-term
Care Facilities** 152
Partial Filling of Schedule II Drugs
for LTCF Patients... 152
Automated Dispensing Systems in LTCFs 152
Emergency Kits for LTCFs 153

**Internet Pharmacies and the
Ryan Haight Amendments**.................................153

**Treatment of Opioid Overdose
and Dependence** 154
The Opioid Epidemic 154
Naloxone 154
Pharmacists and Naloxone Distribution.......... 154
Opioid Treatment Programs 155
Opioid Dependence Treatment in an
Office-Based Setting.. 155

**Distribution of Controlled Substances
Between DEA Registrants** 156
Pharmacy Going Out of Business 156
Pharmacy Selling Controlled Substances 156

Disposal of Controlled Substances 157
Registrants Returning Controlled Substances to
the Wholesaler 157
Registrants Sending Controlled Substances to a
Reverse Distributor 157
Patients Disposing of Controlled Substances . 158
Disposal of Controlled Substance Wastage in an
Institutional Setting 159
Controlled Substance Loss or Theft 159
Reporting In-Transit Losses of
Controlled Substances 160

**Breakage, Damage, or Spillage of
Controlled Substances** 162

Recordkeeping of Controlled Substances 162
Paper Prescription Recordkeeping System 163
Electronic Prescription Recordkeeping
System 163
Institutional Medication Records..................... 163
DEA Controlled Substances Inventory 164

**Nonprescription Products with
Restricted Sales**..164
Pseudoephedrine, Ephedrine, Phenylpropanol-
amine, and Norpseudoephedrine..................... 164
Dextromethorphan 168

Drug Paraphernalia 168

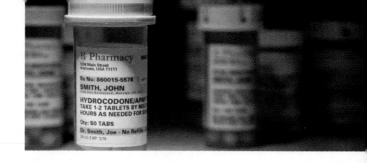

CONTROLLED SUBSTANCES

LAWS, RULES, AND REGULATIONS

CONTROLLED SUBSTANCES ACT

This section begins with a chart of the most common DEA forms and their purpose.

DEA FORM #	PURPOSE
224	Registration Form for Retail Pharmacies, Hospitals/Clinics, Practitioners, Teaching Institutions, or Mid-Level Practitioners
225	Registration Form for Manufacturers, Distributors, Researchers, Analytical Laboratories, Importers, Exporters
363	Registration Form for Narcotic Treatment Programs
222	Ordering Schedule I and II Drugs
106	Reporting the Theft or Significant Loss of Controlled Substances
41	Record of Controlled Substances Destroyed

The U.S. Attorney General, under authority provided by the CSA, is responsible for the enforcement of federal law requirements for the manufacture, importation, possession, use and distribution of controlled substances, which are divided into 5 schedules as shown in the following table. States can classify substances in stricter categories. The DEA works with the FDA to make decisions about the schedule in which a controlled substance is placed. Sometimes, a drug is reclassified to a different schedule (such as the recent move of all hydrocodone-containing products into schedule II) if the perceived risks involving the drug have changed. The DEA is primarily concerned with diversion, whereas the FDA is primarily concerned with legitimate medical need and safety (primarily due to overdose).

This section reviews the Controlled Substance Act (CSA). Pharmacists can use the DEA's Pharmacists Manual as a guide to interpret the CSA and how it applies to pharmacy practice.[44] When state and federal pharmacy law differ, the stricter law would prevail. For example, *Fioricet* is not federally classified as a controlled substance. A handful of states (Maryland, Georgia, Utah, Florida, New Mexico, California) has listed *Fioricet* as schedule III. If a student sitting for the Florida MPJE was asked what schedule the drug *Fioricet* is classified as, the correct answer would be schedule III.

44   https://www.deadiversion.usdoj.gov/pubs/manuals/pharm2/index.html (accessed 2018 Jan 16).

CLASSIFICATION OF CONTROLLED SUBSTANCES

The higher the potential for abuse, the lower the schedule number. Schedule I drugs have the highest potential for abuse and are considered to have no accepted medical use. Drugs in this category (such as heroin and LSD) may be used for research purposes, but are most commonly used illicitly (illegally/unlawfully).

Marijuana is federally classified as schedule I, but is legalized in over half of the states. Marijuana distribution takes place in marijuana dispensaries, not in pharmacies. Even though marijuana is not dispensed in pharmacies, pharmacists should note marijuana in the patient's profile if the patient is taking it and be aware of the potential drug-drug interactions.

Most schedule II – V drugs are dispensed in pharmacies with a prescription. Select schedule V drugs (primarily cough syrups) can be sold without a prescription in some states as long as certain requirements are met, such as keeping a logbook of sales.

Some drugs can be classified in more than one schedule depending on the formulation. Codeine is schedule II if it is a single agent, schedule III if formulated as part of a combination tablet/capsule, and schedule V if formulated as a combination cough syrup. Dronabinol is schedule II as a solution (*Syndros*) and schedule III as a capsule (*Marinol*). In contrast, hydrocodone is schedule II in all single and combination products and tramadol is schedule IV in all single and combination products as well.

Generally, most controlled substances of the same pharmacological class will be in the same schedule. Barbiturates can be schedule II, III, or IV. Single agent formulations of amobarbital, pentobarbital, and secobarbital are schedule II. If amobarbital, secobarbital, or pentobarbital are formulated as a suppository or as a combination product with a non-controlled substance, then it is schedule III. Butabarbital is schedule III. Butabarbital is not to be confused with butalbital. Butalbital is currently only available in combination with non-controlled substances, and is schedule III. Phenobarbital is schedule IV. Phenobarbital is not to be confused with pentobarbital.

It will not be possible to answer some of the questions on the MPJE without knowledge of the categories for the controlled substances. The classification of the drug will determine the requirements for ordering, labeling, refills, emergency fills, and inventory and recordkeeping.

If your state classifies select drugs in a different schedule than the federal classification, list the drugs and the schedules: _____

_____

_____

_____

_____

FEDERAL CONTROLLED SUBSTANCE SCHEDULES

SCHEDULE	EXAMPLES
C-I	3,4-methylenedioxy-methamphetamine or MDMA ("Ecstasy")
	Gamma-hydroxybutyric acid or GHB (the sodium salt form, sodium oxybate, is C-III)
	Heroin
	Lysergic acid diethylamide or LSD
	Marijuana or *cannabis* (tetrahydrocannabinol, cannabidiol) — legalized in some states
	Mescaline
	Peyote
C-II	Amobarbital (*Amytal Sodium*)
	Amphetamine containing products (*Dexedrine, Adderall*)
	Carfentanil — veterinary use only
	Cocaine
	Codeine
	Dronabinol solution (*Syndros*)
	Etorphine HCl — veterinary use only
	Fentanyl (*Duragesic, Actiq, Fentora, Onsolis, Subsys, Lazanda, Abstral*)
	Hydrocodone-containing products (*Zohydro ER, Hysingla ER, Norco, Vicodin, TussiCaps, Tussionex*)
	Hydromorphone (*Dilaudid*)
	Levo-alpha acetyl methadol or LAAM
	Lisdexamfetamine (*Vyvanse*)
	Meperidine (*Demerol*)
	Methadone (*Dolophine, Methadose*)
	Methylphenidate (*Ritalin, Concerta*)
	Morphine (*MS Contin, Kadian, Duramorph, Arymo ER, Infumorph, MorphaBond ER*)
	Oxycodone-containing products (*Percocet, Percodan, OxyContin*)
	Pentobarbital (*Nembutal*)
	Secobarbital (*Seconal*)
	Sufentanil (*Sufenta*)
	Tapentadol (*Nucynta*)

C-III	Anabolic steroids such as testosterone (*AndroGel*)
	Benzphetamine (*Regimex*)
	Buprenorphine (*Suboxone, Subutex*)
	Butabarbital (*Butisol*)
	Butalbital/Acetaminophen/Caffeine/Codeine (*Fioricet with Codeine*)
	Butalbital/Aspirin/Caffeine/Codeine (*Fiorinal with Codeine*)
	Butalbital/Aspirin/Caffeine (*Fiorinal*)
	Codeine/acetaminophen (*Tylenol with Codeine #3, Tylenol with Codeine #4*)
	Dronabinol capsules (*Marinol*)
	Ketamine (*Ketalar*)
	Perampanel (*Fycompa*)
	Phendimetrazine (*Bontril PDM*)
	Sodium oxybate (*Xyrem*)
C-IV	Armodafinil (*Nuvigil*)
	Benzodiazepines such as lorazepam (*Ativan*), diazepam (*Valium*), alprazolam (*Xanax*)
	Butorphanol (*Stadol*)
	Carisoprodol (*Soma*)
	Diethylpropion (*Tenuate*)
	Difenoxin/atropine (*Mofeten*)
	Eluxadoline (*Viberzi*)
	Eszopiclone (*Lunesta*)
	Lorcaserin (*Belviq*)
	Modafinil (*Provigil*)
	Phenobarbital
	Phentermine (*Adipex-P, Suprenza*)
	Phentermine/topiramate (*Qsymia*)
	Suvorexant (*Belsomra*)
	Tramadol-containing products (*Ultram, Ultracet, ConZip*)
	Zaleplon (*Sonata*)
	Zolpidem (*Ambien*)
C-V	Brivaracetam (*Briviact*)
	Codeine-containing cough syrups (codeine/promethazine, codeine/promethazine/phenylephrine, codeine/guaifenisen, others)
	Difenoxin/atropine (*Mofeten* half strength) — discontinued
	Diphenoxylate/atropine (*Lomotil*)
	Ezogabine (*Potiga*)
	Lacosamide (*Vimpat*)
	Pregabalin (*Lyrica*)

DRUGS SCHEDULED DIFFERENTLY THAN THE DEA

STATE	SCHEDULE
Alabama	Schedule III ■ Codeine-containing cough syrups ■ Butalbital-acetaminophen-caffeine *(Fioricet)*
Arizona	Schedule V ■ Ephedrine
Arkansas	Schedule IV ■ Nalbuphine Schedule V ■ Ephedrine ■ Phenylpropanolamine ■ Pseudoephedrine
California	Schedule III ■ Butalbital-acetaminophen-caffeine *(Fioricet)* ■ Human chorionic gonadotropin (hCG)
District of Columbia	Not-scheduled, but monitored in PDMP ■ Butalbital and Cyclobenzaprine
Florida	Schedule III ■ Butalbital-acetaminophen-caffeine *(Fioricet)*
Georgia	Schedule III ■ Butalbital-acetaminophen-caffeine *(Fioricet)* Schedule V ■ Pseudoephedrine
Hawaii	Schedule III ■ Butalbital-acetaminophen-caffeine *(Fioricet)*
Illinois	Schedule III ■ Butalbital-acetaminophen-caffeine *(Fioricet)* Schedule IV ■ Ephedrine Schedule V ■ Pseudoephedrine
Indiana	Schedule III ■ Butalbital-acetaminophen-caffeine *(Fioricet)* Schedule IV ■ Ephedrine ■ Pseudoephedrine
Iowa	Schedule V ■ Pseudoephedrine
Kansas	Schedule V ■ Pseudoephedrine

Kentucky	**Schedule III** ■ Butalbital-acetaminophen-caffeine *(Fioricet)* ■ Pentazocine ■ Barbital ■ Methylphenobarbital ■ Phenobarbital **Schedule IV** ■ Nalbuphine **Schedule V** ■ Gabapentin
Louisiana	**Schedule II** ■ Carisoprodol **Schedule V** ■ Ephedrine ■ Phenylpropanolamine ■ Pseudoephedrine
Maryland	**Schedule III** ■ Butalbital-acetaminophen-caffeine *(Fioricet)*
Michigan	**Schedule V** ■ Gabapentin
Minnesota	**Schedule III** ■ Human chorionic gonadotropin (hCG) ■ Human growth hormone ■ Codeine-containing cough syrups **Schedule V** ■ Ephedrine ■ Pseudoephedrine **Not-scheduled, but monitored in PDMP** ■ Gabapentin
Mississippi	**Schedule III** ■ Butalbital-acetaminophen-caffeine *(Fioricet)* ■ Ephedrine ■ Pseudoephedrine
Missouri	**Schedule IV** ■ Codeine-containing cough syrups ■ Ephedrine **Schedule V** ■ Pseudoephedrine
Montana	**Schedule II** ■ Dronabinol **Schedule IV** ■ Ephedrine
Nevada	**Schedule III** ■ Human growth hormone

New Mexico	**Schedule III** ■ Butalbital-acetaminophen-caffeine *(Fioricet)* **Schedule IV** ■ Dezocine ■ Nalbuphine **Schedule V** ■ Pseudoephedrine
New Jersey	**Schedule V** ■ Gabapentin ■ Human growth hormone
New York	**Schedule II** ■ Anabolic steroids **Schedule III** ■ Human chorionic gonadotropin (hCG)
North Carolina	**Schedule III** ■ Human chorionic gonadotropin (hCG)
North Dakota	Not-scheduled, but monitored in PDMP ■ Gabapentin
Ohio	**Schedule V** ■ Gabapentin
Oklahoma	**Schedule IV** ■ Ephedrine **Schedule V** ■ Pseudoephedrine
Oregon	**Schedule III** ■ Ephedrine ■ Pseudoephedrine ■ Phenylpropanolamine
Pennsylvania	**Schedule III** ■ Human chorionic gonadotropin (hCG)
South Carolina	**Schedule II** ■ Pentazocine injection
Tennessee	**Schedule V** ■ Gabapentin
Utah	**Schedule III** ■ Butalbital-acetaminophen-caffeine *(Fioricet)*
West Virginia	**Schedule III** ■ Butalbital-acetaminophen-caffeine *(Fioricet)* **Schedule V** ■ Gabapentin ■ Pseudoephedrine
Wisconsin	**Schedule IV** ■ Ephedrine **Schedule V** ■ Pseudoephedrine

HCG = human chorionic gonadotropin
HGH = human growth hormone

MAXIMUM LIMITS AND SET OPIOID AMOUNTS

The scheduling of some drugs depend on the opioid concentration. There are some drugs available in a few of the categories that the DEA defines in the following table, including *Paregoric* (an oral liquid containing morphine 2 mg/5 mL) and *Tylenol with Codeine* (which contains acetaminophen and 15 – 60 mg of codeine per tablet). However, in some of the categories, the drugs have been discontinued or are rarely used.

SCHEDULE	NOT MORE THAN (NMT) QUANTITY LIMIT
Schedule III *Typically, these are calculated based on the Rule of Three as many of these numbers are divisible by 3.*	Not more than 1.8 g of codeine per 100 mL or not more than 90 mg per dosage unit when combined with an equal or greater quantity of an isoquinoline alkaloid of opium
	Not more than 1.8 g of codeine per 100 mL or not more than 90 mg per dosage unit when combined with one or more active non-narcotic ingredient
	Not more than 1.8 g of dihydrocodeine per 100 mL or not more than 90 mg per dosage unit when combined with one or more active non-narcotic ingredient
	Not more than 300 mg of ethylmorphine per 100 mL or not more than 15 mg per dosage unit when combined with one or more active non-narcotic ingredient
	Not more than 500 mg of opium per 100 mL or per 100 g or not more than 25 mg per dosage unit when combined with one or more active non-narcotic ingredient
	Not more than 50 mg of morphine per 100 mL or per 100 g when combined with one or more active non-narcotic ingredient
Schedule IV	Not more than 1 mg difenoxin and not less than 25 mcg of atropine sulfate per dosage unit
Schedule V *Typically, these are calculated based on the Rule of Five as many of these numbers are divisible by 5.*	Not more than 200 mg of codeine per 100 mL or per 100 g when combined with one or more active non-narcotic ingredient (such as *Robitussin AC*, promethazine/codeine cough syrup)
	Not more than 100 mg of dihydrocodeine per 100 mL or per 100 g when combined with one or more active non-narcotic ingredient (such as dihydrocodeine/chlorpheniramine/phenylprine cough syrup)
	Not more than 100 mg of ethylmorphine per 100 mL or per 100 g when combined with one or more active non-narcotic ingredient
	Not more than 2.5 mg of diphenoxylate and not less than 25 mcg of atropine sulfate per dosage unit (e.g., *Lomotil*)
	Not more than 100 mg of opium per 100 mL or per 100 g when combined with one or more active non-narcotic ingredient
	Not more than 0.5 mg of difenoxin and not less than 25 mcg of atropine sulfate per dosage unit

ORDERING CONTROLLED SUBSTANCES

DEA FORM 222

Form 222 (or its electronic equivalent) is required for each distribution, purchase, or transfer of schedule I or II drugs. A pharmacist would usually use the Form 222 to order schedule II drugs, sell or lend schedule II drugs to another pharmacy or prescriber, borrow schedule II drugs from another pharmacy, or return controlled substances to the wholesaler or reverse distributer.

The Form 222 is a serially numbered (with a consecutive number series), triplicate form, and is pre-printed with the pharmacy's name, address, DEA number, and the schedules of controlled substances that can be ordered by the registrant. The colors of the triplicate forms are brown (Copy 1), green (Copy 2), and blue (Copy 3). If a registration terminates or the preprinted name

and address needs to be revised, the unused forms are returned to the DEA and new forms will be required.

The registrant <u>requesting/receiving the schedule II drugs</u> (e.g., the pharmacy) will <u>keep Copy 3</u> and send Copies 1 and 2 to the supplier. Upon delivery of the controlled substances to the recipient (e.g., the pharmacy), the registrant supplying the drugs (e.g., the drug wholesaler) will forward <u>Copy 2 to the DEA</u>. Note that the pharmacy keeps Copy 3 when purchasing the controlled substances from the wholesaler — but the pharmacy will <u>keep Copy 1</u> when returning drugs to a wholesaler or sending drugs to a reverse distributor for disposal since, in these cases, the pharmacy is <u>"supplying" the drugs</u>. The table below outlines who must keep which copy of the Form 222 in different scenarios.

ACTION	COPY 1 (BROWN)	COPY 2 (GREEN)	COPY 3 (BLUE)
The pharmacy orders schedule II drugs from a wholesaler	Supplier	DEA	Pharmacy
The pharmacy returns unused schedule II drugs back to a supplier	Pharmacy	DEA	Supplier
The pharmacy sends unused schedule II drugs back to reverse distributor for disposal	Pharmacy	DEA	Reverse distributor
The pharmacy sells or lends schedule II drugs to another pharmacy that is out of stock and needs the drugs to dispense a prescription	Supplying pharmacy	DEA	Receiving Pharmacy
The pharmacy sells or lends schedule II drugs to a physician for administration or dispensing to a patient	Pharmacy	DEA	Physician

A Form 222 is not required if drug products are transferred from a central fill pharmacy to its retail pharmacy or when the schedule II drug is being dispensed to the patient. Other than these two exceptions, Form 222 is to document every distribution, purchase, or transfer of schedule II drugs.

REQUESTING DEA FORM 222

Initial Forms 222 can be requested on the Form 224, which is the application for initial DEA registration. Once a registrant has received a DEA registration number, additional Forms 222 can be ordered on the DEA website or by calling the DEA Headquarters Registration Unit or the nearest DEA Field Office.

ORDERING SCHEDULE II DRUGS WITH DEA FORM 222

Schedule I drugs may be used for research with permission from the DEA and FDA but are neither ordered by pharmacies nor prescribed by healthcare providers. This section on how to use the Form 222 focuses on schedule II drugs. The Form 222 or the electronic equivalent (the Controlled Substance Ordering System or CSOS) is required for the distribution, purchase, or transfer of schedule II drugs. The electronic CSOS can be used for ordering all schedules (I – V).

1. The Form 222 must be completed with a <u>typewriter, ink pen, or indelible (non-erasable) pencil</u>. If the form is filled out by hand with an ink pen or indelible pencil, the purchaser must press firmly to ensure that all three forms will be legible.

2. Each item must be written on a <u>separate line</u> with a total of <u>10 lines</u> on each form. A maximum of 10 items can be ordered. Lines cannot be skipped. The purchaser must fill out the name and address of the supplier, only one supplier can be used on a form. There are three columns for each drug that must be complete:

- ❏ The number of packages (e.g., 25)

- ❏ The size of the package (e.g., 946 mL)

- ❏ The name (brand or generic) and dosage (e.g., methadone HCl 10 mg/mL)

3. The purchaser can leave the NDC entry blank since the supplier may not have the exact product the pharmacy requested, and can substitute a different package size or select a different manufacturer. The same drug in a different size package or from a different manufacturer will have a different NDC number. These substitutions are permitted as long as the quantity provided does not exceed the amount ordered. For example, *Norco* 7.5/325 mg is supplied as bottles of 100 and 500 tablets. If the pharmacy orders 5 of the 500-count bottles and the distributor does not have the 500 count, they can provide 25 of the 100-count bottles. Either option will provide the purchaser with 2500 tablets, which is the quantity that was ordered. Each of the different size bottles and each different manufacturer will have a different NDC number, which is why it is more convenient to leave it blank so the supplier can fill in the NDC number for the exact item that is sent to the purchaser.

4. The last line completed must be indicated in the space provided on the form, which will be the <u>total number of different items ordered</u>. This field must be completed and will be 10 or less, since there are 10 lines on the form. If this is left blank or does not match the number of lines that have been completed, it will be returned to the pharmacy. In the sample Form 222 that follows, since three items are ordered, the purchaser must record "3" in the space marked "last line completed".

5. The Form 222 must be <u>signed</u> and <u>dated</u> by the <u>person authorized to sign the registration application</u> or a <u>person who has been granted power of attorney</u>. If the form is not signed and dated, it will be returned to the pharmacy.

6. If a mistake is made, the purchaser must write "<u>Void</u>" on the Form 222 and begin again with a new Form 222.

7. The Form 222 must be filled <u>completely</u> and <u>legibly</u> or it cannot be filled and will be returned to the purchaser. The Form 222 will be sent back if alterations or cross-outs are present, if the drug name, strength, size, quantify is missing or if the date or signature is missing. Minor errors (for example, misspelling "methodone" for methadone) could be reasonably corrected by the distributor. However, it is best to avoid even simple errors.

8. Once completed, <u>the purchaser keeps Copy 3</u> (<u>blue Copy</u>) sends Copy 1 and 2 (brown and green Copy) to the supplier. The first two Copies must remain together, with the carbon intact. If the top two Copies are not attached, the supplier cannot accept the order and will return the Copies to the pharmacy.

9. On Copies 1 and 2, the supplier records the number of containers furnished per item along with date of shipment. If the supplier cannot provide the entire quantity, the supplier can provide a partial shipment and supply the balance within 60 days from the date the Form 222 was completed by the purchaser. The supplier maintains Copy 1 for its files and sends Copy 2 to the DEA by the <u>end of the month</u> during which the order was fulfilled. If the supplier cannot fulfill the order within the specified time limit, the supplier can endorse the order to another supplier to fill.

10. Shipments of controlled substances can be sent only to the current DEA registered address.

11. The supplier delivers the scheduled drugs to the purchaser in its own container, which is separate from the non-scheduled and OTC drugs. The order is checked in by the pharmacist who will <u>record the number of packages received</u> and the <u>date received</u> on <u>Copy 3</u>.

12. Federal law requires the purchaser to keep copy 3 of the Form 222 (and all scheduled drug forms) for at least <u>2 years</u>. A state can require purchasers to keep records for a longer period of time. All <u>records related to schedule II drugs</u> (orders, invoices, prescriptions, inventory records) are <u>kept separate from other forms.</u>

CANCELLING OR VOIDING DEA FORM 222

If the supplier cannot fulfill the order or if the order form is illegible, incomplete, or altered, then the supplier returns Copies 1 and 2 to the purchaser with a rationale for not filling the order. The purchaser must keep all three copies.

A supplier can void part or all of an order by notifying the purchaser in writing. The supplier must draw a line through the cancelled items on Copies 1 and 2 of the Form 222 and print "Void" in the space provided for the number of items shipped.

A purchaser can cancel all or part of an order by notifying the supplier in writing. The supplier indicates the cancellation on Copies 1 and 2 by drawing a line through the cancelled item/s and writing "Cancelled" in the space where they would usually put the number of items shipped.

LOST OR STOLEN DEA FORM 222

If the Form 222 that was sent to the supplier becomes lost or stolen, the purchaser must re-order with a new form. The pharmacist must prepare a <u>statement that the order was not received</u>, and include the <u>serial number of the lost or stolen form</u>, and the <u>date of the loss.</u> This statement must be attached to the new order form and sent to the supplier. Copy 3 of the new and the original Form 222 and the statement are filed together. If the supplier subsequently receives the original order form, it is marked as "not accepted" and returned to the purchaser who files the original Copies 1 and 2 with the original Copy 3.

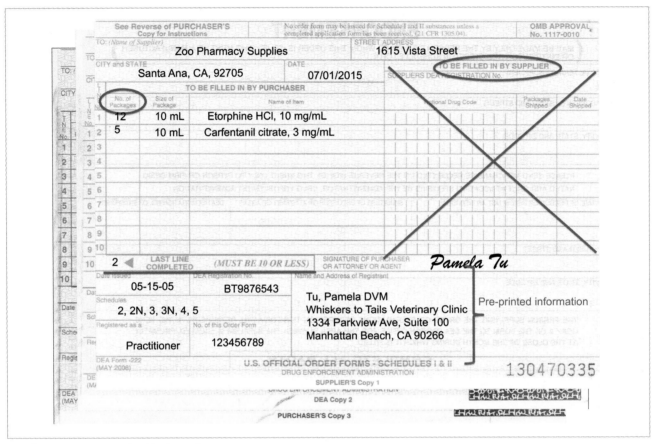

Sample DEA Form 222 completed by the purchaser

ELECTRONIC CONTROLLED SUBSTANCE ORDERING SYSTEM

The electronic Controlled Substance Ordering System (CSOS) is the electronic equivalent to Form 222. CSOS is used to order schedule I and II drugs and, unlike Form 222, can be used to order controlled drugs in schedules III, IV and V and non-controlled drugs.[45] Each Form 222 can only be used to order up to 10 items; the CSOS has no limits on the quantity of items to be ordered. Utilizing CSOS reduces ordering errors, requires less paperwork and reduces administrative costs. Drug delivery is faster with CSOS than with the paper form, which requires additional time for the supplier to receive the form from the pharmacy. With CSOS, the purchaser can order the drugs, have the order electronically sent to the supplier within the same business day, and the supplier can deliver the order to the purchaser by the next business day. Ordering through CSOS improves inventory control. There is less stockpiling and less waiting time to fill up a paper order form. Orders can be placed more often for fewer items.

	PAPER DEA FORM 222	ELECTRONIC CSOS
Limit of items per order	10 items	No limits
What drugs can be ordered	Schedules I, II	Schedules I, II, III, IV, V, and non-scheduled
Typical turnaround time	1-7 business days	1-2 business days
Type of signature used	Wet (handwritten) signature	Digital signature
Can the order be endorsed to another supplier?	Yes	No
When must supplier report transaction to DEA?	By the end of the month during which the order was filled	Within 2 business days of filling the order

CSOS utilizes Public Key Infrastructure (PKI) technology to securely exchange data. The purchaser (such as the pharmacy) enrolls with the DEA to receive a CSOS digital certificate and public-private key pairs. The public key is used to encrypt data, and the private key is used to decrypt data, which enables the purchaser and supplier to securely exchange data.

A CSOS digital certificate is essentially an authorized digital identity that contains information about the registrant, including the name, email address, location name and address, DEA number, the schedules the registrant can order, and the expiration date of the certificate. The purchaser signs the electronic controlled substance order with the digital certificate.

45   https://www.deaecom.gov/overview.pdf (accessed 2018 Jan 19).

ORDERING CONTROLLED SUBSTANCES WITH CSOS

The registrant creates the CSOS order using DEA-approved software which is typically available through the wholesaler's online ordering website. When the order is complete, the purchaser signs it with the digital certificate and electronically transmits it to the supplier. The supplier receives the order, verifies the certificate, and fills the order. <u>Electronic orders can not be endorsed to another supplier</u>. The purchaser will know almost instantaneously that the supplier cannot fill all or part of an order and can simply issue a new electronic order to a different supplier. The supplier must report the order information to the DEA within <u>2 business days</u> from the date the supplier received the order.

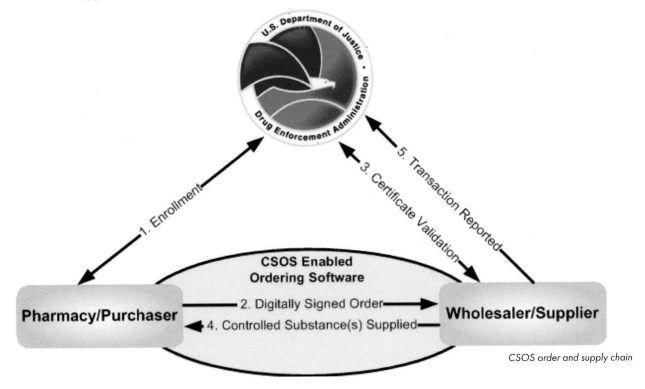

CSOS order and supply chain

CANCELLING OR VOIDING ELECTRONIC ORDERS

An electronic order is invalid if any required data field is missing, if it is not signed with a DEA-sanctioned digital certificate, if the digital certificate is expired, or if the purchaser's public key will not validate the digital signature. The supplier can refuse to fill an order for any reason and must provide the purchaser with a statement of the occurrence. The purchaser must electronically link this statement to the original order. Invalid electronic orders cannot be corrected; a new order must be submitted by the purchaser.

The supplier is not required to keep a record of orders that were not filled, but the purchaser must keep an electronic copy of the voided order. If a supplier partially voids an order, the supplier must indicate in the linked record that nothing was shipped for each voided item.

THEFT OR LOSS OF CONTROLLED SUBSTANCE ORDERS

If an unfulfilled order from Form 222 or CSOS is lost, the purchaser must provide the supplier with the unique tracking number, the date of the loss, and a statement that the goods from the first order were never received. If the purchaser issues another order to replace the lost order, the lost order (along with the statement of loss) and the replacement order must be electronically linked.

GRANTING THE POWER OF ATTORNEY

The DEA registrant orders the controlled substances for the pharmacy with the Form 222 or CSOS. That person may not be present all the time, and can authorize others to order the controlled substances in their place by granting a power of attorney (POA). A POA is a legal document that gives the person the registrant has chosen the power to act in the registrant's place. Licensed or unlicensed individuals can be granted a POA. Multiple POAs can be issued if the registrant requires more than one substitute. The person who granted the POA may revoke it at any time. If a new registrant completes the renewal application, new power of attorney form/s will need to be completed. The POA documents are not submitted to the DEA, but must be filed with the completed Forms 222 and should be readily retrievable in the event that the pharmacy needs to provide them to an inspector. The DEA does not provide an official power of attorney form, but recommends the wording shown on the following page.

Power of Attorney _____

(Name of registrant) _____

(Address of registrant) _____

(DEA registration number)

I,_____ (name of person granting power), the undersigned, who is authorized to sign the current application for registration of the above-named registrant under the Controlled Substances Act or Controlled Substances Import and Export Act, have made, constituted, and appointed, and by these presents, do make, constitute, and appoint _____ (name of attorney-in-fact), my true and lawful attorney for me in my name, place, and stead, to execute applications for Forms 222 and to sign orders for Schedule I and II drugs, whether these orders be on Form 222 or electronic, in accordance with 21 U.S.C. 828 and Part 1305 of Title 21 of the Code of Federal Regulations. I hereby ratify and confirm all that said attorney must lawfully do or cause to be done by virtue hereof.

_____

(Signature of person granting power)

I, _____ (name of attorney-in-fact), hereby affirm that I am the person

named herein as attorney-in-fact and that the signature affixed hereto is my signature.

_____

(Signature of attorney-in-fact)

Witnesses:

1._____ 2. _____

Signed and dated on the _____day of _____, (year), at _____.

Notice of Revocation

The foregoing power of attorney is hereby revoked by the undersigned, who is authorized to sign the current application for registration of the above-named registrant under the Controlled Substances Act or the Controlled Substances Import and Export Act. Written notice of this revocation has been given to the attorney-in-fact this same day.

_____

(Signature of person revoking power)

Witnesses:

1._____ 2. _____

Signed and dated on the _____day of _____, (year), at _____.

Sample of a Power of Attorney Form

ORDERING SCHEDULE III – V DRUGS

The registrant must keep a <u>receipt</u> (e.g., the <u>invoice</u> or <u>packing slip</u>) on which the registrant records the date the drugs were received and confirms that the order was accurate. These receipts must contain the name of each controlled substance, the formulation, the number of dosage units in each commercial container, and the number of containers ordered and received. These receipts must be kept in a readily retrievable manner for inspection.

PRESCRIBING AND FILLING CONTROLLED SUBSTANCES

HEALTHCARE PROVIDERS AUTHORIZED TO PRESCRIBE CONTROLLED SUBSTANCES

A prescription for a controlled substance for a legitimate medical purpose may only be issued by a physician (MD/DO), dentist (DDS, DMD), podiatrist (DPM), veterinarian (DVM), mid-level practitioner (MLP), or other registered practitioner who is:

- <u>Authorized to prescribe</u> controlled substances by the <u>jurisdiction or state</u> in which the practitioner is licensed to practice

- Registered or exempt from <u>DEA registration</u>

- An agent or employee of a hospital or institution acting in the normal course of business <u>under the registration of the hospital or institution</u>

Only physicians have unlimited, independent prescribing authority in all states, although it is preferable to prescribe within the area of expertise. The license to practice medicine is granted by the individual states.

The prescribing authority for all other prescribers is limited to the practitioner's <u>scope of practice</u> in all states and may require a <u>collaborative practice agreement</u> with a physician. For example, naturopathic doctors (NDs) are generally limited to "natural" compounds such as vitamins, natural hormones (e.g., *Armour Thyroid*), or amino acids. The prescribing authority of mid-level practitioners (MLPs) varies by state and by type of practitioner. MLPs vary by state and can include nurse practitioners (NPs), certified nurse midwives (CNMs), anesthetist nurses (ANs), physician assistants (PAs) and optometrists (ODs).

An <u>employee or agent</u> (such as a nurse or office assistant), under the direct supervision of a prescriber, may <u>communicate prescription information to a pharmacist</u>. The agent can also <u>prepare a prescription</u> for the prescriber to sign and date.

My state permits the following MLPs to prescribe the following schedules of controlled substances:

MLP TYPE	SCHEDULES OF DRUGS	PRESCRIBING LIMITATIONS

Healthcare providers employed by the following organizations are <u>exempt from DEA registration</u>: <u>U.S. Public Health Service</u>, the <u>Federal Bureau of Prisons</u>, and the <u>U.S. Armed Forces</u> (Army, Air Force, Navy, Marine Corps and Coast Guard). Additionally, under the Indian Self-Determination and Education Assistance Act, <u>institutions and employees of Indian healthcare facilities are exempt</u>. Prescribers employed by these facilities are not be required to register with the DEA in order to write for controlled substances. Many of these practitioners will still apply for a DEA number in order to work at an outside private practice.

PRESCRIBING CONTROLLED SUBSTANCES FOR ONESELF OR IMMEDIATE FAMILY MEMBERS

The American Medical Association (AMA) does not recommend self-prescribing or treating immediate family members. This ethical and legal issue is discussed in detail in the pharmacy practice section. This type of prescribing is not addressed by the DEA, but individual state medical boards and boards of pharmacy can prohibit treating oneself or immediate family members. Some states prohibit prescribing certain categories of drugs to oneself or to family members, such as schedule II drugs or all controlled drugs.

My state sets limits on prescribing controlled drugs to oneself or family members. Yes / No

If yes, list the limitations on prescribing to oneself or to family members in your state: _____

CHECKING THE VALIDITY OF A DEA NUMBER

Each DEA number is unique and is assigned to an individual healthcare provider or to an institution. The DEA number permits the individual to write for controlled substances, and permits the institution to order and manage controlled substances. DEA numbers must meet in order to be valid. Each DEA number is randomly-generated and begins with <u>2 letters</u>, followed by <u>7 numbers</u>. The last number is called the "<u>check digit</u>". The <u>first letter</u> identifies the <u>type</u> of practitioner or institution:

A/B/F/G – Hospital, clinic, practitioner, teaching institution, pharmacy

M – Mid-level practitioner (nurse practitioners, physician assistants, optometrists, etc.)

P/R – Manufacturer, distributor, researcher, analytical lab, importer, exporter, reverse distributor, narcotic treatment program

The <u>second letter</u> of the DEA number is the <u>first letter of the prescriber's last name</u>. For example: Wendy Clark, MD has the DEA number AC2143799, where A is the initial letter (Dr. Clark is a physician), C is for her last name (Clark), followed by 7 numeric digits.

If a practitioner is authorized to <u>prescribe narcotics</u> (such as buprenorphine) <u>for opioid addiction treatment</u>, the practitioner will receive a <u>DATA 2000 waiver unique identification number</u> (UIN). The number is the same as the DEA number, except that the <u>letter "X" replaces the first letter</u>. The provision that permits this prescribing is called "DATA 2000" and is described further in this manual. If Dr. Clark decided to take this training and could then prescribe for this purpose, her DATA 2000 waiver unique identification number (UIN) would be XC2143799. Both her DEA number and her UIN should be on the prescription. If there is no X with the DEA number and buprenorphine is being used for pain (not addiction) the prescription should state "for pain."

Prescribers in a hospital or other institution, including medical interns, residents, and visiting physicians, can prescribe medication <u>under the DEA registration of that hospital or institution</u>.

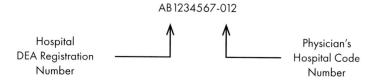

AB1234567-012

Hospital DEA Registration Number → ← Physician's Hospital Code Number

Steps to Verify the Validity of a DEA Number

Step one: Add the 1st, 3rd and 5th digits together.

Step two: Add the 2nd, 4th and 6th digits together.

Step three: Multiply the result of step two by 2.

Step four: Add the results of step one and step three together. The last digit of this sum should match the last digit of the prescriber's DEA number. This is called the <u>check digit</u>.

Example: DEA number BT6835752

Step one: 6 + 3 + 7 = 16
Step two: 8 + 5 + 5 = 18
Step three: 18 x 2 = 36
Step four: 16 + 36 = 52

The last digit of the sum in step four is 2. This should be the same as the last digit of the DEA number. Therefore, this DEA number appears to be valid.

Verify Dr. Mikacich's DEA number (BM6125341):

Step one: _____

Step two: _____

Step three: _____

Step four: _____

The last digit of the sum in step four is: _____

Does Dr. Mikacich's DEA number appear to be valid?* Yes / No

*Answer: Yes

VALIDITY OF PRESCRIPTIONS FOR CONTROLLED SUBSTANCES

Once a prescriber authorizes a prescription, the patient may have a limited amount of time to fill it. Non-scheduled drugs and schedule V drugs do not expire and do not have a refill limit. Schedule III – IV drugs are valid up to 6 months from the issue date and are limited to 5 refills. Despite having the highest abuse potential amongst prescription drugs, schedule II drugs do not expire. Schedule II drugs cannot have refills. Refills for controlled substances are discussed further.

Individual states may have stricter regulations regarding the expiration dates of prescriptions, especially prescriptions for schedule II drugs. Some states may also impose a quantity limit on certain prescriptions.

	EXPIRATION	REFILL LIMIT
Non-scheduled	Never	No limit
Schedule V	Never	No limit
Schedule IV	6 months	5 refills
Schedule III	6 months	5 refills
Schedule II	Never	0 refills

If your state has stricter regulations addressing the expiration date of prescriptions, list them here: _____

_____

WRITTEN PRESCRIPTIONS FOR CONTROLLED SUBSTANCES

The prescription for a controlled substance must be written in ink, indelible pencil, or typewritten by the prescriber or prepared by an agent of the prescriber (such as an office assistant or nurse). It must be signed and dated by the prescriber.

The prescription must include:

The patient's full name and address

- The prescriber's full name, business address, and DEA number

- The drug name, strength, dosage form, quantity prescribed and directions for use

- The number of refills authorized

Orders written for direct administration to patients in facilities such as clinics and hospitals are not considered prescriptions (they are referred to as medication orders) and do not need to meet prescription requirements.

Tamper-Resistant Security Forms

States can require the use of tamper-resistant security forms for all prescriptions, for all scheduled drugs, or for schedule II drugs only. Many states have the same or similar requirements for the security forms. Prescribers can have both security and non-security forms. Some prescribers choose to use security forms for all prescriptions, which is acceptable, but more costly.

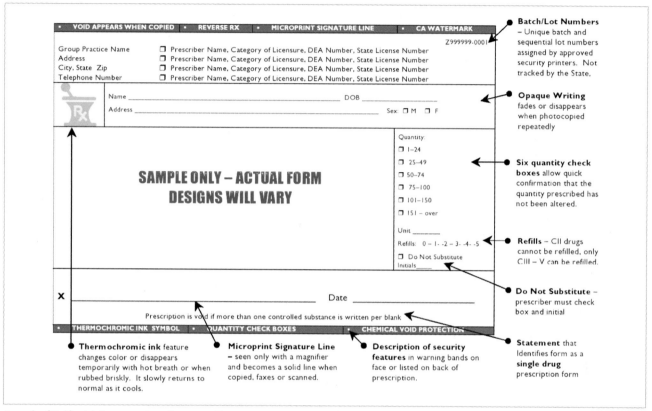

Example of California's Tamper-resistant Prescription Forms

In order for <u>outpatient</u> drugs to be paid for under the <u>federal Medicaid program</u>, all written prescriptions must be on tamper-resistant security forms that contain at least <u>three</u> tamper-resistant security features. This does not apply to electronic, oral, or faxed prescriptions.

My state requires tamper-resistant security forms for these categories of drugs (e.g., all drugs, all scheduled drugs only, schedule II drugs only): _____

_____

If required for certain patient groups, fill in the type of patients: _____

_____

Describe the security elements that must be present on the form in your state: _____

_____

the essential
pasta
cookbook

the essential
pasta
cookbook

bay books

Published by Bay Books, an imprint of Murdoch Books Pty Limited.

Murdoch Books Australia
Pier 8/9, 23 Hickson Road
Millers Point NSW 2000
Phone: +61 (0) 2 8220 2000
Fax: +61 (0) 2 8220 2558
www.murdochbooks.com.au

Editor: Wendy Stephen
Managing Editor: Jane Price
Design Concept and Art Direction: Marylouise Brammer
Designer: Vivien Valk
Food Director: Jody Vassallo
Photographers (special features): Chris Jones, Luis Martin Photographer (cover): Ian Hofstetter
Stylists (special features): Mary Harris, Rosemary Mellish Stylist (cover): Katy Holder
Stylist's Assistants (special features): Kerrie Ray, Tracey Port
Background painter (special features): Sandra Anderson from Painted Vision, Mudgee NSW
Food Editors: Jody Vassallo, Kerrie Ray
Additional text: Joanne Glynn, Justine Upex, Jody Vassallo
Picture Librarian: Denise Martin

Chief Executive: Juliet Rogers
Publisher: Kay Scarlett

ISBN 978 0 68153 378 3

PRINTED IN CHINA.
This edition published in 2010.

OUR STAR RATING: When we test recipes, we rate them for ease of preparation.
The following cookery ratings are used in this book:
★ A single star indicates a recipe that is simple and generally quick to make—perfect for beginners.
★★ Two stars indicate the need for just a little more care, or perhaps a little more time.
★★★ Three stars indicate special dishes that need more investment in time,
care and patience—but the results are worth it. Even beginners can make these
dishes as long as the recipe is followed carefully.

NUTRITION: The nutritional information given for each recipe does not include any
accompaniments, such as rice or pasta, unless they are included in the ingredients list. The
nutritional values are approximations and can be affected by biological and seasonal variations
in foods, the unknown composition of some manufactured foods and uncertainty in the dietary
database. Nutrient data given are derived primarily from the official NUTTAB95 database.

PASTA... A FEAST FOR THE GODS

We have finally discovered a cookery secret the Italians have known for centuries... it is difficult to go wrong with pasta. What could be simpler or more appealing than butter and shavings of Parmesan melting over a bowl of fresh tagliatelle? As comfort food, pasta is unbeatable. It is warming, filling and, above all, mouthwateringly delicious.

It was said that Marco Polo brought pasta noodles to Italy from China in 1295, a rumour that does great disservice to the ancient Italians, who had been tucking in since the days of Imperial Rome. Cicero himself, so legend has it, was inordinately fond of laganum, the flat, ribbon pasta we now call tagliatelle. And, from the middle ages, Tasso's story tells how an innkeeper invented tortellini in the image of Venus' navel. So, if you're enjoying your pasta, you're in good company. *Buon appetito.*

CONTENTS

Pasta... a feast for the gods 5

Pasta secrets 8

Dried and fresh pastas 10

Making pasta 16

Classic sauces 20

Soups 34

Pasta with meat 54

Pasta with chicken 78

Pasta with seafood 92

Pasta with vegetables 114

Creamy pasta 144

Pasta salads 170

Gnocchi   196

  Making gnocchi   202

Filled pasta   210

  Filling pasta   218

Baked pasta   228

Pasta pronto   252

Pasta desserts   284

Index   293

SPECIAL FEATURES

ANTIPASTO   50

COLD MEATS   66

OLIVES   134

CHEESE   166

BREAD   184

PASTA SECRETS

There are good reasons why pasta is such a popular food: it's cheap, it's quick and easy to prepare (you'll notice most of our recipes have an 'easy' rating), it's delicious, it's nutritious and, as this book demonstrates, it's amazingly versatile. You can dress up pasta for a dinner party with a creamy smoked salmon sauce, or serve it simply, with Parmesan or bacon and eggs. You can serve it cold in salads, warm in soups or piping hot from the oven, stuffed with spinach and ricotta. You can serve it for dessert and you can even serve it as a hangover cure... according to the Italians, spaghetti with garlic and chilli oil, eaten before going to sleep, will ward off the aftereffects of too much vino. You can eat pasta every day of the week (as indeed many Italians do) and never tire of it. Pasta goes well with anything, including breads, vegetables and salads, which is why we have included ideas for these throughout the book.

And of course, there is the traditional accompaniment to some pasta dishes, Parmesan. Although small amounts of grated Parmesan, or little shavings, do look *so* attractive, resist the temptation to serve it with everything. Avoid it with seafood sauces, in particular, as the flavours do not always mix well. If you can't resist decorating your pasta, garnish with the gremolata suggested on page 113.

DRIED OR FRESH?

Many people think that fresh pasta must be better than dried. This is not always the case—some sauces are better teamed with fresh pasta and some are best with dried. Fresh pasta works well with rich sauces made from cream, butter and cheese, because its soft texture absorbs the sauce. Alfredo is one of the nicest sauces to serve on fresh home-made pasta, as is a simple topping of butter and grated Parmesan. Dried pasta is the one to choose if you're serving a heartier, tomato-based sauce. If your sauce has olives, anchovies, chilli, meat or seafood, you'll almost certainly need dried.

Pasta is a combination of flour, water and sometimes eggs and oil. Pasta made with wholewheat flour is darker. If dried pasta is made with durum wheat flour, it is considered to be of superior quality. Other dried pastas that are available include those made from different flours and cereals such as buckwheat, corn, rice and soya beans. Pastas are sometimes flavoured with a purée of herbs, tomato, spinach or other vegetables. Dried pasta will last up to six months, stored in an airtight container in a cool dark place. However, dried wholewheat pasta will only last for one month before turning rancid. Fresh pasta can be wrapped in plastic and frozen for five days. If double wrapped, it will last up to four months. Don't thaw before cooking.

WHICH PASTA SHAPE?

There are good reasons for matching one pasta shape with a particular sauce. Apart from the traditional regional preference for a local shape, its ability to hold and support the sauce is all important. Tubular shapes such as penne capture thick sauces, while flat or long pastas are traditionally served with thin, smooth sauces. But there are no hard and fast rules and part of the fun of pasta is trying out all those fabulous colours, flavours and shapes. See the following pages for photographs of some of the many fresh and dried pastas now available.

A lot of information about the pasta contained in the packet can be gleaned from its name. A name ending in *-ricce* means the pasta has a wavy edge; *-nidi* indicates that the lengths are formed into nests; *-rigate* means ridged and *-lisce*, smooth surfaced. And, if your Italian is up to scratch, you can pretty much visualise your pasta from its

name... although sometimes you may find this a little offputting. *Orecchiette* are little ears; *eliche*, propellers; *ditali*, thimbles; *conchiglie*, conch shells; *linguine*, little tongues; and *vermicelli*, little worms. If the name of the pasta ends with *-oni*, this indicates a larger size: for example, *conchiglioni* are large *conchiglie*. Likewise, *-ini* and *-ette* means smaller versions, as in *farfallini*. However, before we become too embroiled in the importance of names, let us point out that they do vary from manufacturer to manufacturer and book to book... one man's tortelloni can be another man's agnolotti. Luckily, if a little commonsense is used, this isn't going to pose problems of life-threatening importance.

HOW MUCH PASTA?

Another highly charged subject as far as pasta aficionados are concerned, is how much pasta each person should be served and, even more controversially, how much sauce should be served on that pasta. As a general guide, use 60 g (2 oz) of fresh pasta per person for a starter, and 125 g (4 oz) for a main dish. You should allow a little bit more if you are using dried (it contains less moisture, so is lighter), about 90 g (3 oz) each for a starter and 150 g (5 oz) per person for a main course.

How much sauce is obviously a matter of personal taste, but the biggest mistake non-Italian cooks make is to use too much sauce: the pasta should be lightly coated, not drenched. When the pasta and sauce are tossed, there shouldn't be extra sauce swimming around at the bottom.

COOKING YOUR PASTA

Unsalted water will come to the boil faster than salted water, so add the salt once the water is boiling. Use a large pan of water, enough so that the pasta has plenty of room to move around, and only add the pasta when the water has reached a rapid boil. Some people like to add a tablespoon of olive oil to help prevent the

water boiling over or the pasta sticking together. After the pasta has been added, cover the pan to help bring the water back to the boil as quickly as possible, then remove the lid as soon as the water returns to the boil.

Perfectly cooked pasta should be *al dente*, tender but still firm 'to the tooth'. It is important to drain the pasta and then turn it immediately into a heated dish, into the pan with the sauce, or back into its cooking pan. It should never be overdrained, as it needs to be slippery for the sauce to coat it well. Never leave it sitting in the colander or it will become a sticky mass. A little oil or butter tossed through the drained pasta will stop it sticking together. Alternatively, lightly spray the pasta with some boiling water and toss it gently (it is always a good idea to keep a little of the cooking water for this, in case you overdrain). Timing can make all the difference between a good pasta meal and a great one. Always read the recipe through first and then coordinate your cooking times. Try to have the sauce ready to dress the pasta as soon as it is cooked, especially if the pasta is fresh (it will continue to cook if it is left to sit around). Pasta that is to be used in cold pasta salads should be rinsed under cold water to remove excess starch and tossed with a small amount of oil. Cover and refrigerate until ready to use.

FAR LEFT: Lemon grass and lime scallop pasta (page 165)
ABOVE: Green olive and eggplant toss (page 120)

DRIED PASTA

Traditionally, long thin pastas, such as spaghetti, are served with thin oily sauces, while shorter fatter pastas hold chunky sauces better.

PAPPARDELLE

SPAGHETTI

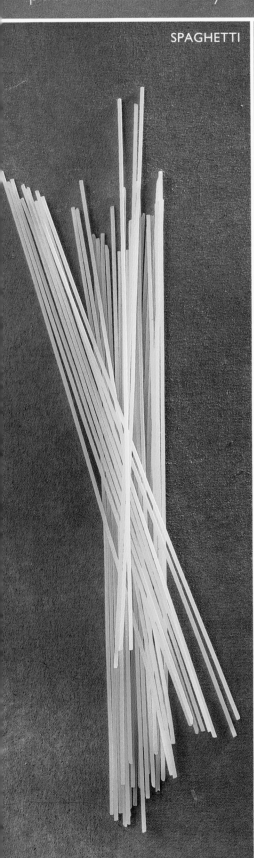

LUMACONI or PIPE RIGATE

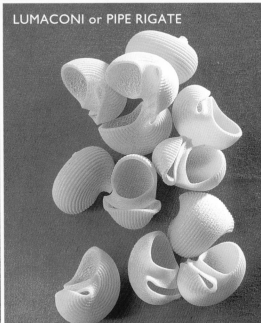

RISSONI

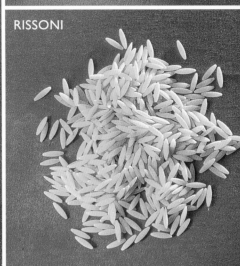

MACARONI or MACCHERONI

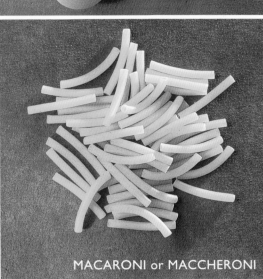

ANELLI

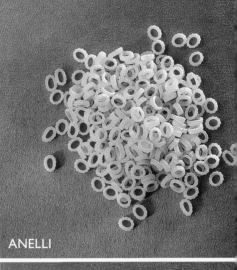

PENNE or PENNE RIGATE

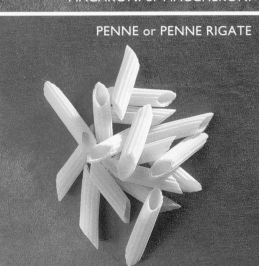

RIGATONI

FUSILLI or ELICHE

ORECCHIETTE

CANNELLONI

FUSILLI or BUCATI LUNGHI

SARDI or GNOBETTI

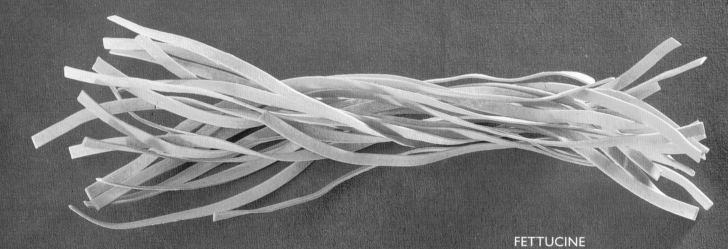

FETTUCINE

LASAGNE

COTELLI or CAVATAPPI

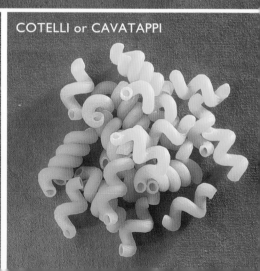

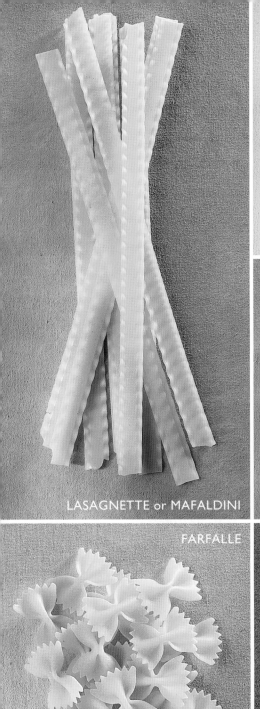

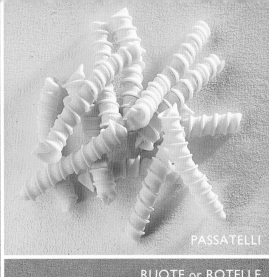

PASSATELLI

CAPELLINI or ANGEL HAIR PASTA

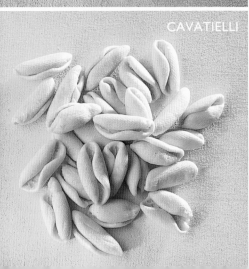

LASAGNETTE or MAFALDINI

RUOTE or ROTELLE

DITALI or DITALINI

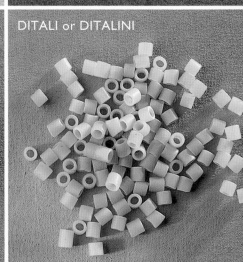

FARFALLE

GNOCCHI

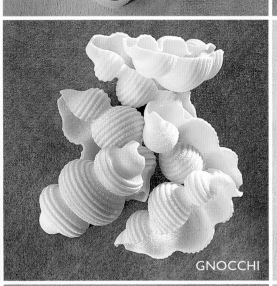

CRESTI DI GALLO

CAVATIELLI

TAGLIATELLE

GARGANELLI

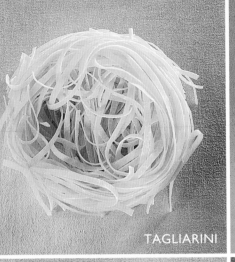
TAGLIARINI

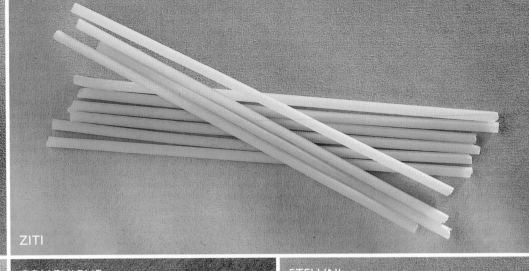
ZITI

FRICELLI

CONCHIGLIE

STELLINI

VERMICELLI

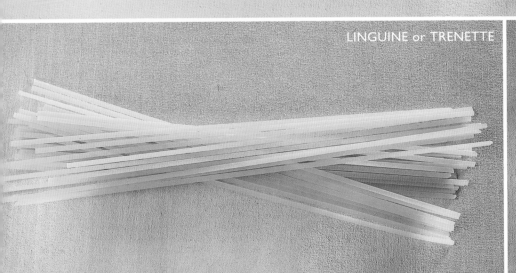
LINGUINE or TRENETTE

TORTELLINI

FRESH PASTA

Wonderful with creamy butter- or cream-based sauces, as the soft texture absorbs the flavours. Make your own or buy one of the supermarket or delicatessen varieties.

MALTAGLIATI

GNOCCHI

TORTELLINI

FETTUCINE

PAPPARDELLE

RAVIOLI

MEZZALUNA

AGNOLOTTI

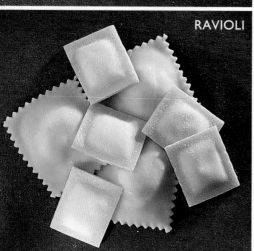

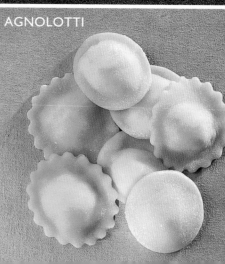

CAPPELLETTI

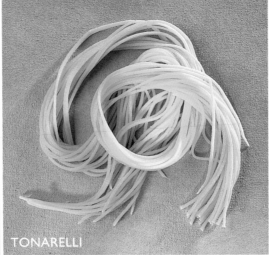
TONARELLI

LASAGNE

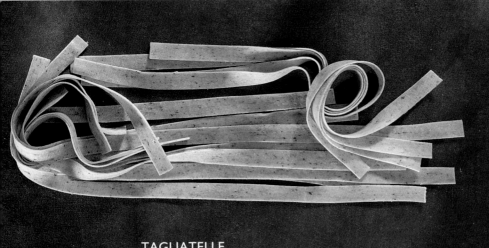
TAGLIATELLE

QUADRUCCI

GARGANELLI

LINGUINE

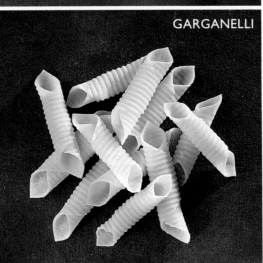

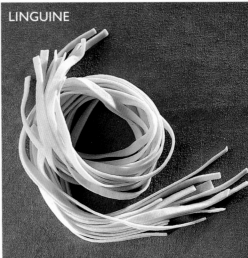

SPAGHETTI PANSOTTI

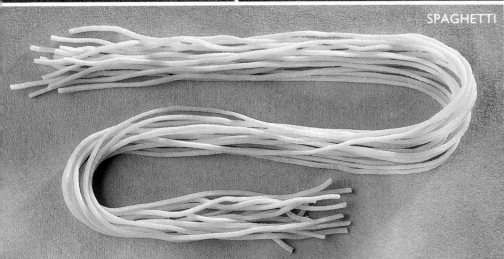

MAKING PASTA What could be more

satisfying and soothing? With a little practice and good-quality ingredients you'll soon

be creating your own pasta in a variety of shapes, tastes and textures.

Making pasta isn't difficult—in fact, it can be extremely relaxing—but there are a few tips that will help. One important element that is often overlooked is a well-ventilated kitchen without breezes or air-conditioning. Also, humidity can cause unruly dough, so don't make pasta on a rainy day.

Kneading is an important part of the process, as it is necessary to work the gluten content of the flour to give a firm but tender dough. Knead the dough until it is pliable, adding small amounts of flour at a time if it is too soft.

Home-made pasta can be refrigerated for up to 48 hours, loosely packed in an airtight container. Turn it over once to check for moisture. Freezing works quite well, but sometimes the pasta becomes brittle. Don't defrost frozen pasta, just put it straight into boiling water. Lasagne sheets store best if blanched first, then stacked between layers of waxed paper before being refrigerated or frozen.

EQUIPMENT

No special equipment is necessary to make pasta but some will save time. Work on a large work area or rolling board with a hard, even surface. Wood or marble is ideal. If making the dough by hand, a long rolling pin gives an evenly-rolled dough and requires less strokes, and a large ceramic bowl makes mixing tidier. A food processor will mix the dough quickly and reduce kneading time. For cutting, you'll need a long,

sharp knife, perhaps a pastry wheel, and a dough scraper is handy. The hand-cranked pasta machines are highly recommended. They knead the dough as it is being rolled, give even sheets of pasta with good texture and are easy to handle. The better brands are sturdy, with a strong holding clamp and rollers that adjust easily as well as crank smoothly.

INGREDIENTS
All the ingredients for pasta dough should be brought to room temperature before you start. The proportion of flour to eggs depends on the weather, the quality of the flour and the age and size of the eggs. Oil makes it easier to work with but you don't have to use it.

Use plain or unbleached flour. It gives a well-textured, light dough with good manageability. A percentage of durum wheat semolina is favoured by some pasta

makers as it improves flavour, colour and texture. However, its hard wheat qualities sometimes make it difficult to work, particularly on a hand-cranked machine, and any proportion greater than equal parts durum wheat semolina to plain flour can cause problems.

BASIC PLAIN DOUGH
To make enough pasta dough to serve 6 as a first course or 4 as a main course, you will need 300 g (10 oz) of plain flour, 3 large (60 g/2 oz) eggs, 30 ml (1 fl oz) of olive oil, optional, and a pinch of salt.

1 To mix the dough by hand, mound the plain flour on a work surface or in a large ceramic bowl and then make a well in the centre.
2 Break the eggs into the well and add the oil, if using, and a large pinch of salt. Using a fork, begin to whisk the eggs

and oil together, incorporating a little of the flour as you do so.
3 Gradually blend the flour with the eggs, working from the centre out. Use your free hand to hold the mound in place and stop leakage if any of the egg escapes.
4 Knead the dough on a lightly floured surface with smooth, light strokes, turning it as you fold and press. It should be soft and pliable, but dry to the touch. If it is sticky, knead in a little flour.
5 It will take at least 6 minutes kneading to achieve a smooth and elastic texture with a slightly glossy appearance. If durum wheat semolina is used, the kneading will take a little longer, at least 8 minutes. Put the dough in a plastic bag without sealing, or cover with a tea towel or an upturned bowl. Allow to rest for 30 minutes. The dough can be made in a food processor.

MAKING PASTA

ROLLING AND CUTTING BY HAND

1 Divide the dough into three or four manageable portions and cover them.

2 Lightly flour a large work surface. Flatten one portion of dough onto the surface and using a long, floured rolling pin, roll out the dough from the centre to the outer edge.

3 Continue rolling, always from in front of you outward, and rotating the dough often. Keep the work surface dusted with just enough flour to prevent sticking. When you have rolled a well-shaped circle, fold the dough in half and roll it out again. Continue in this way seven or eight times to give a smooth circle of pasta about 5 mm (¼ inch) thick.

4 Roll the sheet quickly and smoothly to a thickness of 2.5 mm (⅛ inch). Patch

any tears with a piece of dough from the edge and a little water to help it stick.

5 As each sheet is done, transfer it to a dry tea towel. If the pasta is to be used to make filled pasta keep it covered, but if they are to be cut into lengths or shapes, leave them uncovered while the others are being rolled, so that the surface moisture will dry slightly.

6 For lasagne sheets, simply cut the pasta into the sizes required. The best way to cut lengths such as fettucine is to roll each pasta sheet up like a swiss roll, then cut this into uniform widths with a long, sharp knife. For tagliatelle, cut at 8 mm (⁴⁄10 inch) intervals, 5 mm (¼ inch) for fettucine, or about 3 cm (1¼ inches) for pappardelle. Discard the offcuts. Place the lengths in a single layer on a tea towel to

surface dry for no more than 10 minutes. Or hang long pasta strips to surface dry on broom handles or long wooden spoons between two chairs.

Lengths can also be cut from the flat sheet using a long, sharp knife or a pastry wheel. You may find it easier to run the wheel beside a ruler for straight cutting. A zig-zag pastry wheel will give an interesting edge to pasta shapes such as lasagnette and farfalle.

Don't dry pasta in a cold place or in a draught or it may become brittle. It is better if it dries slowly.

ROLLING AND CUTTING WITH A HAND-CRANKED MACHINE

1 Clamp the machine securely onto the edge of your work surface. Divide the

dough into three or four portions and shape each into a rough log. Keeping the unworked portions covered, take one and flatten it by one or two rolls with a rolling pin. Dust lightly with flour.

2 With the machine's rollers at their widest setting, crank the dough through two or three times. Fold it in thirds, turn the dough 90 degrees and feed through again. If the dough feels damp or tends to stick, lightly flour the outside surfaces each time it is rolled until it passes through cleanly. Repeat this folding and rolling process eight to ten times, or until the dough is a smooth and elastic sheet with a velvety appearance. From now on the dough is not folded.

3 Reduce the width of the rollers by one setting and pass the dough through. Repeat, setting the rollers one notch closer each time until you have rolled the desired thickness. Some machines may roll the sheets too thinly on their last setting, tearing them. A way around this is to stop at the second last setting and roll the dough through several times. It will come out a little thinner each time. This step also applies to machines that don't roll the pasta thinly enough on the last setting.

4 As each sheet is completed, place it on a dry tea towel. Leave uncovered to surface dry for 10 minutes if the sheets are to be cut, but cover them if they are to be used for filled pasta.

5 For lasagne sheets, cut the pasta to the desired size. For narrower lengths, select the appropriate cutters on the machine and crank each pasta sheet through it. Spread them on the tea towel until ready to be cooked, only covering them if they appear to be drying too much. Long pasta such as tagliatelle can be hung to surface dry on broom handles or long wooden spoons between two chairs.

MAKING SHAPES

To make **farfalle** you will need sheets of pasta dough freshly rolled to a standard thickness of 2.5 mm (1/8 inch). Using a zig-zag pastry wheel against a ruler, cut rectangles about 2½ x 5½ cm (1 x 2¼ inches). Pinch the centres together to form a bow tie shape and spread them on a dry tea towel to surface dry for 10–12 minutes. After 5 minutes, re-pinch any that look a little wayward.

To make **orecchiette** start with unrolled, but rested dough. Divide into manageable portions and with your hands, roll each into a long, thin log about 1 cm (1/2 inch) in diameter. Working with one log at a time, cut slices about 2.5 mm (1/8 inch) wide. Roll each slice between your thumb and a lightly floured wooden board. Little ear-like shells form, thicker than most pasta shapes and with an obvious hand-made look. Spread on a tea towel to surface dry.

CLASSIC SAUCES

Sometimes it's difficult to determine whether you're eating pasta with your sauce or sauce with your pasta. While the difference is subtle, the Italians intended their pasta to be evenly dressed by its sauce, rather than swimming in it. Prepare these classic sauces using the freshest ingredients and toss them through a bowl of pasta. And remember the Italian philosophy regarding sauce. To eat your pasta any other way is to do it a great injustice.

After cooking, squeeze the beans out of their skins. If they will not come out easily, gently slit or break the ends first.

Use a small knife to trim the stalks from the sugar snap peas. Break the woody ends from the asparagus.

PRIMAVERA

Preparation time: 25 minutes
Total cooking time: 10– 15 minutes
Serves 4

★

500 g (1 lb) pasta
1 cup (155 g/5 oz) frozen broad beans
200 g (6¹/2 oz) sugar snap peas
155 g (5 oz) fresh aparagus spears
30 g (1 oz) butter
1 cup (250 ml/8 fl oz) cream
60 g (2 oz) freshly grated Parmesan

1 Cook the pasta in a large pan of rapidly boiling salted water until *al dente*. Drain and return to the pan to keep warm.
2 Cook the beans in a pan of boiling water for 2 minutes. Plunge them into iced water and then drain. Remove and discard the skins from the broad beans— you can usually just squeeze them out, otherwise carefully slit the skins first.
3 Trim the stalks from the peas and break the woody ends from the asparagus spears. Cut the asparagus into short lengths.
4 Melt the butter in a heavy-based frying pan. Add the vegetables, cream and Parmesan. Simmer gently over medium heat for 3– 4 minutes, or until the peas and asparagus are bright green and just tender. Season with some salt and pepper. Pour the sauce over the warm pasta and toss to combine. Serve immediately.
NOTE: Traditionally, primavera sauce is served with spaghetti. We have shown it with spaghettini, a thin spaghetti.

NUTRITION PER SERVE: *Protein 30 g; Fat 35 g; Carbohydrate 95 g; Dietary Fibre 12 g; Cholesterol 105 mg; 3420 kJ (815 cal)*

POMODORO

Preparation time: 15 minutes
Total cooking time: 10–15 minutes
Serves 4

500 g (1 lb) pasta
1¹/₂ tablespoons olive oil
1 onion, very finely chopped
2 x 400 g (13 oz) cans Italian tomatoes, chopped
¹/₄ cup (7 g / ¹/₄ oz) fresh basil leaves

1 Cook the pasta in a large pan of rapidly boiling salted water until *al dente*. Drain, return to the pan and keep warm.

2 Heat the oil in a large frying pan. Add the onion and cook over medium heat until softened. Stir in the chopped tomato and simmer for 5–6 minutes, or until the sauce has reduced slightly and thickened. Season with salt and freshly ground pepper. Stir in the basil leaves and cook for another minute. Pour the sauce over the warm pasta and gently toss through. Serve immediately. This is a sauce suitable for serving with freshly grated Parmesan.

NOTE: Traditionally, pomodoro is served with tagliatelle. We have shown it with fettucine.

NUTRITION PER SERVE: *Protein 20 g; Fat 10 g; Carbohydrate 95 g; Dietary Fibre 10 g; Cholesterol 5 mg; 2295 kJ (545 cal)*

STEP-BY-STEP

To finely chop the onion, use a sharp knife to cut it in half, then thinly slice it horizontally, without cutting all the way through.

Next, make cuts close together across one way, and then in the opposite direction, making fine cubes.

STEP-BY-STEP

Finely chop the thick bacon rashers or speck, after removing any rind.

Grate a little of the whole nutmeg, using the finest cutting side of the grater.

CLASSIC BOLOGNESE

Preparation time: 25 minutes
Total cooking time: at least 3 hours
Serves 4

★

50 g (1³/₄ oz) butter
180 g (6 oz) thick bacon rashers or speck, with rind removed, finely chopped
1 large onion, finely chopped
1 carrot, finely chopped
1 celery stick, finely chopped
400 g (13 oz) lean beef mince
150 g (5 oz) chicken livers, finely chopped
2 cups (500 ml/16 fl oz) beef stock
1 cup (250 ml/8 fl oz) tomato purée (passata)
¹/₂ cup (125 ml/4 fl oz) red wine
¹/₄ teaspoon freshly grated nutmeg
500 g (1 lb) pasta
freshly grated Parmesan, for serving

1 Heat half the butter in a heavy-based frying pan. Add the speck and cook until golden. Add the onion, carrot and celery and cook over low heat for 8 minutes, stirring occasionally.
2 Increase the heat, add the remaining butter and, when the pan is hot, add the mince. Break up any lumps with a fork and stir until brown. Add the chicken livers and stir until they change colour. Add the beef stock, tomato purée, wine, nutmeg, and salt and pepper, to taste.
3 Bring to the boil and simmer, covered, over very low heat for 2– 5 hours, adding a little more stock if the sauce becomes too dry. The longer the sauce is cooked, the more flavour it will have.
4 Cook the pasta in a large pan of rapidly boiling salted water until *al dente*. Drain and divide among warmed serving bowls. Serve the sauce over the top and sprinkle with freshly grated Parmesan.
NOTE: Traditionally, bolognese was served with tagliatelle, but now we serve it with spaghetti.

NUTRITION PER SERVE: *Protein 45 g; Fat 35 g; Carbohydrate 95 g; Dietary Fibre 9 g; Cholesterol 145 mg; 3860 kJ (920 cal)*

ALFREDO

Preparation time: 10 minutes
Total cooking time: 15 minutes
Serves 4–6

500 g (1 lb) pasta
90 g (3 oz) butter
1½ cups (150 g / 5 oz) freshly grated
  Parmesan
1¼ cups (315 ml / 10 fl oz) cream
3 tablespoons chopped fresh parsley

1 Cook the pasta in a large pan of rapidly boiling salted water until *al dente*. Drain and return to the pan.
2 While the pasta is cooking, melt the butter in a pan over low heat. Add the Parmesan and cream and bring to the boil, stirring constantly. Reduce the heat and simmer, stirring, until the sauce has thickened slightly. Add the chopped fresh parsley, salt and pepper, to taste, and stir until well combined.
3 Add the sauce to the pasta and toss well so the sauce coats the pasta. This dish can be garnished with chopped herbs or sprigs of fresh herbs such as thyme.
NOTE: Traditionally, plain fettucine, as shown in the picture, is used with this sauce, but you can use any style of pasta. It is a very simple sauce to make and should be prepared just before the pasta is cooked.

NUTRITION PER SERVE (6): *Protein 20 g; Fat 40 g; Carbohydrate 60 g; Dietary Fibre 4 g; Cholesterol 125 mg; 2875 kJ (685 cal)*

STEP-BY-STEP

Ideally, Parmesan is grated from a piece just before using. This prevents loss of flavour and drying out.

Use a large, sharp knife to chop the fresh parsley. A swivel action is easiest, holding the point of the knife in one place.

STEP-BY-STEP

For this sauce, the vegetables should be chopped into quite small pieces before adding to the hot oil.

The tomatoes should also be cut into small pieces, before adding with the parsley, sugar and water.

NAPOLITANA

Preparation time: 20 minutes
Total cooking time: 1 hour
Serves 4– 6

★

2 tablespoons olive oil
1 onion, finely chopped
1 carrot, finely chopped
1 celery stick, finely chopped
500 g (1 lb) very ripe tomatoes, chopped
2 tablespoons chopped fresh parsley
2 teaspoons sugar
500 g (1 lb) pasta

1 Heat the oil in a heavy-based pan. Add the onion, carrot and celery. Cover and cook for 10 minutes over low heat, stirring occasionally.
2 Add the tomato to the vegetables with the parsley, sugar and ½ cup (125 ml/4 fl oz) of water. Bring to the boil, reduce the heat to low,

cover and simmer for 45 minutes, stirring occasionally. Season with salt and freshly ground black pepper, to taste. If necessary, add up to ¾ cup (185 ml/6 fl oz) more water until the required consistency is reached.
3 About 15 minutes before serving, add the pasta to a large pan of rapidly boiling salted water and cook until *al dente*. Drain and return to the pan. Pour the sauce over the pasta and gently toss until combined. Serve in individual bowls or on plates.

NOTE: Traditionally, spaghetti is used with this sauce, but you can use any pasta. We have shown penne rigate. The sauce can be reduced to a concentrated version by cooking it for a longer period. Store it in the refrigerator and add water or stock to thin it, if necessary, when reheating.

NUTRITION PER SERVE (6): *Protein 10 g; Fat 7 g; Carbohydrate 65 g; Dietary Fibre 6 g; Cholesterol 0 mg; 1540 kJ (365 cal)*

CARBONARA
(CREAMY EGG AND BACON SAUCE)

Preparation time: 15 minutes
Total cooking time: 25 minutes
Serves 4– 6

8 bacon rashers
500 g (1 lb) pasta
4 eggs
1/2 cup (50 g / 1³/4 oz) freshly grated
   Parmesan
1¹/4 cups (315 ml / 10 fl oz) cream

1 Remove and discard the bacon rind and cut the bacon into thin strips. Cook in a heavy-based pan over medium heat until crisp. Drain on paper towels.
2 Add the pasta to a large pan of rapidly boiling salted water and cook until *al dente*. Drain and return to the pan.
3 While the pasta is cooking, beat the eggs, Parmesan and cream in a bowl until well combined. Stir the bacon through the mixture. Pour the sauce over the hot pasta and toss gently until the sauce coats the pasta.
4 Return the pan to very low heat and cook for 1/2 – 1 minute, or until the sauce has slightly thickened. Freshly ground black pepper can be added, to taste.
NOTE: Traditionally, fettucine is used with this dish, but you can use any pasta of your choice. It has been pictured with tagliatelle.

NUTRITION PER SERVE (6): *Protein 30 g; Fat 35 g; Carbohydrate 60 g; Dietary Fibre 4 g; Cholesterol 225 mg; 2895 kJ (690 cal)*

STEP-BY-STEP

Cook the bacon strips in a heavy-based pan, stirring until crisp, being careful not to let them burn.

Drain the bacon on paper towels. After beating the eggs, Parmesan and cream together, mix in the bacon.

Process the pine nuts, basil leaves, garlic, salt and cheeses until finely chopped, about 20 seconds.

With the motor running, add the olive oil in a thin steady stream, until a paste is formed.

PESTO

Preparation time: 10–15 minutes
Total cooking time: Nil
Serves 4– 6

★

500 g (1 lb) pasta
3 tablespoons pine nuts
2 cups (100 g/3¹/₂ oz) fresh basil leaves
2 cloves garlic, peeled
¹/₂ teaspoon salt
3 tablespoons freshly grated Parmesan
2 tablespoons freshly grated Pecorino
    cheese, optional
¹/₂ cup (125 ml/4 fl oz) olive oil

1 Cook the pasta in a large pan of rapidly boiling salted water until *al dente*. Drain, return to the pan and keep warm.
2 About 5 minutes before the pasta is cooked, add the pine nuts to a heavy-based pan and stir over low heat for 2– 3 minutes, or until golden. Allow to cool. Process the pine nuts, basil leaves, garlic, salt and cheeses in a food processor for 20 seconds, until finely chopped. Scrape down the sides of the bowl.
3 With the motor running, gradually add the oil in a thin steady stream until a paste is formed. Add freshly ground black pepper, to taste. Toss the sauce with the warm pasta until the pasta is well coated.
NOTE: Traditionally, linguine, as shown, is used with pesto but you can serve it with any pasta of your choice. Pesto sauce can be made up to one week in advance and refrigerated in an airtight container. Ensure the pesto is tightly packed and seal the surface with some plastic wrap or pour some extra oil over the top, to prevent the pesto going black.

NUTRITION PER SERVE (6): *Protein 15 g; Fat 30 g; Carbohydrate 60 g; Dietary Fibre 5 g; Cholesterol 8 mg; 2280 kJ (540 cal)*

AMATRICIANA
(SPICY BACON AND TOMATO SAUCE)

Preparation time: 45 minutes
Total cooking time: 20 minutes
Serves 4– 6

6 thin slices pancetta or 3 bacon rashers

1 kg (2 lb) very ripe tomatoes

500 g (1 lb) pasta

1 tablespoon olive oil

1 small onion, very finely chopped

2 teaspoons very finely chopped fresh chilli

Parmesan shavings, for serving

1 Finely chop the pancetta or bacon. Score a cross in the base of each tomato. Soak in boiling water for 1– 2 minutes, drain and plunge into cold water briefly. Peel back the skin from the cross. Halve, remove the seeds and chop the flesh.

2 Add the pasta to a large pan of rapidly boiling water and cook until *al dente*. Drain and return to the pan.

3 About 5 minutes before the pasta is cooked, heat the oil in a heavy-based frying pan. Add the pancetta or bacon, onion and chilli and stir over medium heat for 3 minutes. Add the tomato and salt and pepper, to taste. Reduce the heat and simmer for another 3 minutes. Add the sauce to the pasta and toss until well combined. Serve garnished with shavings of Parmesan. Freshly ground black pepper can be added, to taste.

NOTE: It is believed this dish originated in the town of Amatrice, where bacon is a prized local product. For a change from regular tomatoes, you can try Roma (egg) tomatoes in this recipe. They are firm-fleshed, with few seeds and have a rich flavour when cooked. Traditionally, bucatini, as shown, is used with this sauce, but you can use any pasta you prefer.

NUTRITION PER SERVE (6): *Protein 15 g; Fat 9 g; Carbohydrate 60 g; Dietary Fibre 6 g; Cholesterol 15 mg; 1640 kJ (390 cal)*

STEP-BY-STEP

Remove the tomatoes from the cold water and peel the skin down from the cross.

Halve the tomatoes and use a teaspoon to scrape out the seeds before chopping the flesh.

STEP-BY-STEP

Add a little of the cream and scrape the bottom of the pan with a wooden spoon to dislodge any bacon that has stuck.

Cook the sauce over high heat until it is thick enough to coat the back of a wooden spoon.

CREAMY BOSCAIOLA

Preparation time: 15 minutes
Total cooking time: 20–25 minutes
Serves 4

500 g (1 lb) pasta
6 bacon rashers, trimmed of rind
  and chopped
200 g (6¹/₂ oz) button mushrooms, sliced
2¹/₂ cups (600 ml/20 fl oz) cream
2 spring onions, sliced
1 tablespoon chopped fresh parsley

1 Cook the pasta in a large pan of rapidly boiling salted water until *al dente*. Drain, return to the pan and keep warm.
2 While the pasta is cooking, heat about 1 tablespoon of oil in a large frying pan, add the bacon and mushroom and cook, stirring, for 5 minutes, or until golden brown.

3 Stir in a little of the cream and scrape the wooden spoon on the bottom of the pan to dislodge any bacon that has stuck.
4 Add the remaining cream, bring to the boil and cook over high heat for 15 minutes, or until the sauce is thick enough to coat the back of a spoon. Stir the spring onion through the mixture. Pour the sauce over the pasta and toss to combine. Serve sprinkled with the chopped fresh parsley.
NOTE: This sauce is normally served with spaghetti, but you can use any pasta. We have shown it with casereccie. If you are short on time and don't have 15 minutes to reduce the sauce, it can be thickened with 2 teaspoons of cornflour mixed in 1 tablespoon of water. Stir until the mixture boils and thickens. 'Boscaiola' means woodcutter—collecting mushrooms is part of the heritage of the woodcutters.

NUTRITION PER SERVE: *Protein 30 g; Fat 60 g; Carbohydrate 95 g; Dietary Fibre 8 g; Cholesterol 200 mg; 4310 kJ (1025 cal)*

PUTTANESCA
(SAUCE WITH CAPERS, OLIVES AND ANCHOVIES)

Preparation time: 20 minutes
Total cooking time: 20 minutes
Serves 4

500 g (1 lb) pasta
2 tablespoons olive oil
3 cloves garlic, crushed
2 tablespoons chopped fresh parsley
1/4 – 1/2 teaspoon chilli flakes
   or powder
2 x 425 g (14 oz) cans chopped
   tomatoes
1 tablespoon capers
3 anchovy fillets, thinly sliced
1/4 cup (45 g/1 1/2 oz) black olives
freshly grated Parmesan, for serving

1 Cook the pasta in a large pan of rapidly boiling salted water until *al dente*. Drain, return to the pan and keep warm.
2 While the pasta is cooking, heat the oil in a large heavy-based frying pan. Add the garlic, parsley and chilli flakes and stir constantly, for about 1 minute, over medium heat.
3 Add the tomato to the pan and bring to the boil. Reduce the heat and simmer, covered, for 5 minutes.
4 Add the capers, anchovies and olives and stir for another 5 minutes. Season, to taste, with black pepper. Add the sauce to the pasta and toss gently until the sauce is evenly distributed. Serve immediately, with freshly grated Parmesan.
NOTE: Traditionally, spaghetti is used with the sauce, but you can use other pasta if you prefer. The lasagnette we have shown here creates an unusual look.

NUTRITION PER SERVE: *Protein 20 g; Fat 15 g; Carbohydrate 95 g; Dietary Fibre 9 g; Cholesterol 8 mg; 2510 kJ (595 cal)*

STEP-BY-STEP

To make peeling easier, squash each clove of garlic with the flat side of a knife, pressing with the palm of your hand.

Roughly chop the garlic, with a little salt, then scrape the knife at an angle to finely crush the garlic.

STEP-BY-STEP

Remove the stalks and slice the chillies in half. Wear rubber gloves to protect your skin.

Finely chop the chillies. The seeds and membrane are left in as this is a fiery sauce, but remove them if you prefer a milder taste.

ARRABBIATA
(FIERY TOMATO SAUCE)

Preparation time: 30 minutes
Total cooking time: 50 minutes
Serves 4

1/2 cup (75 g/2 1/2 oz) bacon fat
2–3 fresh red chillies
2 tablespoons olive oil
1 large onion, finely chopped
1 clove garlic, finely chopped
500 g (1 lb) very ripe tomatoes, finely chopped
500 g (1 lb) pasta
2 tablespoons chopped fresh parsley
freshly grated Parmesan or Pecorino cheese, for serving

1 Use a large knife to finely chop the bacon fat. Chop the chillies, taking care to avoid skin irritation—wearing rubber gloves will help. Heat the oil in a heavy-based pan and add the bacon fat, chilli, onion and garlic. Cook for 8 minutes over medium heat, stirring occasionally.
2 Add the chopped tomato along with 1/2 cup (125 ml/4 fl oz) of water and season with salt and freshly ground black pepper, to taste. Cover and simmer for about 40 minutes, or until the sauce is thick and rich.
3 When the sauce is almost cooked, cook the pasta in a large pan of rapidly boiling salted water until *al dente*. Drain and return to the pan.
4 Add the parsley to the sauce. Taste and season again, if necessary. Pour the sauce over the pasta in the pan and toss gently. Serve with the freshly grated Parmesan or Pecorino cheese sprinkled over the top.
NOTE: Penne rigate, as shown, is traditionally used with this sauce, but you can use other pasta.

NUTRITION PER SERVE: *Protein 20 g; Fat 25 g; Carbohydrate 95 g; Dietary Fibre 9 g; Cholesterol 20 mg; 2880 kJ (685 cal)*

MARINARA

Preparation time: 50 minutes
Total cooking time: 30 minutes
Serves 4

★

1 onion, chopped

2 cloves garlic, crushed

1/2 cup (125 ml/4 fl oz) red wine

2 tablespoons tomato paste

425 g (14 oz) can chopped tomatoes

1 cup (250 ml/8 fl oz) bottled tomato pasta sauce

1 tablespoon each of chopped fresh
   basil and oregano

12 mussels, beards removed, and scrubbed
   (discard any which are already open)

30 g (1 oz) butter

125 g (4 oz) small calamari tubes, sliced

125 g (4 oz) boneless white fish fillets, cubed

200 g (6 1/2 oz) raw prawns, shelled and
   deveined, leaving tails intact

500 g (1 lb) pasta

1 Heat a little olive oil in a large pan. Add the onion and garlic and cook over low heat for 2–3 minutes. Increase the heat to medium and add the wine, tomato paste, tomato and pasta sauce. Simmer, stirring occasionally, for 5–10 minutes or until the sauce reduces and thickens slightly. Stir in the herbs and season, to taste. Keep warm.

2 While the sauce is simmering, heat 1/2 cup (125 ml/4 fl oz) water in a pan. Add the mussels, cover and steam for 3–5 minutes, or until the mussels have changed colour and opened. Discard any unopened mussels. Remove and set aside. Stir the remaining liquid into the tomato sauce.

3 Heat the butter in a pan and sauté the calamari, fish and prawns, in batches, for 1–2 minutes, or until cooked. Add the seafood to the warm tomato sauce and stir gently.

4 Cook the pasta in a large pan of rapidly boiling salted water until *al dente*; drain. Combine the seafood sauce with the hot pasta and serve.

NOTE: Traditionally served with spaghetti.

NUTRITION PER SERVE: *Protein 40 g; Fat 10 g; Carbohydrate 100 g; Dietary Fibre 10 g; Cholesterol 205 mg; 2840 kJ (675 cal)*

STEP-BY-STEP

Pull the beards away from the mussels and discard any open mussels. Scrub the shells to remove any dirt or grit.

Remove the quills from inside the calamari tubes and slice the tubes into thin rings.

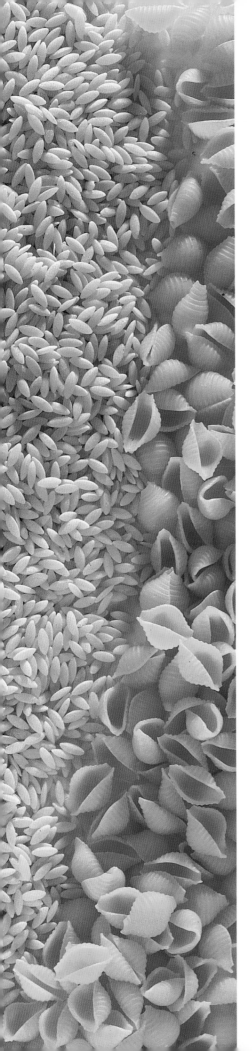

SOUPS

Soup is food for the soul—spreading warmth and comfort and memories of winter suppers. The best kind of soup is made by simmering all your favourite ingredients in a tasty stock, and what better way to beef it up than by throwing in a handful of pasta? Conchiglie and fusilli make a soup almost a stew, while tortellini or ravioli make a meal of any elegant clear consommé. There are even special tiny pastas for floating in your soup. In fact, pasta and soup go together like, well, like macaroni and minestrone.

ABOVE: *Lemon-scented broth with tortellini*

low heat. Remove the lemon rind from the pan and bring the mixture to the boil.

3 Add the tortellini and parsley to the pan and season with black pepper. Cook for 6– 7 minutes, or until the pasta is *al dente*. Garnish with the fine strips of lemon rind.

NOTE: You can use chopped fresh basil instead of parsley. Serve with a sprinkling of freshly grated Parmesan if you wish.

NUTRITION PER SERVE (6): *Protein 10 g; Fat 2 g; Carbohydrate 45 g; Dietary Fibre 4 g; Cholesterol 10 mg; 1060 kJ (250 cal)*

CHICKEN, LEEK AND CHICKPEA SOUP

Preparation time: 15 minutes
Total cooking time: 20 minutes
Serves 4

4 cups (1 litre) chicken stock
125 g (4 oz) miniature pasta shapes
20 g (³/4 oz) butter
1 leek, sliced
1 clove garlic, crushed
¹/2 cup (110 g/3¹/2 oz) roasted chickpeas
1 tablespoon plain flour
2 tablespoons finely chopped fresh
   flat-leaf parsley
pinch of cayenne pepper
200 g (6¹/2 oz) chopped cooked chicken meat

1 Bring the chicken stock to the boil in a large saucepan. Add the pasta to the stock and cook until just tender. Remove the pasta with a slotted spoon, keeping the stock on the heat and just boiling.

2 Meanwhile, melt the butter in a large saucepan, add the leek and garlic and stir until golden, but not brown. Add the chickpeas, toss for a minute and then sprinkle with the flour. Fry for about 10 seconds, then gradually blend in the boiling stock.

3 Add the parsley, cayenne, and salt and black pepper, to taste. Add the pasta and the chicken meat to the saucepan and bring back to the boil before serving.

NUTRITION PER SERVE: *Protein 15 g; Fat 8 g; Carbohydrate 30 g; Dietary Fibre 4 g; Cholesterol 50 mg; 1075 kJ (255 cal)*

LEMON-SCENTED BROTH WITH TORTELLINI

Preparation time: 10 minutes
Total cooking time: 20 minutes
Serves 4– 6

1 lemon
¹/2 cup (125 ml/4 fl oz) good-quality white wine
440 g (14 oz) can chicken consommé
375 g (12 oz) fresh or dried veal- or
   chicken-filled tortellini
4 tablespoons chopped fresh parsley

1 Using a vegetable peeler, peel wide strips from the lemon. Remove the white pith with a small sharp knife and cut three of the wide pieces into fine strips. Set aside for garnishing.

2 Combine the wide lemon strips, white wine, consommé and 3 cups (750 ml/24 fl oz) of water in a large deep pan. Cook for 10 minutes over

MINESTRONE

Preparation time: 30 minutes + overnight
soaking
Total cooking time: 3 hours
Serves 6– 8

250 g (8 oz) dried borlotti beans, soaked
   in water overnight
2 onions, chopped
2 cloves garlic, crushed
3 bacon rashers, chopped
4 egg (Roma) tomatoes, peeled and chopped
3 tablespoons chopped fresh parsley
9 cups (2.25 litres) beef or vegetable stock
1/4 cup (60 ml/2 fl oz) red wine
1 carrot, chopped
1 swede, diced
2 potatoes, diced
3 tablespoons tomato paste (tomato purée,
   double concentrate)

2 zucchini (courgettes), sliced
1/2 cup (80 g/2 3/4 oz) peas
1/2 cup (80 g/2 3/4 oz) small macaroni
freshly grated Parmesan and pesto, for serving

1 Drain and rinse the borlotti beans, cover with
cold water in a pan. Bring to the boil, stir, lower
the heat and simmer for 15 minutes. Drain.
2 Heat 2 tablespoons of oil in a large heavy-
based pan and cook the onion, garlic and
bacon, stirring, until the onion is soft and the
bacon golden.
3 Add the tomato, parsley, borlotti beans, stock
and red wine. Simmer, covered, over low heat
for 2 hours. Add the carrot, swede, potato and
tomato paste, cover and simmer for 20 minutes.
4 Add the zucchini, peas and macaroni. Cover
and simmer for 10– 15 minutes, or until the
vegetables and macaroni are tender. Season, to
taste, and serve topped with Parmesan and a
little pesto. Fresh herbs can be used to garnish.

NUTRITION PER SERVE (8): *Protein 15 g; Fat 7 g;
Carbohydrate 35 g; Dietary Fibre 8 g; Cholesterol 8 mg;
1135 kJ (270 cal)*

BORLOTTI BEANS
Borlotti beans, also known
as cranberry or red
haricot, are the large,
beautifully marked kidney
beans so loved in northern
and central Italy. They
have a nutty flavour and
creamy flesh that is
especially fine in soups
and stews, but they are
also suited to salads and
puréeing. They can be
found fresh in spring and
summer. Otherwise, dried
are used, or pre-cooked
from cans for convenience.

ABOVE: Minestrone

SNOW PEA (MANGETOUT), PRAWN AND PASTA SOUP

Preparation time: 30 minutes
Total cooking time: 15 minutes
Serves 4

★

12 raw king prawns
100 g (3¹/2 oz) snow peas (mangetout)
1 tablespoon oil
2 onions, chopped
6 cups (1.5 litres) chicken stock
¹/2 teaspoon grated fresh ginger
200 g (6¹/2 oz) angel hair pasta or spaghettini
fresh basil leaves, to garnish

BELOW: Snow pea, prawn and pasta soup

1 Peel and devein the prawns, leaving the tails intact. Trim the snow peas and if they are big ones, slice them into smaller pieces.
2 Heat the oil in a pan, add the onion and cook over low heat until soft. Add the chicken stock to the pan and bring to the boil.
3 Add the fresh ginger, snow peas, prawns and pasta. Cook over medium heat for 4 minutes. Season with salt and pepper and serve immediately, garnished with fresh basil leaves.

NUTRITION PER SERVE: *Protein 20 g; Fat 6 g; Carbohydrate 40 g; Dietary Fibre 4 g; Cholesterol 85 mg; 1255 kJ (300 cal)*

RISSONI AND MUSHROOM BROTH

Preparation time: 15 minutes
Total cooking time: 20– 25 minutes
Serves 4

★

90 g (3 oz) butter
2 cloves garlic, sliced
2 large onions, sliced
375 g (12 oz) mushrooms, thinly sliced
5 cups (1.25 litres) chicken stock
125 g (4 oz) rissoni
1¹/4 cups (315 ml/10 fl oz) cream

1 Melt the butter in a large pan over low heat. Add the garlic and onion and cook for 1 minute. Add the sliced mushrooms and cook gently, without colouring, for 5 minutes. Set aside a few mushroom slices to use as a garnish. Add the chicken stock and cook for 10 minutes.
2 Meanwhile, add the rissoni to a large pan of rapidly boiling salted water and cook until *al dente*. Drain and set aside.
3 Allow the mushroom mixture to cool a little before mixing in a blender or food processor until smooth.
4 Return the mixture to the pan and stir in the rissoni and cream. Heat through and season with salt and pepper, to taste. Serve from a soup terrine or in individual bowls. Garnish with the reserved mushrooms.

NUTRITION PER SERVE: *Protein 10 g; Fat 55 g; Carbohydrate 30 g; Dietary Fibre 5 g; Cholesterol 165 mg; 2660 kJ (635 cal)*

BEAN SOUP WITH SAUSAGE

Preparation time: 25 minutes
Total cooking time: 40 minutes
Serves 4–6

4 Italian sausages

2 teaspoons olive oil

2 leeks, sliced

1 clove garlic, crushed

1 large carrot, chopped into
   small cubes

2 celery sticks, sliced

2 tablespoons plain flour

2 beef stock cubes, crumbled

8 cups (2 litres) hot water

1/2 cup (125 ml/4 fl oz) white wine

125 g (4 oz) conchiglie
   (shell pasta)

440 g (14 oz) can three-bean
   mix, drained

1 Cut the sausages into small pieces. Heat the oil in a large heavy-based pan and add the sausage pieces. Cook over medium heat for 5 minutes or until golden, stirring regularly. Remove from the pan and drain on paper towels.

2 Add the leek, garlic, carrot and celery to the pan and cook for 2–3 minutes or until soft, stirring occasionally.

3 Add the flour and stir for 1 minute. Gradually stir in the combined stock cubes and water and the wine. Bring to the boil, reduce the heat and simmer for 10 minutes.

4 Add the pasta and beans to the pan. Increase the heat and cook for 8–10 minutes, or until the pasta is tender. Return the sausage to the pan and season with salt and pepper, to taste. Serve with chopped fresh parsley, if desired.

NOTE: Use dried beans, if preferred. Put them in a bowl, cover with water and soak overnight. Drain and add to a large pan with enough water to cover the beans well. Bring to the boil, reduce the heat and simmer for 1 hour. Drain well before adding to the soup.

NUTRITION PER SERVE (6): *Protein 15 g; Fat 10 g; Carbohydrate 30 g; Dietary Fibre 9 g; Cholesterol 20 mg; 1145 kJ (270 cal)*

*ABOVE: Bean
soup with sausage*

ABOVE: Spicy chicken broth with coriander pasta

FRESH CORIANDER

Coriander, also known as cilantro or Chinese parsley, is widely used throughout the world. All parts of the plant are eaten, in one country or another. In Asia and the Middle East, the dried seeds are used for their fragrance, and they form the basis for curry powders when ground. In Mexican cooking, fresh leaves are used extensively, while in Thailand the stems and roots are eaten as well as the leaves.

SPICY CHICKEN BROTH WITH CORIANDER PASTA

Preparation time: 1 hour
Total cooking time: 50 minutes
Serves 4

★★★

350 g (11 oz) chicken thighs or wings, skin removed

2 carrots, finely chopped

2 celery sticks, finely chopped

2 small leeks, finely chopped

3 egg whites

6 cups (1.5 litres) chicken stock

Tabasco sauce

Coriander pasta

1/2 cup (60 g/2 oz) plain flour

1 egg

1/2 teaspoon sesame oil

90 g (3 oz) coriander leaves

1 Put the chicken pieces, carrot, celery and leek in a large heavy-based pan. Push the chicken to one side and add the egg whites to the vegetables. Using a wire whisk, beat for a minute or so, until frothy (take care not to use a pan that can be scratched by the whisk).

2 Warm the stock in another pan, then add gradually to the first pan, whisking continuously to froth the egg whites. Continue whisking while slowly bringing to the boil. Make a hole in the froth on top with a spoon and leave to simmer for 30 minutes, without stirring.

3 Line a large strainer with a damp tea towel or double thickness of muslin and strain the broth into a clean bowl (discard the chicken and vegetables). Season with salt, pepper and Tabasco sauce, to taste. Set aside until you are ready to serve.

4 To make the coriander pasta, sift the flour into a bowl and make a well in the centre. Whisk the egg and oil together and pour into the well. Mix together to make a soft pasta dough and knead on a lightly floured surface for 2 minutes, until smooth.

5 Divide the pasta dough into four even portions. Roll one portion out very thinly and cover with a layer of evenly spaced coriander leaves. Roll out another portion of pasta and lay this on top of the leaves, then gently roll the layers together. Repeat with the remaining pasta and coriander.

6 Cut out squares of pasta around the leaves. The pasta may then be left to sit and dry out if it is not needed immediately. When you are ready to serve, heat the chicken broth gently in a pan. As the broth simmers, add the pasta and cook for 1 minute. Serve immediately.

NOTE: The egg whites added to the vegetable and chicken stock make the broth very clear, rather than leaving it with the normal cloudy appearance of chicken stock. This is called clarifying the stock. When you strain the broth through muslin or a tea towel, don't press the solids to extract the extra liquid or the broth will become cloudy. It is necessary to make a hole in the froth on top to prevent the stock boiling over.

NUTRITION PER SERVE: *Protein 25 g; Fat 5 g; Carbohydrate 20 g; Dietary Fibre 5 g; Cholesterol 95 mg; 920 kJ (220 cal)*

TOMATO SOUP WITH PASTA AND BASIL

Preparation time: 25 minutes
Total cooking time: 35– 40 minutes
Serves 4

3 large very ripe tomatoes (about 750 g/1 ½ lb)
2 tablespoons olive oil
1 onion, finely chopped
1 clove garlic, crushed
1 small red pepper (capsicum),
    finely chopped
4 cups (1 litre) chicken or vegetable
    stock
¼ cup (60 g/2 oz) tomato paste
    (tomato purée, double concentrate)
1 teaspoon sugar
¼ cup (15 g/½ oz) fresh basil leaves
1 cup (155 g/5 oz) conchiglie (shell pasta)
    or macaroni

1 Score a small cross in the top of each tomato. Plunge the tomatoes into boiling water for 1– 2 minutes, then into cold water. Peel the skin down from the cross and discard. Remove the seeds and roughly chop the tomatoes. Heat the oil in a large heavy-based pan and cook the onion, garlic and red pepper, stirring, for 10 minutes, or until soft. Add the tomato and cook for another 10 minutes.

2 Add the stock, tomato paste, sugar and salt and pepper, to taste. Cover and simmer for 15 minutes. Remove from the heat and add the basil leaves. Allow to cool slightly before processing the mixture, in batches, in a food processor or blender until smooth. Return the mixture to the pan and reheat gently.

3 While the soup is cooking, add the pasta to a large pan of rapidly boiling salted water and cook until *al dente*. Drain, add to the soup and heat through. Garnish with basil leaves if you wish.
NOTE: Basil is added at the end of cooking so that its flavour is not impaired.

NUTRITION PER SERVE: *Protein 10 g; Fat 10 g; Carbohydrate 40 g; Dietary Fibre 5 g; Cholesterol 0 mg; 1200 kJ (285 cal)*

BASIL
There are many varieties of this spicy, aromatic herb, but sweet basil is the most commonly used. Basil plays an important role in Italian and Asian, especially Indonesian, cuisine. It is most often used fresh and added at the last minute, the dried form only being successful in dishes of complex flavours needing long cooking. Basil leaves have a high moisture content and bruise easily. They are best if shredded, not chopped, and the less they are cut, the less blackening will occur.

LEFT: Tomato soup with pasta and basil

1 In a large pan, heat the oil and butter. Add the peeled whole garlic cloves and the onion and cook over low heat for 2– 3 minutes.

2 Add the celery and carrot and fry until the vegetables are golden but do not allow them to brown. Add the parsley, basil and cayenne. Stir briefly, add the prawns and toss through. Remove the garlic cloves.

3 Pour in the sherry, increase the heat and cook for 2– 3 minutes. Add the chicken stock, bring back to the boil, reduce the heat and simmer for 5 minutes.

4 Add the conchiglie and simmer until the pasta is *al dente*. Stir in the cream and add salt and freshly ground black pepper, to taste.

NUTRITION PER SERVE: *Protein 25 g; Fat 20 g; Carbohydrate 20 g; Dietary Fibre 5 g; Cholesterol 270 mg; 1710 kJ (410 cal)*

BROCCOLI SOUP

Preparation time: 15 minutes
Total cooking time: 20 minutes
Serves 4

2 tablespoons olive oil

1 large onion, thinly sliced

50 g (1³/₄ oz) diced prosciutto or unsmoked ham

1 clove garlic, crushed

5 cups (1.25 litres) chicken stock

50 g (1³/₄ oz) stellini or other miniature pasta shapes

250 g (8 oz) broccoli, tops cut into small florets and the tender stems julienned

freshly grated Parmesan, for serving

1 Heat the oil in a large pan over low heat, add the onion, prosciutto and garlic and cook for 4– 5 minutes.

2 Pour in the chicken stock, bring to the boil, reduce the heat slightly and simmer for 10 minutes with the lid three-quarters on.

3 Add the stellini and broccoli and cook until the pasta is *al dente* and the broccoli is crisp but tender. Season, to taste, with salt and freshly ground black pepper. Serve in warm bowls with the grated Parmesan.

NUTRITION PER SERVE: *Protein 10 g; Fat 15 g; Carbohydrate 10 g; Dietary Fibre 5 g; Cholesterol 10 mg; 850 kJ (250 cal)*

BROCCOLI

Broccoli belongs to the cabbage family. It is so closely related to the cauliflower that they both have the same varietal name, *botrytis*, from the Greek meaning "formed in a cluster" like a bunch of grapes. Broccoli adds not only colour and flavour to a meal, but nutritive value, as it has high levels of vitamins and essential minerals. It boils or steams well and, if trimmed and cut into separate florets, will cook fast and evenly. Broccoli is also suitable for puréeing and the bulk of the florets gives volume to salads and stir-fries.

ABOVE: Prawn and basil soup (top); Broccoli soup

PRAWN AND BASIL SOUP

Preparation time: 45 minutes
Total cooking time: 15– 20 minutes
Serves 4

2 tablespoons olive oil

20 g (³/₄ oz) butter

2 cloves garlic

1 small red onion, thinly sliced

2 celery sticks, cut into julienne strips

3 small carrots, cut into julienne strips

1 tablespoon finely chopped fresh parsley

1¹/₂ tablespoons finely chopped fresh basil

pinch of cayenne pepper

500 g (1 lb) raw prawns, peeled and deveined

¹/₂ cup (125 ml/4 fl oz) medium-dry sherry

4 cups (1 litre) chicken stock

70 g (2¹/₄ oz) conchiglie (shell pasta)

3 tablespoons cream

BACON AND PEA SOUP

Preparation time: 20 minutes
Total cooking time: 15 minutes
Serves 4–6

4 bacon rashers
50 g (1¾ oz) butter
1 large onion, finely chopped
1 celery stick, thinly sliced
8 cups (2 litres) chicken stock
1 cup (155 g/5 oz) frozen peas
250 g (8 oz) rissoni
2 tablespoons chopped fresh parsley

1 Trim the rind and excess fat from the bacon and chop into small pieces.
2 Melt the butter in a large heavy-based pan and cook the bacon, onion and celery over low heat for 5 minutes, stirring occasionally. Add the stock and peas and simmer, covered, for 5 minutes. Increase the heat, add the rissoni and cook, uncovered, stirring occasionally, for 5 minutes, or until the rissoni is tender.

3 Add the chopped fresh parsley and season with salt and pepper, to taste, just before serving.

NUTRITION PER SERVE (6): *Protein 10 g; Fat 10 g; Carbohydrate 35 g; Dietary Fibre 5 g; Cholesterol 35 mg; 1130 kJ (270 cal)*

ON THE SIDE

HERB BREAD To make herb bread, combine 125 g (4 oz) of softened butter with ½ cup (30 g/1 oz) of chopped mixed herbs and a finely chopped garlic clove. Slice a breadstick diagonally, almost all the way through, and spread each piece with the herb butter. Reshape into a loaf, wrap in aluminium foil and bake in a moderate 180°C (350°F/Gas 4) oven for 30 minutes, or until the loaf is crisp and hot. If you don't want the garlic flavour, you can leave it out.

CELERY

An important flavouring vegetable for many dishes, celery is also delicious in its own right, whether it be braised, baked or served fresh in a salad. All the sticks are stringy, and the darker, outer ones might need to be stripped before use. These are more likely to be chopped for use in stews, while the pale, milder inner stalks can be eaten raw. Celery hearts do not need stringing and are ideal for braising. The dried seeds of the plant, aromatic and slightly bitter, are used as a seasoning.

ABOVE: Bacon and pea soup

EGGPLANT (AUBERGINE)
One of the most attractive of vegetables, the eggplant or aubergine comes in an amazing range of shapes and colours. It can be large and bulbous, thin and finger-like, or small and round like a cherry tomato. The colours range from deep purple to green or white and sometimes they are striped. Look for a glossy wrinkle-free skin, and firm, not hard, flesh.

ABOVE: Ratatouille and pasta soup

RATATOUILLE AND PASTA SOUP

Preparation time: 25 minutes + standing
Total cooking time: 40 minutes
Serves 6

1 medium eggplant (aubergine)
2 tablespoons olive oil
1 large onion, chopped
1 large red pepper (capsicum), chopped
1 large green pepper (capsicum), chopped
2 cloves garlic, crushed
3 zucchini (courgettes), sliced
2 x 400 g (13 oz) cans crushed tomatoes
1 teaspoon dried oregano leaves
1/2 teaspoon dried thyme leaves
4 cups (1 litre) vegetable stock
1/2 cup (45 g/1 1/2 oz) fusilli
Parmesan shavings, for serving

1 Chop the eggplant. To remove any bitterness, spread the eggplant pieces out in a colander and sprinkle generously with salt. Set aside for 20 minutes and then rinse thoroughly and pat dry with paper towels.

2 Heat the oil in a large heavy-based pan and cook the onion over medium heat for 10 minutes, or until soft and lightly golden. Add the peppers, garlic, zucchini and eggplant and stir-fry for 5 minutes.

3 Add the tomato, herbs and vegetable stock to the pan. Bring to the boil, reduce the heat and simmer for 10 minutes, or until the vegetables are tender. Add the fusilli and cook for another 15 minutes, or until the fusilli is tender. Serve with shavings of Parmesan.

NOTE: This delicious soup can be served with Italian bread.

NUTRITION PER SERVE: *Protein 5 g; Fat 5 g; Carbohydrate 20 g; Dietary Fibre 5 g; Cholesterol 0 mg; 640 kJ (150 cal)*

SOUPE AU PISTOU
(VEGETABLE SOUP WITH BASIL SAUCE)

Preparation time: 1 hour
Total cooking time: 35–40 minutes
Serves 8

3 stalks fresh parsley
1 large sprig fresh rosemary
1 large sprig fresh thyme
1 large sprig fresh marjoram
1 bay leaf
1/4 cup (60 ml/2 fl oz) olive oil
2 onions, thinly sliced
1 leek, thinly sliced
375 g (12 oz) pumpkin, cut into
    small pieces
250 g (8 oz) potato, cut into small pieces
1 carrot, cut in half lengthways and
    thinly sliced
2 small zucchini (courgettes),
    thinly sliced
1 teaspoon salt
8 cups (2 litres) water or vegetable stock
1/2 cup (80 g/2 3/4 oz) fresh or frozen
    broad beans
1/2 cup (80 g/2 3/4 oz) fresh or frozen peas
2 very ripe tomatoes, peeled and chopped
1/2 cup (80 g/2 3/4 oz) short macaroni
    or conchiglie (shell pasta)

Pistou

1/2 cup (25 g/3/4 oz) fresh basil leaves
2 large cloves garlic, crushed
1/2 teaspoon black pepper
1/3 cup (35 g/1 1/4 oz) freshly grated Parmesan
1/3 cup (80 ml/2 3/4 fl oz) olive oil

1 Tie the fresh parsley, rosemary, thyme, marjoram and the bay leaf together with string. Heat the oil in a heavy-based pan, add the sliced onion and leek and cook over low heat for 10 minutes, or until soft.
2 Add the herb bunch, pumpkin, potato, carrot, zucchini, salt, and water or stock to the pan. Cover and simmer for 10 minutes, or until the vegetables are almost tender.
3 Add the broad beans, peas, tomato and pasta. Cover and cook for another 15 minutes, or until

the vegetables are very tender and the pasta is cooked (add more water if necessary). Remove the herbs. While the soup is cooking, prepare the pistou.
4 To make the pistou, process the fresh basil leaves with the garlic, pepper and Parmesan in a food processor for 20 seconds, or until finely chopped. With the motor running, pour in the oil gradually, processing until smooth. Serve small amounts of the pistou spooned over the top.
NOTE: This hearty soup is suitable for a main course. It can be made with any seasonal vegetable of your choice. Serve the soup with slices of fresh bread, bread rolls or pieces of Lebanese bread.

NUTRITION PER SERVE: *Protein 5 g; Fat 20 g; Carbohydrate 20 g; Dietary Fibre 5 g; Cholesterol 5 mg; 1150 kJ (275 cal)*

BROAD BEANS
Broad beans, also known as fava, Windsor and horse beans, are the most widely used bean in Europe. Only the bean itself is eaten. Very young broad beans can be eaten raw. When older, the skin toughens and should be removed unless going into a stew or soup, where they will be cooked until tender. Skinning can be done easily once the bean has been steamed or boiled. Dried broad beans have a unique flavour, mealy flesh and dull colour.

ABOVE: Soupe au pistou

PASTA AND BEANS

Combining pasta and beans may seem strange, but they have an affinity recognised in a number of cuisines. In Italy, each region seems to have its own version of *pasta e fagioli*, with the local pasta and favourite beans matched with vegetables, sausage, or perhaps just Parmesan. Pasta combined with beans creates a complete protein, making it a good vegetarian meal.

*BELOW: Pasta
and bean soup*

PASTA AND BEAN SOUP

Preparation time: 20 minutes
+ overnight soaking
Total cooking time: 1 hour 25 minutes
Serves 4–6

250 g (8 oz) borlotti beans, soaked
    in water overnight
1 ham hock
1 onion, chopped
pinch of ground cinnamon
pinch of cayenne pepper
2 teaspoons olive oil
2 cups (500 ml/16 fl oz) chicken stock
125 g (4 oz) tagliatelle (plain or spinach),
    broken into short lengths

1 Drain and rinse the borlotti beans, cover with cold water in a pan and bring to the boil. Stir, lower the heat and simmer for 15 minutes.
2 Drain the beans and transfer to a large pan, with a tight-fitting lid. Add the ham hock, onion, cinnamon, cayenne, olive oil and stock, and cold water to cover. Cover the pan and simmer over low heat for 1 hour, or until the beans are cooked and have begun to thicken the stock. Remove the hock and cut off any meat. Chop the meat and return to the pan, discarding the bone.
3 Taste for seasonings and add salt, if necessary. Bring the soup back to the boil, toss in the tagliatelle and cook until *al dente*. Remove the pan from the heat and set aside for 1–2 minutes before serving. Can be garnished with fresh herbs.

NUTRITION PER SERVE (6): *Protein 15 g; Fat 3 g; Carbohydrate 40 g; Dietary Fibre 6 g; Cholesterol 4 mg; 1025 kJ (245 cal)*

CHICKEN AND PASTA SOUP

Preparation time: 20 minutes
Total cooking time: 20 minutes
Serves 4

2 chicken breast fillets

90 g (3 oz) mushrooms

2 tablespoons olive oil

I onion, finely diced

180 g (6 oz) spaghetti, broken into
   short lengths

6 cups (1.5 litres) chicken stock

I cup (35 g/1 1/4 oz) torn fresh basil leaves

I Finely dice the chicken breast fillets and
roughly chop the mushrooms. Heat the olive oil
in a pan and cook the onion until soft and
golden. Add the chicken, mushrooms, spaghetti
pieces and chicken stock. Bring to the boil.
2 Reduce the heat and simmer for 10 minutes.
Stir in the fresh basil leaves. Season with salt and
freshly ground black pepper, to taste.
NOTE: This is quite a chunky soup. If you prefer
a thinner style of soup, you can add more stock.
The soup is best enjoyed immediately.

NUTRITION PER SERVE: *Protein 20 g; Fat 10 g;
Carbohydrate 35 g; Dietary Fibre 4 g; Cholesterol 30 mg;
1380 kJ (330 cal)*

GARLIC, PASTA AND FISH SOUP

Preparation time: 30 minutes
Total cooking time: 40 minutes
Serves 4–6

4 tablespoons olive oil

I leek, sliced

20–30 cloves garlic, thinly sliced

2 potatoes, chopped

2 litres fish stock

1/2 cup (75 g/2 1/2 oz) miniature pasta shapes

10 baby yellow squash, halved

2 zucchini, cut into thick slices

300 g (10 oz) ling fillets, cut into
   large pieces

1–2 tablespoons lemon juice

2 tablespoons shredded fresh basil

I Heat the oil in a large pan, add the leek, garlic
and potato and cook over medium heat for
10 minutes. Add 500 ml (16 fl oz) of the stock
and cook for 10 minutes.
2 Allow to cool slightly before puréeing, in
batches, in a food processor or blender.
3 Pour the remaining stock into the pan and
bring to the boil. Add the pasta, squash and
zucchini, along with the purée, and simmer
for 15 minutes.
4 When the pasta is soft, add the fish and cook
for 5 minutes, or until tender. Add the lemon
juice and basil, and season with salt and pepper,
to taste.

NUTRITION PER SERVE (6): *Protein 15 g; Fat 15 g;
Carbohydrate 20 g; Dietary Fibre 4 g; Cholesterol 35 mg;
1165 kJ (275 cal)*

*ABOVE: Chicken
and pasta soup*

47

PUMPKIN

Pumpkins are related to marrows and squash. Because of their relatively high moisture content, they cook more quickly than vegetables such as potatoes. When cooking pumpkin for a puréed soup, try baking the pumpkin instead of boiling it. The resulting texture is firmer and the flavour is richer and has a slightly nutty edge.

ABOVE: Country pumpkin and pasta soup

COUNTRY PUMPKIN AND PASTA SOUP

Preparation time: 25 minutes
Total cooking time: 20 minutes
Serves 4– 6

★

700 g (1 lb 6¹/₂ oz) pumpkin

2 potatoes

1 tablespoon olive oil

30 g (1 oz) butter

1 large onion, finely chopped

2 cloves garlic, crushed

12 cups (3 litres) ready-made liquid chicken stock

125 g (4 oz) stellini or rissoni

chopped fresh parsley, for serving

1 Chop the peeled pumpkin and potatoes into small cubes. Heat the oil and butter in a large pan. Add the onion and garlic and stir over low heat for 5 minutes.

2 Add the chopped pumpkin, potato and chicken stock. Increase the heat, cover the pan and cook for 10 minutes, or until the vegetables are tender.

3 Add the pasta and cook, stirring occasionally, for 5 minutes or until the pasta is just tender. Sprinkle with the chopped fresh parsley. Serve immediately.

NOTE: Butternut or jap pumpkin will give the sweetest flavour. Use a good-quality chicken stock to give the best flavour and to ensure that the soup does not finish up too salty.

NUTRITION PER SERVE (6): *Protein 5 g; Fat 10 g; Carbohydrate 35 g; Dietary Fibre 5 g; Cholesterol 15 mg; 1000 kJ (240 cal)*

LAMB AND FUSILLI SOUP

Preparation time: 25 minutes
Total cooking time: 40 minutes
Serves 6–8

500 g (1 lb) lean lamb meat, cut
   into cubes

2 onions, finely chopped

2 carrots, diced

4 celery sticks, diced

425 g (14 oz) can crushed
   tomatoes

8 cups (2 litres) beef stock

500 g (1 lb) fusilli

chopped fresh parsley,
   for serving

1 Heat a little oil in a large pan and cook the cubed lamb, in batches, until golden brown. Remove each batch as it is done and drain on paper towels. Add the onion to the pan and cook for 2 minutes or until softened. Return the meat to the pan.

2 Add the carrot, celery, tomato, and beef stock. Stir to combine and bring to the boil. Reduce the heat to low and simmer, covered, for 15 minutes.

3 Add the fusilli to the pan. Stir briefly to prevent the pasta from sticking to the pan. Simmer, uncovered, for another 10 minutes or until the lamb and pasta are tender. Sprinkle with chopped fresh parsley before serving.

NUTRITION PER SERVE (8): *Protein 25 g; Fat 5 g; Carbohydrate 50 g; Dietary Fibre 5 g; Cholesterol 40 mg; 1400 kJ (330 cal)*

BEEF STOCK
Beef stock is the base of many soups and adds flavour to casseroles and stews. A good stock can be drunk as a light broth. When reduced to a concentrated form, it becomes a flavouring agent for sauces. Beef or chicken stock is used in recipes containing lamb and pork, as lamb gives a strong, muttony stock and pork, a thin, sweet flavour.

ABOVE: Lamb and fusilli soup

ANTIPASTO What better way to whet the

appetite? Literally translated as 'before the pasta', the antipasto platter is a colourful

reminder of the days of the Roman banquet. Excellent for serving at parties.

SALAMI AND POTATO FRITTATA WEDGES
Fry 2 finely diced potatoes in about 2 tablespoons of oil in a 20 cm (8 inch) diameter non-stick frying pan. Add 50 g (1¾ oz) of roughly chopped spicy Italian salami and fry, stirring occasionally, for 10 minutes, or until the potato softens. Add 8 lightly beaten eggs and cook over medium heat for 10 minutes. Transfer the pan to a preheated grill and cook for 3 minutes or until the frittata is set. Remove from the pan and allow to cool slightly before cutting into wedges. Serves 6–8.

NUTRITION PER SERVE (8): *Protein 8 g; Fat 10 g; Carbohydrate 4 g; Dietary Fibre 1 g; Cholesterol 185 mg; 660 kJ (155 cal)*

STUFFED MUSSELS
Scrub 500 g (1 lb) of mussels and remove the beards. Discard any open mussels. Cook in boiling water for 3 minutes, or until the mussels open (discard any that don't open). Drain and cool. Remove the top shells and put the mussels in the shell in a baking dish. Preheat the oven to moderately hot 200°C (400°F/Gas 6).

Fry 1 finely chopped onion in 1 tablespoon of olive oil until golden. Add 2 chopped ripe tomatoes and 2 crushed cloves of garlic. Remove from the heat and season, to taste. Spoon a little sauce into each shell. Combine 1 cup (80 g/2¾ oz) of fresh breadcrumbs and 20 g (¾ oz) of finely grated Parmesan and sprinkle on top. Bake for 10 minutes, or until the crumbs are crisp. Serves 6–8.

NUTRITION PER SERVE (8): *Protein 15 g; Fat 5 g; Carbohydrate 8 g; Dietary Fibre 1 g; Cholesterol 65 mg; 545 kJ (130 cal)*

POLENTA SHAPES WITH CHORIZO AND SALSA

Bring 3 cups (750 ml/24 fl oz) of water to the boil in a saucepan. Gradually add ¾ cup (110 g/3½ oz) of polenta (cornmeal) and stir constantly over medium heat until the mixture comes away from the side of the pan. Stir in 100 g (3½ oz) of grated Cheddar cheese, 50 g (1¾ oz) of grated Mozzarella cheese and 1 tablespoon of chopped fresh oregano. Spread the mixture into a greased tin, about 28 x 18 cm (11 x 7 inches). Chill for 2 hours, or until set. Cut out shapes using biscuit cutters about 5 cm (2 inches) in diameter. Brush lightly with oil and cook under a preheated grill until golden. Thinly slice 4 chorizo sausages and brown on both sides in a non-stick frying pan. Top the polenta shapes with bottled tomato salsa and a piece of chorizo. Garnish with fresh oregano leaves. Serves 6–8.

NUTRITION PER SERVE (8): *Protein 9 g; Fat 15 g; Carbohydrate 10 g; Dietary Fibre 1 g; Cholesterol 30 mg; 945 kJ (225 cal)*

BARBECUED SARDINES

Combine 3 tablespoons of lemon juice, 2 tablespoons of olive oil and 1 or 2 peeled and halved garlic cloves. Lightly oil a preheated barbecue or chargrill pan and brown 20 butterflied sardine fillets over high heat. Brush the sardines with the lemon mixture during cooking. Arrange the sardines on a platter. Makes 20.

NUTRITION PER SARDINE: *Protein 3 g; Fat 4 g; Carbohydrate 0 g; Dietary Fibre 0 g; Cholesterol 15 mg; 220 kJ (50 cal)*

ABOVE, FROM LEFT: Salami and potato frittata wedges; Stuffed mussels; Polenta shapes with chorizo and salsa; Barbecued sardines

ANTIPASTO

GRILLED EGGPLANT (AUBERGINE) AND PEPPERS (CAPSICUMS)

Cut 1 large eggplant into 1 cm (½ inch) thick slices. Cut 2 large red peppers (capsicums) in half and remove the seeds and membrane. Put the red pepper, skin-side-up, under a hot grill and cook for 8 minutes, or until the skins blister and blacken. Remove from the heat and cover with a damp tea towel. When cool enough to handle, peel away the skin and cut the pepper flesh into thick strips. Brush the eggplant slices liberally with olive oil and cook under a medium grill until deep golden brown. Carefully turn the slices over, brush the other sides with oil and grill again until golden. Do not rush this process by having the grill too hot, as slow cooking allows the sugar in the eggplant to caramelize. Combine the eggplant and peppers in a bowl with 2 crushed cloves of garlic, 2 tablespoons of extra virgin olive oil, a pinch of sugar and about 2 tablespoons of chopped fresh parsley. Cover and marinate in the refrigerator overnight. Bring to room temperature for serving. Serves 4–6.

NUTRITION PER SERVE (6): *Protein 1 g; Fat 15 g; Carbohydrate 3 g; Dietary Fibre 2 g; Cholesterol 0 mg; 670 kJ (160 cal)*

PESTO BOCCONCINI BALLS

Blend 1 cup (50 g/1¾ oz) of fresh basil leaves, 3 tablespoons each of pine nuts and freshly grated Parmesan with 2 cloves of garlic, in a food processor until finely chopped. With the motor running, gradually add ⅓ cup (80 ml/2¾ fl oz) of olive oil and process until a paste is formed. Transfer the pesto to a bowl and add 300 g (10 oz) of baby bocconcini. Mix very gently, cover and marinate in the refrigerator for 2 hours. Serves 4–6.

NUTRITION PER SERVE (6): *Protein 15 g; Fat 30 g; Carbohydrate 1 g; Dietary Fibre 1 g; Cholesterol 35 mg; 1400 kJ (335 cal)*

SLOW-ROASTED BALSAMIC TOMATOES

Preheat the oven to warm 160°C (315°F/Gas 2). Cut 500 g (1 lb) of egg (Roma) tomatoes in half. Put them on a non-stick baking tray and brush lightly with extra virgin olive oil. Sprinkle with salt and drizzle with 2 tablespoons of balsamic vinegar. Roast for 1 hour, basting every 15 minutes with another 2 tablespoons of balsamic vinegar. Serves 6– 8.

NUTRITION PER SERVE (8): *Protein 1 g; Fat 2 g; Carbohydrate 1 g; Dietary Fibre 1 g; Cholesterol 0 mg; 135 kJ (30 cal)*

BRUSCHETTA

Cut 1 loaf of Italian bread into thick slices. Chop 500 g (1 lb) of ripe tomatoes into very small cubes. Finely dice 1 red (Spanish) onion. Combine the tomato and onion in a bowl with 2 tablespoons of olive oil. Season, to taste, with salt and freshly ground pepper. Lightly toast the bread and, while still hot, rub both sides with a whole garlic clove. Top each piece with some of the tomato mixture and serve warm, topped with strips of finely shredded fresh basil leaves. Serves 6– 8.

NUTRITION PER SERVE (8): *Protein 6 g; Fat 6 g; Carbohydrate 30 g; Dietary Fibre 3 g; Cholesterol 0 mg; 875 kJ (210 cal)*

CAULIFLOWER FRITTERS

Cut 300 g (10 oz) of cauliflower into large florets. Cook the florets in a large pan of salted boiling water until just tender. Be careful that you do not overcook them or they will fall apart. Drain thoroughly and set aside to cool slightly. Cut 200 g (6½ oz) of fontina cheese into small cubes and carefully tuck the cheese inside the florets. Beat 3 eggs together in a bowl and dip each floret in the egg. Next, roll the florets in ½ cup (40 g/1¼ oz) of fresh breadcrumbs. When they are all crumbed, deep-fry them in hot oil, in batches, until they are crisp and golden. Serve hot. Serves 4– 6.

NUTRITION PER SERVE (6): *Protein 15 g; Fat 30 g; Carbohydrate 5 g; Dietary Fibre 1 g; Cholesterol 120 mg; 1440 kJ (340 cal)*

ABOVE, FROM LEFT: Grilled eggplant and peppers; Pesto bocconcini balls; Slow-roasted balsamic tomatoes; Bruschetta; Cauliflower fritters

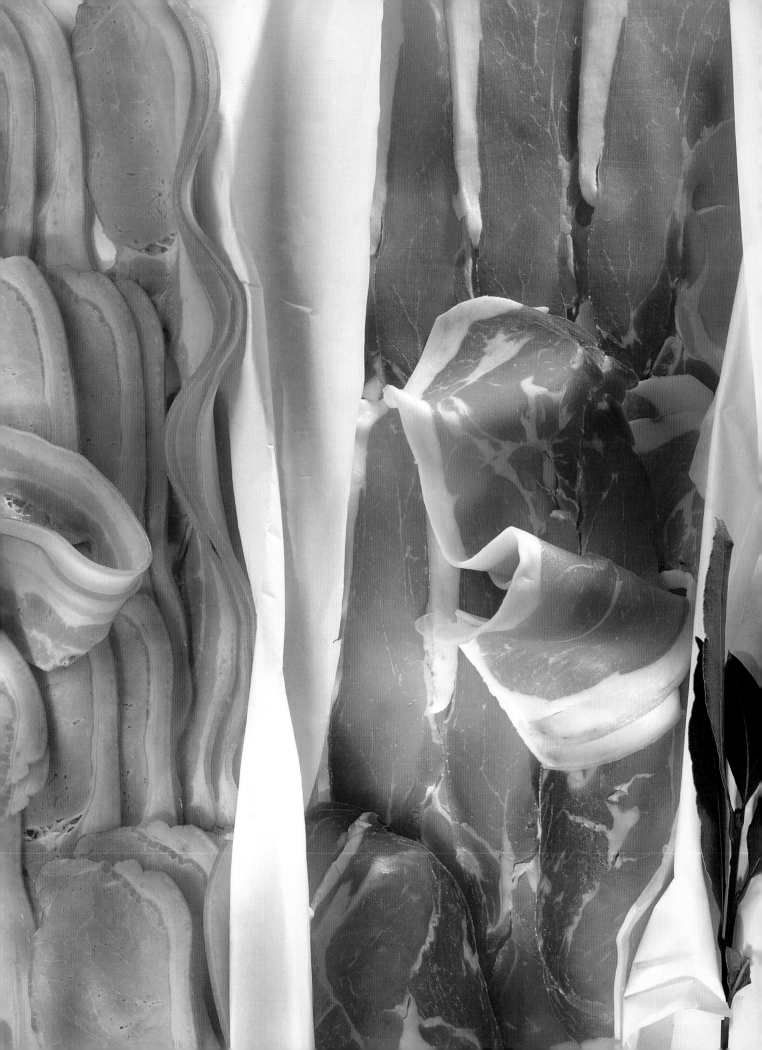

PASTA WITH MEAT

Undoubtedly the most famous pasta dish of all, and the most popular standby meal for many families, is spaghetti bolognese, the superb combination of minced meat sauce with pasta. Although most commonly made with beef, in Bologna pork is often added and sometimes lamb is used. All these meats, and many others, when flavoured with herbs, and married with tomatoes, vegetables and wine, turn a straightforward bowl of pasta into a hearty, nutritious and truly delicious meal.

SPAGHETTI BOLOGNESE
This is one of the most popular pasta dishes ever created and almost every family has their own favourite unique version. Within this book you will find three different recipes for this well-loved classic: the traditional (page 24), flavoured with chicken livers and requiring several hours of loving attention; a quick bolognese (page 60); and this recipe (right), ideal for family dinners.

ABOVE: Spaghetti bolognese

SPAGHETTI BOLOGNESE

Preparation time: 20 minutes
Total cooking time: 1 hour 40 minutes
Serves 4– 6

★

2 tablespoons olive oil
2 cloves garlic, crushed
1 large onion, chopped
1 carrot, chopped
1 celery stick, chopped
500 g (1 lb) beef mince
2 cups (500 ml/16 fl oz) beef stock
1½ cups (375 ml/12 fl oz) red wine
2 x 425 g (14 oz) cans crushed tomatoes
1 teaspoon sugar
¼ cup (7 g/¼ oz) fresh parsley, chopped
500 g (1 lb) spaghetti
freshly grated Parmesan, for serving

1 Heat the olive oil in a large deep pan. Add the garlic, onion, carrot and celery and stir for 5 minutes over low heat until the vegetables are golden.
2 Increase the heat, add the mince and brown well, stirring and breaking up any lumps with a fork as it cooks. Add the stock, wine, tomato, sugar and parsley.
3 Bring the mixture to the boil, reduce the heat and simmer for 1½ hours, stirring occasionally. Season, to taste.
4 While the sauce is cooking and shortly before serving, cook the pasta in a large pan of rapidly boiling salted water until *al dente*. Drain and then divide among serving bowls. Serve the sauce over the top of the pasta and sprinkle with the freshly grated Parmesan.

NUTRITION PER SERVE (6): *Protein 30 g; Fat 20 g; Carbohydrate 65 g; Dietary Fibre 5 g; Cholesterol 55 mg; 2470 kJ (590 cal)*

TAGLIATELLE WITH VEAL, WINE AND CREAM

Preparation time: 15 minutes
Total cooking time: 20 minutes
Serves 4

500 g (1 lb) veal scaloppine or escalopes,
   cut into thin strips
plain flour, seasoned with salt and pepper
60 g (2 oz) butter
1 onion, sliced
1/2 cup (125 ml/4 fl oz) dry white wine
3–4 tablespoons beef stock or chicken stock
2/3 cup (170 ml/5 1/2 fl oz) cream
600 g (1 1/4 lb) fresh plain or spinach tagliatelle
   (or a mixture of both)
freshly grated Parmesan

1 Coat the veal strips with the seasoned flour. Melt the butter in a pan. Add the veal strips and fry quickly until browned. Remove with a slotted spoon and set aside.
2 Add the onion slices to the pan and stir until soft and golden, about 8–10 minutes. Pour in the wine and cook rapidly to reduce the liquid. Add the stock and cream and season with salt and pepper, to taste. Reduce the sauce again, and add the veal towards the end.
3 Meanwhile, cook the tagliatelle in a large pan of rapidly boiling salted water until *al dente*. Drain and transfer to a warm serving dish.
4 Stir 1 tablespoon of Parmesan through the sauce. Pour the sauce over the pasta. Serve with a sprinkle of Parmesan. Some chopped herbs can be used as an extra garnish and will add flavour.
NOTE: This dish is lovely served with a mixed salad. If you prefer a lighter sauce, you can omit the cream. The flavour is just as delicious.

NUTRITION PER SERVE: *Protein 45 g; Fat 35 g; Carbohydrate 75 g; Dietary Fibre 5 g; Cholesterol 205 mg; 3355 kJ (800 cal)*

ON THE SIDE

ROAST PUMPKIN WITH SAGE
Preheat the oven to 220°C (425°C/Gas 7). Cut a pumpkin into small cubes and toss well in olive oil. Transfer to a baking dish and scatter with 2 tablespoons of chopped fresh sage and salt and pepper, to taste. Bake for 20 minutes, or a little longer, to brown the cubes a little more. Serve scattered with a little more fresh sage.

CUCUMBER WITH TOASTED SESAME SEEDS
Thinly slice a long cucumber, season and add 2 tablespoons of sesame oil and 1 tablespoon of toasted sesame seeds. Toss and leave to stand for about 20 minutes before serving.

WHITE WINE
White wine contributes a delicate body to dishes. The taste should never be discernible and only a small amount should be used, which must then be completely cooked off to dispel the alcohol. The wine should be the same quality as a good drinking wine. Non-fruity dry white wines are used in savoury cooking, particularly with seafood, and for sweet dishes fortified wines or liqueurs are chosen, but not sweet white wine.

ABOVE: Tagliatelle with veal, wine and cream

PASTA WITH BRAISED OXTAIL AND CELERY

Preparation time: 20 minutes
Total cooking time: 3 hours 45 minutes
Serves 4

1.5 kg (3 lb) oxtail, jointed
¹/₄ cup (30 g/1 oz) plain flour, seasoned
¹/₄ cup (60 ml/2 fl oz) olive oil
1 onion, finely chopped
2 cloves garlic, crushed
2 cups (500 ml/16 fl oz) beef stock
425 g (14 oz) can crushed tomatoes
1 cup (250 ml/8 fl oz) dry white wine
6 whole cloves
2 bay leaves
3 celery sticks, finely chopped
500 g (1 lb) penne
30 g (1 oz) butter
3 tablespoons freshly grated Parmesan

1 Preheat the oven to warm 160°C (315°F/Gas 2– 3).
2 Dust the oxtail in seasoned flour and shake off any excess. Heat half the oil in a large pan and brown the oxtail over high heat, a few pieces at a time. Transfer to a large casserole dish.
3 Wipe the pan clean with paper towels. Heat the remaining oil in the pan and add the onion and garlic. Cook over low heat until the onion is tender. Stir in the stock, tomato, wine, cloves, bay leaves and salt and pepper, to taste. Bring to the boil. Pour over the oxtail.
4 Bake, covered, for 2¹/₂– 3 hours. Add the celery to the dish. Bake, uncovered, for another 30 minutes. Towards the end of cooking time, cook the pasta in a large pan of rapidly boiling salted water until *al dente*. Drain and toss with the butter and Parmesan. Serve the oxtail and sauce with the pasta.
NOTE: Seasoned flour is plain flour to which seasonings of your choice have been added, for example, herbs, salt, pepper, dried mustard.

NUTRITION PER SERVE: *Protein 50 g; Fat 70 g; Carbohydrate 100 g; Dietary Fibre 10 g; Cholesterol 110 mg; 5200 kJ (1240 cal)*

ABOVE: Pasta with braised oxtail and celery

SPAGHETTI WITH SALAMI AND PEPPERS (CAPSICUMS)

Preparation time: 15 minutes
Total cooking time: 55 minutes
Serves 4–6

2 tablespoons olive oil
1 large onion, finely chopped
2 cloves garlic, crushed
150 g (5 oz) sliced spicy salami,
　cut into strips
2 large red peppers (capsicums), chopped
825 g (1 lb 11 oz) can crushed tomatoes
1/2 cup (125 ml/4 fl oz) dry white wine
500 g (1 lb) spaghetti

1 Heat the oil in a heavy-based frying pan. Add the onion, garlic and salami and cook for 5 minutes, stirring, over medium heat. Add the pepper, cover and cook for 5 minutes.
2 Add the tomato and the dry white wine and bring to the boil. Reduce the heat and simmer, covered, for 15 minutes. Remove the lid and cook for another 15 minutes, or until the liquid is reduced and the sauce is the desired consistency. Add salt and pepper, to taste.
3 About 15 minutes before the sauce is ready, cook the spaghetti in a large pan of rapidly boiling salted water until *al dente*. Drain and return to the pan. Toss half the sauce with the pasta and divide among serving dishes. Top with the remaining sauce and serve.

NUTRITION PER SERVE (6): *Protein 20 g; Fat 15 g; Carbohydrate 70 g; Dietary Fibre 5 g; Cholesterol 25 mg; 2150 kJ (510 cal)*

ON THE SIDE

POTATO SALAD Cook 1 kg (2 lb) of baby potatoes, with the skins left on, in boiling salted water. Drain and set aside to cool. In a large bowl, thoroughly mix 2 tablespoons of mayonnaise, 2 tablespoons of sour cream and 4 finely chopped spring onions. Add the potatoes and toss until covered in the mixture. Sprinkle with a little cayenne pepper.

SALAMI

Salami, uncooked cured sausage, comes in numerous shapes, flavours and blends of meats. They can be mild or strong, fresh or mature, hard or soft, fine or coarse grained. The meats that are favoured are beef, pork and pork fat in varying proportions, and game meat is sometimes used. Most salamis are cured in salt, but there are some types that originated in mountainous regions which are air-cured. Salami should not be cooked too long as this draws out the fat content.

BELOW: Spaghetti with salami and peppers

EXTRA VIRGIN OLIVE OIL

Extra virgin olive oil is traditionally made from the first pressing of slightly under-ripe olives, where no heating of the fruit takes place (cold pressed) and no chemicals are used. It has almost no acidity and is thick and rich in colour, and often unfiltered. However, by the terms set down by the European Union, the only distinction an olive oil must have to qualify as extra virgin is to have less then 1% acidity. So it is more economical for large olive oil companies in Spain, Italy and France to chemically rectify lower grade oils. This reduces the acid level to the required percentage. Ironically, farmers and small co-ops find this refining too expensive and stick to their traditional methods. It is almost impossible for the consumer to tell the difference, so the only ways to judge quality are by tasting and testing.

ABOVE: Quick spaghetti bolognese

QUICK SPAGHETTI BOLOGNESE

Preparation time: 15 minutes
Total cooking time: 30 minutes
Serves 4

2 teaspoons extra virgin olive oil
75 g (2½ oz) bacon or pancetta, finely chopped
400 g (13 oz) lean beef mince
2 cups (500 g/1 lb) ready-made tomato pasta sauce
2 teaspoons red wine vinegar
2 teaspoons sugar
1 teaspoon dried oregano
500 g (1 lb) spaghetti
freshly grated Parmesan, for serving

1 Heat the oil in a large frying pan and fry the bacon or pancetta until lightly browned. Add the beef mince and brown well over high heat, breaking up any lumps with a fork.
2 Add the pasta sauce, wine vinegar, sugar and dried oregano to the pan and bring to the boil. Lower the heat and simmer for 15 minutes, stirring often to prevent the sauce from catching on the bottom of the pan.
3 About 10 minutes before the sauce is ready, cook the spaghetti in a large pan of rapidly boiling salted water and cook until *al dente*. Drain and divide among four serving bowls. Top with a generous portion of Bolognese sauce and serve sprinkled with the freshly grated Parmesan.

NUTRITION PER SERVE: *Protein 40 g; Fat 30 g; Carbohydrate 100 g; Dietary Fibre 10g; Cholesterol 150 mg; 3505 kJ (835 cal)*

BAKED PASTA AND MINCE

Preparation time: 20 minutes
Total cooking time: 2 hours
Serves 8

2 tablespoons olive oil
1 large onion, chopped
1 kg (2 lb) beef mince
1/4 cup (60 ml/2 fl oz) red wine
700 ml (23 fl oz) chunky tomato pasta sauce
2 chicken stock cubes, crumbled
2 tablespoons finely chopped
    fresh parsley
500 g (1 lb) bucatini
2 egg whites, lightly beaten
2 tablespoons dry breadcrumbs

Cheese sauce

50 g (1 3/4 oz) butter
2 tablespoons plain flour
2 1/2 cups (600 ml/20 fl oz) milk
2 egg yolks, lightly beaten
1 cup (125 g/4 oz) grated
    Cheddar cheese

1 Heat the oil in a heavy-based pan. Add the onion and cook over medium heat for 2 minutes, or until soft. Add the mince and stir over high heat until well browned and almost all the liquid has evaporated.
2 Add the wine, sauce and stock cubes and bring to the boil. Reduce to a simmer and cook, covered, for 1 hour, stirring occasionally. Remove from the heat. Add the parsley and allow to cool.
3 To make the cheese sauce, heat the butter in a medium pan over low heat, add the flour and stir for 1 minute, or until golden and smooth. Remove from the heat and gradually stir in the milk. Return to the heat and stir constantly over medium heat for 5 minutes, or until the sauce boils and begins to thicken. Simmer for another minute. Remove from the heat, allow to cool slightly and stir in the egg yolks and cheese.
4 Preheat the oven to moderate 180°C (350°F/Gas 4). Cook the bucatini in a large pan of rapidly boiling salted water until *al dente*. Drain, rinse under cold water and drain thoroughly, then mix with the egg whites. Place half the bucatini over the base of a lightly oiled, deep ovenproof dish. Cover with the mince mixture.
5 Combine the remaining bucatini with the cheese sauce and spread over the mince.

Sprinkle with the dry breadcrumbs. Bake in the oven for 45 minutes, or until the top is lightly golden.

NUTRITION PER SERVE: *Protein 40 g; Fat 30 g; Carbohydrate 80 g; Dietary Fibre 5 g; Cholesterol 160 mg; 3210 kJ (765 cal)*

ON THE SIDE

BEAN SALAD WITH VINAIGRETTE
Toss cooked cannellini or haricot beans in a vinaigrette dressing made by thoroughly whisking together some walnut oil and balsamic vinegar with a crushed clove of garlic. Add 2 tablespoons of finely chopped fresh parsley, 4 finely chopped spring onions and a handful of torn basil. Season well with salt and pepper. Before serving, allow to stand for about 10 minutes so the beans soak up the flavour.

ABOVE: Baked pasta and mince

CHORIZO SAUSAGE

Chorizo is a hard, deep red sausage from Spain. It is well spiced and coarsely grained and is made primarily from pork and pork fat with garlic and paprika. Some types are intended for eating raw, while others with less fat are suited to cooking in stews and soups. If unobtainable, substitute Italian pepperoni or any other firm, spicy garlic sausage.

ABOVE: Rigatoni with chorizo and tomato

RIGATONI WITH CHORIZO AND TOMATO

Preparation time: 15 minutes
Total cooking time: 20– 25 minutes
Serves 4

2 tablespoons olive oil
1 onion, sliced
250 g (8 oz) chorizo sausage, sliced
425 g (14 oz) can crushed tomatoes
1/2 cup (125 ml/4 fl oz) dry white wine
1/2– 1 teaspoon chopped chilli, optional
375 g (12 oz) rigatoni
2 tablespoons chopped fresh parsley
2 tablespoons freshly grated Parmesan

1 Heat the oil in a frying pan. Add the onion and stir over low heat until tender.
2 Add the sausage to the pan and cook, turning frequently, for 2– 3 minutes. Add the tomato, wine, chilli and salt and pepper, to taste, and stir. Bring to the boil, reduce the heat and simmer for 15– 20 minutes.
3 While the sauce is cooking, cook the rigatoni in a large pan of rapidly boiling salted water until *al dente*. Drain and return to the pan. Add the sauce to the hot pasta. Toss well to combine. Serve sprinkled with the combined fresh parsley and grated Parmesan.

NUTRITION PER SERVE: *Protein 25 g; Fat 30 g; Carbohydrate 70 g; Dietary Fibre 5 g; Cholesterol 50 mg; 2990 kJ (715 cal)*

ZITI WITH VEGETABLES AND SAUSAGE

Preparation time: 30 minutes
Total cooking time: 40 minutes
Serves 4

1 red pepper (capsicum)
1 green pepper (capsicum)
1 small eggplant (aubergine), sliced
1/4 cup (60 ml/2 fl oz) olive oil
1 onion, sliced
1 clove garlic, crushed
250 g (8 oz) chipolatas, sliced
425 g (14 oz) can crushed tomatoes
1/2 cup (125 ml/4 fl oz) red wine
1/4 cup (35 g/1 1/4 oz) halved pitted
   black olives
1 tablespoon chopped fresh basil
1 tablespoon chopped fresh parsley
500 g (1 lb) ziti
freshly grated Parmesan, for serving

1 Cut the peppers into large flat pieces and discard the seeds and membrane. Put, skin-side-up, under a hot grill and cook for 8 minutes, or until the skin is black and blistered. Remove from the heat and cover with a damp tea towel. When cool, peel away the skin, chop the flesh and set aside.
2 Brush the eggplant with a little of the oil. Grill until golden on each side, brushing with more oil as required. Set aside.
3 Heat the remaining oil in a frying pan. Add the onion and garlic and stir over low heat until the onion is tender. Add the chipolatas and cook until well browned.
4 Stir in the tomato, wine, olives, basil, parsley and salt and pepper, to taste. Bring to the boil, reduce the heat and simmer for 15 minutes. Add the vegetables and then heat through.
5 While the sauce is cooking, cook the ziti in a large pan of rapidly boiling salted water until *al dente*. Drain and return to the pan. Toss the vegetables and sauce through the hot pasta. Sprinkle with Parmesan before serving.
NOTE: Ziti is a wide tubular pasta that is excellent with this dish but you can substitute fettucine or spaghetti if you prefer.

NUTRITION PER SERVE: *Protein 30 g; Fat 35 g; Carbohydrate 105 g; Dietary Fibre 10 g; Cholesterol 35 mg; 3760 kJ (900 cal)*

ON THE SIDE

ASPARAGUS WITH LEMON HAZELNUT BUTTER Lightly steam or microwave fresh asparagus spears until just tender. Heat a little butter in a small pan until it starts to turn a nutty brown. Stir in some toasted and roughly chopped hazelnuts and finely grated lemon rind. Spoon over the asparagus and serve at once.

CHIVE AND GARLIC CORN COBS Boil, steam or microwave corn cobs in the husk until tender. Remove the husks and silks. Cut the cobs into three and toss in a little extra virgin olive oil, butter, crushed garlic and chopped fresh chives. Sprinkle generously with cracked black pepper and sea salt.

ABOVE: Ziti with vegetables and sausage

RED WINE

Where a richer, more mellow taste is called for in a dish, red wine is used. Its earthy, robust flavours make it a good companion to red meats and game and the colour makes it better suited to tomato-based sauces and gravies. Very rarely is it used with dairy produce, such as in a cream sauce. The red wine best suited for cooking is young, full-bodied and well balanced, one that would be enjoyed as a table wine.

BELOW: Rigatoni with Italian-style oxtail sauce

RIGATONI WITH ITALIAN-STYLE OXTAIL SAUCE

Preparation time: 25 minutes
Total cooking time: 2 hours
Serves 4

2 tablespoons olive oil
1.5 kg (3 lb) oxtail, jointed
2 large onions, sliced
4 cloves garlic, chopped
2 celery sticks, sliced
2 carrots, thinly sliced
2 large sprigs rosemary
1/4 cup (60 ml/2 fl oz) red wine
1/4 cup (60 g/2 oz) tomato paste (tomato purée, double concentrate)
4 tomatoes, peeled and chopped
6 cups (1.5 litres) beef stock
500 g (1 lb) rigatoni or ditaloni

1 Heat the oil in a large heavy-based pan. Brown the oxtail, remove from the pan and set aside. Add the onion, garlic, celery and carrot to the pan and stir for 3– 4 minutes, or until the onion is lightly browned.
2 Return the oxtail to the pan and add the rosemary and red wine. Cover and cook for 10 minutes, shaking the pan occasionally to prevent the meat from sticking to the bottom. Add the tomato paste and chopped tomato to the pan with 2 cups (500 ml/16 fl oz) of the beef stock and simmer, uncovered, for 30 minutes, stirring the mixture occasionally.
3 Add another 2 cups of beef stock to the pan and cook for 30 minutes. Add 1 cup of stock and cook for 30 minutes. Finally, add the remaining stock and cook until the oxtail is tender and the meat is falling from the bone. The liquid should have reduced to produce a thick sauce.
4 Just before the meat is cooked, cook the pasta in a large pan of rapidly boiling salted water until *al dente*. Serve the meat and sauce over the hot pasta.
NOTE: For a different flavour, you can add 250 g (8 oz) of bacon to the cooked onion, garlic and vegetables. Proceed as above.

NUTRITION PER SERVE: *Protein 50 g; Fat 55 g; Carbohydrate 100 g; Dietary Fibre 10 g; Cholesterol 90 mg; 4600 kJ (1100 cal)*

ON THE SIDE

SPICY CUCUMBER SALAD Peel and slice a long cucumber and arrange the slices on a platter. Mix 1 finely chopped spring onion with 2 tablespoons of rice vinegar or white wine vinegar, 1 teaspoon of honey, 1 tablespoon of sesame oil and a finely chopped red chilli. Drizzle the dressing over the cucumber slices and sprinkle with about 3 tablespoons of chopped roasted peanuts.

GARLIC DILL MUSHROOMS Fry sliced button mushrooms in a mixture of olive oil and butter. Add some finely chopped garlic and some sliced spring onions and cook until the mushrooms are browned and tender. Drain off any excess liquid, fold through a little chopped fresh dill and season, to taste, with salt and cracked black pepper.

RIGATONI WITH KIDNEY BEANS AND ITALIAN SAUSAGE

Preparation time: 25 minutes
Total cooking time: 30 minutes
Serves 4– 6

1 tablespoon olive oil

1 large onion, chopped

2 cloves garlic, crushed

4 Italian sausages, chopped

825 g (1 lb 11 oz) can crushed tomatoes

425 g (14 oz) can kidney or borlotti
    beans, drained

2 tablespoons chopped fresh basil

1 tablespoon chopped fresh sage

1 tablespoon chopped fresh parsley

500 g (1 lb) rigatoni

freshly grated Parmesan, for serving

1 Heat the oil in a heavy-based pan. Add the onion, garlic and sausage to the pan and cook, stirring occasionally, over medium heat for 5 minutes.

2 Add the tomato, beans, basil, sage, parsley and salt and pepper, to taste. Reduce the heat and simmer for 20 minutes.

3 While the sauce is cooking, add the pasta to a large pan of rapidly boiling salted water and cook until *al dente*. Drain. Divide the pasta among serving bowls and top with the sauce. Sprinkle with Parmesan and serve immediately.

NOTE: Dried beans can be used. Soak them overnight in water, drain and transfer to a pan. Cover well with water, bring to the boil and cook for 20 minutes, or until tender. Giant conchiglie (shell pasta) can be used instead of rigatoni as they hold the sauce well.

NUTRITION PER SERVE (6): *Protein 25 g; Fat 30 g; Carbohydrate 75 g; Dietary Fibre 10 g; Cholesterol 60 mg; 2810 kJ (670 cal)*

FRESH ITALIAN SAUSAGES
Italian sausages are distinguished by a coarse grain and well-balanced spicing. They are made with various combinations of pork, pork fat and beef, and rely on the quality of these for good flavour and texture. For use in a stew or sauce, choose one that is compact, with good meat to fat ratio and an even grain. The skins can be removed before cooking without the sausage losing shape. Italian sausages are available at delicatessens.

ABOVE: Rigatoni with kidney beans and Italian sausage

65

COLD MEATS
While Italy is famous for its pasta, cold meats and salamis are also close to the Italian cook's heart. Each region is passionately adamant about the superiority of its own speciality.

PANCETTA is the Italian version of bacon. The rind is removed and the meat is seasoned with salt and pepper and spices which include nutmeg, juniper, cloves, cinnamon, depending on the person who is packing it. It is cured for two weeks, then tightly rolled and packed in a case similar to that used for salami. The flavour is less salty than prosciutto, though it can be eaten raw as you would

prosciutto. It is prized for the flavour it imparts to cooked dishes where it has no real substitute for its savoury sweet taste.

PROSCIUTTO is the salt- and air-dried hind leg of a pig. The salt removes the moisture from the meat and the slow process of air-curing produces a soft delicate flavour. Prosciutto can be cured for up 18 months and the most prized

are judged against genuine Italian Parma ham. Sliced prosciutto should be consumed as soon as possible after cutting as it gradually loses its flavour. Remove it from the refrigerator 1 hour before you plan to serve it. Parma ham gets its unique flavour from the pigs being fed the whey left over from cheese-making. Traditionally served with melon or figs on an antipasto platter.

MORTADELLA from Bologna takes its name from the mortar used to grind the pork. Flavoured with peppercorns, stuffed olives, pistachios and garlic and flecked with strips of fat, it can measure up to 40 cm (16 inches) in diameter. Mortadella is chopped and used on pizzas, in sandwiches or in tortellini.

SALAMI
A cured dry sausage made from minced pork and seasoned with garlic, herbs and spices. Thought to have originated in Salamis in Cyprus, most Italian salamis take their names from the towns in which they are produced. Distinctive types of salami are also made in Denmark, Spain, Hungary, Austria and Germany.

CACCIATORE is made from pork and beef, garlic and spices, and can be mild or hot.

MILANO SALAMI is a mildly-flavoured Italian salami made with lean pork, beef and pork fat. It has a fine texture and is seasoned with garlic, pepper and wine.

FINOCCHIONA TOSCANA is a salami made from pork and seasoned with fennel seeds that are distributed throughout the salami. Mild or hot.

PEPPERONI is a dried Italian sausage made from ground pork and beef, highly seasoned with pepper. It is used as a topping for pizzas and in pasta sauces.

COPPA is made from the pork shoulder that has been cured. It is fattier than prosciutto and is sold rolled and cased like salami. Coppa is frequently served as a part of an antipasto platter.

SPECK is the fatty top part of a leg of bacon, usually smoked and salted. It is available in small pieces. Austrian in origin, it can be sliced for a cold snack or chopped into small cubes to use to add flavour to cooked dishes.

CHORIZO is a coarsely-textured Spanish sausage that comes in many varieties, although it is always made from pork and seasoned with pimiento. It is sliced, fried and used in pasta sauces or, as it is best known, in paella.

CLOCKWISE, FROM TOP LEFT: Prosciutto on the bone, pancetta, prosciutto slices off the bone, Milano, Finocchiona Toscana, Coppa, Cacciatore, Speck, Chorizo, Pepperoni, Mortadella

PORK, PAPRIKA AND POPPY SEEDS WITH PASTA

Preparation time: 15 minutes
Total cooking time: 15–20 minutes
Serves 4

★

500 g (1 lb) pappardelle
20 g (3/4 oz) butter
1 1/2 tablespoons vegetable oil
1 onion, thinly sliced
1 clove garlic, crushed
2 teaspoons sweet paprika
pinch of cayenne pepper
500 g (1 lb) lean pork (fillet or leg steaks),
    thinly sliced
1 tablespoon finely chopped fresh parsley
1 tablespoon port or other dry
    fortified wine
1 tablespoon tomato paste (tomato purée,
    double concentrate)
300 g (10 oz) sour cream
150 g (5 oz) button mushrooms, sliced
2 teaspoons poppy seeds
2 tablespoons chopped fresh parsley

1 Cook the pappardelle in a large pan of rapidly boiling salted water until *al dente*. Drain and return to the pan.
2 Heat the butter and 1/2 tablespoon of oil in a frying pan and gently fry the sliced onion for 6–8 minutes, or until soft. Add the garlic, paprika, cayenne pepper, pork and parsley and season, to taste, with freshly ground pepper. Sauté quickly over high heat until the pork is cooked. Add the port, bring to the boil and stir briefly, for about 10 seconds. Add the tomato paste and sour cream and stir until combined. Stir in the mushrooms and adjust the seasoning. Reduce the heat to low.
3 Stir the remaining oil and the poppy seeds through the warm pasta. Serve the pork spooned over the pasta. Garnish with fresh parsley just before serving.

NUTRITION PER SERVE: *Protein 40 g; Fat 45 g; Carbohydrate 65 g; Dietary Fibre 6 g; Cholesterol 170 mg; 3525 kJ (840 cal)*

ABOVE: Pork, paprika and poppy seeds with pasta

TURKISH RAVIOLI

Preparation time: 1 hour
Total cooking time: 30 minutes
Serves 4–6

Filling

1 tablespoon oil
1 small onion, finely grated
1 red chilli, finely chopped
1 teaspoon ground cinnamon
1 teaspoon ground cloves
500 g (1 lb) finely minced lamb
2 teaspoons grated lemon rind
2 teaspoons chopped fresh dill
3 tablespoons chopped fresh flat-leaf parsley

Sauce

1 cup (250 ml/8 fl oz) chicken stock
2 cups (500 ml/16 fl oz) natural yoghurt
4 cloves garlic, crushed

1³/₄ cups (215 g/7 oz) plain flour
¹/₃ cup (50 g/1³/₄ oz) plain wholemeal flour
¹/₂ cup (125 ml/4 fl oz) water
1 egg
1 egg yolk
¹/₂ cup fresh mint leaves, finely chopped

1 To make the filling, heat the oil in a large frying pan, add the onion, chilli and spices and cook over medium heat for 5 minutes, or until the onion is golden. Add the mince and cook over high heat until the meat is browned, stirring constantly to break up any lumps. Remove from the heat, stir in the lemon rind and chopped herbs. Set aside to cool.

2 To make the sauce, bring the chicken stock to the boil in a pan and cook until the stock is reduced by half. Remove from the heat, and whisk the stock with the yoghurt and garlic. Season, to taste, with salt and pepper.

3 Combine the flours, water, egg and yolk in a food processor until the mixture comes together to form a smooth dough. Turn the dough out onto a lightly floured surface. If the dough is too sticky you may need to add a little extra flour. (It is much easier to add more flour to a wet dough than add more egg to a dry dough.)

4 Divide the dough into quarters, open the rollers on your pasta machine to the widest setting, sprinkle the rollers generously with flour and roll the dough through the machine.

Fold the dough into three, so that the width of the pasta remains the same and the length should now be one-third of what it was.

5 Pass the dough through the rollers again, and repeat the folding and rolling process, turning the dough right on a 90 degree angle each time. Repeat this at least ten times, dusting the machine and dough lightly with flour if you need to. When the pasta is smooth, set the rollers in a groove closer, pass the pasta through and keep setting the rollers closer until the pasta is 1 mm (¹/₁₆ inch) thick. Cover and set aside. Repeat with the remaining dough.

6 Cut the dough into 12 cm (5 inch) squares and place 1 tablespoon of the filling on the centre of each square, brush the edges lightly with water and fold each square into a triangle. Press the edges together to seal and place the ravioli in a single layer on a lightly floured baking tray. Keep them covered while making the rest of the ravioli.

7 Cook the ravioli, in batches, in a large pan of rapidly boiling salted water for 3 minutes, or until *al dente*. Drain and toss through the sauce. Garnish with chopped mint.

NUTRITION PER SERVE (6): *Protein 25 g; Fat 20 g; Carbohydrate 30 g; Dietary Fibre 3 g; Cholesterol 120 mg; 1595 kJ (380 cal)*

NATURAL YOGHURT

Made by fermenting cow's or ewe's milk, yoghurt originated in the Balkans. It was used then as a pharmaceutical remedy but is now enjoyed for the fresh, slightly sour flavour and used in cooking for the complexity of tastes that its acidity creates. Yoghurt is produced when selected milk is treated with an active lactic culture. Under controlled temperatures, this action brings about a natural fermentation. The resulting curd is semi-set, smooth and a clean white colour. Fresh yoghurt keeps for 4–5 days, refrigerated, before deteriorating.

BELOW: Turkish ravioli

GINGER
Ginger is a rhizome, the root of a tropical plant which originated in Bengal and the Malabar Coast of southern India. It is used as a condiment for savoury foods and as a flavouring ingredient for savoury and sweet dishes. Ginger has a fresh but hot taste and a very firm flesh. The fragrance, which is clean and aromatic, is intensified when heated. The longer ginger is in the ground, the stronger the flavour becomes, but unfortunately this is accompanied by an increase in the fibrousness of the root, which makes it harder to chop or grate. When buying fresh ginger choose a plump, firm root that isn't limp or spongey, and store it in the refrigerator, wrapped first in a paper towel and then a plastic bag.

OPPOSITE PAGE:
Stir-fried chilli beef with spaghettini (top);
Moroccan lamb and roasted pepper with fusilli

STIR-FRIED CHILLI BEEF WITH SPAGHETTINI

Preparation time: 40 minutes
Total cooking time: 20 minutes
Serves 4

500 g (1 lb) spaghettini
3 tablespoons peanut oil
1 onion, sliced
1 clove garlic, crushed
1/2 teaspoon finely chopped fresh ginger
1/4 teaspoon chilli flakes
400 g (13 oz) lean beef (rump or scotch fillet), cut into thin strips
1 1/2 teaspoons soy sauce
few drops sesame oil
155 g (5 oz) bean sprouts, trimmed
1 heaped tablespoon chopped fresh coriander

1 Cook the spaghettini in a large pan of rapidly boiling salted water until *al dente*. Drain, return to the pan and cover with cold water. Drain again and return to the pan. Stir 1 tablespoon of peanut oil through the pasta and set aside.
2 Heat 1 tablespoon of peanut oil in a large frying pan or wok and cook the onion, without browning, until softened. Stir in the garlic, ginger and chilli flakes. Add the beef and stir-fry over high heat until browned.
3 Stir in the soy sauce, sesame oil, bean sprouts and coriander. Taste for salt, pepper and chilli, adjust if necessary, and continue stirring until all the ingredients have heated through. Remove from the pan or wok. Add some peanut oil to the wok or pan and add the pasta, tossing it briefly over high heat to heat it through. Serve the spaghettini topped with the beef.
NOTE: As with all stir-fries, this dish requires quick, attentive cooking over high heat. Although it's tempting to take short cuts, rinsing the spaghettini in cold water is necessary to stop the cooking process and give the correct texture and flavour to the pasta.

NUTRITION PER SERVE: *Protein 35 g; Fat 20 g; Carbohydrate 70 g; Dietary Fibre 7 g; Cholesterol 65 mg; 2455 kJ (585 cal)*

MOROCCAN LAMB AND ROASTED PEPPER (CAPSICUM) WITH FUSILLI

Preparation time: 25 minutes
  + overnight marinating
Total cooking time: 25 minutes
Serves 4– 6

500 g (1 lb) lamb fillets
3 teaspoons ground cumin
1 tablespoon ground coriander
2 teaspoons ground allspice
1 teaspoon ground cinnamon
1/2 teaspoon ground cayenne pepper
4 cloves garlic, crushed
1/3 cup 80 ml (2 3/4 fl oz) olive oil
1/2 cup (125 ml/4 fl oz) lemon juice
2 red peppers (capsicums)
400 g (13 oz) fusilli
1/4 cup (60 ml/2 fl oz) extra virgin olive oil
2 teaspoons harissa
150 g (5 oz) rocket

1 Cut the fillets in half if they are very long. Mix the cumin, coriander, allspice, cinnamon, cayenne, garlic, olive oil and half the lemon juice in a bowl. Add the lamb, stir to coat and marinate, covered, in the refrigerator overnight.
2 Cut the peppers into large pieces and discard the seeds and membrane. Put skin-side-up, under a hot grill and cook for 8 minutes, or until the skin is black and blistered. Remove from the heat and cover with a damp tea towel. When cool, peel away the skin and slice thinly.
3 Cook the fusilli in a large pan of rapidly boiling salted water until *al dente*. Drain; keep warm.
4 Drain the lamb, heat 1 tablespoon of the extra virgin olive oil in a large frying pan and cook the lamb over high heat until done to your liking. Remove from the pan; cover with foil.
5 Heat 1 teaspoon of the oil in the frying pan and cook the harissa over medium heat for a few seconds. Be careful as the mixture may spit. Remove and place in a small screw top jar with the remaining oil and lemon juice and shake the jar until well combined. Season, to taste.
6 Thinly slice the lamb fillets and toss with the warm pasta, sliced pepper and rocket. Toss the harissa dressing through the pasta. Serve warm.

NUTRITION PER SERVE (6): *Protein 25 g; Fat 30 g; Carbohydrate 50 g; Dietary Fibre 5 g; Cholesterol 55 mg; 2365 kJ (565 cal)*

MARJORAM

Also known as sweet or knotted marjoram, common marjoram (*majorana hortensis*) is very closely related to oregano. Sweet marjoram is milder and more subtle in flavour, and has a fresh, fragrant aroma. It is used in soups and with fish, and goes well with most vegetables. It is easy to grow and it dries easily. For best results when drying, cut sprigs just before the flowers come into bloom as this is when the herb is in full fragrance.

ABOVE: Rigatoni with salami and fresh herbs

RIGATONI WITH SALAMI AND FRESH HERBS

Preparation time: 35 minutes
Total cooking time: 40 minutes
Serves 4

★

20 g (³/₄ oz) butter

1 tablespoon olive oil

1 onion, thinly sliced

1 carrot, cut into julienne strips

1 bay leaf

75 g (2¹/₂ oz) bacon rashers, chopped

200 g (6¹/₂ oz) spicy Italian salami, skinned and sliced

400 g (13 oz) can peeled egg (Roma) tomatoes

¹/₂ cup (125 ml/4 fl oz) beef or chicken stock

400 g (13 oz) rigatoni

1 tablespoon fresh oregano or marjoram leaves

1 Heat the butter and oil in a frying pan and cook the onion and carrot with the bay leaf until the onion is transparent and softened. Add the chopped bacon and sliced salami and cook, stirring often, until brown.

2 Squeeze half the tomatoes dry over the sink, pulp the flesh with your hand and add to the pan. Add the rest whole and break up loosely with the spoon while stirring. Season well with salt and pepper, to taste, and simmer for 30 minutes over low heat, gradually adding the stock as the sauce reduces.

3 Cook the rigatoni in a large pan of rapidly boiling salted water until *al dente*. Drain and transfer to a warm serving dish. Add the oregano or marjoram and sauce, and toss together lightly before serving.

NOTE: Use good-quality salami to ensure the success of this sauce. The use of fresh herbs is also important to produce the best flavour.

NUTRITION PER SERVE: *Protein 25 g; Fat 25 g; Carbohydrate 75 g; Dietary Fibre 10 g; Cholesterol 65 mg; 2755 kJ (660 cal)*

MEATBALLS WITH FUSILLI

Preparation time: 35 minutes
Total cooking time: 35 minutes
Serves 4

750 g (1 1/2 lb) pork and veal or beef mince

1 cup (80 g/2 3/4 oz) fresh breadcrumbs

3 tablespoons freshly grated Parmesan

1 onion, finely chopped

2 tablespoons chopped fresh parsley

1 egg, beaten

1 clove garlic, crushed

rind and juice of 1/2 lemon

1/4 cup (30 g/1 oz) plain flour, seasoned

2 tablespoons olive oil

500 g (1 lb) fusilli

Sauce

425 g (14 oz) can tomato purée (passata)

1/2 cup (125 ml/4 fl oz) beef stock

1/2 cup (125 ml/4 fl oz) red wine

2 tablespoons chopped fresh basil

1 clove garlic, crushed

1 In a large bowl, combine the mince, breadcrumbs, Parmesan, onion, parsley, egg, garlic, lemon rind and juice and salt and pepper, to taste. Roll tablespoons of the mixture into balls and roll the balls in the seasoned flour.
2 Heat the oil in a large frying pan and fry the meatballs until golden. Remove from the pan and drain on paper towels. Remove the excess fat and meat juices from the pan.
3 To make the sauce, in the same pan, combine the tomato purée, stock, wine, basil, garlic, salt and pepper. Bring to the boil.
4 Reduce the heat and return the meatballs to the pan. Allow to simmer for 10–15 minutes.
5 While the meatballs and sauce are cooking, add the fusilli to a large pan of rapidly boiling salted water and cook until *al dente*. Drain and serve with meatballs and sauce over the top.

NUTRITION PER SERVE: *Protein 60 g; Fat 35 g; Carbohydrate 115 g; Dietary Fibre 10 g; Cholesterol 170 mg; 4110 kJ (980 cal)*

ON THE SIDE

BEETROOT, GOATS CHEESE AND PISTACHIO NUT SALAD

Boil, steam or microwave about 1 kg (2 lb) of trimmed baby beetroot until quite tender. Allow to cool slightly before cutting into quarters. Line a serving plate with rocket leaves, top with the beetroot quarters, along with 1 thinly sliced red (Spanish) onion, 100 g (3 1/2 oz) of crumbled goats cheese and 100 g (3 1/2 oz) of toasted and roughly chopped pistachio nuts. Make a dressing by whisking together 3 tablespoons of raspberry vinegar, 1 teaspoon of Dijon mustard, 1 teaspoon of honey and 1/3 cup (80 ml/2 3/4 fl oz) of oil. Drizzle over the salad ingredients and serve immediately.

SEASONED FLOUR

When plain flour has salt added to it, it is called seasoned flour. Pepper, and sometimes other spices or herbs, may be included. It is used to dredge meats and vegetables before searing them for braising. The flour gives an even coating that colours well and helps to thicken sauce. It also enhances the flavour of the dish.

ABOVE: Meatballs with fusilli

MACARONI

Macaroni, or *maccheroni*, is short tubular lengths of pasta. It can be quite short and thin, or fat and as long as 4 cm (1¹/2 inches), but it is always hollow. Various sizes are known by specific names, and different regions in Italy may have different names for the same shape and size. Along with many of the improbable stories regarding the origins of macaroni, one fact is known, that it has been called *maccherone* since at least 1041 when it was a word used to describe a man who was a bit of a dunce.

ABOVE: Penne with prosciutto

PENNE WITH PROSCIUTTO

Preparation time: 15 minutes
Total cooking time: 25 minutes
Serves 4

1 tablespoon olive oil

6 thin slices prosciutto, chopped

1 onion, finely chopped

1 tablespoon chopped fresh rosemary

825 g (1 lb 11 oz) can crushed tomatoes

500 g (1 lb) penne or macaroni

¹/2 cup (50 g/1³/4 oz) freshly grated Parmesan

1 Heat the oil in a heavy-based frying pan. Add the prosciutto and onion and cook, stirring occasionally, over low heat for 5 minutes, or until golden.

2 Add the rosemary, tomato and salt and pepper, to taste. Simmer for 10 minutes.

3 While the sauce is cooking, add the pasta to a large pan of rapidly boiling salted water and cook until *al dente*. Drain. Divide the pasta among serving bowls and top with the sauce. Sprinkle with grated Parmesan.

NOTE: Rosemary, commonly used in Mediterranean cookery, adds a distinctive flavour to this dish.

NUTRITION PER SERVE: *Protein 20 g; Fat 9 g; Carbohydrate 65 g; Dietary Fibre 6 g; Cholesterol 20 mg; 1725 kJ (410 cal)*

PARSEE LAMB WITH CUMIN, EGGS AND TAGLIATELLE

Preparation time: 40 minutes
Total cooking time: 1 hour 15 minutes
Serves 4

20 g (3/4 oz) butter
1 large onion, finely chopped
2 cloves garlic, crushed
1 teaspoon finely chopped fresh ginger
3/4 teaspoon each of chilli flakes, turmeric, garam masala and ground cumin
600 g (1 1/4 lb) minced lamb
2 large very ripe tomatoes, chopped
1/2 teaspoon sugar
1 tablespoon lemon juice
3 tablespoons finely chopped fresh coriander
1 small red chilli, finely chopped, optional
350 g (11 oz) tagliatelle
1 tablespoon vegetable oil
3 hard-boiled eggs, chopped

1 Heat the butter in a frying pan and add the onion, garlic and ginger. Fry over low heat until the onion is soft but not browned. Stir in the chilli flakes, turmeric, garam masala and cumin.
2 Add the mince, increase the heat and cook until the meat is well browned, stirring occasionally. Stir in the tomato, sugar, a good pinch of salt and 1 cup (250 ml/8 fl oz) of water. Reduce the heat and simmer, covered, for 50–60 minutes, or until the sauce thickens and darkens. Increase the heat and add the lemon juice, 2 tablespoons of the chopped coriander and the red chilli. Check the seasoning, add salt if required and cook, uncovered, for 2–3 minutes.
3 Cook the tagliatelle in a large pan of rapidly boiling salted water until *al dente*. Drain, return to the pan and stir in the oil. Transfer to warmed serving dishes and spoon the lamb mixture on top. Sprinkle with hard-boiled eggs and the remaining fresh coriander before serving.

NUTRITION PER SERVE: *Protein 45 g; Fat 35 g; Carbohydrate 65 g; Dietary Fibre 7 g; Cholesterol 275 mg; 3270 kJ (780 cal)*

GARAM MASALA
Garam masala is a blend of ground spices used in Indian cooking. If stored in an airtight container and kept in a cool, dark spot it will keep for 3 months. There are many versions of garam masala, probably as many as there are cooks in India, but they will always include cardamom, cloves, nutmeg and cinnamon. Other possible components are cumin, coriander or black peppercorns. In Kashmir, black cumin is popular.

ABOVE: Parsee lamb with cumin, eggs and tagliatelle

MEATBALLS STROGANOFF

Preparation time: 40 minutes
Total cooking time: 20– 25 minutes
Serves 4

★

500 g (1 lb) macaroni

750 g (1 ½ lb) lean beef mince

2 cloves garlic, crushed

2– 3 tablespoons plain flour

1 teaspoon sweet paprika

2 tablespoons oil

50 g (1¾ oz) butter

1 large onion, thinly sliced

250 g (8 oz) small button mushrooms, halved

2 tablespoons tomato paste (tomato purée, double concentrate)

2– 3 teaspoons Dijon mustard

¼ cup (60 ml/2 fl oz) white wine

½ cup (125 ml/4 fl oz) beef stock

¾ cup (185 g/6 oz) sour cream

3 tablespoons finely chopped fresh parsley

1 Cook the macaroni in a large pan of rapidly boiling water until *al dente*. Drain; keep warm.
2 Combine the beef mince, garlic and some salt and cracked pepper in a bowl. Use your hands to mix well. Roll 2 heaped teaspoons of the mince into balls. Combine the flour, paprika and some freshly ground black pepper on a clean surface or sheet of greaseproof paper. Dust the meatballs in the seasoned flour.
3 Heat the oil and half the butter in a frying pan. When foaming, cook the meatballs over medium heat, in batches, until brown. Remove from the pan and drain on paper towels.
4 Melt the remaining butter in the pan, add the onion and cook until soft. Stir in the mushrooms and cook until the mushrooms are tender. Pour in the combined tomato paste, mustard, wine and stock. Return the meatballs to the pan and gently reheat. Bring the mixture to the boil, reduce the heat and simmer for 5 minutes, stirring occasionally. Season to taste. Stir the sour cream through until smooth. Sprinkle with a little parsley and serve with the pasta.

NUTRITION PER SERVE: *Protein 60 g; Fat 50 g; Carbohydrate 100 g; Dietary Fibre 10 g; Cholesterol 205 mg; 4615 kJ (1095 cal)*

ABOVE: Meatballs stroganoff

PASTA WITH LAMB AND VEGETABLES

Preparation time: 20 minutes
Total cooking time: 20 minutes
Serves 4

2 tablespoons oil

1 large onion, chopped

2 cloves garlic, crushed

500 g (1 lb) minced lamb

125 g (4 oz) small mushroom
  caps, halved

1 red pepper (capsicum), seeded and chopped

150 g (5 oz) shelled broad beans

440 g (14 oz) can crushed tomatoes

2 tablespoons tomato paste (tomato purée,
  double concentrate)

500 g (1 lb) penne

125 g (4 oz) feta cheese

2 tablespoons shredded fresh basil

1 Heat the oil in a heavy-based pan over medium heat. Add the onion and garlic and stir-fry for 2 minutes or until lightly browned. Add the mince and stir-fry over high heat for 4 minutes or until the meat is well browned and all the liquid has evaporated. Use a fork to break up any lumps as the mince cooks.

2 Add the mushrooms, red pepper, broad beans, undrained tomato and tomato paste to the pan. Bring to the boil, reduce the heat and simmer, covered, for 10 minutes or until the vegetables are tender. Stir occasionally.

3 While the sauce is cooking, cook the pasta in a large pan of rapidly boiling salted water until *al dente*. Drain. Spoon into serving bowls, top with the lamb and vegetable sauce, crumble cheese over the top and sprinkle with basil.

NOTE: The sauce can be made up to two days ahead. Refrigerate, covered with plastic wrap. Reheat the sauce and cook the pasta just before serving. Unsuitable for freezing.

NUTRITION PER SERVE: *Protein 50 g; Fat 30 g; Carbohydrate 100 g; Dietary Fibre 15 g; Cholesterol 100 mg; 3730 kJ (890 cal)*

GARLIC

Garlic is a bulbous liliaceous plant and the most pungent member of the *allium* family, which includes onions and leeks. Straight from the ground it has a crisp, sharp taste which mellows and becomes less intense as the bulb dries. Garlic has a high oil content and this is what determines pungency; the fresher the bulb, the more oil it contains and the stronger the flavour. Used with discretion, garlic gives a kick to otherwise flat flavours, and when subjected to slow cooking it gives body to a dish. As well, it has medicinal properties and stimulates the gastric juices, thus acting as a digestive and as a flavouring.

ABOVE: Pasta with lamb and vegetables

PASTA WITH CHICKEN

As tradition has it chicken would not, in days gone by, have been served with pasta, but we can now look back and wonder 'whyever not?' With the added flavour of fresh herbs, spices, tomatoes or mushrooms, chicken combines perfectly with pasta, especially as a filling for tiny parcels such as tortellini or ravioli. The versatility of chicken is shown in dishes such as meatballs, lasagne and even bolognese: a new twist on recipes in which you would normally expect to find meat.

BAY LEAVES

Bay or bay laurel is a symbol of fame and victory. Wreaths of laurel have been presented to honour achievement ever since the Ancient Greeks wove it into crowns for victorious athletes, poets and statesmen. The leaves have been used in the kitchen for just as long, although at first they were favoured as a flavouring for sweet dishes. Nowadays they are used mainly in marinades and in pickling, and to enhance the taste of white sauces, soups and stews.

SPAGHETTI WITH CHICKEN MEATBALLS

Preparation time: 45 minutes + chilling
Total cooking time: 1 hour 30 minutes
Serves 4–6

500 g (1 lb) chicken mince
60 g (2 oz) freshly grated Parmesan
2 cups (160 g/5½ oz) fresh white breadcrumbs
2 cloves garlic, crushed
1 egg
1 tablespoon chopped fresh flat-leaf parsley
1 tablespoon chopped fresh sage
3 tablespoons vegetable oil
500 g (1 lb) spaghetti
2 tablespoons chopped fresh oregano, to serve

Tomato sauce

1 tablespoon olive oil
1 onion, finely chopped
2 kg (4 lb) very ripe tomatoes, chopped
2 bay leaves
1 cup (30 g/1 oz) fresh basil leaves,
  loosely packed
1 teaspoon coarsely ground black pepper

1 In a large bowl, mix the chicken mince, Parmesan, breadcrumbs, garlic, egg and herbs. Season, to taste, with salt and freshly ground black pepper. Shape tablespoonsful of the mixture into small balls and chill for about 30 minutes, to firm.

2 Heat the oil in a shallow pan and fry the balls, in batches, until golden brown. Turn them often by gently shaking the pan. Drain on paper towels.

3 To make the tomato sauce, heat the oil in a large pan, add the onion and fry for about 1–2 minutes, until softened. Add the tomato and bay leaves, cover and bring to the boil, stirring occasionally. Reduce the heat to low, partially cover and cook for 50–60 minutes.

4 Add the meatballs to the sauce, along with the basil leaves and freshly ground black pepper and simmer, uncovered, for 10–15 minutes.

5 While the sauce is simmering, cook the spaghetti in a large pan of rapidly boiling salted water until *al dente*. Drain and return to the pan. Add some sauce to the pasta and toss to distribute. Serve the pasta in individual bowls with sauce and meatballs, sprinkled with chopped fresh oregano and perhaps some extra Parmesan.

NUTRITION PER SERVE (6): *Protein 40 g; Fat 20 g; Carbohydrate 85 g; Dietary Fibre 10 g; Cholesterol 95 mg; 2915 kJ (670 cal)*

ABOVE: Spaghetti with chicken meatballs

CHICKEN TORTELLINI WITH TOMATO SAUCE

Preparation time: 1 hour
  + resting of dough
Total cooking time: 30 minutes
Serves 4

Pasta

2 cups (250 g/8 oz) plain flour

3 eggs

1 tablespoon olive oil

Filling

20 g (3/4 oz) butter

90 g (3 oz) chicken breast fillet, cubed

2 slices pancetta, chopped

1/2 cup (50 g/1 3/4 oz) freshly grated Parmesan

1/2 teaspoon nutmeg

1 egg, lightly beaten

Tomato sauce

1/3 cup (80 ml/2 3/4 fl oz) olive oil

1 1/2 kg (3 lb) very ripe tomatoes, peeled
  and chopped

1/4 cup (7 g/1/4 oz) chopped fresh oregano

1/2 cup (50 g/1 3/4 oz) freshly grated Parmesan

100 g (3 1/2 oz) bocconcini, thinly sliced,
  for serving

1 To make the pasta, sift the flour and a pinch of salt into a bowl and make a well in the centre. In a jug, whisk together the eggs, oil and 1 tablespoon of water. Add the egg mixture gradually to the flour, mixing to a firm dough. Gather together into a ball, adding a little extra water if necessary.

2 Knead on a lightly floured surface for 5 minutes, or until the dough is smooth and elastic. Put in a lightly oiled bowl, cover with plastic wrap and set aside for 30 minutes.

3 To make the filling, heat the butter in a frying pan, add the chicken cubes and cook, stirring, until golden brown. Drain and allow to cool slightly. Process the chicken and pancetta in a food processor or mincer until finely chopped. Transfer to a bowl and add the Parmesan, nutmeg, egg and salt and pepper, to taste. Set aside.

4 Roll out the dough very thinly on a lightly floured surface. Using a floured cutter, cut into 5 cm (2 inch) rounds and spoon 1/2 teaspoon of filling into the centre of each. Brush the edges with a little water. Fold in half to form semi-circles, pressing the edges together. Wrap each around your finger to form a ring and then press the ends of the dough together firmly.

5 To make the tomato sauce, put the oil, tomato and oregano in a frying pan and cook over high heat for 10 minutes. Stir the Parmesan through and set aside.

6 Cook the tortellini in two batches in a large pan of rapidly boiling water for about 6 minutes each batch, or until *al dente*. Drain and return to the pan. Reheat the tomato sauce, add to the tortellini and toss to combine. Divide the tortellini among individual bowls, top with bocconcini and allow the cheese to melt a little before serving.

NUTRITION PER SERVE: *Protein 40 g; Fat 55 g; Carbohydrate 55 g; Dietary Fibre 5 g; Cholesterol 300 mg; 3660 kJ (875 cal)*

TORTELLINI AND CAPPELLETTI

Manufacturers invariably sell cappelletti as tortellini. The difference is minimal. Tortellini are small rolls of filled pasta that were originally twisted around a finger so that the two ends folded over each other. Cappelletti are like little hats and their ends are pinched together. The two are interchangeable.

ABOVE: Chicken tortellini with tomato sauce

CHICKEN AND SPINACH LASAGNE

Preparation time: 30 minutes
Total cooking time: I hour 10 minutes
Serves 8

500 g (I lb) English spinach
I kg (2 lb) chicken mince
I clove garlic, crushed
3 bacon rashers, chopped
425 g (14 oz) can crushed tomatoes
1/2 cup (125 g/4 oz) tomato paste (tomato purée, double concentrate)
1/2 cup (125 ml/4 fl oz) tomato sauce
1/2 cup (125 ml/4 fl oz) chicken stock
12 instant lasagne sheets
I cup (125 g/4 oz) grated Cheddar cheese

Cheese sauce

60 g (2 oz) butter
1/3 cup (40 g/1 1/4 oz) plain flour
2 1/2 cups (600 ml/20 fl oz) milk
I cup (125 g/4 oz) grated Cheddar cheese

1 Preheat the oven to moderate 180°C (350°F/Gas 4). Remove and discard the stalks from the spinach leaves. Plunge the leaves in a pan of boiling water for 2 minutes, or until

ABOVE: Chicken and spinach lasagne

tender. Remove, plunge immediately into a bowl of iced water and then drain.
2 Heat a little oil in a heavy-based frying pan. Add the mince, garlic and bacon. Cook over medium heat for 5 minutes, or until browned. Stir in the tomato, tomato paste, sauce and stock and bring to the boil. Reduce the heat and simmer, partially covered, for 10 minutes, or until the sauce is slightly thickened. Season with salt and pepper, to taste.
3 To make the cheese sauce, melt the butter in a medium pan, add the flour and stir over low heat for 1 minute, or until the mixture is lightly golden and smooth. Remove from the heat and gradually stir in the milk. Return to the heat and stir constantly over medium heat for 4 minutes, or until the sauce boils and thickens. Remove from the heat and stir in the cheese.
4 To assemble the lasagne, brush a deep, 3-litre, ovenproof dish with melted butter or oil. Spread one-quarter of the chicken mixture over the base. Top with 4 sheets of lasagne. Spread with one-third of the cheese sauce, then another layer of the chicken filling. Top with all of the spinach, a layer of lasagne, a layer of cheese sauce and the remaining chicken filling. Spread evenly with the remaining cheese sauce and sprinkle with the grated cheese. Bake for 50 minutes, or until cooked through and golden brown.

NUTRITION PER SERVE: *Protein 50 g; Fat 45 g; Carbohydrate 35 g; Dietary Fibre 5 g; Cholesterol 230 mg; 3145 kJ (750 cal)*

The rind, flesh and juice of lemons are all put to good use in savoury foods as well as desserts, cakes and sweets. The lemon is perhaps the most acid of citrus fruits and is highly scented. Bush lemons, with their thick and crinkly skins, are valued for their clean acid taste, which stays pure when blended with other flavours. The many types of smooth-skinned lemons tend to be sweeter and the fresh fruit is more attractive for use as a decoration or garnish.

CHICKEN WITH LEMON, PARSLEY AND ORECCHIETTE

Preparation time: 10 minutes
Total cooking time: 20 minutes
Serves 4

375 g (12 oz) orecchiette
1 tablespoon oil
60 g (2 oz) butter
4 small chicken breast fillets
1/3 cup (80 ml/2 3/4 fl oz) lemon juice
1/3 cup (20 g/3/4 oz) finely chopped fresh parsley
    plus some extra, to garnish
lemon slices, to garnish

1 Cook the pasta in a large pan of rapidly boiling salted water until *al dente*. Drain.
2 While the pasta is cooking, heat the oil and half the butter in a large, heavy-based pan. Add the chicken fillets and cook for 2 minutes each side; set aside. Add the lemon juice, parsley and the remaining butter to the pan. Stir to combine and return the fillets to the pan. Cook over low heat for 3– 4 minutes, turning once, or until cooked through. Season, to taste, with salt and freshly ground black pepper.
3 Serve the pasta topped with a chicken fillet and sauce. Garnish with lemon slices and sprinkle with some chopped fresh parsley.

NUTRITION PER SERVE: *Protein 40 g; Fat 20 g; Carbohydrate 25 g; Dietary Fibre 0 g; Cholesterol 120 mg; 1880 kJ (450 cal)*

ON THE SIDE

BACON, LETTUCE AND TOMATO SALAD Grill or fry 4 rashers of bacon until they are crisp. Allow to cool on paper towels before roughly chopping. Combine in a bowl with the leaves of a cos lettuce, 200 g (6 1/2 oz) of halved cherry tomatoes, and 1 chopped avocado. Toss gently to combine. Top with a dressing made by mixing together 1/2 cup (125 g/4 oz) of natural yoghurt with 1 tablespoon of wholegrain mustard, 1 tablespoon of lemon juice and 1 teaspoon of honey.

ABOVE: Chicken with lemon, parsley and orecchiette

ORIENTAL CHICKEN PASTA

Preparation time: 25 minutes
Total cooking time: 10 minutes
Serves 4

★

1 barbecued chicken

1 onion

1 carrot

150 g (5 oz) tagliatelle

1 tablespoon oil

1 clove garlic, crushed

2 teaspoons curry powder

2 teaspoons bottled crushed chilli

1 large red pepper (capsicum), thinly sliced

150 g (5 oz) snow peas (mangetout), halved

3 spring onions, sliced

2 teaspoons sesame oil

1/4 cup (60 ml/2 fl oz) soy sauce

1 Remove the chicken meat from the bones and discard the bones. Slice the chicken into thin strips. Cut the onion into thin wedges and the carrot into long strips.

2 Cook the tagliatelle in a large pan of rapidly boiling salted water until *al dente*. Drain well.

3 Heat the oil in a wok or heavy-based pan, swirling gently to coat the base and sides. Add the onion, carrot, garlic, curry powder and chilli. Stir until aromatic and the garlic is soft. Add the pasta and the remaining ingredients. Stir-fry over medium heat for 4 minutes, or until heated through. Add salt, to taste.

NUTRITION PER SERVE: *Protein 40 g; Fat 25 g; Carbohydrate 40 g; Dietary Fibre 5 g; Cholesterol 105 mg; 2355 kJ (560 cal)*

RIGHT: Oriental chicken pasta

Rosemary is an important herb in European cookery where it is used in particular for outdoor cooking and to flavour meats. It should be added to food towards the end of cooking, as the essential oils that contain the flavour evaporate with lengthy cooking. The perennial plant is not difficult to grow as it tolerates most conditions, and the leaves, when dried, carry a true rosemary taste, rich and piney.

SPAGHETTI WITH CHICKEN BOLOGNESE

Preparation time: 20 minutes
Total cooking time: 15 minutes
Serves 4

2 tablespoons olive oil

2 leeks, thinly sliced

1 red pepper (capsicum), diced

2 cloves garlic, crushed

500 g (1 lb) chicken mince

2 cups (500 g/1 lb) tomato pasta sauce

1 tablespoon chopped fresh thyme

1 tablespoon chopped fresh rosemary

2 tablespoons seeded and chopped black olives

400 g (13 oz) spaghetti

125 g (4 oz) feta cheese, crumbled

1 Heat the oil in a large, heavy-based pan. Add the leek, pepper and garlic and cook over medium-high heat for 2 minutes, or until lightly browned.

2 Add the chicken mince and cook over high heat for 3 minutes, or until browned and any liquid has evaporated. Stir occasionally and break up any lumps as the mince cooks.

3 Add the tomato pasta sauce, thyme and rosemary and bring to the boil. Reduce the heat and simmer for 5 minutes, or until the sauce has reduced and thickened. Add the olives and stir to combine. Season, to taste.

4 Cook the spaghetti in a large pan of rapidly boiling salted water until *al dente*. Drain. Place the spaghetti on individual serving plates or pile into a large deep serving dish and pour the Chicken Bolognese over the top. (The sauce can be mixed through the pasta.) Sprinkle with feta and serve immediately.

NOTE: Chicken Bolognese can be cooked up to 2 days ahead. Refrigerate, covered, or freeze for up to four weeks. Reheat the sauce and cook the spaghetti just before serving. Any type of pasta, dried or fresh, is suitable to use. Freshly grated Parmesan or pecorino can be used instead of feta cheese.

NUTRITION PER SERVE: *Protein 45 g; Fat 35 g; Carbohydrate 85 g; Dietary Fibre 10 g; Cholesterol 120 mg; 3540 kJ (845 cal)*

ABOVE: Spaghetti with chicken bolognese

REHEATING PASTA

Most sauced pasta dishes can be reheated. Dishes with a good amount of sauce or a lot of oil in the dressing, such as pesto, can be stirred over high heat in a pan or heated in a moderate oven in a greased, ovenproof dish, covered with foil. Cooked pasta without sauce can be reheated by putting it in a colander and pouring boiling water over it, or immersing it in a pan of boiling water for about 30 seconds. A microwave is also ideal.

ABOVE: Fettucine with chicken and mushroom sauce

FETTUCINE WITH CHICKEN AND MUSHROOM SAUCE

Preparation time: 20 minutes
Total cooking time: 20 minutes
Serves 4

400 g (13 oz) fettucine
2 large chicken breast fillets
1 tablespoon olive oil
30 g (1 oz) butter
2 bacon rashers, chopped
2 cloves garlic, crushed
250 g (8 oz) button mushrooms, sliced
1/3 cup (80 ml/2³/4 fl oz) white wine
2/3 cup (170 ml/5¹/2 fl oz) cream
4 spring onions, chopped
1 tablespoon plain flour
2 tablespoons water
1/3 cup (35 g/1¹/4 oz) freshly grated Parmesan, for serving

1 Cook the fettucine in a large pan of rapidly boiling salted water until *al dente*. Drain and return to the pan.

2 Trim the chicken of excess fat and cut into thin strips. Heat the oil and butter in a heavy-based frying pan, add the chicken and cook over medium heat for 3 minutes, or until browned. Add the bacon, garlic and mushrooms and cook for 2 minutes, stirring occasionally.

3 Add the wine and cook until the liquid has reduced by half. Add the cream and spring onion and bring to the boil. Blend the flour with the water until smooth, add to the pan and stir until the mixture boils and thickens. Reduce the heat and simmer for 2 minutes. Season with salt and pepper, to taste.

4 Add the sauce to the pasta and stir over low heat until combined. Sprinkle with Parmesan. Serve immediately with a green salad and perhaps some hot herb bread.

NUTRITION PER SERVE: *Protein 40 g; Fat 35 g; Carbohydrate 75 g; Dietary Fibre 5 g; Cholesterol 135 mg; 3355 kJ (800 cal)*

PESTO CHICKEN PASTA

Preparation time: 20 minutes
Total cooking time: 20 minutes
Serves 4

250 g (8 oz) fusilli or penne
1 small barbecued chicken
1 cup (125 g/4 oz) walnuts
4 bacon rashers
250 g (8 oz) cherry tomatoes, halved
60 g (2 oz) pitted and sliced olives
1/2 cup (125 g/4 oz) bottled pesto sauce
1/2 cup (30 g/1 oz) finely shredded fresh basil
shavings of Parmesan, for serving

1 Cook the pasta in a large pan of rapidly boiling salted water until *al dente*. Drain.
2 While the pasta is cooking, discard the skin of the chicken. Remove the meat from the chicken, cut or shred it into bite-sized pieces and put in a large bowl.
3 Toast the walnuts for 2–3 minutes under a hot grill, allow to cool and then chop roughly.

4 Remove the rind from the bacon rashers and grill the bacon for 3–4 minutes, or until crisp. Allow to cool and then chop into small pieces. Add the nuts, bacon, cherry tomatoes and olives to the chicken.
5 Add the pasta to the chicken mixture, along with the pesto sauce and the fresh basil. Toss until thoroughly mixed. Serve at room temperature, with Parmesan shavings.

NUTRITION PER SERVE: *Protein 55 g; Fat 45 g; Carbohydrate 25 g; Dietary Fibre 5 g; Cholesterol 190 mg; 2960 kJ (705 cal)*

ON THE SIDE

ROASTED TOMATOES TOPPED WITH HERBED GOATS CHEESE

Brush halved egg (Roma) tomatoes with a little olive oil, sprinkle with salt, sugar and pepper and bake in a moderate 180°C (350°F/Gas 4) oven for 30 minutes, or until tender and slightly dried. Make a mixture of goats cheese and fresh herbs and press a little onto the top of each piece of cooked tomato. Cook under a grill until the goats cheese begins to soften and colour.

BELOW: Pesto chicken pasta

based pan. Cook the chicken quickly over high heat until browned but not cooked through; drain on paper towels. Add the onion, carrot and bacon to the pan. Stir over medium heat for 10 minutes. Add the zucchini and soup, bring to the boil and simmer for 5 minutes. Remove from the heat.

3 Combine the pasta, chicken, tomato mixture and sour cream. Season with salt and pepper, to taste. Spread into a shallow ovenproof dish and top with cheese. Bake for 20 minutes, or until golden and cooked through.

NUTRITION PER SERVE: *Protein 45 g; Fat 30 g; Carbohydrate 45 g; Dietary Fibre 5 g; Cholesterol 115 mg; 2665 kJ (635 cal)*

LASAGNETTE WITH MUSHROOMS AND CHICKEN

Preparation time: 15 minutes
Total cooking time: 20 minutes
Serves 4

1/4 cup (60 ml/2 fl oz) milk
1/2 teaspoon dried tarragon or
   2 teaspoons chopped fresh
400 g (13 oz) lasagnette
25 g (3/4 oz) butter
2 cloves garlic
200 g (61/2 oz) chicken breast fillet, sliced
100 g (31/2 oz) button mushrooms,
   thinly sliced
ground nutmeg
2 cups (500 ml/16 fl oz) cream
few sprigs fresh tarragon, to garnish

CHICKEN AND MACARONI BAKE

Preparation time: 20 minutes
Total cooking time: 55 minutes
Serves 6

4 chicken breast fillets
2 cups (310 g/10 oz) macaroni elbows
1/4 cup (60 ml/2 fl oz) olive oil
1 onion, chopped
1 carrot, chopped
3 bacon rashers, chopped
2 zucchini, chopped
440 g (14 oz) can tomato soup
1/3 cup (90 g/3 oz) sour cream
1 1/2 cups (185 g/6 oz) grated Cheddar cheese

1 Trim the chicken of excess fat and sinew. Preheat the oven to moderate 180°C (350°F/ Gas 4). Cook the macaroni in a large pan of rapidly boiling salted water until *al dente*; drain.
2 Slice the chicken breasts into long strips and then cut into cubes. Heat the oil in a heavy-

ABOVE: Chicken and macaroni bake
RIGHT: Lasagnette with mushrooms and chicken

1 Bring the milk and tarragon to the boil in a small pan. Remove from the heat, strain and reserve the milk. Set aside.

2 Cook the lasagnette in a large pan of rapidly boiling salted water until *al dente*. Drain and return to the pan.

3 While the pasta is cooking, melt the butter in a frying pan and gently sauté the whole garlic cloves, sliced chicken and button mushrooms until the chicken is golden and cooked through. Discard the garlic cloves and add the nutmeg and salt and pepper, to taste. Stir for 10 seconds before stirring in the cream and tarragon milk. Bring to the boil, reduce the heat and simmer until the sauce thickens. Spoon the sauce over the pasta and decorate with fresh tarragon.

NUTRITION PER SERVE: *Protein 25 g; Fat 60 g; Carbohydrate 75 g; Dietary Fibre 5 g; Cholesterol 215 mg; 4005 kJ (955 cal)*

CHICKEN LIVERS WITH PENNE

Preparation time: 15 minutes
Total cooking time: 15 minutes
Serves 4

★ ★

350 g (11 oz) chicken livers

500 g (1 lb) penne

50 g (1 3/4 oz) butter

1 onion, diced

2 cloves garlic, crushed

2 teaspoons finely grated orange rind

2 bay leaves

1/2 cup (125 ml/4 fl oz) red wine

2 tablespoons tomato paste (tomato purée, double concentrate)

2 tablespoons cream

1 Wash the chicken livers and trim off any membrane. Cut each liver into six pieces.

2 Cook the penne in a large pan of rapidly boiling salted water until *al dente*. Drain and keep warm.

3 While the pasta is cooking, melt the butter in a frying pan and cook the onion until softened. Add the crushed garlic, chicken livers, orange rind and bay leaves, and stir for 3 minutes. Remove the chicken livers with a slotted spoon. Stir in the red wine, tomato paste and cream. Simmer until the sauce reduces and thickens.

4 Return the chicken livers to the pan and warm through. Season with salt and freshly ground pepper, to taste. Spoon the chicken liver sauce over the pasta.

NUTRITION PER SERVE: *Protein 35 g; Fat 20 g; Carbohydrate 90 g; Dietary Fibre 10 g; Cholesterol 460 mg; 3010 kJ (720 cal)*

ON THE SIDE

ROAST BROCCOLI WITH CUMIN SEEDS Gently boil or steam some evenly sized broccoli florets for a couple of minutes. Drain thoroughly and then toss them in a mixture of olive oil, crushed garlic and lightly toasted crushed cumin seeds. Put on an oven tray and bake in a very hot oven until the broccoli is browned at the edges.

CHERRY TOMATOES WITH BUTTER AND DILL Pan-fry some cherry tomatoes in a little butter until the skins are beginning to split, season well with salt and cracked black pepper and sprinkle with some chopped dill. Gently toss and serve immediately.

ABOVE: Chicken livers with penne

CHICKEN RAVIOLI WITH FRESH TOMATO SAUCE

Preparation time: 40 minutes
Total cooking time: 40 minutes
Serves 4

★ ★

1 tablespoon oil
1 large onion, chopped
2 cloves garlic, crushed
1/3 cup (90 g/3 oz) tomato paste (tomato purée, double concentrate)
1/4 cup (60 ml/2 fl oz) red wine
2/3 cup (170 ml/5 1/2 fl oz) chicken stock
2 very ripe tomatoes, chopped
1 tablespoon chopped fresh basil

Ravioli

200 g (6 1/2 oz) chicken mince
1 tablespoon chopped fresh basil
1/4 cup (25 g/3/4 oz) grated Parmesan

BELOW: Chicken ravioli with fresh tomato sauce

3 spring onions, finely chopped
50 g (1 3/4 oz) fresh ricotta cheese
250 g (8 oz) packet (48) gow gee wrappers

1 Heat the oil in a medium pan and add the onion and garlic. Cook for 2–3 minutes and stir in the tomato paste, red wine, chicken stock and chopped tomato and simmer for 20 minutes. Stir in the basil and season, to taste.
2 To make the ravioli, combine the chicken mince, basil, Parmesan, spring onion, ricotta and some salt and pepper. Lay 24 of the wrappers on a flat surface and brush with a little water. Place slightly heaped teaspoons of mixture in the centre of each wrapper. Place another wrapper on top and press the edges firmly together.
3 Bring a large pan of water to the boil and cook the ravioli a few at a time for 2–3 minutes, or until tender. Drain well. Serve with sauce.

NUTRITION PER SERVE: *Protein 20 g; Fat 25 g; Carbohydrate 50 g; Dietary Fibre 5 g; Cholesterol 75 mg; 2210 kJ (530 cal)*

BRANDY CHICKEN FETTUCINE

Preparation time: 40 minutes
Total cooking time: 40 minutes
Serves 4– 6

10 g (1/4 oz) porcini mushrooms

2 tablespoons olive oil

2 cloves garlic, crushed

200 g (6 1/2 oz) button mushrooms, sliced

125 g (4 oz) prosciutto, chopped

375 g (12 oz) fettucine

1/4 cup (60 ml/2 fl oz) brandy

1 cup (250 ml/8 fl oz) cream

1 barbecued chicken, shredded

1 cup (155 g/5 oz) frozen peas

1/3 cup (20 g/3/4 oz) finely chopped
   fresh parsley

1 Put the porcini mushrooms in a bowl and cover with boiling water. Set aside for 10 minutes, then drain, squeeze dry and chop.
2 Heat the oil in a large, heavy-based pan. Add the crushed garlic and cook, stirring, for 1 minute over low heat. Add the button and porcini mushrooms, along with the prosciutto, and cook over low heat, stirring often, for 5 minutes.
3 Meanwhile, cook the pasta in a large pan of rapidly boiling salted water until *al dente*. Drain and return to the pan.
4 Add the brandy and cream to the mushroom mixture. Cook, stirring, over low heat for 2 minutes. Add the chicken, peas and parsley. Cook, stirring, for 4– 5 minutes, until heated through. Add the chicken mixture to the hot pasta and mix through.
NOTE: Cut the slices of prosciutto separately, otherwise they stick together. Use bacon slices instead, if preferred. If porcini mushrooms are not available, use 30 g (1 oz) of dried Chinese mushrooms.

NUTRITION PER SERVE (6): *Protein 40 g; Fat 35 g; Carbohydrate 45 g; Dietary Fibre 5 g; Cholesterol 130 mg; 2900 kJ (690 cal)*

ON THE SIDE

PANZANELLA Tear 2 slices of day-old country-style bread into pieces and sprinkle with crushed garlic and oil. Toss it in a bowl with chopped cucumber, tomatoes, red (Spanish) onion and some fresh basil leaves. Drizzle with olive oil and red wine vinegar and season well. The bread should be slightly moist but not too soggy. You can also add anchovies or hard-boiled eggs.

BEANS WITH PARSLEY BUTTER Cook some green beans in salted boiling water until they are tender but still bright green. Drain and place in a bowl with some pieces of herb butter and some salt and black pepper. Toss well so that the beans are all coated in the buttery mixture.

ABOVE: Brandy chicken fettucine

PASTA WITH SEAFOOD

It is hardly a mystery why pasta and seafood go together so well. Italy is surrounded on almost all sides by the tranquil blueness of the Mediterranean sea and the Italians have been reaping its fruits since the dawn of their civilization. It's only natural that they should cook up their catch of fresh prawns, clams and succulent fish and toss them together with their beloved pasta to come up with some spectacular dishes.

CALAMARI

Calamari, Italian for squid, is a member of the *cephalopod* family, along with octopus and cuttlefish. Like the octopus, the squid has eight limbs, but also two longer tentacles with suckers on the end. The body sac is elongated and does not contain a true skeleton, and both this body and the tentacles can be eaten. The flesh is firm, mildy sweet and doesn't have a 'fishy' flavour. Calamari is eaten whole, stuffed and stewed, or cut into strips or rings and fried. It can be rubbery and tasteless if cooked without care.

ABOVE: Spaghetti marinara

SPAGHETTI MARINARA

Preparation time: 40 minutes
Total cooking time: 50 minutes
Serves 6

12 fresh mussels

Tomato Sauce

2 tablespoons olive oil
1 onion, finely diced
1 carrot, sliced
1 red chilli, seeded and chopped
2 cloves garlic, crushed
425 g (14 oz) can crushed tomatoes

1/2 cup (125 ml/4 fl oz) white wine
1 teaspoon sugar
pinch of cayenne pepper

1/4 cup (60 ml/2 fl oz) white wine
1/4 cup (60 ml/2 fl oz) fish stock
1 clove garlic, crushed
375 g (12 oz) spaghetti
30 g (1 oz) butter
125 g (4 oz) small calamari tubes, sliced
125 g (4 oz) boneless white fish fillets, cut into cubes
200 g (6 1/2 oz) raw prawns, shelled and deveined
1/2 cup (30 g/1 oz) fresh parsley, chopped
200 g (6 1/2 oz) can clams, drained

1 Remove the beards from the mussels and scrub away any grit. Discard any opened or damaged mussels.

2 To make the tomato sauce, heat the oil in a medium pan, add the onion and carrot and stir over medium heat for about 10 minutes, or until the vegetables are lightly browned. Add the chilli, garlic, tomato, white wine, sugar and cayenne pepper and simmer for 30 minutes, stirring occasionally.

3 Meanwhile, heat the ¼ cup wine with the stock and garlic in a large pan and add the unopened mussels. Cover the pan and shake it over high heat for 3–5 minutes. After 3 minutes, start removing any opened mussels and set them aside. After 5 minutes discard any unopened mussels and reserve the wine mixture.

4 Cook the pasta in a large pan of rapidly boiling salted water until *al dente*. Drain and keep warm. Meanwhile, melt the butter in a frying pan, add the calamari rings, fish and prawns and stir-fry for 2 minutes. Set aside. Add the reserved wine mixture, mussels, calamari, fish, prawns, parsley and clams to the tomato sauce and reheat gently. Gently combine the sauce with the pasta and serve at once.

NUTRITION PER SERVE: *Protein 30 g; Fat 15 g; Carbohydrate 50 g; Dietary Fibre 5 g; Cholesterol 225 mg; 2000 kJ (480 cal)*

FARFALLE WITH TUNA, MUSHROOMS AND CREAM

Preparation time: 15 minutes
Total cooking time: 15 minutes
Serves 4

500 g (1 lb) farfalle
60 g (2 oz) butter
1 tablespoon olive oil
1 onion, chopped
1 clove garlic, crushed
125 g (4 oz) button mushrooms, sliced
1 cup (250 ml/4 fl oz) cream
450 g (14 oz) can tuna, drained
  and flaked
1 tablespoon lemon juice
1 tablespoon chopped fresh parsley

1 Cook the farfalle in a large pan of rapidly boiling salted water until *al dente*. Drain and return to the pan.

2 While the pasta is cooking, heat the butter and oil in a large frying pan. Add the chopped onion and crushed garlic and stir over low heat until the onion is tender. Add the sliced mushroom and cook for 2 minutes. Pour in the cream and bring to the boil. Reduce the heat and simmer until the sauce begins to thicken.

3 Add the flaked tuna, lemon juice, parsley and salt and pepper, to taste, to the cream mixture and stir to combine. Heat gently, stirring constantly. Add the sauce to the farfalle and toss gently to combine.

NOTE: You can use a can of salmon, drained and flaked, instead of tuna.

NUTRITION PER SERVE: *Protein 45 g; Fat 50 g; Carbohydrate 90 g; Dietary Fibre 10 g; Cholesterol 145 mg; 4100 kJ (980 cal)*

TUNA

Tuna are surface fish and strong swimmers so they have tight, muscular and close-grained flesh. This makes tuna well suited to stewing and long cooking, but it is also eaten lightly sautéed or uncooked, as in Japanese sashimi. The raw flesh is an attractive dark rose colour and can be cut into firm slices without breaking up.

ABOVE: Farfalle with tuna, mushrooms and cream

CREAMY PRAWNS WITH FETTUCINE

Preparation time: 30 minutes
Total cooking time: 15 minutes
Serves 4

500 g (1 lb) fettucine
500 g (1 lb) raw prawns
30 g (1 oz) butter
1 tablespoon olive oil
6 spring onions, chopped
1 clove garlic, crushed
1 cup (250 ml/8 fl oz) cream
2 tablespoons chopped fresh parsley,
    for serving

*BELOW: Creamy
prawns with fettucine*

1 Cook the fettucine in a large pan of rapidly boiling water until *al dente*. Drain and return to the pan.
2 While the fettucine is cooking, peel and devein the prawns. Heat the butter and oil in a frying pan, add the spring onion and garlic and stir over low heat for 1 minute. Add the prawns and cook for 2–3 minutes, or until the flesh changes colour. Remove the prawns from the pan and set aside. Add the cream to the pan and bring to the boil. Reduce the heat and simmer until the sauce begins to thicken. Return the prawns to the pan, add salt and pepper, to taste, and simmer for 1 minute.
3 Add the prawns and sauce to the warm fettucine and toss gently. Serve sprinkled with chopped parsley.
NOTE: For variations, in step 1, add 1 sliced red pepper (capsicum) and 1 very finely sliced leek. Use scallops instead of prawns or a mixture of both.

NUTRITION PER SERVE: *Protein 35 g; Fat 40 g; Carbohydrate 90 g; Dietary Fibre 7 g; Cholesterol 320 mg; 3660 kJ (875 cal)*

ON THE SIDE

WATERCRESS, SALMON AND CAMEMBERT SALAD Remove the sprigs of watercress (about 500 g/1 lb) from the tough stems and arrange the sprigs over the base of a large platter. Top with ten slices of smoked salmon, 200 g (6½ oz) of thinly sliced camembert cheese, 2 tablespoons of capers and 1 thinly sliced red (Spanish) onion. Make a dressing by thoroughly combining 2 tablespoons of freshly squeezed lime juice, 1 teaspoon of honey and ⅓ cup (90 ml/3 fl oz) of olive oil. Drizzle over the salad and garnish generously with cracked black pepper and snipped fresh chives.

MARINATED MUSHROOM SALAD Trim and halve 500 g (1 lb) of button mushrooms. Put them in a large bowl, add 4 thinly sliced spring onions, 1 finely diced red pepper (capsicum) and 2 tablespoons of chopped fresh flat-leaf parsley. Make a dressing by combining 3 crushed cloves of garlic, 3 tablespoons of white wine vinegar, 2 teaspoons of Dijon mustard and ⅓ cup (80 ml/2¾ fl oz) of olive oil. Pour the dressing over the mushrooms and toss to coat. Cover and refrigerate for 3 hours before serving.

CRAB CAKES WITH HOT SALSA

Preparation time: 40 minutes
  + 30 minutes refrigeration
Total cooking time: 35 minutes
Serves 6

Hot salsa

2 large very ripe tomatoes

1 onion, finely chopped

2 cloves garlic, crushed

1 teaspoon dried oregano leaves

2 tablespoons sweet chilli sauce

100 g (3½ oz) angel hair pasta, broken into
  short lengths

600 g (1¼ lb) crab meat

2 tablespoons finely chopped fresh parsley

1 small red pepper (capsicum), finely chopped

3 tablespoons freshly grated Parmesan

¼ cup (30 g/1 oz) plain flour

2 spring onions, finely chopped

2 eggs, lightly beaten

2–3 tablespoons oil, for frying

1 To make the hot salsa, combine all the
ingredients in a small bowl and allow to stand
at room temperature for 1 hour.
2 Cook the pasta in a large pan of rapidly
boiling salted water until *al dente*. Drain.
3 Squeeze the excess moisture from the crab
meat and combine in a large bowl with the
pasta, parsley, red pepper, grated Parmesan,
flour, onions and pepper, to taste. Add the
beaten egg and mix well.
4 Shape the mixture into twelve flat patties,
cover and refrigerate for 30 minutes.
5 Heat the oil in a large heavy-based pan and
cook the crab cakes, in batches, over medium
high heat until golden brown. Serve
immediately with hot salsa.

NUTRITION PER SERVE: *Protein 20 g; Fat 10 g;
Carbohydrate 25 g; Dietary Fibre 3 g; Cholesterol 150 mg;
1200 kJ (290 cal)*

ON THE SIDE

**BLACK BEANS WITH TOMATO,
LIME AND CORIANDER** Peel
3 large very ripe tomatoes, remove the
seeds and finely chop the flesh. Combine in
a bowl with the juice of 1 lime, some finely
chopped cucumber and a large handful of
fresh coriander leaves. Mix with 2 cups of
cooked black beans (turtle beans) and
1 tablespoon of olive oil and season well.

**ZUCCHINI WITH TOMATO
AND GARLIC** Fry little cubes of
zucchini in olive oil with a crushed clove of
garlic until they are crisp and browned on
all sides. Add some fresh chopped tomato
and season well with salt and pepper. Serve
while the zucchini is still crisp.

CRAB

Crab, a crustacean, does
not have a high flesh to
bulk ratio. Small swimmer
and shore crabs have a
low meat yield and are
used for flavouring stocks
and stews. But if caught
while their new shells are
still soft, they can be eaten
whole, shells, claws and all.
Some, such as the Alaskan
crab, have huge claws and
the amount of flesh is
significant. Crab meat is
mild and sweet.

*ABOVE: Crab cakes
with hot salsa*

SALMON

Salmon is prized for its delicate taste, warm pink colour and the fine, succulent grain of the flesh. It conserves well and can be dried, smoked or canned. Salmon are a migratory fish that live in the sea but spawn in fresh water. They do not feed when in fresh water so their meat is at its worst by the time they head back to the sea. There are exceptions to this rule, however, and salmon in some places are known to live in fresh water lakes, travelling up their tributaries to spawn. The flesh of these fish is considered by some to be inferior in both flavour and texture, but in these days of farming and controlled production the quality of salmon in the marketplace is consistently high.

ABOVE: Salmon and pasta mornay

SALMON AND PASTA MORNAY

Preparation time: 15 minutes
Total cooking time: 10–15 minutes
Serves 4

400 g (13 oz) conchiglie (shell pasta)
30 g (1 oz) butter
6 spring onions, chopped
2 cloves garlic, crushed
1 tablespoon plain flour
1 cup (250 ml/8 fl oz) milk
1 cup (250 g/8 oz) sour cream
1 tablespoon lemon juice
425 g (14 oz) can salmon, drained and flaked
1/2 cup (30 g/1 oz) chopped fresh parsley

1 Cook the pasta in a large pan of rapidly boiling salted water until *al dente*. Drain and return to the pan.

2 While the pasta is cooking, melt the butter in a medium pan, add the onion and garlic and stir over low heat for 3 minutes, or until tender. Add the flour and stir for 1 minute. Combine the milk, sour cream and lemon juice in a jug. Add gradually to the onion mixture, stirring constantly. Stir over medium heat for 3 minutes, or until the mixture boils and thickens.

3 Add the salmon and parsley to the pan and stir for 1 minute, or until heated through. Add to the drained pasta and toss until well combined. Season with salt and pepper, to taste, before serving.

NOTE: As a variation, use a can of drained and flaked tuna instead of salmon, or add 1 teaspoon of mustard to the sauce.

NUTRITION PER SERVE: *Protein 40 g; Fat 40 g; Carbohydrate 80 g; Dietary Fibre 5 g; Cholesterol 190 mg; 3550 kJ (850 cal)*

SPAGHETTI WITH CHILLI CALAMARI

Preparation time: 20 minutes
Total cooking time: 20 minutes
Serves 4

500 g (1 lb) calamari, cleaned

500 g (1 lb) spaghetti

2 tablespoons olive oil

1 leek, chopped

2 cloves garlic, crushed

1–2 teaspoons chopped chilli

1/2 teaspoon cayenne pepper

425 g (14 oz) can crushed tomatoes

1/2 cup (125 ml/4 fl oz) fish stock (see margin note)

1 tablespoon chopped fresh basil

2 teaspoons chopped fresh sage

1 teaspoon chopped fresh marjoram

1 Pull the tentacles from the body of the calamari. Using your fingers, pull the quill from the pouch of the calamari. Pull the skin away from the flesh and discard. Use a sharp knife to slit the tubes up one side. Lay out flat and score one side in a diamond pattern. Cut each tube into four.

2 Cook the spaghetti in a large pan of rapidly boiling salted water until *al dente*. Drain and keep warm.

3 While the pasta is cooking, heat the oil in a large frying pan. Add the leek and cook for 2 minutes. Add the garlic and stir over low heat for 1 minute. Stir in the chilli and cayenne. Add the tomato, stock and herbs and bring to the boil. Reduce the heat and simmer for 5 minutes.

4 Add the calamari to the pan. Simmer for another 5 – 10 minutes, or until tender. Serve the chilli calamari over the spaghetti.

NUTRITION PER SERVE: *Protein 35 g; Fat 15 g; Carbohydrate 90 g; Dietary Fibre 10 g; Cholesterol 250 mg; 2670 kJ (640 cal)*

FISH STOCK

Fish stock is not widely available ready-made, so you may want to make your own and freeze it. Melt 1 tablespoon butter in a large pan and cook 2 finely chopped onions over low heat for 10 minutes, or until soft but not browned. Add 2 litres of water, 1.5 kg (3 lb) of fish bones, heads and tails and a bouquet garni. Simmer for about 20 minutes, skimming off any froth. Strain the stock through a fine sieve before refrigerating. Use white-fleshed fish for stock as darker, oily fish tends to make it greasy.

ABOVE: Spaghetti with chilli calamari

3 Add the prawns and cook for 5 minutes, or until the prawns are browned. Stir in the salsa and cream and bring to the boil. Reduce the heat and simmer for 3–5 minutes, or until the sauce thickens slightly. Divide the pasta among four plates, top with sauce and garnish with parsley.

NUTRITION PER SERVE: *Protein 55 g; Fat 40 g; Carbohydrate 95 g; Dietary Fibre 8 g; Cholesterol 385 mg; 4105 kJ (975 cal)*

FRAGRANT HERB TAGLIATELLE WITH KAFFIR LIME AND PRAWNS

Preparation time: 1½ hours + 1 hour drying
Total cooking time: 12–15 minutes
Serves 4

⭐ ⭐ ⭐

Tagliatelle

2 cups (250 g/8 oz) plain flour, sifted, plus
   extra flour
¼ cup (15 g/½ oz) parsley, minced or very
   finely chopped
3 teaspoons herb-flavoured oil
3 teaspoons pure lime oil
1 teaspoon salt
3 eggs, beaten

Sauce

20 g (¾ oz) butter
1 onion, chopped
1 teaspoon grated fresh ginger
½ cup (125 ml/3½ fl oz) fish sauce
⅓ cup (90 ml/3 fl oz) sweet chilli sauce
juice and rind of 1 lime
6 kaffir lime leaves, roughly chopped
1¾ cups (440 ml/14 fl oz) coconut milk
1 kg (2 lb) raw king prawns, peeled
   and deveined, leaving tails intact
½ cup (125 ml/4 fl oz) cream

1 To make the tagliatelle, mix the flour, parsley, oils, salt and eggs in a food processor for 2–3 minutes, or until the mixture forms a soft dough. It will not form a ball, but will come together. Transfer to a lightly floured cutting board and cut into three or four equal pieces, using a floured knife. Cover with a damp cloth.
2 Adjust the rollers of the pasta machine to fully open. Lightly flour one piece of dough and pass it through the rollers to a lightly floured surface.

SPICY PRAWN MEXICANA

Preparation time: 20 minutes
Total cooking time: 15 minutes
Serves 4

⭐

500 g (1 lb) rigatoni
1 tablespoon oil
2 cloves garlic, crushed
2 red chillies, finely chopped
3 spring onions, sliced
750 g (1½ lb) raw prawns, peeled
   and deveined
300 g (10 oz) hot bottled salsa
1½ cups (375 ml/12 fl oz) cream
2 tablespoons chopped fresh parsley

1 Cook the rigatoni in a large pan of rapidly boiling salted water until *al dente*. Drain.
2 Heat the oil, add the garlic, chilli and spring onion and cook over medium heat for 2 minutes, or until the garlic is soft and golden.

ABOVE: Spicy prawn mexicana

KAFFIR LIME LEAVES
The kaffir lime tree has dark green fruit with a hard, knobbly rind, and distinctive leaves that look like two smaller leaves joined end to end. The rind and juice of the fruit is strong in both aroma and taste and is used in Asian soups and curries. The fresh leaves, which should not be replaced by those from a standard lime tree, are used whole to flavour curries, and shredded in salads. They can be bought from Asian food stores and the whole leaves freeze well if stored in airtight bags. Dried leaves are available, but can only be used in cooked dishes.

Fold the dough into thirds, turn the dough by 90 degrees and feed through again. Lightly dust with flour so that the dough does not stick to the rollers. This process kneads the dough and must be repeated about ten times. Gradually decrease the width of the dough by adjusting the notches. This is a thinning process and the dough should not be folded. Each time you pass the dough through, tighten a notch until it has reached the third narrowest setting (the narrowest is too thin). You may want to cut the thinned pasta strip in half as you reach notch 3 or 4. If the pasta strip gets too long, it is hard to handle.

3 Trim rough edges of the pasta sheets and cut the sheets into tagliatelle with cutters. Hang the pasta up to dry, over a clean stick, supported by the backs of two chairs, for 10–15 minutes. (Be careful not to leave it too long or in a draught, or it will dry out and crack.) Place in loosely coiled piles and dust well with flour. Leave on a floured tea towel to dry for at least 1 hour.

4 Add 1 teaspoon each of lime oil, olive oil and salt to a large pan of water. Bring to the boil, add the tagliatelle and cook until *al dente*. Drain and keep warm.

5 To make the sauce, melt the butter in heavy-based pan, add the onion and cook over medium heat until tender. Add the ginger, fish sauce, sweet chilli sauce, lime juice and rind, and kaffir lime leaves. Cook for 1–2 minutes. Stir in the coconut milk and simmer over low heat for 10 minutes.

6 Add the prawns and cream. Simmer for another 3–4 minutes, being careful not to overcook the prawns or they will become tough.

7 To serve, divide the tagliatelle among warmed plates and spoon the sauce over the top.

NOTE: Fragrant herb oil can be made by mincing ½ cup (30 g/1 oz) basil leaves and ½ cup (15 g/½ oz) parsley leaves in a food processor. Add to ½ cup (125 ml/4 fl oz) of extra virgin olive oil and simmer very gently for 2 minutes. Cool and strain. As an alternative to lime oil, use 3 teaspoons of olive oil with 2 teaspoons of finely grated lime rind.

NUTRITION PER SERVE: *Protein 70 g; Fat 50 g; Carbohydrate 70 g; Dietary Fibre 4 g; Cholesterol 555 mg; 4245 kJ (1010 cal)*

ABOVE: Fragrant herb tagliatelle with kaffir lime and prawns

RED CAVIAR
The roe of various members of the sturgeon family is known as caviar. There are different qualities, depending on the fish from which the roe is extracted, and the colour can be black, dark brown, grey, golden or salmon. What is known as red caviar is actually a pale orange. The eggs should be glossy and firm, and taste neither too salty nor too fishy.

BELOW: Fettucine with caviar

FETTUCINE WITH CAVIAR

Preparation time: 15 minutes
Total cooking time: 15 minutes
Serves 4

2 hard-boiled eggs
4 spring onions
1 cup (150 g/5 oz) light sour cream
50 g (1 3/4 oz) red caviar
2 tablespoons chopped fresh dill
1 tablespoon lemon juice
500 g (1 lb) fettucine

1 Peel the eggs and chop into small pieces. Trim the spring onions, discarding the dark green tops, and chop finely.
2 In a small bowl, mix the sour cream, egg, spring onion, caviar, dill, lemon juice and pepper, to taste. Set aside.

3 Cook the fettucine in a large pan of rapidly boiling salted water until *al dente*. Drain and return to the pan.
4 Toss the caviar mixture through the hot pasta. Serve garnished with a sprig of fresh dill, if desired.
NOTE: Use large red roe, not the small supermarket variety.

NUTRITION PER SERVE: *Protein 20 g; Fat 15 g; Carbohydrate 90 g; Dietary Fibre 5 g; Cholesterol 165 mg; 2950 kJ (700 cal)*

FRAGRANT SEAFOOD PASTA

Preparation time: 30 minutes
Total cooking time: 20 minutes
Serves 4

500 g (1 lb) conchiglie (shell pasta)
2–3 tablespoons light olive oil
4 spring onions, finely sliced
1 small chilli, finely chopped
500 g (1 lb) raw prawns, peeled and deveined, tails intact
250 g (8 oz) scallops, halved
1/4 cup (15 g/1/2 oz) chopped fresh coriander
1/4 cup (60 ml/2 fl oz) lime juice
2 tablespoons sweet chilli sauce
1 tablespoon fish sauce
1 tablespoon sesame oil
shredded lime rind, to garnish

1 Cook the conchiglie in a large pan of rapidly boiling salted water until *al dente*.
2 While the pasta is cooking, heat the oil in a pan and add the spring onion, chilli, prawns and scallops. Stir constantly over medium heat until the prawns turn pink and the scallops are lightly cooked. Remove from the heat immediately. Stir in the coriander, lime juice, chilli sauce and fish sauce.
3 Drain the pasta and return to the pan. Toss the sesame oil through, add the prawn mixture and mix gently to combine. Serve the pasta garnished with lime rind, if desired.

NUTRITION PER SERVE: *Protein 45 g; Fat 40 g; Carbohydrate 90 g; Dietary Fibre 5 g; Cholesterol 260 mg; 3885 kJ (925 cal)*

CHILLI SEAFOOD IN TOMATO SAUCE

Preparation time: 25 minutes
Total cooking time: 30 minutes
Serves 4

★

8 fresh mussels

1 teaspoon olive oil

1 large onion, chopped

3 cloves garlic, finely chopped

2 small red chillies, seeded and finely
   chopped

820 g (1 lb 13 oz) can tomatoes

2 tablespoons tomato paste (tomato purée,
   double concentrate)

1/2 teaspoon cracked black pepper

1/2 cup (125 ml/4 fl oz) vegetable stock

2 tablespoons Pernod

650 g (1 lb 5 oz) marinara mix

2 tablespoons chopped fresh flat-leaf parsley

1 tablespoon chopped fresh dill

350 g (11 oz) bucatini

1 Remove the beards from the mussels and
scrub away any grit.
2 Heat the oil in a large pan. Add the onion,
garlic and chilli and cook for 1—2 minutes.
Stir in the tomato, tomato paste, pepper, stock
and Pernod. Reduce the heat and simmer for
8—10 minutes. Remove the sauce from the heat
and cool slightly. Transfer to a food processor
and process until smooth.

3 Return the tomato mixture to the pan, add
the marinara mix and simmer for 4 minutes.
Add the mussels and herbs to the pan and
simmer for another 1—2 minutes, or until the
mussels have opened. Discard any mussels that
do not open.
4 Meanwhile, cook the pasta in a large pan
of rapidly boiling water until *al dente*; drain
thoroughly. Divide the pasta among 4 serving
bowls and spoon the sauce over the top.
NOTE: Marinara mix is a combination of
uncooked seafood available from fish shops. It
usually contains scallops, prawns, mussels and
calamari rings. You can use just one favourite
type of seafood, such as prawns or calamari.

NUTRITION PER SERVE: *Protein 45 g; Fat 5 g;
Carbohydrate 80 g; Dietary Fibre 10 g; Cholesterol 265 mg;
2380 kJ (570 cal)*

*ABOVE: Fragrant
seafood pasta
BELOW: Chilli seafood
in tomato sauce*

2 While the pasta is cooking, heat 2 tablespoons of olive oil in a heavy-based pan and cook the garlic and chilli for 1 minute over low heat. Add the chopped tomato with any juices, and the sugar. Stir gently over low heat for 5 minutes, or until the tomato is just warmed through.

3 Add the salmon and basil and season with salt and pepper, to taste. Toss the sauce through the pasta before serving.

NUTRITION PER SERVE: *Protein 25 g; Fat 10 g; Carbohydrate 60 g; Dietary Fibre 5 g; Cholesterol 55 mg; 1930 kJ (460 cal)*

SPAGHETTINI WITH ROASTED SALMON AND GARLIC

Preparation time: 10 minutes
Total cooking time: 20 minutes
Serves 4– 6

4 small fillets fresh baby salmon, about
    100 g (3 1/2 oz) each
4– 5 tablespoons extra virgin olive oil
8– 10 cloves garlic, peeled
300 g (10 oz) dry spaghettini
50 g (1 3/4 oz) thinly sliced fennel
1 1/2 teaspoons finely grated lime rind
2 tablespoons lime juice
4 sprigs fennel fronds, to garnish

1 Preheat the oven to hot 220°C (425°F/Gas 7) and oil a ceramic baking dish. Brush the salmon fillets with 2 tablespoons of the olive oil, salt lightly and position in a single layer in the dish.

2 Slice the garlic cloves lengthways and spread them all over the salmon fillets. Brush lightly with olive oil. Bake for 10– 15 minutes, or until the salmon is cooked through.

3 Meanwhile, cook the spaghettini in a large pan of rapidly boiling salted water until *al dente*. Drain and stir through enough extra virgin olive oil to make it glisten. Toss the fennel and lime rind through the pasta and arrange on warmed serving plates.

4 Top each serving with a salmon fillet then spoon the pan juices over them, with any stray slices of garlic. Drizzle with lime juice. Garnish with fennel fronds and serve accompanied by a plain tomato salad.

NUTRITION PER SERVE (6): *Protein 30 g; Fat 30 g; Carbohydrate 55 g; Dietary Fibre 5 g; Cholesterol 70 mg; 2640 kJ (630 cal)*

PAPPARDELLE

Pappardelle are long flat noodles, similar to fettucine but a lot wider at around 30 mm (1 1/4 inches). They are excellent for sauces that are strong, rich or heavy and ideal with game and offal. Sometimes one or both sides are crimped, causing confusion with lasagnette, which is only half the width. One can be substituted for the other in most recipes.

ABOVE: Pappardelle with salmon

PAPPARDELLE WITH SALMON

Preparation time: 15 minutes
Total cooking time: 25 minutes
Serves 6

500 g (1 lb) pappardelle
2 cloves garlic, finely chopped
1 teaspoon chopped fresh chilli
500 g (1 lb) very ripe tomatoes, chopped
1 teaspoon soft brown sugar
425 g (14 oz) can pink salmon, drained
    and flaked
1/2 cup (30g/1 oz) fresh basil leaves, chopped

1 Cook the pappardelle in a large pan of rapidly boiling salted water until *al dente*. Drain and return to the pan.

TAGLIATELLE WITH OCTOPUS

Preparation time: 30 minutes
Total cooking time: 25 minutes
Serves 4

500 g (1 lb) mixed tagliatelle

1 kg (2 lb) baby octopus

2 tablespoons olive oil

1 onion, sliced

1 clove garlic, crushed

425 g (14 oz) can tomato purée (passata)

1/2 cup (125 ml/4 fl oz) dry white wine

1 tablespoon bottled chilli sauce

1 tablespoon chopped fresh basil

1 Cook the tagliatelle in a large pan of rapidly boiling salted water until *al dente*. Drain and return to the pan.

2 Clean the octopus by using a small sharp knife to remove the gut—either cut off the head entirely or slice open the head and remove the gut. Pick up the body and use your index finger to push the beak up. Remove the beak and discard. Clean the octopus thoroughly, pat dry and, if you prefer, cut in half. Set aside.

3 While the pasta is cooking, heat the oil in a large frying pan. Add the onion and garlic and stir over low heat until the onion is tender. Add the tomato purée, wine, chilli sauce, basil, and salt and pepper, to taste, to the pan. Bring to the boil, reduce the heat and simmer for 10 minutes.

4 Add the octopus to the pan and simmer for 5–10 minutes, or until tender. Serve over the pasta.

NUTRITION PER SERVE: *Protein 50 g; Fat 15 g; Carbohydrate 95 g; Dietary Fibre 10 g; Cholesterol 00 mg; 3130 kJ (750 cal)*

ABOVE: Tagliatelle with octopus

TOMATO PASTA WITH SMOKED COD AND SESAME

Preparation time: 25 minutes
Total cooking time: 10 minutes
Serves 4

320 g (11 oz) smoked cod or other fresh
   smoked large fish, e.g. haddock
1/2 cup (125 ml/4 fl oz) milk
400 g (13 oz) tomato casereccie
1 carrot
4 tablespoons peanut oil
1 small onion, sliced
150 g (5 oz) bean sprouts
1 1/2 teaspoons soy sauce
1 teaspoon sesame oil
1 tablespoon sesame seeds, toasted

1 Put the fish in a pan with the milk, add enough water to cover, and poach for 5 minutes, or until tender. Rinse under cold water to cool and to remove milk scum. Break the fish into large flakes, discarding the skin and bones. Set aside.
2 Cook the pasta in a large pan of rapidly boiling salted water until *al dente*. Drain.
3 Thinly slice the carrot diagonally. Heat 3 tablespoons of the peanut oil in a large frying pan or wok and toss the carrot and onion until cooked but still crisp. Stir in the bean sprouts, soy sauce and sesame oil. Season, to taste, with salt and freshly ground black pepper.
4 Add the pasta to the pan with the sesame seeds, prepared fish and the remaining 1 tablespoon peanut oil. Lightly toss and serve immediately.

NUTRITION PER SERVE: *Protein 30 g; Fat 25 g; Carbohydrate 75 g; Dietary Fibre 8 g; Cholesterol 45 mg; 2725 kJ (650 cal)*

TROUT, FETTUCINE AND FENNEL FRITTATA

Preparation time: 20 minutes
Total cooking time: 1 hour
Serves 4

250 g (8 oz) whole smoked trout
200 g (6 1/2 oz) dried fettucine
1 cup (250 ml/8 fl oz) milk
1/2 cup (125 ml/4 fl oz) cream
4 eggs
pinch of nutmeg
40 g (1 1/4 oz) finely sliced fennel, plus fennel
   greens for garnish
4 spring onions, sliced
2/3 cup (85 g/3 oz) grated Cheddar cheese

1 Preheat the oven to moderate 180°C (350°F/Gas 4). Lightly brush a 23 cm (9 inch) ovenproof frying pan or flan dish with oil. Remove and discard the skin and bones from the trout.
2 Cook the fettucine in a large pan of rapidly boiling salted water until *al dente*. Drain.
3 Combine the milk, cream, eggs and nutmeg in a large bowl and whisk until smooth. Season with salt and pepper, to taste. Add the trout, fettucine, fennel and spring onion and toss to distribute evenly. Pour into the prepared dish, sprinkle with the cheese and bake until set, about 1 hour. Garnish with 2– 3 sprigs of fennel greens and serve.

NUTRITION PER SERVE: *Protein 25 g; Fat 20 g; Carbohydrate 25 g; Dietary Fibre 2 g; Cholesterol 195 mg; 1615 kJ (385 cal)*

ON THE SIDE

TABOULI Soak 3/4 cup (130 g/4 1/4 oz) of burghul in 3/4 cup (185 ml/6 fl oz) of water for about 15 minutes, or until the water has been absorbed. Finely chop the leaves from 2 bunches (300 g/10 oz) of flat-leaf parsley and combine with 1/2 cup (25 g/3/4 oz) of chopped fresh mint, 3 chopped vine-ripened tomatoes and 4 finely chopped spring onions. Make a dressing by thoroughly combining 3 crushed cloves of garlic, 1/3 cup (80 ml/2 3/4 fl oz) of lemon juice and 1/4 cup (60 ml/2 fl oz) of olive oil. Pour the dressing over the salad and toss well to combine.

FENNEL
Bulb fennel has an unmistakable aniseed flavour and a crunchy texture. Uncooked and sliced, it is used in salads and as antipasto. Cooked, it braises well and is a good companion to seafood and pork. Look for crisp bulbs that are fully formed with many stalks. The white inner stalks are used as well as the leaves, which are very good chopped and sprinkled on salads and fish, or as a flavouring in seafood sauces. Dried fennel seeds are important in spice mixtures and are used to flavour a diverse range of foods, from bread to salami.

OPPOSITE PAGE: Tomato pasta with smoked cod and sesame (top); Trout, fettucine and fennel frittata

SCALLOPS

Scallops are one of the molluscs that are cooked for eating. Out of the shell they may be poached, sautéed or baked; in the half shell they are lightly grilled, and often with a minimum of flavourings. Scallops are complemented well by milk, butter and cream, and are often put with white wine. The cooking time should be brief to avoid the flesh becoming rubbery.

ABOVE: Creamy seafood ravioli

CREAMY SEAFOOD RAVIOLI

Preparation time: 1 hour
  + 30 minutes standing
Total cooking time: 30 minutes
Serves 4

☆

Pasta

2 cups (250 g/8 oz) plain flour
3 eggs
1 tablespoon olive oil
1 egg yolk, extra

Filling

50 g (1³/₄ oz) butter, softened
3 cloves garlic, finely chopped
2 tablespoons finely chopped flat-leaf parsley
100 g (3¹/₂ oz) scallops, cleaned and
  finely chopped
100 g (3¹/₂ oz) raw prawn meat, finely chopped

Sauce

75 g (2¹/₂ oz) butter
3 tablespoons plain flour
1¹/₂ cups (375 ml/12 fl oz) milk
300 ml (10 fl oz) cream
¹/₂ cup (125 ml/4 fl oz) white wine
¹/₂ cup (50 g/1³/₄ oz) grated Parmesan
2 tablespoons chopped flat-leaf parsley

1 To make the pasta, sift the flour and a pinch of salt into a bowl and make a well in the centre. Whisk the eggs, oil and 1 tablespoon water in a jug, then add gradually to the flour and mix to a firm dough. Gather into a ball.
2 Knead on a lightly floured surface for 5 minutes, or until smooth and elastic. Transfer to a lightly oiled bowl, cover with plastic wrap and set aside for 30 minutes.
3 To make the filling, mix together the softened butter, chopped garlic, parsley, scallops and prawn meat. Set aside.

4 Roll out a quarter of the pasta dough at a time until very thin (each portion of dough should be roughly 10 cm/4 inches wide when rolled). Place 1 teaspoonful of filling at 5 cm (2 inch) intervals down one side of each strip. Whisk the extra egg yolk with 3 tablespoons water. Brush along one side of the dough and between the filling. Fold the dough over the filling to meet the other side. Repeat with the remaining filling and dough. Press the edges of the dough together firmly to seal.

5 Cut between the mounds with a knife or a fluted pastry cutter. Cook, in batches, in a large pan of rapidly boiling salted water for 6 minutes each batch (while the pasta is cooking make the sauce). Drain well and return to the pan to keep warm.

6 To make the sauce, melt the butter in a pan, add the flour and cook over low heat for 2 minutes. Remove from the heat and gradually stir in the combined milk, cream and wine. Cook over low heat until the sauce begins to thicken, stirring constantly to prevent lumps forming. Bring to the boil and simmer gently for 5 minutes. Add the Parmesan and parsley and stir until combined. Remove from the heat, add to the ravioli and toss well.

NOTE: The pasta dough is set aside for 30 minutes to let the gluten in the flour relax. If you don't do this, you run the risk of making tough pasta.

NUTRITION PER SERVE: *Protein 30 g; Fat 70 g; Carbohydrate 60 g; Dietary Fibre 5 g; Cholesterol 430 mg; 4255 kJ (1020 cal)*

MUSSELS WITH TOMATO SAUCE

Preparation time: 20 minutes
Total cooking time: 20 minutes
Serves 4

500 g (1 lb) penne or rigatoni
1 tablespoon olive oil
1 small onion, finely chopped
1 clove garlic, chopped
1 large carrot, diced
1 stick celery, diced
3 tablespoons chopped fresh parsley
800 ml (24 fl oz) tomato pasta sauce
1/2 cup (125 ml/4 fl oz) white wine
375 g (12 oz) tub marinated green mussels
1/4 cup (60 ml/2 fl oz) cream, optional

1 Cook the pasta in a large pan of rapidly boiling salted water until *al dente*. Drain and return to the pan.

2 Heat the oil in a pan and add the onion, garlic, carrot and celery. Cook until the vegetables are tender and add the parsley, tomato pasta sauce and wine. Simmer, stirring occasionally, for 15 minutes.

3 Drain the mussels, add to the sauce with the cream, if using, and stir to combine. Add to the pasta and stir to combine.

NOTE: If you can't buy bottled tomato pasta sauce, use canned crushed tomatoes.

NUTRITION PER SERVE: *Protein 35 g; Fat 25 g; Carbohydrate 100 g; Dietary Fibre 10 g; Cholesterol 105 mg; 3280 kJ (780 cal)*

ABOVE: Mussels with tomato sauce

SPAGHETTI

Spaghetti arrived in Italy via Sicily, where it was introduced by the Arabs after they invaded in 827 A.D. Being great wanderers and traders, they needed their pasta in a form that could be stored and easily transported and so their preference for dried spaghetti was passed on. Known then as *itriyah* (Persian for string), it developed into *tria* and then *trii*, a form of spaghetti still popular in Sicily and parts of southern Italy.

BELOW: Spaghetti with creamy garlic mussels

SPAGHETTI WITH CREAMY GARLIC MUSSELS

Preparation time: 20 minutes
Total cooking time: 10–15 minutes
Serves 4

500 g (1 lb) spaghetti
1.5 kg (3 lb) fresh mussels
2 tablespoons olive oil
2 cloves garlic, crushed
1/2 cup (125 ml/4 fl oz) white wine
1 cup (250 ml/8 fl oz) cream
2 tablespoons chopped fresh basil

1 Cook the spaghetti in a large pan of rapidly boiling salted water until *al dente*. Drain.
2 While the spaghetti is cooking, remove the beards from the mussels and scrub away any grit. Discard any open mussels. Set aside. Heat the oil in a large pan. Add the garlic and stir over low heat for 30 seconds.

3 Add the wine and mussels. Simmer, covered, for 5 minutes. Remove the mussels, discarding any that don't open, and set aside.
4 Add the cream, basil and salt and pepper, to taste, to the pan. Simmer for 2 minutes, stirring occasionally. Serve the sauce and mussels over the spaghetti.

NUTRITION PER SERVE: *Protein 80 g; Fat 40 g; Carbohydrate 90 g; Dietary Fibre 7 g; Cholesterol 445 mg; 4510 kJ (1075 cal)*

ON THE SIDE

ROASTED VEGETABLE AND BRIE SALAD Roast 300 g (10 oz) each of peeled and halved potatoes, parsnips, sweet potato and baby carrots and onions in oil until crisp and tender. While still hot, drizzle with a dressing made by whisking together 2 tablespoons of orange juice, 1 teaspoon of horseradish cream and 2 tablespoons of oil. Serve warm, topped with 200 g (6 1/2 oz) of sliced Brie cheese and plenty of cracked black pepper.

SUN-DRIED TOMATOES
These preserved tomatoes are available dry, loosely packed, or in jars. They are useful in pasta dishes and salads or on top of pizzas. The flavour is intense and sweet. Some come packed in olive or canola oil and need to be drained. Others are available dry and must be soaked in boiling water for 5 minutes before use. Sun-dried tomatoes combine well with cheese, salad greens, olives, seafood, chicken and meat.

FETTUCINE WITH SMOKED SALMON

Preparation time: 10 minutes
Total cooking time: 10–15 minutes
Serves 4

100 g (3½ oz) smoked salmon

¼ cup (35 g/1¼ oz) sun-dried tomatoes

1 tablespoon olive oil

1 clove garlic, crushed

1 cup (250 ml/8 fl oz) cream

¼ cup (15 g/½ oz) snipped fresh chives, plus extra, to garnish

¼ teaspoon mustard powder

2 teaspoons lemon juice

375 g (12 oz) fettucine

2 tablespoons freshly grated Parmesan, for serving

1 Cut the smoked salmon into bite-sized pieces and the sun-dried tomatoes into small pieces.
2 Heat the olive oil in a frying pan, add the garlic and stir over low heat for 30 seconds. Add the cream, chives, mustard powder, and salt and pepper, to taste. Bring to the boil, reduce the heat and simmer, stirring, until the sauce begins to thicken.
3 Add the salmon and lemon juice to the pan and stir to combine. Heat gently.
4 While the sauce is cooking, cook the fettucine in a large pan of rapidly boiling salted water until *al dente*. Drain well and return to the pan. Toss the sauce through the hot pasta. Serve immediately topped with the sun-dried tomato, Parmesan and chives.

NUTRITION PER SERVE: *Protein 20 g; Fat 30 g; Carbohydrate 70 g; Dietary Fibre 5 g; Cholesterol 90 mg; 2685 kJ (640 cal)*

ABOVE: Fettucine with smoked salmon

CLAMS

Long thought of as the poor relative in the mollusc family, clams are used for their succulent flesh and mild flavour. When bought live in the shells, they are eaten raw or lightly cooked. Shelled, they are preserved in cans or bottles and in this form the flesh is used in sauces and stews. Jars of cooked clams still in their shell are also available, and are an excellent alternative to preparing clams from scratch. The juice in which clams are preserved makes a lightly flavoured seafood stock, good for use in soups and sauces.

ABOVE: Spaghetti vongole

SPAGHETTI VONGOLE
(SPAGHETTI WITH CLAM SAUCE)

Preparation time: 25 minutes + soaking
Total cooking time: 20– 35 minutes
Serves 4

1 kg (2 lb) fresh small clams in shells or
  750 g (1 1/2 lb) can clams in brine
1 tablespoon lemon juice
1/3 cup (80 ml/2 3/4 fl oz) olive oil
3 cloves garlic, crushed
2 x 425 g (14 oz) cans crushed tomatoes
250 g (8 oz) spaghetti
4 tablespoons chopped fresh parsley

1 If using fresh clams, clean thoroughly (see Note). Place in a large pan with the lemon juice. Cover the pan and shake over medium heat for 7– 8 minutes until the shells open, discarding any that don't open. Remove the clam flesh from the shell of the opened clams and set aside; discard the empty shells. If using canned clams, drain, rinse well and set aside.

2 Heat the oil in a large pan. Add the garlic and cook over low heat for 5 minutes. Add the tomato and stir to combine. Bring to the boil and simmer, covered, for 20 minutes. Add freshly ground black pepper, to taste, and the clams, and stir until heated through.

3 While the sauce is cooking, cook the spaghetti in a large pan of rapidly boiling salted water until *al dente*. Drain and return to the pan. Gently stir in the sauce and the chopped parsley until combined. Serve immediately in a warm dish. Caperberries and a slice of lemon peel make an attractive garnish for special occasions.

NOTE: To clean the clams, any sand and grit needs to be drawn out of the shells. Combine 2 tablespoons each of salt and plain flour with enough water to make a paste. Add to a large bucket or bowl of cold water and soak the clams in this mixture overnight. Drain and scrub the shells well, then rinse thoroughly and drain again.

NUTRITION PER SERVE: *Protein 35 g; Fat 25 g; Carbohydrate 55 g; Dietary Fibre 7 g; Cholesterol 355 mg; 2420 kJ (580 cal)*

SPAGHETTI AND MUSSELS IN TOMATO AND HERB SAUCE

Preparation time: 15 minutes
Total cooking time: 30 minutes
Serves 4

1.5 kg (3 lb) fresh mussels
2 tablespoons olive oil
1 onion, finely sliced
2 cloves garlic, crushed
425 g (14 oz) can crushed tomatoes
1 cup (250 ml/8 fl oz) white wine
1 tablespoon chopped fresh basil
2 tablespoons chopped fresh parsley
500 g (1 lb) spaghetti

1 Remove the beards from the mussels and scrub away any grit. Discard any open mussels.
2 Heat the olive oil in a large pan. Add the onion and garlic and stir over low heat until the onion is tender. Add the tomato, white wine, fresh basil and parsley, and salt and pepper, to taste. Bring the sauce to the boil, reduce the heat and simmer for 15– 20 minutes, or until the sauce begins to thicken.
3 Add the prepared mussels to the pan and cook, covered, for 5 minutes, shaking the pan occasionally. Be sure to discard any mussels that don't open.
4 While the sauce is cooking, add the spaghetti to a large pan of rapidly boiling salted water and cook until *al dente*. Drain. Serve the mussels and sauce over the pasta.

NUTRITION PER SERVE: *Protein 50 g; Fat 15 g; Carbohydrate 95 g; Dietary Fibre 10 g; Cholesterol 190 mg; 3050 kJ (730 cal)*

ON THE SIDE

POTATO, EGG AND BACON SALAD Boil, steam or microwave 1 kg (2 lb) of whole baby potatoes. Fry 4 sliced rashers of bacon until crisp; drain on paper towels. Peel and quarter 6 hard-boiled eggs and combine with the warm potatoes, 4 sliced spring onions and 2 tablespoons each of chopped fresh mint and chives. Fold through 1 cup (250 g/8 oz) of natural yoghurt and top with the crisp bacon.

GREMOLATA
It is not usual to serve grated cheese with seafood pasta sauces, but for those who can't resist sprinkling a little something on top, there is an alternative! Mix the grated rind of half a lemon, with a finely chopped clove of garlic and about a cup of loosely packed chopped fresh parsley. Adjust the proportions to suit your tastes. Called gremolata or gremolada, this mix was traditionally used to accompany osso buco.

ABOVE: Spaghetti and mussels in tomato and herb sauce

PASTA WITH VEGETABLES

The key to great food is freshness. While the Italian cook makes good use of pantry staples such as canned tomatoes and olive oil, it is the fresh vegetables and herbs which lift the dishes into the sublime. Herbs are generally used fresh, often gathered from the surrounding area in great basketfuls. Tomatoes, peppers and artichokes ripen under the Mediterranean sun and, tossed together with a bowl of pasta, are as colourful and delicious as they are good for you.

ZUCCHINI

Zucchini or courgettes are Italian summer squash. Green or yellow in colour, they should be harvested within 4–6 days of flowering to give a tender rind and crisp flesh. If they are too old or too big, the flesh tends to be bitter. Zucchini require little preparation and short cooking time. They can be steamed, boiled, sautéed, baked or deep-fried, and larger ones can be stuffed and baked.

ABOVE: Fettucine with zucchini and crisp-fried basil

FETTUCINE WITH ZUCCHINI (COURGETTES) AND CRISP-FRIED BASIL

Preparation time: 15 minutes
Total cooking time: 15 minutes
Serves 6

1 cup (250 ml/8 fl oz) olive oil
a handful of fresh basil leaves
500 g (1 lb) fettucine or tagliatelle
60 g (2 oz) butter
2 cloves garlic, crushed
500 g (1 lb) zucchini (courgettes), grated
3/4 cup (75 g/2 1/2 oz) freshly grated Parmesan

1 To crisp-fry the basil leaves, heat the oil in a small pan, add 2 leaves at a time and cook for 1 minute, or until crisp. Remove with a slotted spoon and drain on paper towels. Repeat with the remaining basil leaves.
2 Cook the pasta in a large pan of rapidly boiling salted water until *al dente*. Drain and return to the pan.
3 While the pasta is cooking, heat the butter in a deep heavy-based pan over low heat until the butter is foaming. Add the garlic and cook for 1 minute. Add the zucchini and cook, stirring occasionally, for 1–2 minutes or until softened. Add to the hot pasta. Add the Parmesan and toss well. Serve the pasta garnished with the crisp basil leaves.
NOTE: The basil leaves can be fried up to 2 hours in advance. Store in an airtight container after cooling.

NUTRITION PER SERVE: *Protein 15 g; Fat 55 g; Carbohydrate 60 g; Dietary Fibre 5 g; Cholesterol 35 mg; 3245 kJ (775 cal)*

OLIVE AND MOZZARELLA SPAGHETTI

Preparation time: 20 minutes
Total cooking time: 15 minutes
Serves 4

500 g (1 lb) spaghetti
50 g (1 3/4 oz) butter
2 cloves garlic, crushed
1/2 cup (70 g/2 1/4 oz) pitted black olives, halved
3 tablespoons olive oil
1/3 cup (20 g/3/4 oz) chopped fresh parsley
150 g (5 oz) mozzarella cheese, cut into small cubes

1 Cook the spaghetti in a large pan of rapidly boiling salted water until *al dente*. Drain and return to the pan.

2 While the spaghetti is cooking, heat the butter in a small pan until it begins to turn nutty brown. Add the crushed garlic and cook over low heat for 1 minute.

3 Add to the pasta with the black olives, olive oil, fresh parsley and mozzarella cheese. Toss until well combined.

NUTRITION PER SERVE: *Protein 25 g; Fat 35 g; Carbohydrate 90 g; Dietary Fibre 5 g; Cholesterol 55 mg; 3320 kJ (770cal)*

FARFALLE WITH ARTICHOKE HEARTS AND OLIVES

Preparation time: 20 minutes
Total cooking time: 20 minutes
Serves 4

500 g (1 lb) farfalle
400 g (13 oz) marinated
    artichoke hearts
3 tablespoons olive oil
3 cloves garlic, crushed
1/2 cup (95 g/3 oz) pitted black
    olives, chopped
2 tablespoons chopped fresh chives
200 g (6 1/2 oz) fresh ricotta cheese

1 Cook the farfalle in a large pan of rapidly boiling salted water until *al dente*. Drain and return to the pan.

2 While the pasta is cooking, drain and thinly slice the artichoke hearts. Heat the olive oil in a large frying pan. Add the garlic and cook over low heat until softened, but don't let the garlic burn or brown or it will become bitter.

3 Add the artichoke hearts and olives to the pan and stir until heated through. Add the chives and ricotta, breaking up the ricotta with a spoon. Cook until the ricotta is heated through.

4 Combine the sauce with the pasta. Season with salt and freshly ground black pepper and serve immediately.

NOTE: This dish is wonderful made with fresh cooked artichoke hearts. Use 5 artichoke hearts and follow the recipe as above.

NUTRITION PER SERVE: *Protein 15 g; Fat 15 g; Carbohydrate 60 g; Dietary Fibre 5 g; Cholesterol 15 mg; 1840 kJ (440 cal)*

ABOVE: Olive and mozzarella spaghetti (left); Farfalle with artichoke hearts and olives

SUN-DRIED TOMATO SAUCE ON TAGLIATELLE

Preparation time: 20 minutes
Total cooking time: 20 minutes
Serves 4

500 g (1 lb) tagliatelle
2 tablespoons olive oil
1 onion, chopped
1/2 cup (80 g/2 3/4 oz) thinly sliced
   sun-dried tomatoes
2 cloves garlic, crushed
425 g (14 oz) can chopped tomatoes
1 cup (125 g/4 oz) pitted black olives
1/3 cup (20 g/3/4 oz) chopped fresh basil
freshly grated Parmesan, for serving

1 Cook the tagliatelle in a large pan of rapidly boiling salted water until *al dente*. Drain and return to the pan.
2 Meanwhile, heat the oil in a large frying pan. Add the onion and cook for 3 minutes, stirring occasionally, until soft. Add the sliced sun-dried tomato along with the crushed garlic and cook for another minute.
3 Add the chopped tomato, olives and basil to the pan and season with freshly ground black pepper. Bring to the boil, reduce the heat, and simmer for 10 minutes.
4 Add the sauce to the hot pasta and gently toss through. Serve immediately, topped with some Parmesan.
NOTE: Sun-dried tomatoes are available either dry or loosely packed, or in jars with olive or canola oil. The tomatoes in oil need only to be drained, but the dry tomatoes must be soaked in boiling water for 5 minutes to rehydrate and soften before using.

NUTRITION PER SERVE: *Protein 20 g; Fat 15 g; Carbohydrate 95 g; Dietary Fibre 10 g; Cholesterol 5 mg; 2415 kJ (575 cal)*

CREAMY ASPARAGUS LINGUINE

Preparation time: 15 minutes
Total cooking time: 15 minutes
Serves 4

200 g (6 1/2 oz) fresh full-fat ricotta cheese
1 cup (250 ml/8 fl oz) cream
3/4 cup (75 g/2 1/2 oz) freshly grated Parmesan
freshly ground nutmeg, to taste
500 g (1 lb) linguine
500 g (1 lb) fresh asparagus spears, cut into
   short lengths
1/2 cup (45 g/1 1/2 oz) toasted flaked almonds,
   for serving

1 Put the ricotta in a bowl and stir until smooth. Stir in the cream, Parmesan and nutmeg and season with salt and freshly ground black pepper, to taste.
2 Cook the linguine in a large pan of rapidly boiling salted water until not quite tender. Add the asparagus to the pan and cook for another 3 minutes.
3 Drain the pasta and asparagus, reserving 2 tablespoons of the cooking water. Return the pasta and asparagus to the pan.
4 Add the reserved cooking water to the ricotta mixture, stirring well to combine. Spoon the mixture over the pasta and toss gently. Serve sprinkled with the toasted almonds.
NOTE: To toast flaked almonds, you can heat them under a moderately hot grill for about 2 minutes. Stir them occasionally and be careful to avoid burning them.

NUTRITION PER SERVE: *Protein 35 g; Fat 45 g; Carbohydrate 90 g; Dietary Fibre 10 g; Cholesterol 125 mg; 3850kJ (920 cal)*

BLACK OLIVES
Olives when picked young are green and hard. They ripen and darken on the tree. Olives are preserved in oil, sometimes with herbs, or in brine. Featured in a great many Mediterranean dishes, olives are suitable for salads and stuffings, are baked into breads and are an attractive addition to pasta and rice dishes. Olives should be used as soon after purchase as possible, and it is wisest to buy the best you can afford. Greek and Italian olives are thought to be the finest.

OPPOSITE PAGE: Sun-dried tomato sauce on tagliatelle (top); Creamy asparagus linguine

GREEN OLIVE AND EGGPLANT (AUBERGINE) TOSS

Preparation time: 20 minutes
Total cooking time: 20 minutes
Serves 4

★

500 g (1 lb) fettucine or tagliatelle
1 cup (175 g/6 oz) green olives
1 large eggplant (aubergine)
2 tablespoons olive oil
2 cloves garlic, crushed
1/2 cup (125 ml/4 fl oz) lemon juice
2 tablespoons chopped fresh parsley
1/2 cup (50 g/1 3/4 oz) freshly grated Parmesan

1 Cook the pasta in a large pan of rapidly boiling salted water until *al dente*. Drain and return to the pan.
2 While the pasta is cooking, slice the olives and cut the eggplant into small cubes.
3 Heat the oil in a heavy-based frying pan. Add the garlic and stir for 30 seconds. Add the eggplant and cook over medium heat, stirring frequently, for 6 minutes, or until tender. Add the olives, lemon juice and salt and pepper, to taste. Add the sauce to the pasta and toss. Sprinkle with parsley and grated Parmesan.

NOTE: To draw out bitter juices, eggplant can be chopped and salted, left to stand for 30 minutes, then rinsed well before using.

NUTRITION PER SERVE: *Protein 20 g; Fat 15 g; Carbohydrate 95 g; Dietary Fibre 10 g; Cholesterol 10 mg; 2585 kJ (615 cal)*

ON THE SIDE

WARM VEGETABLE SALAD Boil or steam 200 g (6 1/2 oz) each of baby carrots, sugar snap peas, yellow squash, zucchini and new potatoes until just tender. Do not overcook or the vegetables will lose their bright colours. To make the dressing, combine 2 crushed cloves of garlic, 2 tablespoons each of chopped fresh dill and chives, 1 tablespoon lime juice, 1 tablespoon Dijon mustard and 1/3 cup (80 ml/2 3/4 fl oz) of olive oil.

BELOW: Green olive and eggplant toss

SPAGHETTI WITH FRESH TOMATO SAUCE

Preparation time: 15 minutes
+ 2 hours refrigeration
Total cooking time: 10– 15 minutes
Serves 4

4 firm ripe tomatoes

8 stuffed green olives

2 tablespoons capers

4 spring onions, finely chopped

2 cloves garlic, crushed

1/2 teaspoon dried oregano

1/3 cup (20 g/3/4 oz) fresh parsley, chopped

1/3 cup (80 ml/23/4 fl oz) olive oil

375 g (12 oz) spaghetti or spaghettini

1 Chop the tomatoes into small pieces. Chop the olives and capers. Combine all the ingredients, except the pasta, in a bowl and mix well. Cover and refrigerate for at least 2 hours.
2 Cook the pasta in a large pan of rapidly boiling salted water until *al dente*. Drain and return to the pan. Add the cold sauce to the hot pasta and mix well.
NOTE: For a different taste, add 1/2 cup (30 g/1 oz) of shredded fresh basil leaves to the sauce.

NUTRITION PER SERVE: *Protein 15 g; Fat 20 g; Carbohydrate 70 g; Dietary Fibre 10 g; Cholesterol 0 mg; 2190 kJ (525cal)*

LINGUINE WITH ROASTED VEGETABLE SAUCE

Preparation time: 30 minutes
Total cooking time: 50 minutes
Serves 4

4 large red peppers (capsicums)

500 g (1 lb) firm ripe tomatoes

3 large red (Spanish) onions, peeled

1 bulb garlic

1/2 cup (125 ml/4 fl oz) balsamic vinegar

1/4 cup (60 ml/2 fl oz) olive oil

2 teaspoons coarse salt

2 teaspoons freshly ground black pepper

500 g (1 lb) linguine

100 g (31/2 oz) fresh Parmesan, shaved

100 g (31/2 oz) black olives

1 Preheat the oven to moderate 180°C (350°F/Gas 4). Cut the peppers in half and remove the seeds and membrane. Cut the tomatoes and onions in half and separate and peel the garlic cloves.
2 Arrange the vegetables in a large baking dish in a single layer. Pour the vinegar and oil over them and sprinkle with the salt and pepper.
3 Bake for 50 minutes. Allow to cool for 5 minutes before puréeing in a food processor for 3 minutes, or until the mixture is smooth. Season with more salt and pepper, if necessary.
4 When the vegetables are almost cooked, cook the linguine in a large pan of rapidly boiling salted water until *al dente*. Drain.
5 Serve the roasted vegetable sauce over the linguine with the Parmesan, olives and some extra black pepper.

NUTRITION PER SERVE: *Protein 30 g; Fat 30 g; Carbohydrate 100 g; Dietary Fibre 10 g; Cholesterol 25 mg; 3320 kJ (790 cal)*

ABOVE: Spaghetti with fresh tomato sauce

EGG TOMATOES
Favoured for their high flesh-to-seed ratio, egg tomatoes are ideal for cooking. Also known as Roma or plum tomatoes, their colour is a bright, even red and their walls are thick and firm, thus making peeling easy. They are perfect for preserving and are used for canned peeled tomatoes and sun-dried tomatoes.

ABOVE: Grilled vegetables on pasta

GRILLED VEGETABLES ON PASTA

Preparation time: 30 minutes
Total cooking time: 20 minutes
Serves 4

500 g (1 lb) tomato- or chilli-flavoured
fettucine or tagliatelle
1 red pepper (capsicum)
1 yellow pepper (capsicum)
250 g (8 oz) egg (Roma) tomatoes,
thickly sliced
2 large zucchini (courgettes), sliced
1/3 cup (80 ml/2³/4 fl oz) olive oil
3 cloves garlic, crushed
10 fresh basil leaves, roughly chopped
4 bocconcini, sliced

1 Cook the pasta in a large pan of rapidly boiling salted water until *al dente*. Drain and return to the pan. Cut the peppers into large flat pieces and discard the seeds and membrane. Cook skin-side-up under a hot grill for 8 minutes, or until the skin is black and blistered. Remove from the heat and cover with a damp tea towel. When cool, peel the skin away and finely chop the pepper flesh.
2 Sprinkle the cut sides of the tomatoes lightly with salt. Brush the zucchini with 1 tablespoon of the oil. Cook the vegetables under a hot grill for 10 minutes, or until tender, turning once.
3 Toss the pasta with the vegetables, garlic, basil, the remaining oil and the sliced bocconcini. Season with salt and freshly ground black pepper, to taste. Serve immediately.
NOTE: Use plain pasta if flavoured is not available. Add a little chopped chilli to the dish, if you like the spicy taste.

NUTRITION PER SERVE: *Protein 25 g; Fat 30 g; Carbohydrate 95 g; Dietary Fibre 10 g; Cholesterol 20 mg; 3060 kJ (730 cal)*

VEGETABLE LASAGNE

Preparation time: 40 minutes
Total cooking time: 1 hour 15 minutes
Serves 6

3 large red peppers (capsicums)
2 large eggplants (aubergines)
2 tablespoons oil
1 large onion, chopped
3 cloves garlic, crushed
1 teaspoon dried mixed herbs
1 teaspoon dried oregano
500 g (1 lb) mushrooms, sliced
440 g (14 oz) can crushed tomatoes
440 g (14 oz) can red kidney beans, drained
1 tablespoon sweet chilli sauce
250 g (8 oz) packet instant lasagne
500 g (1 lb) English spinach, chopped
1 cup (30 g/1 oz) fresh basil leaves
90 g (3 oz) sun-dried tomatoes, sliced
3 tablespoons grated Parmesan
3 tablespoons grated Cheddar cheese

Cheese sauce

60 g (2 oz) butter
3 tablespoons plain flour
2 cups (500 ml/16 fl oz) milk
600 g (1 1/4 lb) ricotta cheese

1 Preheat the oven to moderate 180°C (350°F/Gas 4). Brush a 35 x 28 cm (14 x 11 inch) ovenproof baking dish with oil.
2 Cut the red peppers into large flat pieces and remove the seeds and membrane. Cook, skin-side-up, under a hot grill for 8 minutes, or until the skin is black and blistered. Cover with a damp tea towel and when cool, peel away the skin and cut the flesh into long thin strips. Set aside.
3 Slice the eggplant into 1 cm (1/2 inch) rounds and place in a large pan of boiling water. Cook for 1 minute, or until just tender. Drain, pat dry with paper towels and set aside.
4 Heat the oil in a large heavy-based frying pan and add the onion, garlic and herbs. Cook over medium heat for 5 minutes, or until the onion is soft. Add the sliced mushrooms and cook for 1 minute.
5 Add the tomato, red kidney beans, chilli sauce and salt and pepper, to taste. Bring to the boil, reduce the heat and simmer for 15 minutes, or until the sauce thickens. Remove from the heat and set aside.
6 To make the cheese sauce, heat the butter in a pan and stir in the flour over medium heat for 1 minute, or until smooth. Remove from the heat and gradually stir in the milk. Return to the heat and stir constantly until the sauce boils and begins to thicken. Simmer for another minute. Add the ricotta and stir until smooth.
7 Dip the lasagne sheets, if necessary, in hot water to soften slightly and arrange 4 sheets on the base of the prepared dish. Build up layers on top of the pasta, using half of the eggplant, the spinach, the basil, the grilled pepper strips, the mushroom sauce and then the sun-dried tomatoes. Top with a layer of pasta and press gently. Repeat the layers, finishing with a layer of lasagne. Top with the cheese sauce and sprinkle with the combined cheeses. Bake for 45 minutes, or until the pasta is soft.

NUTRITION PER SERVE: *Protein 35 g; Fat 35 g; Carbohydrate 65 g; Dietary Fibre 15 g; Cholesterol 95 mg; 2965 kJ (710 cal)*

ABOVE: Vegetable lasagne

FLAT-LEAF PARSLEY
Also known as Italian or continental parsley, the flat-leafed variety is stronger tasting than curly-leafed and more widely used as a flavouring agent. However, it is mild enough to use in quantity and so can be added to thicken dishes and also to temper other ingredients. The taste of the stems is more delicate and they can be used instead of the leaves for a milder flavour.

ABOVE: Chunky spaghetti napolitana

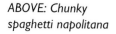

CHUNKY SPAGHETTI NAPOLITANA

Preparation time: 20 minutes
Total cooking time: 1 hour
Serves 6

2 tablespoons olive oil
1 onion, finely chopped
1 carrot, diced
1 celery stick, diced
500 g (1 lb) very ripe tomatoes
1/2 cup (125 ml/4 fl oz) white wine
2 teaspoons sugar
500 g (1 lb) spaghetti
1 tablespoon chopped fresh parsley
1 tablespoon chopped fresh oregano

1 Heat the oil in a heavy-based pan. Add the onion, carrot and celery, cover and cook for 10 minutes over low heat, stirring occasionally, taking care not to let the vegetables colour.
2 Chop the tomatoes and add to the vegetables with the wine and sugar. Bring the sauce to the boil, reduce the heat to low, cover and simmer for 45 minutes, stirring occasionally. Season with salt and freshly ground black pepper. If the sauce becomes too thick, add up to 3/4 cup (185 ml/6 fl oz) of water to thin it out.
3 About 15 minutes before serving time, cook the spaghetti in a large pan of rapidly boiling salted water until *al dente*. Drain and return to the pan. Pour two-thirds of the sauce over the pasta, add the parsley and oregano and gently toss. Serve in bowls or on a platter with the remaining sauce in a jug at the table.

NUTRITION PER SERVE: *Protein 10 g; Fat 7 g; Carbohydrate 65 g; Dietary Fibre 7 g; Cholesterol 0 mg; 1595 kJ (380 cal)*

Capers are the small, unripe bud of the caper bush. They are preserved in vinegar or salt and their piquant flavour makes them an ideal companion for fish and meat dishes. Salted ones have a more subtle flavour without vinegar overtones, but they need to have the salt rinsed off before use. Tiny capers have a finer flavour and a crunchier texture, but are more expensive because of the extra labour required for picking.

SPAGHETTI WITH OLIVES AND CAPERS

Preparation time: 20 minutes
Total cooking time: 20 minutes
Serves 4

2/3 cup (170 ml/5 1/2 fl oz) extra virgin olive oil
1 1/2 cups (125 g/4 oz) fresh white breadcrumbs
3 cloves garlic, finely chopped
45 g (1 1/2 oz) can anchovies, drained and finely chopped, optional
300 g (10 oz) black olives, finely chopped
6 Roma (egg) tomatoes, peeled and chopped
2 tablespoons tiny capers
500 g (1 lb) spaghetti or spaghettini

1 Heat 2 tablespoons of the olive oil in a medium frying pan. Add the breadcrumbs and cook, stirring continuously, until golden brown and crispy. Remove from the pan and set aside to cool completely.

2 Add the remaining oil to the pan and heat for 1 minute. Add the garlic, anchovies and black olives and cook over medium heat for 30 seconds. Add the tomato and capers and cook for 3 minutes.

3 Cook the pasta in a large pan of rapidly boiling salted water until *al dente*. Drain and return to the pan. Add the tomato mixture and breadcrumbs and toss to combine. Serve immediately, with herbs as a garnish if you like.

NUTRITION PER SERVE: *Protein 25 g; Fat 45 g; Carbohydrate 11.5 g; Dietary Fibre 15 g; Cholesterol 10 mg; 4065 kJ (970 cal)*

ABOVE: Spaghetti with olives and capers

4 While the pasta is cooking, heat the oil in a heavy-based frying pan. Cook the bacon and spring onion over medium heat, stirring occasionally, for 5 minutes. Add the basil, cream and salt and pepper, to taste, and simmer for 5 minutes. Add the tomato and cook for 2– 3 minutes, or until heated through. Serve the sauce over the pasta.

NUTRITION PER SERVE: *Protein 15 g; Fat 25 g; Carbohydrate 65 g; Dietary Fibre 6 g; Cholesterol 80 mg; 2325 kJ (555 cal)*

FARFALLE WITH MUSHROOMS

Preparation time: 20 minutes
Total cooking time: 15 minutes
Serves 4

500 g (1 lb) farfalle
50 g (1³/4 oz) butter
2 cloves garlic, thinly sliced
500 g (1 lb) button mushrooms, thinly sliced
2 tablespoons dry sherry
1/4 cup (60 ml/2 fl oz) chicken stock
1/3 cup (90 g/3 oz) sour cream
2 tablespoons fresh thyme leaves
2 tablespoons chopped fresh chives
2 tablespoons chopped fresh parsley
freshly grated Parmesan, for serving

1 Cook the farfalle in a large pan of rapidly boiling salted water until *al dente*. Drain and return to the pan.
2 While the pasta is cooking, melt the butter in a large frying pan, add the garlic and cook for 1 minute over medium heat.
3 Add the mushrooms and, when all the butter is absorbed, add the sherry, stock and sour cream. Stir to combine and bring to the boil. Reduce the heat and simmer for 4 minutes.
4 Add the mushroom sauce and herbs to the pasta and toss to combine. Serve sprinkled with grated Parmesan and maybe some cracked black pepper or seasoned pepper.

NUTRITION PER SERVE: *Protein 20 g; Fat 25 g; Carbohydrate 90 g; Dietary Fibre 10 g; Cholesterol 65 mg; 2790 kJ (665 cal)*

PENNE WITH CREAMY TOMATO SAUCE

Preparation time: 25 minutes
Total cooking time: 20 minutes
Serves 6

2 bacon rashers, optional
4 large ripe tomatoes
500 g (1 lb) penne
1 tablespoon olive oil
2 spring onions, chopped
2 tablespoons chopped fresh basil
1 1/4 cups (315 ml/10 fl oz) cream

1 Discard the bacon rind and cut the bacon into small pieces. Cut a small cross on the base of each tomato. Put in boiling water for 1– 2 minutes and then plunge into cold water. Peel the skin down from the cross.
2 Cut the tomatoes in half and scoop out the seeds with a teaspoon. Finely chop the tomatoes.
3 Cook the pasta in a large pan of rapidly boiling salted water until *al dente*. Drain and keep warm.

ABOVE: Penne with creamy tomato sauce

RIGATONI WITH PUMPKIN SAUCE

Preparation time: 15 minutes
Total cooking time: 25 minutes
Serves 6

500 g (1 lb) rigatoni or large penne
1 kg (2 lb) pumpkin
2 leeks
30 g (1 oz) butter
1/2 teaspoon ground nutmeg
1 1/4 cups (315 ml/10 fl oz) cream
3 tablespoons pine nuts, toasted

1 Cook the pasta in a large pan of rapidly boiling salted water until *al dente*. Drain and return to the pan.
2 Peel the pumpkin, remove and discard the seeds and cut the pumpkin into small cubes. Wash the leeks thoroughly to remove all traces of grit and then slice very finely. Heat the butter in a large pan over low heat. Add the sliced leek, cover the pan and cook, stirring occasionally, for 5 minutes.
3 Add the pumpkin and nutmeg, cover and cook for 8 minutes. Add the cream and 3 tablespoons of water to the pumpkin and bring the sauce to the boil. Cook, stirring occasionally, for 8 minutes, or until the pumpkin is tender.
4 Divide the pasta among serving bowls and top with sauce. Sprinkle with pine nuts and serve immediately.
NOTE: Butternut or jap pumpkin will give the sweetest flavour to this sauce. To toast pine nuts, stir over low heat in a non-stick frying pan until lightly golden. Alternatively, spread on a baking tray and grill. Be sure to check frequently as they brown quickly.

NUTRITION PER SERVE: *Protein 15 g; Fat 35 g; Carbohydrate 70 g; Dietary Fibre 7 g; Cholesterol 85 mg; 2710 kJ (645 cal)*

BELOW: Rigatoni with pumpkin sauce

LINGUINE WITH RED PEPPER (CAPSICUM) SAUCE

Preparation time: 20 minutes
Total cooking time: 30 minutes
Serves 6

3 red peppers (capsicums)
3 tablespoons olive oil
1 large onion, sliced
2 cloves garlic, crushed
1/4 – 1/2 teaspoon chilli powder or flakes
1/2 cup (125 ml/4 oz) cream
2 tablespoons chopped fresh oregano
500 g (1 lb) linguine or spaghetti (plain
  or spinach)

1 Cut the red peppers into large flat pieces and discard the seeds and membrane. Place skin-side up, under a hot grill and cook for 8 minutes, or until black and blistered. Remove from the heat, cover with a damp tea towel and, when cool, peel away the skin and cut the flesh into thin strips.
2 Heat the oil in a large heavy-based pan. Add the onion and stir over low heat for 8 minutes, or until soft. Add the pepper strips, garlic, chilli and cream and cook for 2 minutes, stirring occasionally. Add the oregano and salt and pepper, to taste.
3 About 15 minutes before the sauce is cooked, cook the pasta in a large pan of rapidly boiling salted water until *al dente*. Drain and return to the pan. Add the sauce to the hot pasta and toss until well combined.
NOTE: If necessary, you can substitute dried oregano. Use about one-third of the quantity as dried herbs have a much stronger flavour. For a stronger red pepper flavour, just omit the cream.

NUTRITION PER SERVE: *Protein 10 g; Fat 20 g; Carbohydrate 65 g; Dietary Fibre 5 g; Cholesterol 30 mg; 2050 kJ (490 cal)*

FUSILLI WITH GREEN SAUCE

Preparation time: 10 minutes
Total cooking time: 15 minutes
Serves 6

500 g (1 lb) fusilli or spiral pasta
1 onion
2 zucchini (courgettes)
5– 6 large silverbeet leaves
2 anchovies, optional
2 tablespoons olive oil
1 tablespoon capers
50 g (1 3/4 oz) butter
1/4 cup (60 ml/2 fl oz) white wine

1 Cook the pasta in a large pan of rapidly boiling salted water until *al dente*. Drain and return to the pan.
2 While the pasta is cooking, chop the onion very finely and grate the zucchini into fine pieces. Remove and discard the stalks from the silverbeet and chop or shred the leaves into small pieces. Roughly chop the anchovies, if using. Heat the olive oil and butter in a large heavy-based pan. Add the onion and zucchini and stir with a wooden spoon for 3 minutes over medium heat.
3 Add the anchovies, capers, wine and salt and pepper, to taste, to the pan and cook, stirring, for 2 minutes. Add the prepared silverbeet to the pan and cook for 1– 2 minutes, or until the silverbeet has softened. Add the green sauce to the warm pasta and toss until well distributed through the sauce.
NOTE: If you prefer, you can use 500 g (1 lb) of English spinach instead of silverbeet. Cut the ends off and shred the leaves into small pieces.

NUTRITION PER SERVE: *Protein 10 g; Fat 15 g; Carbohydrate 60 g; Dietary Fibre 10 g; Cholesterol 20 mg; 1815 kJ (430 cal)*

SILVERBEET
Silverbeet, also known as Swiss chard or seakale spinach, is unusual in that the stalks and leaves are used as separate vegetables. The white stalks or ribs have a sweet and nutty flavour. They are cut from the leaves, then rinsed and trimmed of the stringy outer membrane before being boiled or par-boiled for braising. Silverbeet leaves are tougher and less sweet than those of English spinach, but they can be used in fillings and stuffings and they are strong enough to roll up into parcels for baking or braising.

OPPOSITE PAGE:
Linguine with red pepper sauce (top); Fusilli with green sauce

MAKING FRESH BREADCRUMBS

Fresh breadcrumbs are easily made in a food processor. Discard the crusts, cut the bread into chunks and process until crumbed. For smaller, more even crumbs, simply grate frozen bread and use straight away. Don't use bread that is more than two days old as the flavour of some breads deteriorates with age and their crumbs will carry the stale taste into your dish.

ABOVE: Spaghetti with herbs and tomato

SPAGHETTI WITH HERBS AND TOMATO

Preparation time: 20 minutes
Total cooking time: 15 minutes
Serves 4

1/4 cup (20 g/3/4 oz) fresh breadcrumbs

500 g (1 lb) spaghetti

3 tablespoons olive oil

2 cloves garlic, diced

1 cup (30 g/1 oz) chopped fresh herbs
   (basil, coriander, parsley)

4 tomatoes, chopped

1/4 cup (30 g/1 oz) chopped walnuts

1/4 cup (25 g/3/4 oz) grated Parmesan, plus
   extra for serving

1 Heat the grill to medium and put the fresh breadcrumbs under for a few seconds, or until slightly golden.
2 Cook the spaghetti in boiling salted water until *al dente*, then drain.

3 Heat 2 tablespoons of the olive oil in a large frying pan and cook the garlic until soft.
4 Add the remaining oil and the herbs, tomato, walnuts and Parmesan. Add the pasta to the pan and toss for 1–2 minutes. Top with the breadcrumbs and extra Parmesan.

NUTRITION PER SERVE: *Protein 20 g; Fat 25 g; Carbohydrate 95 g; Dietary Fibre 9 g; Cholesterol 6 mg; 2825 kJ (620 cal)*

ON THE SIDE

WALDORF SALAD Combine in a bowl 3 cored and chopped red apples, 100 g (3½ oz) of toasted walnuts, 2 sliced sticks of celery, and 200 g (6½ oz) of black grapes. Remove the skin and bones from a barbecued chicken, finely shred the chicken flesh and add it to the salad. To make the dressing, combine 1 cup (250 g/8 oz) whole egg mayonnaise, ¼ cup (60 g/2 oz) of natural yoghurt and 1 teaspoon of mild curry powder. Fold through the salad just before serving.

FETTUCINE PRIMAVERA

Preparation time: 35 minutes
Total cooking time: 15 minutes
Serves 6

500 g (1 lb) fettucine
155 g (5 oz) fresh asparagus spears
1 cup (155 g/5 oz) frozen (or fresh)
    broad beans
30 g (1 oz) butter
1 celery stick, sliced
1 cup (155 g/5 oz) peas
1¼ cups (315 ml/10 fl oz) cream
½ cup (50 g/1¾ oz) freshly grated Parmesan

1 Cook the pasta in a large pan of rapidly boiling salted water until *al dente*. Drain and return to the pan.
2 While the pasta is cooking, cut the asparagus into small pieces. Bring a pan of water to the boil, add the asparagus and cook for 2 minutes. Using a slotted spoon, remove the asparagus from the pan and plunge the pieces into a bowl of ice cold water.
3 Add the broad beans to the pan of boiling water. Remove immediately and cool in cold water. Drain, then peel and discard any rough outside skin. If fresh broad beans are used, cook them for 2–5 minutes or until tender. If the beans are young, the skin can be left on, but old beans should be peeled.
4 Heat the butter in a heavy-based frying pan. Add the celery and stir for 2 minutes. Add the peas and the cream and cook gently for 3 minutes. Add the asparagus, broad beans, Parmesan, and salt and pepper, to taste. Bring the sauce to the boil and cook for 1 minute. Add the sauce to the cooked fettucine and toss well to combine.

NOTE: In this classic dish, any vegetables, usually spring vegetables, may be used. Choose your favourite such as leeks, zucchini, beans, sugar snap peas or snowpeas.

NUTRITION PER SERVE: *Protein 20 g; Fat 10 g; Carbohydrate 95 g; Dietary Fibre 10 g; Cholesterol 5 mg; 2295 kJ (545 cal)*

ON THE SIDE

BEETROOT AND NECTARINE SALAD Boil, steam or microwave 2 bunches of trimmed baby beetroot until tender. Drain and allow to cool before cutting into quarters. Cut 4 fresh nectarines into thick wedges. Combine the beetroot, nectarines, 2 tablespoons of toasted sunflower seeds and 2 tablespoons of fresh chervil leaves. Make up a dressing by mixing together 1 tablespoon of wholegrain mustard, 2 tablespoons of raspberry vinegar, 2 tablespoons of honey, 3 tablespoons of natural yoghurt and 3 tablespoons of oil. Drizzle the dressing over the salad just before serving.

WARM BROCCOLI FLORETS WITH ALMONDS Cook broccoli florets until tender, then refresh in iced water, sprinkle with toasted flaked almonds and drizzle with a dressing made by mixing together melted butter, crushed garlic and lemon juice.

ABOVE: Fettucine primavera

CHICKPEAS

Chickpeas, garbanzos or ceci originated in the Mediterranean regions and are particularly popular today in Spain, southern Italy and North Africa. Their nut-like taste makes them highly suitable for blending with other flavours and their crunchy texture works well in salads. Chickpea flour (besan) is used in both sweet and savoury pastry making. Dried chickpeas must be soaked overnight before use. Canned, pre-cooked chickpeas are a time-saving alternative.

PENNE WITH PUMPKIN AND CINNAMON SAUCE

Preparation time: 25 minutes
Total cooking time: 30 minutes
Serves 4

340 g (11 oz) pumpkin
500 g (1 lb) penne
25 g (3/4 oz) butter
1 onion, finely chopped
2 cloves garlic, crushed
1 teaspoon ground cinnamon
1 cup (250 ml/8 fl oz) cream
1 tablespoon honey
1/3 cup (35 g/1 1/4 oz) freshly grated Parmesan
chopped fresh chives, to garnish

1 Peel the pumpkin, remove the seeds and cut the flesh into small cubes. Boil, steam or microwave the pumpkin until just tender. Drain well.
2 Cook the penne in a large pan of rapidly boiling salted water until *al dente*. Drain and return to the pan.
3 While the pasta is cooking, melt the butter in a frying pan and cook the onion over medium heat until soft and golden. Add the garlic and cinnamon and cook for another minute.
4 Pour the cream into the pan, add the pumpkin and the honey and simmer for 5 minutes, until the sauce reduces and thickens slightly and is heated through.
5 Add the Parmesan and stir until it has melted. Season, to taste, with salt and freshly ground black pepper. Pour the sauce over the penne and toss until well combined. Serve sprinkled with chopped fresh chives.

NUTRITION PER SERVE: *Protein 20 g; Fat 35 g; Carbohydrate 105 g; Dietary Fibre 10 g; Cholesterol 110 mg; 3465 kJ (830 cal)*

CONCHIGLIE WITH CHICKPEAS

Preparation time: 15 minutes
Total cooking time: 20 minutes
Serves 4

500 g (1 lb) conchiglie (pasta shells)
2 tablespoons extra virgin olive oil
1 red (Spanish) onion, finely sliced
2–3 cloves garlic, crushed
425 g (14 oz) can chickpeas
1/2 cup (75 g/2 1/2 oz) sun-dried tomatoes, drained and thinly sliced
1 teaspoon finely grated lemon rind
1 teaspoon chopped fresh red chilli
2 tablespoons lemon juice
1 tablespoon chopped fresh oregano leaves
1 tablespoon finely chopped fresh parsley
fresh Parmesan shavings, for serving

1 Cook the conchiglie in a large pan of rapidly boiling salted water until *al dente*. Drain and return to the pan.
2 While the pasta is cooking, heat the oil in a frying pan, add the onion and cook until soft and lightly golden.
3 Add the garlic to the pan and cook for another minute. Add the rinsed and drained chickpeas, sun-dried tomato, lemon rind and chopped chilli and cook over high heat until heated through. Stir in the lemon juice along with the chopped fresh herbs.
4 Toss the chickpea mixture through the pasta. Season with salt and pepper, to taste, and serve immediately, scattered with Parmesan shavings.

NUTRITION PER SERVE: *Protein 40 g; Fat 20 g; Carbohydrate 145 g; Dietary Fibre 25 g; Cholesterol 2 mg; 3725 kJ (890 cal)*

OPPOSITE PAGE:
Penne with pumpkin and cinnamon sauce (top);
Conchiglie with chickpeas

OLIVES
The sour, pungent taste of these shiny black, green or brown fruits makes a vital contribution to the flavour, not only of the myriad Mediterranean dishes with which we associate them, but many others as well.

OLIVES

The olive tree is the oldest cultivated tree. It originated in Africa and Asia Minor and has been grown in the Mediterranean for over 6,000 years. An olive tree takes five years to bear fruit, but its life span is usually over 100 years. Known as a symbol of longevity, it is able to withstand harsh climates. The olive branch has long been used as a symbol of peace. Black and green olives come from the same tree, green is merely the unripe fruit. To preserve your own fresh olives, soak 1 kg (2 lb) of fresh black olives in a bucket of cold water for 6 weeks, draining and replacing the water every second day. After 6 weeks, drain the olives in a large colander and cover completely with rock salt. Set aside for 2 days. Rinse and set aside to dry thoroughly. Layer the olives in sterilised jars with slivers of preserved lemon skin, slivers of garlic, coriander seeds and sprigs of lemon thyme. Cover with a mixture of half oil and half white wine vinegar. Seal; set aside for 2 weeks. Store in a cool dark place for up to 6 months.

SAUTÉED BLACK OLIVES

Soak 500 g (1 lb) wrinkled cured black olives in warm water overnight. Rinse and drain. Heat 3 tablespoons of oil in a large frying pan, add 1 sliced onion and cook over medium heat for 2 minutes. Add the olives and cook for 10 minutes, or until soft. Remove the olives and onion with a slotted spoon and drain in a colander. Add several sprigs of oregano, toss and cool completely. Transfer to a sterilised jar. Refrigerate up to 3 weeks.

NUTRITION PER 100 G: *Protein 0 g; Fat 25 g; Carbohydrate 1 g; Dietary Fibre 0 g; Cholesterol 0 mg; 770 kJ (185 cal)*

CHILLI GARLIC OLIVES

Rinse and drain 500 g (1 lb) of brined Kalamata olives. Make a small incision in the side of each olive. Layer the olives in a sterilised jar with fine strips of orange rind, 1 teaspoon of chilli flakes, 4 halved small red chillies, 2 finely sliced cloves of garlic and 4 sprigs of rosemary. Combine 2 tablespoons of lemon juice with 1 cup (250 ml/8 fl oz) of olive oil and pour it over the olives. Add extra olive oil to cover, if necessary. Cover and marinate in a cool dark place for 2 weeks.

NUTRITION PER 100 G: *Protein 0 g; Fat 40 g; Carbohydrate 1 g; Dietary Fibre 0 g; Cholesterol 0 mg; 1380 kJ (330 cal)*

OLIVE AND TOMATO TAPENADE

Soak 3 anchovy fillets in milk for 10 minutes. Rinse and drain. Roughly chop the anchovies, 1 cup (155 g/5 oz) of pitted black Niçoise olives, 2 garlic cloves, 2 tablespoons chopped capers and the rind of 1 lemon in a food processor for a few seconds. Transfer to a bowl, add ½ cup (80 g/2¾ oz) chopped sun-dried tomato, 2 tablespoons lemon juice, 1 tablespoon of chopped parsley and 2 tablespoons of extra virgin olive oil. Serve on sliced woodfired Italian bread.

NUTRITION PER 100 G: *Protein 2 g; Fat 15 g; Carbohydrate 2 g; Dietary Fibre 1 g; Cholesterol 3 mg; 620 kJ (145 cal)*

ABOVE, FROM TOP LEFT: Preserved fresh olives; Sautéed black olives; Chilli garlic olives; Olive and tomato tapenade

135

SPAGHETTI SIRACUSANI

Preparation time: 15 minutes
Total cooking time: 1 hour
Serves 6

☆

1 large green pepper (capsicum)

2 tablespoons olive oil

2 cloves garlic, crushed

2 x 425g (14oz) cans crushed tomatoes

2 zucchini (courgettes), chopped

2 anchovy fillets, chopped, optional

1 tablespoon capers, chopped

1/4 cup (35g/1 1/4oz) black olives, pitted
    and halved

2 tablespoons chopped fresh basil leaves

500g (1 lb) spagetti or linguine

1/2 cup (50g/1 3/4oz) freshly grated Parmesan,
    for serving

*BELOW: Spaghetti
siracusani*

1 Remove the membrane and seeds from the green pepper. Slice the flesh into thin strips. Heat the oil in a large deep pan. Add the garlic and stir for 30 seconds over low heat. Add 1/2 cup (125ml/4 fl oz) of water along with teh green pepper, tomato, zucchini, anchovies, if using, capers and olives. Cook for 20 minutes, stirring occasionally. Stir in the basil and salt and pepper, to taste.

2 While the sauce si cooking, cook the pasta in a large pan of rapidly boiling salted water until *al dente*. Drain. Serve the sauce over the pasta. Sprinkle with Parmesan.

NUTRITION PER SERVE: *Protein 15 g; Fat 10 g; Carbohydrate 65 g; Dietary Fibre 10 g; Cholesterol 0 mg; 1790 kJ (430 cal)*

ON THE SIDE

WARM GINGER AND SESAME CARROT SALAD Scrub or peel 500 g (1 lb) of baby carrots and steam or microwave until just tender. Transfer to a bowl, add 1 tablespoon honey, 1/4 teaspoon of ground ginger, 50 g (1 3/4 oz) of melted butter, 1 teaspoon of lemon thyme leaves and 1 tablespoon of toasted sesame seeds. Toss lightly to coat and serve immediately.

BUTTON MUSHROOMS
Cultivated button mushrooms would have to be the most widely used mushroom today. Because of their mild flavour, clean colour and appearance, and compact size, they are suited to most cooking styles. As well as being good for flavouring sauces and fillings, they can be eaten raw. As they mature, their caps partially open and become known as cup or cap mushrooms. These taste stronger and have more visible and browner gills. Cap mushrooms complement foods of a robust nature and make rich sauces when sautéed in butter or cooked with red wine.

FETTUCINE BOSCAIOLA
(FETTUCINE WITH MUSHROOM AND TOMATO SAUCE)

Preparation time: 20 minutes
Total cooking time: 25 minutes
Serves 6

500 g (1 lb) button mushrooms
1 large onion
2 tablespoons olive oil
2 cloves garlic, finely chopped
2 x 425 g (14 oz) cans tomatoes,
   roughly chopped
500 g (1 lb) fettucine
2 tablespoons chopped fresh parsley

1 Carefully wipe the mushrooms with a damp paper towel and then slice finely, including the stems.
2 Chop the onion roughly. Heat the oil in a heavy-based frying pan and cook the onion and garlic over medium heat, stirring occasionally, for about 6 minutes, or until the vegetables are light golden. Add the tomato including the juice, along with the mushrooms, to the pan and bring the mixture to the boil. Reduce the heat, cover the pan and simmer for 15 minutes.
3 While the sauce is cooking, cook the fettucine in a large pan of rapidly boiling salted water until *al dente*. Drain and return to the pan.
4 Stir the parsley into the sauce and season well with salt and pepper, to taste. Toss the sauce through the pasta.
NOTE: If you would like a creamy sauce, add ½ cup (125 ml/4 fl oz) of cream when adding the parsley (do not reboil or it may curdle).

NUTRITION PER SERVE: *Protein 15 g; Fat 10 g; Carbohydrate 65 g; Dietary Fibre 10 g; Cholesterol 0 mg; 1640 kJ (390 cal)*

ABOVE: Fettucine boscaiola

BLUE CHEESE AND BROCCOLI WITH RIGATONI

Preparation time: 15 minutes
Total cooking time: 15 minutes
Serves 4

500 g (1 lb) rigatoni
500 g (1 lb) broccoli
1 tablespoon vegetable oil
1 onion, sliced
1/2 cup (125 ml/4 fl oz) dry white wine
1 cup (250 ml/8 fl oz) cream
1/2 teaspoon spicy paprika
150 g (5 oz) blue Brie, chopped
    into small pieces
2 tablespoons flaked almonds, toasted

1 Cook the rigatoni in a large pan of rapidly boiling salted water until *al dente*. Drain and return to the pan.
2 Cut the broccoli into florets, steam or microwave them for 2–3 minutes, until tender, and drain well.
3 Heat the oil in a large pan and fry the onion until soft. Add the wine and cream and simmer for 4–5 minutes, until reduced and thickened slightly. Stir in the paprika and cheese, and season with salt and pepper, to taste.
4 Add the broccoli and sauce to the pasta and gently toss over low heat until well mixed and heated through. Serve sprinkled with the toasted, flaked almonds.
NOTE: You can use a stronger blue cheese, such as gorgonzola, if you like.

NUTRITION PER SERVE: *Protein 30 g; Fat 50 g; Carbohydrate 95 g; Dietary Fibre 15 g; Cholesterol 120 mg; 4005 kJ (955 cal)*

ON THE SIDE

CRISPY ZUCCHINI RIBBONS

Using a sharp vegetable peeler, cut large zucchinis into ribbons by running the peeler along them horizontally. Lightly coat the ribbons firstly in beaten egg, then in a mixture of dried breadcrumbs, finely grated Parmesan and some chopped fresh herbs. Deep-fry the ribbons, in batches, in hot oil until crisp and golden brown. Serve with a tangy tomato salsa.

PUMPKIN AND PINE NUT TAGLIATELLE

Preparation time: 25 minutes
Total cooking time: 25 minutes
Serves 4

30 g (1 oz) butter
1 large onion, chopped
2 cloves garlic, crushed
1 1/2 cups (375 ml/12 fl oz) vegetable stock
750 g (1 1/2 lb) butternut pumpkin, peeled
    and chopped into small pieces
1/4 teaspoon ground nutmeg
1/2 teaspoon freshly ground black pepper
1 cup (250 ml/8 fl oz) cream
500 g (1 lb) fresh tagliatelle
1/2 cup (80 g/2 3/4 oz) pine nuts, toasted
2 tablespoons chopped fresh chives
freshly grated Parmesan, for serving

1 Melt the butter in a large pan. Add the onion and cook for 3 minutes, or until soft and golden. Add the garlic and cook for another minute. Stir in the vegetable stock and add the pumpkin. Bring to the boil, reduce the heat slightly and cook until the pumpkin is tender.
2 Reduce the heat to very low and season with the nutmeg and pepper. Stir in the cream until just warmed through; do not boil. Transfer to a food processor and process for about 30 seconds, until the mixture forms a smooth sauce.
3 Meanwhile, cook the tagliatelle in a large pan of rapidly boiling salted water until *al dente*. Drain and return to the pan.
4 Return the sauce to the pan and gently reheat. Add to the pasta with the pine nuts and toss well. Serve sprinkled with chives and offer Parmesan in a separate bowl. Pictured garnished with bay leaves.
NOTE: To toast pine nuts, stir over low heat in a non-stick frying pan until lightly golden.

NUTRITION PER SERVE: *Protein 25 g; Fat 50 g; Carbohydrate 105 g; Dietary Fibre 10 g; Cholesterol 110 mg; 4115 kJ (980 cal)*

PINE NUTS
These are small, elongated, creamy white kernels taken from the nuts of pine trees, in particular the Pinon and Stone pines. Sometimes these trees are called parasol pines because of their umbrella shape, and they typify the Mediterranean landscape, where they are native. The nuts are always sold shelled and blanched, and their flavour can be enhanced by toasting or roasting them before use. Pine nuts are used in dessert and sweet making as well as in savoury dishes.

OPPOSITE PAGE: Blue cheese and broccoli with rigatoni (top); Pumpkin and pine nut tagliatelle

SPICY PENNE WITH PEPPERS (CAPSICUMS)

Preparation time: 30 minutes
Total cooking time: 12 minutes
Serves 4

1 large red pepper (capsicum)
1 large green pepper (capsicum)
1 large yellow pepper (capsicum)
500 g (1 lb) penne
1/3 cup (80 ml/2³/4 fl oz) olive oil
2 tablespoons sweet chilli sauce
1 tablespoon red wine vinegar
1/3 cup (20 g/³/4 oz) chopped fresh coriander
250 g (8 oz) cherry tomatoes, halved
freshly grated Parmesan, for serving

1 Cut the peppers into large flat pieces, and discard the seeds and membrane. Cook skin-side-up under a hot grill for 8 minutes, or until the skin is black and blistered. Remove from the heat and cover with a damp tea towel. When cool, peel away the skin and cut the pepper flesh into thin strips.
2 Meanwhile, cook the penne in a large pan of rapidly boiling salted water until *al dente*. Drain and return to the pan.
3 While the penne is cooking, whisk together the oil, chilli sauce and red wine vinegar, and season with salt and pepper, to taste.
4 Add the oil mixture, fresh coriander, peppers and cherry tomatoes to the pasta. Serve sprinkled with Parmesan.
NOTE: This dish can be served warm as a main meal, or at room temperature as a salad. It makes an excellent accompaniment to chicken or barbecued meat.

NUTRITION PER SERVE: *Protein 20 g; Fat 25 g; Carbohydrate 95 g; Dietary Fibre 10 g; Cholesterol 5 mg; 2795 kJ (665 cal)*

FETTUCINE WITH SNOW PEAS (MANGETOUT) AND WALNUTS

Preparation time: 30 minutes
Total cooking time: 15 minutes
Serves 4

500 g (1 lb) fettucine or linguine
1/2 cup (60 g/2 oz) chopped walnuts
30 g (1 oz) butter
1 large onion, chopped
4 bacon rashers, chopped, optional
1 clove garlic, crushed
3/4 cup (185 ml/6 fl oz) dry white wine
1 cup (250 ml/8 fl oz) cream
250 g (8 oz) snow peas (mangetout), cut into pieces

1 Cook the fettucine in a large pan of rapidly boiling salted water until *al dente*. Drain and return to the pan.
2 While the pasta is cooking, scatter the walnuts on a foil-lined grill tray. Cook under a moderately hot grill for 2 minutes, or until lightly toasted. Stir after 1 minute, and be careful they don't burn. Set aside to cool.
3 Melt the butter in a large pan. Add the onion and bacon and cook until the onion is soft and the bacon lightly browned. Add the garlic and cook for another minute.
4 Pour in the white wine and cream, bring to the boil and reduce the heat. Simmer for 4 minutes, add the snow peas and simmer for another minute. Toss the sauce and walnuts through the pasta. Season with salt and pepper, to taste.
NOTE: Don't be tempted to save time by not toasting the nuts. Raw nuts may be bitter and stale in flavour, particularly if they are old, or have been kept in the refrigerator.

NUTRITION PER SERVE: *Protein 30 g; Fat 45 g; Carbohydrate 95 g; Dietary Fibre 10 g; Cholesterol 125 mg; 3930 kJ (940 cal)*

CHERRY TOMATOES

Cherry tomatoes come in a number of varieties including Red Currant, Green Grape, Sweet 100 and Yellow Pear. All are perfect for use in salads and some, such as the Sweet 100, can withstand quick cooking. They are all low in acid and can be extremely sweet. At approximately 5 mm (1/4 inch) diameter, Red Currant is the smallest and is often displayed for sale in loose clusters.

OPPOSITE PAGE: Spicy penne with peppers (top); Fettucine with snow peas and walnuts

WALNUTS

Walnuts are encased in a hard, round shell, with two distinct halves. The nut inside consists of two deeply ridged, creamy-white lobes of mild-flavoured flesh. Chopped walnuts are used in pasta sauces as well as fruit cakes, salads and biscuits. Walnuts in their shells can be refrigerated for up to 6 months. Shelled nuts should be bought in airtight containers or cans and stored, after opening, in a glass, airtight jar in the refrigerator.

ABOVE: Tagliatelle with tomato and walnuts

TAGLIATELLE WITH TOMATO AND WALNUTS

Preparation time: 20 minutes
Total cooking time: 45 minutes
Serves 6

4 very ripe tomatoes

I carrot

2 tablespoons oil

I onion, finely chopped

I celery stick, finely chopped

2 tablespoons chopped fresh parsley

I teaspoon red wine vinegar

1/4 cup (60 ml/2 fl oz) white wine

500 g (1 lb) tagliatelle or fettucine

3/4 cup (90 g/3 oz) walnuts, roughly chopped

1/3 cup (35 g/1 1/4 oz) freshly grated Parmesan, for serving

1 Score a small cross on the base of each tomato. Place in a bowl of boiling water for 1–2 minutes and then plunge into cold water. Peel the skin down from the cross and roughly chop the flesh. Peel and grate the carrot.

2 Heat 1 tablespoon of the oil in a large heavy-based pan and cook the onion and celery for 5 minutes over low heat, stirring regularly. Add the tomato, carrot, parsley and combined vinegar and wine. Reduce the heat and simmer for 25 minutes. Season with salt and pepper.

3 About 15 minutes before the sauce is ready, cook the pasta in a large pan of rapidly boiling water until *al dente*. Drain and return to the pan. Add the sauce to the pasta and toss.

4 Before the sauce is cooked, heat the remaining oil in a frying pan, add the chopped walnuts and stir over low heat for 5 minutes. Serve the pasta and sauce topped with walnuts and sprinkled with Parmesan.

NUTRITION PER SERVE: *Protein 15 g; Fat 20 g; Carbohydrate 65 g; Dietary Fibre 10 g; Cholesterol 5 mg; 2105 kJ (500 cal)*

Once, an innkeeper, a local gastronome, had the good fortune of being host to the goddess Venus. Overtaken with curiosity, he couldn't help taking a peek at her through the keyhole of her door. One look at her bellybutton, surrounded by the outline of the keyhole, was enough to inspire him to rush to his kitchen and create something in its image —the tortellini. This tale reflects the love the citizens of Bologna have for one of their most famous pastas.

TORTELLINI WITH EGGPLANT (AUBERGINE)

Preparation time: 10 minutes
Total cooking time: 20 minutes
Serves 4

500 g (1 lb) fresh cheese and
    spinach tortellini

1/4 cup (60 ml/2 fl oz) oil

2 cloves garlic, crushed

1 red pepper (capsicum), cut into
    small squares

500 g (1 lb) eggplant (aubergine), cut into
    small cubes

425 g (14 oz) can crushed tomatoes

1 cup (250 ml/8 fl oz) vegetable stock

1/2 cup (125 ml/4 fl oz) chopped fresh basil

1 Cook the tortellini in a large pan of rapidly boiling salted water until *al dente*. Drain and return to the pan.
2 While the pasta is cooking, heat the oil in a large pan, add the garlic and red pepper and stir over medium heat for 1 minute.
3 Add the cubed eggplant to the pan and stir gently over medium heat for 5 minutes, or until lightly browned.
4 Add the undrained tomato and vegetable stock to the pan. Stir and bring to the boil. Reduce the heat to low, cover the pan and cook for 10 minutes, or until the vegetables are tender. Add the basil and pasta and stir until mixed through.
NOTE: Cut the eggplant just before using. It turns brown when exposed to the air.

NUTRITION PER SERVE: *Protein 20 g; Fat 15 g; Carbohydrate 100 g; Dietary Fibre 10 g; Cholesterol 0 mg; 2555 kJ (610 cal)*

ABOVE: Tortellini with eggplant

CREAMY PASTA

Pasta and cream, a culinary marriage made in heaven. There are times when only the best will do... when only a bowl of fresh tagliatelle, tossed in a rich creamy sauce and topped with Parmesan shavings and cracked black pepper will satisfy your hunger for a taste of decadence. Traditionally, the long thin pastas are served with cream sauces, but these days, the possibilities are limitless.

FUSILLI WITH BROAD BEAN SAUCE

Preparation time: 30 minutes
Total cooking time: 25 minutes
Serves 6

2 cups (310 g/10 oz) frozen broad beans
4 bacon rashers
2 leeks
2 tablespoons olive oil
1¼ cups (315 ml/10 fl oz) cream
2 teaspoons grated lemon rind
500 g (1 lb) fusilli or penne

1 Plunge the broad beans into a pan of boiling water. Remove, drain and plunge immediately in cold water. Drain again and allow to cool before peeling (see note) and discard any rough outside skin.
2 Remove and discard the bacon rind. Chop the bacon into small pieces. Wash the leeks thoroughly to remove any dirt and grit and slice finely.
3 Heat the oil in a heavy-based frying pan. Add the leek and bacon and cook over medium heat, stirring occasionally, for 8 minutes, or until the leek is golden. Add the cream and lemon rind, bring to the boil, reduce the heat and simmer until the sauce thickens and coats the back of a spoon. Add the broad beans and season with salt and pepper, to taste.
4 While the sauce is simmering, cook the pasta in a large pan of rapidly boiling salted water until *al dente*. Drain and return to the pan.
5 Add the sauce to the pasta and toss well to combine. Serve at once in warmed pasta bowls.
NOTE: Broad beans can be cooked and peeled in advance and refrigerated in a covered container until needed. To peel them, slit or break off the top and squeeze the beans out. Leaving the hard outside skin on the broad bean will change the delicate texture and flavour of this dish so it is worth the extra effort of peeling them.
Fresh broad beans can also be used. If very young, leave the skin on. Old beans should be peeled before cooking. Cook for 15 minutes and then add to the dish.

NUTRITION PER SERVE: *Protein 20 g; Fat 30 g; Carbohydrate 60 g; Dietary Fibre 10 g; Cholesterol 85 mg; 2575 kJ (615 cal)*

ON THE SIDE

WARM SPRING VEGETABLE SALAD Lightly blanch some baby carrots, broccoli, snow peas (mangetout), beans, squash and baby corn in boiling water until just tender. Drain and toss through some chopped fresh herbs and some melted butter and honey mustard.

GREEK SALAD Mix together 1 red (Spanish) onion, cut into thin wedges, 1 red, yellow and green pepper (capsicum), all chopped, 200 g (6½ oz) of halved cherry tomatoes, 50 g (1¾ oz) of marinated black olives, 2 thickly sliced Lebanese cucumbers and 200 g (6½ oz) of feta broken into large pieces. Top with a dressing of 2 crushed cloves of garlic, 1 tablespoon of red wine vinegar and 3 tablespoons of olive oil.

ABOVE: Fusilli with broad bean sauce

TAGLIATELLE WITH CHICKEN LIVERS AND CREAM

Preparation time: 20 minutes
Total cooking time: 15 minutes
Serves 4

375 g (12 oz) tagliatelle

300 g (10 oz) chicken livers

2 tablespoons olive oil

1 onion, finely chopped

1 clove garlic, crushed

1 cup (250 ml/8 fl oz) cream

1 tablespoon snipped fresh chives

1 teaspoon seeded mustard

2 eggs, beaten

freshly grated Parmesan and some snipped
   chives, for serving

1 Cook the tagliatelle in a large pan of rapidly boiling salted water until *al dente*. Drain and return to the pan.
2 While the pasta is cooking, trim the chicken livers and slice. Heat the oil in a large frying pan. Add the onion and garlic and stir over low heat until the onion is tender.
3 Add the chicken livers to the pan and cook gently for 2–3 minutes. Remove from the heat and stir in the cream, chives, mustard, and salt and pepper, to taste. Return to the heat and bring to the boil. Add the beaten eggs and stir quickly to combine. Remove from the heat.
4 Add the sauce to the hot pasta and toss well to combine. Serve sprinkled with Parmesan and snipped chives.

NUTRITION PER SERVE: *Protein 35 g; Fat 50 g; Carbohydrate 70 g; Dietary Fibre 5 g; Cholesterol 575 mg; 3675 kJ (880 cal)*

MUSTARD
The condiment mustard is made by blending mustard seeds, sometimes ground, with vinegar or wine, food acid, salt and aromatic herbs and spices. The seeds come from various species of the mustard plant and have differing strengths, colours and sizes. Mustard powder is a mix of ground mustard seeds and wheat flour, often flavoured with turmeric and other spices.

ABOVE: Tagliatelle with chicken livers and cream

PENNE WITH CHICKEN AND MUSHROOMS

Preparation time: 30 minutes
Total cooking time: 25 minutes
Serves 4

30 g (1 oz) butter
1 tablespoon olive oil
1 onion, sliced
1 clove garlic, crushed
60 g (2 oz) prosciutto, chopped
250 g (8 oz) chicken thigh fillets, trimmed
    and sliced
125 g (4 oz) mushrooms, sliced
1 tomato, peeled, halved and sliced
1 tablespoon tomato paste (tomato purée,
    double concentrate)
1/2 cup (125 ml/4 fl oz) white wine
1 cup (250 ml/8 fl oz) cream
500 g (1 lb) penne
freshly grated Parmesan, for serving

1 Heat the butter and oil in a large frying pan.
Add the onion and garlic and stir over low heat
until the onion is tender. Add the prosciutto to
the pan and fry until crisp.
2 Add the chicken and cook over medium heat
for 3 minutes. Add the mushrooms and cook for
another 2 minutes. Add the tomato and tomato
paste and stir until combined. Stir in the wine
and bring to the boil. Reduce the heat and
simmer until the liquid is reduced by half.
3 Stir in the cream and salt and pepper, to taste,
and bring to the boil. Reduce the heat and
simmer until the sauce begins to thicken.
4 While the sauce is cooking, cook the penne
in a large pan of rapidly boiling salted water until
al dente. Drain well and return to the pan. Add
the sauce to the pasta and toss to combine. Serve
immediately, sprinkled with Parmesan.
NOTE: If you prefer, you can use chicken
mince in this recipe instead of the sliced
chicken thigh fillets.

NUTRITION PER SERVE: *Protein 35 g; Fat 45 g;
Carbohydrate 95 g; Dietary Fibre 10 g; Cholesterol 145 mg;
3980 kJ (950 cal)*

RIGATONI WITH SAUSAGE AND PARMESAN

Preparation time: 15 minutes
Total cooking time: 15 minutes
Serves 4

2 tablespoons olive oil
1 onion, sliced
1 clove garlic, crushed
500 g (1 lb) Italian pork sausage, cut
    into chunks
60 g (2 oz) mushrooms, sliced
1/2 cup (125 ml/4 fl oz) dry white wine
500 g (1 lb) rigatoni
1 cup (250 ml/8 fl oz) cream
2 eggs
1/2 cup (50 g/1 3/4 oz) freshly grated Parmesan
2 tablespoons chopped fresh parsley

1 Heat the oil in a large frying pan. Add the
onion and garlic and stir over low heat until
the onion is tender. Add the sausage and
mushroom and cook until the sausage is cooked
through. Stir in the wine and bring to the boil.
Reduce the heat and simmer until the liquid is
reduced by half.
2 While the sauce is cooking, cook the rigatoni
in a large pan of rapidly boiling salted water until
al dente. Drain and return to the pan.
3 In a large jug, whisk together the cream, eggs,
half the Parmesan, the parsley and salt and
pepper, to taste. Add to the rigatoni with the
sausage mixture and toss. Serve sprinkled with
the remaining Parmesan.
NOTE: You can freeze leftover wine for use in
recipes such as this one. You can use salami
instead of Italian pork sausage.

NUTRITION PER SERVE: *Protein 40 g; Fat 85 g;
Carbohydrate 90 g; Dietary Fibre 5 g; Cholesterol 295 mg;
5585 kJ (1335 cal)*

BLACK PEPPER
Peppercorns are the berry
of the tropical vine *Piper
nigrum*. They are green
and soft when immature,
and red or yellow when
ripe. Black peppercorns
are picked when ripe then
sun-dried, which gives
them their hard, black,
wrinkled appearance.
These have the strongest
flavour and aroma.
Peppercorns lose their
sharpness once ground,
and it is recommended to
keep them whole and
grind just before use.

*OPPOSITE PAGE: Penne
with chicken and
mushrooms (top);
Rigatoni with sausage
and parmesan*

BUCATINI WITH GORGONZOLA SAUCE

Preparation time: 10 minutes
Total cooking time: 20 minutes
Serves 6

375 g (12 oz) bucatini or spaghetti
200 g (6½ oz) gorgonzola cheese
20 g (¾ oz) butter
1 celery stick, chopped
1¼ cups (315 ml/10 fl oz) cream
250 g (8 oz) fresh ricotta cheese, beaten until
   smooth

1 Cook the pasta in a large pan of rapidly boiling salted water until *al dente*. Drain and return to the pan.
2 While the pasta is cooking, chop the gorgonzola cheese into small cubes.
3 Heat the butter in a medium pan, add the celery and stir for 2 minutes. Add the cream, ricotta and gorgonzola and season, to taste, with freshly ground black pepper.

4 Bring to the boil over low heat, stirring constantly, and then simmer for 1 minute. Add the sauce to the warm pasta and toss well.

NUTRITION PER SERVE: *Protein 20 g; Fat 40 g; Carbohydrate 45 g; Dietary Fibre 5 g; Cholesterol 135 mg; 2690 kJ (640 cal)*

ON THE SIDE

KUMERA, YOGHURT AND DILL SALAD Boil, steam or microwave 1 kg (2 lb) of peeled and thickly sliced sweet potato until just tender. Transfer to a bowl and cool slightly before adding 1 red (Spanish) onion, cut into thin wedges, 200 g (6½ oz) of natural yoghurt and plenty of chopped fresh dill, to your taste.

TOMATO AND FETA SALAD Slice egg (Roma) tomatoes in half lengthways and roast in a slow 150°C (300°F/Gas 2) oven until sweet and tender. Arrange on a platter, top with crumbled feta cheese, sliced anchovies and some fresh oregano leaves. Drizzle with olive oil.

GORGONZOLA CHEESE
Gorgonzola is an Italian blue-veined cheese. It is creamy and sweet when young, and sharp, strong and slightly crumbly when mature. As well as being a delicious table cheese which goes well with apples and pears, it is a good companion for cooked vegetables and meats. It melts well when heated and makes a rich, mellow flavouring for cream-based sauces. It can be replaced by a creamy mild blue-vein such as Blue Castello, or half Blue Castello and half Danish Blue for a stronger taste.

RIGHT: Bucatini with gorgonzola sauce

FETTUCINE WITH CREAMY MUSHROOM AND BEAN SAUCE

Preparation time: 20 minutes
Total cooking time: 20 minutes
Serves 4

280 g (9 oz) fettucine
250 g (8 oz) green beans
2 tablespoons oil
1 onion, chopped
2 cloves garlic, crushed
250 g (8 oz) mushrooms, thinly sliced
1/2 cup (125 ml/4 fl oz) white wine
1 1/4 cups (315 ml/10 fl oz) cream
1/2 cup (125 ml/4 fl oz) vegetable stock
1 egg
3 tablespoons chopped fresh basil
2/3 cup (100 g/3 1/2 oz) pine nuts, toasted
1/4 cup (35 g/1 1/4 oz) sun-dried tomatoes, cut into thin strips
50 g (1 3/4 oz) shaved Parmesan

1 Cook the fettucine in a large pan of rapidly boiling salted water until *al dente*. Drain, return to the pan and keep warm.
2 Trim the tops and tails of the beans and cut into long thin strips. Heat the oil in a large heavy-based frying pan. Add the onion and garlic and cook over medium heat for 3 minutes or until softened. Add the sliced mushrooms and cook, stirring, for 1 minute. Add the wine, cream and stock. Bring to the boil, reduce the heat and simmer for 10 minutes.
3 Lightly beat the egg in a small bowl. Stirring constantly, add a little cooking liquid. Pour the mixture slowly into the pan, stirring constantly for 30 seconds. Keep the heat low because if the mixture boils, it will curdle. Add the beans, basil, pine nuts and tomato and stir until heated through. Season, to taste, with salt and pepper. Serve the sauce over the pasta. Garnish with shavings of Parmesan, as well as sprigs of fresh herbs if you like.

NUTRITION PER SERVE: *Protein 25 g; Fat 70 g; Carbohydrate 55 g; Dietary Fibre 10 g; Cholesterol 165 mg; 3955 kJ (945 cal)*

VEGETABLE STOCK
A good vegetable stock has a delicate balance of flavours suitable for meat and seafood dishes as well as vegetable sauces, soups and braises. Any combination of aromatic, non-starchy vegetables such as carrots, onions, leeks, celery or turnips are simmered for 30 minutes with a bouquet garni, a clove of garlic and a little salt. The result will be a pale and clear stock with a mild flavour. A simple alternative is to use the water in which vegetables such as carrots or green beans have been boiled.

ABOVE: Fettucine with creamy mushroom and bean sauce

CONCHIGLIE WITH BROCCOLI AND ANCHOVY

Preparation time: 15 minutes
Total cooking time: 20 minutes
Serves 6

500 g (1 lb) conchiglie (shell pasta)
450 g (14 oz) broccoli
1 tablespoon oil
1 onion, chopped
1 clove garlic, crushed
3 anchovy fillets, chopped
1 1/4 cups (315 ml/10 fl oz) cream
1/2 cup (50 g/1 3/4 oz) freshly grated Parmesan, for serving

1 Cook the conchiglie in a large pan of rapidly boiling salted water until *al dente*. Drain and return to the pan.
2 While the conchiglie is cooking, cut the broccoli into small florets and cook in a pan of boiling water for 1 minute. Drain, plunge in cold water and drain again. Set aside.
3 Heat the oil in a heavy-based frying pan. Add the onion, garlic and anchovies and cook over low heat, stirring, for 3 minutes.
4 Add the cream to the pan and, stirring constantly, bring to the boil. Reduce the heat and simmer for 2 minutes. Add the broccoli florets and cook for 1 minute. Add salt and freshly ground black pepper, to taste. Add the sauce to the pasta and toss well to combine. Sprinkle with Parmesan and serve immediately.
NOTE: When tossing the sauce with the pasta, make sure all pieces of conchiglie are thoroughly coated with sauce. You can substitute different pastas such as macaroni or farfalle if you prefer.

NUTRITION PER SERVE: *Protein 20 g; Fat 30 g; Carbohydrate 60 g; Dietary Fibre 8 g; Cholesterol 85 mg; 2490 kJ (590 cal)*

SPINACH FETTUCINE WITH MUSHROOM SAUCE

Preparation time: 15 minutes
Total cooking time: 25 minutes
Serves 6

500 g (1 lb) spinach or plain fettucine
300 g (10 oz) baby mushrooms
3 spring onions
6 slices smoked ham or pancetta (50 g/1 3/4 oz)
40 g (1 1/4 oz) butter
1 1/4 cups (315 ml/10 fl oz) cream
4 tablespoons chopped fresh parsley

1 Cook the fettucine in a large pan of rapidly boiling salted water until *al dente*. Drain and return to the pan.
2 While the fettucine is cooking, slice the mushrooms finely. Trim the spring onions, removing the dark green section, and chop finely. Slice the smoked ham or pancetta into thin strips.
3 Heat the butter in a medium pan and cook the spring onion and ham over medium heat for 3 minutes. Add the mushrooms, cover, reduce the heat and cook, stirring occasionally, for 5 minutes.
4 Add the cream, half the parsley and salt and pepper, to taste. Simmer for 2 minutes, add the sauce to the fettucine and toss well to combine. Serve immediately, sprinkled with the remaining parsley.
NOTE: Don't add all the pasta to the boiling water at once—add it gradually, making sure that the water continues to boil. If spinach fettucine is unavailable, you can use other varieties of pasta.

NUTRITION PER SERVE: *Protein 15 g; Fat 30 g; Carbohydrate 60 g; Dietary Fibre 6 g; Cholesterol 100 mg; 2430 kJ (580 cal)*

ANCHOVY FILLETS

The most convenient way to buy anchovy fillets is in little tins or jars, preserved in oil. They should be pink, not grey, and have good definable fillets. If they are a little too strong for your taste, drain the amount needed and cover with milk. Leave for 30 minutes before discarding the milk, then pat the fillets dry with a paper towel. For a very mild flavour, use only the oil. Also available are anchovy fillets preserved in salt. These have a more delicate flavour, but must be soaked for 30 minutes before use.

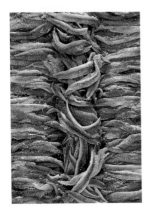

OPPOSITE PAGE:
Conchiglie with broccoli and anchovy (top); Spinach fettucine with mushroom sauce

ASPARAGUS

Preparing asparagus for cooking takes just a minute. The woody base of the stalk should be removed by simply snapping it off. Starting at the base and moving up towards the tip, gently bend the stalk. The tough end will snap off when you reach crisp flesh. Only thick stalks with coarse skins need to be peeled. This is done with a vegetable peeler or a small sharp knife, and the paring should taper off as you near the tip. When these steps are followed, the stalks will cook evenly from top to bottom and it shouldn't be necessary to tie the bunches together for boiling. The cooking time is critical; too short, and the asparagus will be hard and have a metallic taste; too long, and the flesh becomes stringy and water-logged. Asparagus of average thickness take only 3 minutes to cook. For thick stalks an extra 30–50 seconds is needed.

ABOVE: Tagliatelle with asparagus and fresh herbs

TAGLIATELLE WITH ASPARAGUS AND FRESH HERBS

Preparation time: 15 minutes
Total cooking time: 15 minutes
Serves 6

500 g (1 lb) tagliatelle
155 g (5 oz) asparagus spears
40 g (1 1/4 oz) butter
1 tablespoon chopped fresh parsley
1 tablespoon chopped fresh basil
1 1/4 cups (315 ml/10 fl oz) cream
1/2 cup (50 g/1 3/4 oz) freshly grated Parmesan

1 Cook the pasta in a large pan of rapidly boiling salted water until *al dente*. Drain and return to the pan.
2 While the pasta is cooking, cut the asparagus spears into short pieces. Heat the butter in a medium pan, add the asparagus and stir over medium heat for 2 minutes or until just tender. Add the parsley and basil, cream, and salt and pepper, to taste. Cook for 2 minutes.
3 Add the grated Parmesan to the pan and stir well. When thoroughly mixed, add to the warm pasta in the pan and toss gently to distribute ingredients evenly. If serving as a first course, this dish will be sufficient for eight.

NUTRITION PER SERVE: *Protein 15 g; Fat 30 g; Carbohydrate 60 g; Dietary Fibre 5 g; Cholesterol 100 mg; 2470 kJ (590 cal)*

SPAGHETTI CARBONARA
(SPAGHETTI WITH CREAMY EGG AND BACON SAUCE)

Preparation time: 10 minutes
Total cooking time: 20 minutes
Serves 6

⭐

500 g (1 lb) spaghetti

8 bacon rashers

4 eggs

1/2 cup (50 g/1³/4 oz) freshly grated
  Parmesan

1¹/4 cups (315 ml/10 fl oz) cream

1 Cook the spaghetti in a large pan of rapidly boiling salted water until *al dente*. Drain and return to the pan.

2 While the pasta is cooking, discard the bacon rind and cut the bacon into thin strips. Cook in a heavy-based pan over medium heat until crisp. Remove and drain on paper towels.

3 Beat the eggs, Parmesan and cream in a bowl until well combined. Add the bacon and pour the sauce over the warm pasta. Toss gently until pasta is well coated.

4 Return the pan to the heat and cook over very low heat for 1/2 – 1 minute, or until slightly thickened. Serve seasoned with freshly ground pepper. Garnish with herb sprigs if you wish.

NUTRITION PER SERVE: *Protein 25 g; Fat 30 g; Carbohydrate 60 g; Dietary Fibre 5 g; Cholesterol 225 mg; 2665 kJ (635 cal)*

CARBONARA

There is some mystery surrounding the invention and naming of this simple sauce. Some say that Carbonara is relatively new, having appeared in Rome during the Second World War, when American GIs combined their rations of bacon and eggs with the local spaghetti. It is likely that the dish has been around a lot longer than that. Was it simply that it was a quick and easy meal whipped up by the coal vendors, *carbonari*, over street charcoal burners, or was it so named because the flecks of black pepper spotting the creamy sauce looked like coal dust? However it came about, the concept of using egg to thicken and flavour a simple bacon and cream sauce was truly inventive.

ABOVE: Spaghetti carbonara

RAVIOLI WITH MASCARPONE AND PANCETTA

Preparation time: 10 minutes
Total cooking time: 20 minutes
Serves 4

500 g (1 lb) fresh spinach ravioli
2 teaspoons vegetable oil
90 g (3 oz) pancetta, finely chopped
1/2 cup (125 ml/4 fl oz) chicken stock
185 g (6 oz) mascarpone
1/2 cup (80 g/2 3/4 oz) finely sliced sun-dried
   tomatoes
2 tablespoons finely shredded fresh basil
1/2 teaspoon cracked black pepper

1 Cook the ravioli in a large pan of rapidly boiling salted water until *al dente*.
2 While the pasta is cooking, heat the oil in a frying pan and cook the pancetta for 2–3 minutes. Stir in the stock, mascarpone and sun-dried tomatoes.
3 Bring to the boil, reduce the heat and simmer for 5 minutes, until the sauce reduces and thickens. Stir in the basil and pepper.
4 Drain the ravioli and add to the pan with the sauce. Toss together gently to combine. Serve immediately.

NUTRITION PER SERVE: *Protein 20 g; Fat 35 g; Carbohydrate 90 g; Dietary Fibre 5 g; Cholesterol 145 mg; 3220 kJ (770 cal)*

ON THE SIDE

TOMATO AND BOCCONCINI SALAD Thickly slice 4 large vine-ripened tomatoes and 8 baby bocconcini. Arrange the tomato slices, bocconcini and basil leaves on a serving plate. Drizzle with a little extra virgin olive oil and balsamic vinegar. Sprinkle with pepper and sea salt.

ANTIPASTO SALAD Combine about 200 g (6 1/2 oz) each of sun-dried tomatoes, marinated black olives, chopped marinated eggplant (aubergine), artichoke and sun-dried pepper (capsicum). Toss through 3 tablespoons of chopped basil. Drizzle with a little balsamic vinegar.

FETTUCINE WITH SMOKED CHEESE AND SALAMI

Preparation time: 20 minutes
Total cooking time: 15 minutes
Serves 4

375 g (12 oz) tomato fettucine
200 g (6 1/2 oz) sun-dried tomatoes in oil
3 bacon rashers
1 large red onion, sliced
2 large cloves garlic, finely chopped
150 g (5 oz) hot or mild salami, sliced
   into strips
2 teaspoons plain flour
1 tablespoon tomato paste (tomato purée,
   double concentrate)
1 1/2 cups (375 ml/12 fl oz) evaporated milk
1/2 cup (60 g/2 oz) grated smoked cheese
1/4 teaspoon cayenne pepper
2 tablespoons chopped fresh flat-leaf parsley
shavings of fresh Parmesan, for serving

1 Cook the fettucine in a large pan of rapidly boiling salted water until *al dente*. Drain and return to the pan.
2 While the pasta is cooking, drain the sun-dried tomatoes, reserving the oil, and cut into strips; set aside. Finely chop the bacon and set aside.
3 Heat the reserved oil in a pan and cook the onion for 3 minutes, or until soft and golden. Add the garlic and cook for another minute. Add the sun-dried tomato, bacon and salami and cook for another 2–3 minutes.
4 Stir in the flour, then the tomato paste and cook for 1 minute. Gradually add the evaporated milk, stirring continuously. Bring to the boil and reduce the heat. Add the smoked cheese, cayenne pepper, parsley and black pepper, to taste, and simmer until the cheese melts.
5 Toss the sauce through the hot pasta. Serve immediately, with shavings of Parmesan.

NUTRITION PER SERVE: *Protein 40 g; Fat 35 g; Carbohydrate 85 g; Dietary Fibre 5 g; Cholesterol 110 mg; 3495 kJ (835 cal)*

CAYENNE PEPPER
Sometimes called Nepal pepper, cayenne pepper is an attractive bright reddish-orange colour and has a pungency somewhere between that of ground chilli and black pepper. It is named after Cayenne, the main port of French Guiana. Cayenne pepper is made by grinding the dried fruit, minus the seeds, of different members of the capsicum family, namely *capsicum frutescens* and *capsicum minimum*, and it is favoured because it has a slight sweetness underlying the hot pepper taste. Cayenne pepper can be used as a flavouring in dishes which require long cooking, but it has an intensity that is equally strong when used at the last minute as a condiment.

OPPOSITE PAGE: Ravioli with mascarpone and pancetta (top); Fettucine with smoked cheese and salami

HONEY

The flavour, consistency, aroma, colour and degree of sweetness in honey is determined by the flowers from which the bees gather their nectar. Most prized for cooking uses is honey from herbs such as thyme and rosemary that have a subtle flavouring and a savoury fragrance. Flowers such as apple blossom give a highly floral perfume and flavour, while others make almost bitter honey.

ABOVE: Linguine in honey basil cream

LINGUINE IN HONEY BASIL CREAM

Preparation time: 15 minutes
Total cooking time: 20 minutes
Serves 6

500 g (1 lb) linguine
240 g (7 1/2 oz) fresh basil
1 small red chilli, chopped
3 cloves garlic, crushed
3 tablespoons pine nuts, toasted
3 tablespoons freshly grated Parmesan
juice of 1 lemon
1/2 cup (125 ml/4 fl oz) olive oil
3 tablespoons honey
1 1/2 cups (375 ml/12 fl oz) cream
1/2 cup (125 ml/4 fl oz) chicken stock
shavings of fresh Parmesan, for serving

1 Cook the linguine in a large pan of rapidly boiling salted water until *al dente*. Drain and keep warm.
2 While the pasta is cooking, discard the stems of basil and mix the basil leaves, chilli, garlic, pine nuts, Parmesan, lemon juice, oil and honey in a food processor or blender until smooth.
3 Combine the basil mixture, cream and chicken stock in a large pan, bring to the boil and simmer for 15– 20 minutes, or until the sauce has thickened. Season, to taste, with cracked pepper.
4 Add the pasta to the pan and toss well. Sprinkle with shavings of Parmesan.

NUTRITION PER SERVE: *Protein 15 g; Fat 70 g; Carbohydrate 75 g; Dietary Fibre 7 g; Cholesterol 100 mg; 4005 kJ (955 cal)*

CARAMELIZED ONION AND BLUE CHEESE RISSONI

Preparation time: 20 minutes
Total cooking time: 35 minutes
Serves 4

★ ★

500 g (1 lb) rissoni
30 g (1 oz) butter
3 tablespoons olive oil
4 onions, sliced
185 g (6 oz) blue cheese
100 g (3¹/₂ oz) mascarpone
2 cups (130 g/4¹/₂ oz) shredded English
    spinach leaves

 Cook the rissoni in rapidly boiling salted water until *al dente*. Drain well and return to the pan.
2 While the pasta is cooking, heat the butter and the olive oil in a large heavy-based frying pan.

Add the sliced onion and cook over low heat for about 20–30 minutes, until golden brown and caramelized. Remove from the pan with a slotted spoon and drain on paper towels.
3 Mix the blue cheese, mascarpone and onion in a bowl.
4 Add the cheese and onion mixture, as well as the spinach, to the rissoni and toss through. Season, to taste, with salt and freshly ground black pepper before serving.

NUTRITION PER SERVE: *Protein 30 g; Fat 45 g; Carbohydrate 95 g; Dietary Fibre 9 g; Cholesterol 90 mg; 3755 kJ (895 cal)*

ABOVE: Caramelized onion and blue cheese rissoni

GRILLED CARBONARA

Preparation time: 10 minutes
Total cooking time: 15 minutes
Serves 4

250 g (8 oz) linguine
4 eggs
³/4 cup (185 ml/6 fl oz) cream
6 slices prosciutto, chopped
³/4 cup (75 g/2¹/2 oz) freshly grated Parmesan
2 tablespoons chopped fresh chives
30 g (1 oz) butter

1 Brush a 23 cm (9 inch) shallow heatproof dish with some melted butter or oil. Preheat the grill to moderately hot.
2 Cook the linguine in a large pan of rapidly boiling salted water until *al dente*. Drain and return to the pan.
3 While the pasta is cooking, whisk the eggs and cream together in a bowl, stir in the prosciutto, the Parmesan (reserving 3 tablespoons) and chives and season with freshly ground black pepper, to taste.
4 Add the egg mixture and the butter to the hot pasta and stir continuously over low heat for 1 minute, or until the egg mixture begins to thicken slightly. Take care not to overcook the mixture, or you will end up with scrambled eggs. The mixture should be quite creamy and moist.
5 Pour the pasta into the prepared dish and sprinkle the top with the reserved Parmesan. Place under the grill for a few minutes, until just set and lightly browned on top. Serve with crusty Italian bread.

NUTRITION PER SERVE: *Protein 25 g; Fat 40 g; Carbohydrate 45 g; Dietary Fibre 5 g; Cholesterol 300 mg; 2710 kJ (645 cal)*

ORECCHIETTE WITH TUNA, LEMON AND CAPER SAUCE

Preparation time: 10 minutes
Total cooking time: 20 minutes
Serves 4

500 g (1 lb) orecchiette
30 g (1 oz) butter
1 clove garlic, crushed
1 onion, finely chopped
425 g (14 oz) can tuna in brine, drained
2 tablespoons lemon juice
1 cup (250 ml/8 fl oz) cream
2 tablespoons chopped fresh flat-leaf parsley
1 tablespoon capers, drained
¹/4 teaspoon cayenne pepper, optional

1 Cook the orecchiette in a large pan of rapidly boiling salted water until *al dente*. Drain and return to the pan.
2 While the pasta is cooking, heat the butter in a pan and cook the garlic and onion for 1–2 minutes. Add the tuna, lemon juice, cream, half the parsley and the capers. Season with black pepper and cayenne, if using. Simmer over low heat for 5 minutes.
3 Add the tuna sauce to the pasta and toss until thoroughly combined. Serve the pasta sprinkled with the remaining chopped fresh parsley. Pictured here garnished with caperberries.
NOTE: Use two wooden spoons to toss the mixture together.

NUTRITION PER SERVE: *Protein 40 g; Fat 35 g; Carbohydrate 90 g; Dietary Fibre 5 g; Cholesterol 155 mg; 3570 kJ (850 cal)*

PROSCIUTTO

In Italy, prosciutto simply means ham, and it can be bought cooked, *cotto*, which is similar to boiled hams elsewhere, or raw, *crudo*, which is cured on the bone by salting and air-drying. This is the one referred to in recipes and known for its versatility and mellow flavour. It is used in salads, on bread and tossed through pasta sauces, or used to add flavour to cooked sauces, stews and soups. It can be mature, with dark ruby flesh, creamy fat and a concentrated flavour and aroma, or younger and more succulent, with pale pink flesh and white fat.

ON THE SIDE

SESAME COLESLAW Finely shred one-quarter each of a red cabbage and a green cabbage. Cut 100 g (3¹/2 oz) of snow peas (mangetout), 2 celery sticks, 2 carrots and 1 red pepper (capsicum) into julienne strips. Combine the cabbage and other vegetables in a large bowl and toss through enough whole egg mayonnaise to lightly dress the salad. Top with finely shredded fresh mint leaves and toasted sesame seeds.

OPPOSITE PAGE: Grilled carbonara (top); Orecchiette with tuna, lemon and caper sauce

ALFREDO SAUCE
Immortalised by Alfredo in his Rome restaurant, this sauce is a rich blend of butter, cream and Parmesan. Traditionally, it is served with fettucine and eaten as soon as the sauce is tossed through the pasta, to prevent the dish becoming clammy. For this reason it is one of the few pasta dishes that is compiled at the table in restaurants.

ABOVE: Fettucine alfredo

FETTUCINE ALFREDO

Preparation time: 10 minutes
Total cooking time: 15 minutes
Serves 6

500 g (1 lb) fettucine or tagliatelle
90 g (3 oz) butter
1½ cups (150 g/5 oz) freshly shredded Parmesan
1¼ cups (315 ml/10 fl oz) cream
3 tablespoons chopped fresh parsley

1 Cook the pasta in a large pan of rapidly boiling salted water until *al dente*. Drain and return to the pan.
2 While the pasta is cooking, heat the butter in a medium pan over low heat. Add the Parmesan and cream and bring to the boil, stirring constantly. Reduce the heat and simmer for 10 minutes, or until the sauce has thickened slightly. Add the parsley, and salt and pepper, to taste, and stir well to combine. Add the sauce to the warm pasta and toss well to combine. Serve garnished with a fresh herb sprig, if desired.

NUTRITION PER SERVE: *Protein 20 g; Fat 45 g; Carbohydrate 60 g; Dietary Fibre 5 g; Cholesterol 135 mg; 2985 kJ (710 cal)*

ON THE SIDE

GREEN HERB PILAF Fry a finely sliced onion in a little butter in a large deep frying pan. Add 1 tablespoon each of chopped fresh coriander and parsley. Stir in 1 cup (200 g/6½ oz) of washed basmati rice and 1½ cups (375 ml/12 fl oz) of chicken or vegetable stock. Season, to taste. Bring to the boil and simmer for about 20 minutes, or until the rice is cooked. Drain off any excess liquid and add another tablespoon of each herb. Top with tiny knobs of butter and cracked black pepper.

LINGUINE WITH CREAMY LEMON SAUCE

Preparation time: 10 minutes
Total cooking time: 20 minutes
Serves 4

400 g (13 oz) fresh linguine or spaghetti
¼ teaspoon saffron threads or
   powder, optional
1¼ cups (315 ml/10 fl oz) cream
1 cup (250 ml/8 fl oz) chicken stock
1 tablespoon grated lemon rind

1 Cook the pasta in a large pan of rapidly boiling salted water until *al dente*. Drain and keep warm.
2 If using saffron threads, soak them in a little hot water for 5 minutes. While the pasta is cooking, combine the cream, chicken stock and grated lemon rind in a large frying pan. Bring to the boil, stirring occasionally.
3 Reduce the heat and simmer for 10 minutes. Season, to taste, with salt and pepper. Add the cooked pasta and cook for another 2–3 minutes.
4 Add the saffron threads and liquid and stir. Serve garnished with fine strips of lemon rind, if desired.
NOTE: Saffron is available from delicatessens and speciality food shops. If unavailable, use ¼ teaspoon of turmeric.

NUTRITION PER SERVE: *Protein 15 g; Fat 35 g; Carbohydrate 75 g; Dietary Fibre 5 g; Cholesterol 105 mg; 2755 kJ (660 cal)*

SAFFRON

Saffron is the dried stamens of the saffron or autumn crocus. Available in threads or as a powdered form, it has a dark orange colour that carries into the food, and a sharp taste that mellows when cooked. Steep the threads in tepid water to extract the flavour, or to intensify the flavour, toast until darkened, cool, then crumble to a coarse powder. Saffron is costly because of the labour required to pluck the stamens from each flower.

ABOVE: Linguine with creamy lemon sauce

1 To make the dough, combine the flour, beaten eggs and oil with ⅓ cup (80 ml/2¾ fl oz) of water in a food processor, for 5 seconds, or until the mixture comes together in a ball. Cover with plastic wrap and refrigerate for 15 minutes. If you don't have a food processor, combine the ingredients in a large bowl, using your fingertips.

2 To make the filling, heat the oil in a heavy-based pan, add the spring onion and garlic and stir-fry over medium heat for 2 minutes. Add the mince and stir-fry over high heat for 4 minutes, or until well browned and all the liquid has evaporated. Use a fork to break up any lumps as the mince cooks. Allow to cool and stir in the egg.

3 Roll half the dough out very thinly on a lightly floured surface. Use a large sharp knife to cut the dough into 6 cm (2½ inch) squares. Brush half the squares very lightly with water and place a teaspoon of filling on each. Place another square over each and press down firmly to seal the filling inside. Place in a single layer on well-floured oven trays. Repeat with the remaining dough and filling.

4 To make the sauce, melt the butter in a medium pan, add the mascarpone cheese and stir over medium heat until melted. Add the Parmesan and sage and gently heat while stirring, for 1 minute.

5 Cook the ravioli in a large pan of rapidly boiling water for 5 minutes, or until tender. Drain and serve with the sauce.

NUTRITION PER SERVE: *Protein 35 g; Fat 65 g; Carbohydrate 50 g; Dietary Fibre 4 g; Cholesterol 270 mg; 3855 kJ (915 cal)*

GRATED PARMESAN

For an interesting variation on serving freshly grated Parmesan or Pecorino with pasta dishes, combine grated lemon rind with one of these cheeses. It gives a delicious piquancy that enhances many sauces, especially cream-based ones, and works well with meat-filled ravioli. Mix in proportions that will best complement your sauce. A ratio of 1 tablespoon of cheese to 1 teaspoon of lemon rind is a good starting point.

PORK AND VEAL RAVIOLI WITH CHEESY SAUCE

Preparation time: 1 hour
Total cooking time: 15 minutes
Serves 4

Dough

2 cups (250 g/8 oz) plain flour
2 eggs, lightly beaten
2 tablespoons oil

Filling

1 tablespoon oil
4 spring onions, finely chopped
3 cloves garlic, crushed
250 g (8 oz) pork and veal mince
1 egg, lightly beaten

Sauce

60 g (2 oz) butter
1 cup (220 g/7 oz) mascarpone cheese
⅓ cup (35 g/1¼ oz) freshly grated Parmesan
2 tablespoons chopped fresh sage

ABOVE: Pork and veal ravioli with cheesy sauce

ON THE SIDE

DILLED ORANGE CARROTS

Boil, steam or microwave baby carrots until tender. Heat a little orange juice, a cinnamon stick and orange liqueur and honey in a pan, bring to the boil and simmer for 3 minutes. Remove the cinnamon stick. Drizzle the sauce over the carrots and sprinkle with chopped fresh dill.

BRAISED LEEKS WITH PINE NUTS

Fry sliced leeks in a little oil and butter until golden brown. Add enough vegetable stock and white wine to just cover the leeks. Cook until the leeks are tender and fold through lots of chopped fresh herbs. Sprinkle with toasted pine nuts and grated Parmesan.

LEMON GRASS AND LIME SCALLOP PASTA

Preparation time: 20 minutes
Total cooking time: 15 minutes
Serves 4

500 g (1 lb) spaghetti or chilli fettucine
1 tablespoon oil
1 onion, sliced
2 tablespoons finely chopped lemon grass
500 g (1 lb) scallops
1 cup (250 ml/8 fl oz) coconut milk
2 kaffir lime leaves, finely shredded
1/2 cup (15 g/1/2 oz) coriander leaves

1 Cook the pasta in rapidly boiling salted water until *al dente*. Drain.
2 Meanwhile, heat the oil in a large heavy-based frying pan, add the onion and lemon grass and cook over medium heat for 5 minutes, or until the onion is soft. Add the scallops in batches and cook until tender and lightly browned. Remove and keep warm.
3 Add the coconut milk and kaffir lime leaves to the pan and simmer for 5 minutes, or until the sauce thickens slightly.
4 Return the scallops to the pan and cook until heated through. Toss the pasta through the sauce with the coriander leaves. Season, to taste, with salt and pepper.

NUTRITION PER SERVE: *Protein 30 g; Fat 20 g; Carbohydrate 90 g; Dietary Fibre 7 g; Cholesterol 40 mg; 2775 kJ (660 cal)*

LEMON GRASS

Lemon grass is an aromatic plant with a bulbous base and grass-like leaves, used all over Asia for its balmy lemon flavour. The base is trimmed of coarse outer layers and the crisp white heart is chopped or pounded to go into broths, curry pastes and stir-fries. The fresh whole stem or the dried leaves can be added to soups or curries. Dried leaves need to be soaked in water for about 30 minutes before use and the flavour is adequate as a substitute for fresh. Fresh lemon grass can be bought from some greengrocers while Asian food stores stock fresh and dried.

LEFT: Lemon grass and lime scallop pasta

CHEESE
Pasta and Parmesan are a famous combination, but the Italians produce many other cheeses, from soft creamy-white table cheeses to strong blue-veined varieties, of which they are rightfully proud.

MOZZARELLA
A smooth, matured mild-flavoured cheese, originally made from buffalo milk, but now sometimes made from cow's milk or a mixture of the two. Manufactured in large quantities around the world, it is available in a variety of shapes, from pear to block, and has a stringy texture when melted. It is famous for its use in pizzas but can be diced and added to sauces or sliced and melted over veal steaks.

BOCCONCINI AND OVOLINI
Small mozzarella balls are called bocconcini, although sometimes referred to as baby mozzarella. They are fresh, unripened cheeses still made following the traditional method and, unlike matured mozzarella, are enjoyed as a table cheese. Smaller ones are called ovolini. Stored in the refrigerator fully covered in the whey in which they are sold, they will last for up to three weeks. If they show any signs of

yellowing, they should be discarded. Serve drained and cut into thin slices. Used in salads, as a topping for pizzas or bruschetta or in baked pasta dishes.

RICOTTA
A fresh curd cheese made from whey, usually the whey drained off when making mozzarella. It can be made from sheep (ricotta pecora) or cow milk (ricotta vaccina) and is usually sold in the

basket it is produced in, as it is very delicate. Ricotta has a short shelf life and should be bought as required. Avoid any that is discoloured or dry. Drain off the excess whey before using. The flavour is mild, so ricotta can be used in savoury or sweet dishes. Often used in fillings for cannelloni, with pancakes or as a spread. Dried ricotta balls are suitable for grating.

GORGONZOLA

Originally produced in a small village in Milan, gorgonzola is now made throughout the world. It is prized for its rich creamy texture and soft blue flavour. It is less salty than most blue cheeses. Only buy what you need as, like most blues, it has a strong aroma that will permeate other foods in the refrigerator. Gorgonzola is delicious as a cream sauce for pasta, in salads, melted over pears or served with figs. Return to room temperature before serving.

PROVOLONE

Usually sold encased in wax and hanging by a striped red and white string. The younger the cheese, the milder the flavour (it sharpens on ageing). Provolone is often lightly smoked and works well as part of a cheese platter. It is delicious grated in pasta sauces, in fondues or melted over meats. Refrigerate in plastic wrap for up to two weeks.

PECORINO

The name given to a range of hard, cooked sheep milk curd cheeses. These have a grainy texture, similar to that of Parmesan, and are generally grated for cooking, in the same way as Parmesan. *Pecorino romano* is aged for the longest time and is therefore harder and more suitable for grating. *Pecorino pepato* has had black peppercorns added to the curd, and has a subtle peppery flavour.

Pecorino fresco is the name given to the young fresh cheese. Pecorino will keep in the refrigerator for months. Fully enclose it in plastic wrap as it has a strong aroma that can permeate other foods.

MASCARPONE

A fresh curd triple cream cheese that looks more like cream than cheese. It is very high in fat and has a mild yet slightly acidic taste. It can be used in a four-cheese sauce or in a baked béchamel sauce topping. Commonly served with fresh or poached fruit for dessert. Refrigerate for up to five days.

CLOCKWISE, FROM TOP LEFT:
Mozzarella, ricotta, gorgonzola, provolone, mascarpone, pecorino, fresh pecorino, pecorino pepato, baby ricotta, ovolini, bocconcini

CHEESE

FONTINA

A sweet, nutty-flavoured cheese with a soft velvety texture and a few tiny air holes. Fontina is sold in wheels, with a golden brown rind. It is a semi-hard cheese, prized for its melting quality and is the vital ingredient in the Italian-style fondue dish, *fonduta*. Italian law restricts the use of the name *fontina* to cheese produced in the Aosta Valley, near Mount Fontin. There are many copies in other regions of Italy and elsewhere. These are known as *fontal* and are generally softer than fontina. Fontina is delicious melted over polenta or gnocchi as well as in sauces. Will keep in the refrigerator, sealed in plastic wrap, for up to one week.

PARMIGIANO REGGIANO

Parmesan derives its name from the Parma region in northern Italy where it is made. It is a hard cheese with a crumbly texture. Parmesan is aged for 2–3 years in large wooden wheels and can only be stamped *Parmigiano reggiano* if it is produced within the provinces of Parma and Reggio, where it is still made using the original method. It is best to buy Parmesan in a wedge and grate it yourself as pre-grated cheese is often dry and lacking flavour. Select Parmesan with the rind still attached, with no evidence of whitening at the rim. Parmesan can be served on its own or grated or shaved on top of pasta sauces, in salads or soups. Wrap it in greaseproof paper and foil and store on the bottom shelf of your refrigerator.

GRANA

Like Parmesan, this is a hard grating cheese and, as the name implies, it has a grainy texture. It is easily identified by the imprint on the rind of the cheese that guarantees its authenticity. Grana can be served as a table cheese as it has a more delicate flavour than Parmesan. Refrigerate, wrapped in plastic.

BEL PAESE

Easily identified by the silver and green foil wrapper with a map of Italy on the top, this is a mild, creamy, slightly sweet cheese that can be used on sandwiches, as

a table cheese or melted over casseroles or pizzas. The creamy cheese ripens quickly, in about 4–6 weeks, and should be kept wrapped in the foil until ready to use. It is sold in large wheels or tiny individual serves.

TALEGGIO

This cheese takes its name from the town where it is produced and can be classified into two varieties. One is the cooked curd, with a thin greyish rind and straw-coloured interior with a mild flavour. The uncooked curd is a surface-ripened cheese with a thin, reddish moulded skin with a pale yellow buttery interior. It has a delicate sweet flavour with a slightly acidic tang in towards the centre. Taleggio should be purchased only as required. Return to room temperature before serving as a table cheese. Taleggio is also known as *stracchino*.

ASIAGO

This can either be a table cheese or a grating cheese, depending on how it has been aged and pressed. The younger cheese, *Asiago d'Allevo*, has a thin golden rind that darkens to a rusty brown colour as the cheese ripens. The interior is pale yellow with a slightly grainy texture that is scattered with small holes. The flavour sharpens with age. The aged and pressed cheese, *Asiago Pressato* has a deep golden rind and a very pale straw-coloured interior. It has a pleasant mild flavour and is often used as a dessert cheese. Asiago stores well in the refrigerator, wrapped in plastic.

GOATS CHEESE

Goats cheese has a distinctive, sharp taste. It varies in texture from a soft, crumbly cheese to a firm chalky cheese, depending on the age and method of production. When young and crumbly it can easily be spread on bread, as a table cheese or crumbled over salad and pasta dishes. The firmer cheese can be cut into pieces and marinated in oil and herbs. The cheese should be a clean white with no evidence of drying around the edges. Purchase as required. It should keep for up to two weeks in the refrigerator. Depending on the variety, the rind may vary from black (ash-covered goats cheese) to off-white. Ash goats cheese is made by rolling goats cheese in fresh herbs that have been cooked in a pan until blackened. The cheese is rolled until it has an even coating.

CLOCKWISE, FROM TOP LEFT: Fontina, Parmigiano-Reggiano, Bel Paese, Goats cheese, Ash goats cheese, Asiago, Grana

PASTA SALADS

Pasta salads have come about as part of the evolution of pasta. While they are not an authentic Italian creation, the combination of fresh vegetables, finest-quality olive oil and cold *al dente* pasta certainly has a Mediterranean flavour. Few foods are so adaptable that they are delicious when served either hot or cold. Pasta is one exception and these salads are guaranteed to leave Italian cooks with just one thought: 'why didn't we think of that?'

OREGANO

Italian oregano (also known as wild marjoram) is closely related to rigani, which is used in Greek kitchens, and to sweet marjoram, common to French and Northern Italian cooking. It is milder than rigani but more pungent than sweet marjoram. Oregano is very compatible with tomatoes, garlic and onion and is the herb most often found on pizzas. The plants are hardy and the leaves dry well, ensuring a constant supply.

ABOVE: Farfalle salad with sun-dried tomatoes and spinach

FARFALLE SALAD WITH SUN-DRIED TOMATOES AND SPINACH

Preparation time: 20 minutes
Total cooking time: 12 minutes
Serves 6

500 g (1 lb) farfalle or spiral pasta
3 spring onions
50 g (1¾ oz) sun-dried tomatoes,
    cut into strips
1 kg (2 lb) English spinach, stalks trimmed and
    leaves shredded
⅓ cup (50 g/1¾ oz) toasted pine nuts
1 tablespoon chopped fresh oregano
¼ cup (60 ml/2 fl oz) olive oil
1 teaspoon fresh chopped chilli
1 clove garlic, crushed

1 Cook the pasta in a large pan of rapidly boiling salted water until *al dente*. Drain, rinse under cold water and drain again. Allow to cool and transfer to a large salad bowl.
2 Trim the spring onions and finely slice diagonally. Add to the pasta with the tomato, spinach, pine nuts and oregano.
3 To make the dressing, combine the oil, chilli, garlic and salt and pepper, to taste, in a small screw top jar and shake well.
4 Pour the dressing over the top of the salad. Toss well and serve.

NUTRITION PER SERVE: *Protein 15 g; Fat 15 g; Carbohydrate 60 g; Dietary Fibre 10 g; Cholesterol 0 mg; 1930 kJ (460 cal)*

SPAGHETTI TOMATO SALAD

Preparation time: 25 minutes
Total cooking time: 15 minutes
Serves 6

500 g (1 lb) spaghetti or bucatini
1 cup (50 g/1¾ oz) fresh basil leaves, shredded
250 g (8 oz) cherry tomatoes, halved
1 clove garlic, crushed
½ cup (75 g/2½ oz) chopped black olives
¼ cup (60 ml/2 fl oz) olive oil
1 tablespoon balsamic vinegar
½ cup (50 g/1¾ oz) freshly grated Parmesan

1 Cook the pasta in a large pan of rapidly boiling salted water until *al dente*. Drain, rinse under cold water and drain again.
2 Combine the basil, tomato, garlic, olives, oil and vinegar in a salad bowl. Set aside for about 15 minutes. Mix in the drained pasta.

3 Add the Parmesan and salt and pepper, to taste. Toss well and serve immediately.

NUTRITION PER SERVE: *Protein 15 g; Fat 15 g; Carbohydrate 60 g; Dietary Fibre 5 g; Cholesterol 10 mg; 1780 kJ (425 cal)*

ON THE SIDE

PUMPKIN AND SAGE SCONES

Sift 2 cups (250 g/8 oz) of self-raising flour into a bowl with a pinch of salt. Rub 250 g of cooked and puréed pumpkin and 20 g (¾ oz) of butter into the flour and then add 1 tablespoon of chopped fresh sage. Bring the mixture together with a little milk and turn it out onto a baking tray. Shape the mixture into a round and roll it out to about 3 cm (1¼ inches) thick. Gently mark or cut the scone into segments and bake in a moderate 180°C (350°F/Gas 4) oven for 15–20 minutes, until lightly browned and cooked through.

ABOVE: Spaghetti tomato salad

2 While the pasta is cooking, mix the olive oil, garlic, lemon rind and juice, basil, tomato, olives and oregano in a large bowl. Season with salt and pepper, to taste.

3 Cut the chicken into thin strips. Heat the oil in a medium heavy-based frying pan. Add the chicken strips and cook over medium heat, stirring occasionally, for 4 minutes, or until cooked through.

4 Add the drained chicken and warm pasta to the tomato mixture and toss to combine. Serve with the rocket leaves.

NUTRITION PER SERVE: *Protein 20 g; Fat 15 g; Carbohydrate 25 g; Dietary Fibre 5 g; Cholesterol 45 mg; 1330 kJ (320 cal)*

TOMATO AND BASIL PASTA SALAD

Preparation time: 15 minutes
Total cooking time: 10 minutes
Serves 6

500 g (1 lb) cooked penne rigate

1/4 cup (15 g/1/2 oz) finely shredded fresh basil

1–2 cloves garlic, crushed

2 tablespoons olive oil

1 tablespoon balsamic vinegar

1 teaspoon soft brown sugar

4 egg (Roma) tomatoes

60 g (2 oz) prosciutto

WARM SALADS

A salad where all or some of the ingredients are warm makes a very appetising first course or light meal. The cooked components, straight from the heat, are still bright and succulent and full of flavour, while the more traditional salad vegetables contribute a contrasting crisp freshness.

ABOVE: Warm chicken and pasta salad
RIGHT: Tomato and basil pasta salad

WARM CHICKEN AND PASTA SALAD

Preparation time: 20 minutes
Total cooking time: 15 minutes
Serves 6

180 g (6 oz) penne rigate

1/4 cup (60 ml/2 fl oz) virgin olive oil

2 cloves garlic, crushed

rind of 1 lemon, cut into fine strips

1 tablespoon lemon juice

3 tablespoons shredded fresh basil

4 medium tomatoes, seeded and chopped

18 black olives, pitted and sliced

1/2 teaspoon chopped fresh oregano leaves

400 g (13 oz) chicken breast tenderloins

1 tablespoon oil

1/2 cup (20 g/3/4 oz) rocket leaves

1 Cook the pasta in a large pan of rapidly boiling salted water until *al dente*; drain.

1 Combine the penne, basil, garlic, oil, vinegar, brown sugar and salt and pepper, to taste.
2 Cut the egg tomatoes into wedges and toss with the other ingredients until well distributed.
3 Grill the prosciutto until crisp, crumble into small pieces and sprinkle on top of the salad before serving.

NUTRITION PER SERVE: *Protein 5 g; Fat 5 g; Carbohydrate 30 g; Dietary Fibre 5 g; Cholesterol 5 mg; 910 kJ (215 cal)*

TUNA AND PASTA SALAD

Preparation time: 20 minutes
Total cooking time: 15 minutes
Serves 6

500 g (1 lb) conchiglie (shell pasta) or fusilli
200 g (6¹/₂ oz) beans, cut into short lengths
2 red peppers (capsicums), thinly sliced
2 spring onions, chopped
425 g (14 oz) can tuna, in oil
2 tablespoons oil
¹/₄ cup (60 ml/2 fl oz) white wine vinegar
1 tablespoon lemon juice
1 clove garlic, crushed
1 teaspoon sugar
1 large cucumber, thinly sliced
6 eggs, hard-boiled and quartered
4 tomatoes, cut into eighths
¹/₂ cup (80 g/2³/₄ oz) black olives
2 tablespoons chopped fresh basil

1 Cook the pasta in a large pan of rapidly boiling salted water until *al dente*. Drain, rinse under cold water and drain again.
2 Combine the pasta, beans, peppers and the spring onions in a large bowl, mixing well. Drain the tuna, reserving the oil, and flake with a fork.
3 Combine the reserved tuna oil, oil, vinegar, lemon juice, garlic and sugar in a small screw top jar. Shake vigorously for 2 minutes, or until well combined.
4 Spoon the pasta into the centre of a large serving platter. Arrange the cucumber, egg and tomato around the edge of the platter, and drizzle with half the dressing. Scatter the flaked tuna, olives and basil over the salad and drizzle with the remaining dressing just before serving.

NUTRITION PER SERVE: *Protein 35 g; Fat 25 g; Carbohydrate 65 g; Dietary Fibre 10 g; Cholesterol 235 mg; 2650 kJ (630 cal)*

ON THE SIDE

POLENTA BREAD Stir ¹/₂ cup (50 g/1³/₄ oz) finely grated Parmesan, some chopped fresh herbs (basil, parsley, oregano, sage), a crushed clove of garlic and a little cream into some cooked polenta. Mix well and season, to taste. Pour into a baking dish and bake at moderately hot 200°C (400°F/Gas 6) until the crust is golden and the polenta well set. Cut into slices and serve warm.

KUMERA AND PARSNIP CHIPS Peel and cut kumera (orange sweet potato) and parsnip into very thin slices or ribbons, using a sharp vegetable peeler. Deep-fry in batches, in hot oil, until crisp. Drain and keep warm in a moderate 180°C (350°F/Gas 4) oven whilst cooking the remainder. Serve with a garlic mayonnaise.

ABOVE: Tuna and pasta salad

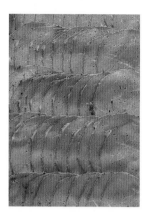

PASTRAMI

Pastrami is a cured, highly seasoned cut of lean beef made popular in the United States. It is believed to have originated in the Balkans and is closely related to the pastirma of Turkey. Spiced with paprika, pepper, cumin and garlic, and sometimes smoked, pastrami is delicious sliced thinly and eaten cold.

OPPOSITE PAGE: Tuna, green bean and onion salad (top); Pastrami, mushroom and cucumber salad

TUNA, GREEN BEAN AND ONION SALAD

Preparation time: 20 minutes
Total cooking time: 10– 15 minutes
Serves 4

200 g (6¹/2 oz) green beans, trimmed
  and cut into short lengths
300 g (10 oz) penne rigate
¹/2 cup (125 ml/4 fl oz) olive oil
250 g (8 oz) fresh tuna steak, cut into
  thick slices
1 red (Spanish) onion, thinly sliced
1 tablespoon balsamic vinegar

1 In a large pan of boiling water, cook the prepared beans for 1– 2 minutes, until tender but still crisp. Remove with a slotted spoon and rinse under cold water. Drain and transfer to a serving bowl.
2 Cook the pasta in a large pan of rapidly boiling salted water until *al dente*. Drain, rinse under cold water and drain again before adding to the beans.
3 Heat half the oil in a frying pan. Add the tuna and onion and gently sauté until the tuna is just cooked through. Stir the tuna carefully to prevent it from breaking up. Add the vinegar, turn heat to high and quickly cook until the dressing has reduced and lightly coats the tuna. Transfer the tuna and onion to a bowl, leaving behind any bits on the bottom of the pan.
4 Toss the beans, pasta, tuna and onion together lightly and mix with the remaining oil, and salt and pepper, to taste. Cool to room temperature before serving.

NUTRITION PER SERVE: *Protein 25 g; Fat 30 g; Carbohydrate 55 g; Dietary Fibre 6 g; Cholesterol 45 mg; 2535 kJ (605 cal)*

PASTRAMI, MUSHROOM AND CUCUMBER SALAD

Preparation time: 20 minutes
Total cooking time: 5– 10 minutes
Serves 4

200 g (6¹/2 oz) lasagnette, broken
  into quarters
250 g (8 oz) sliced pastrami,
  cut in strips
1 celery stick, sliced
2 small tomatoes, cut into wedges
1 Lebanese cucumber, thinly sliced
80 g (2³/4 oz) button mushrooms,
  thinly sliced
1 tablespoon finely chopped fresh
  coriander, to garnish

Dressing

¹/4 cup (60 ml/2 fl oz) olive oil
2 tablespoons red wine vinegar
¹/2 teaspoon Dijon mustard
1 clove garlic, crushed
¹/4 teaspoon hot chilli oil

1 Cook the lasagnette in a large pan of rapidly boiling salted water until *al dente*. Drain, rinse under cold water and drain again. Allow to cool and transfer to a large salad bowl.
2 Add the pastrami, celery, tomato wedges, cucumber and mushrooms to the pasta.
3 To prepare the dressing, combine all the ingredients in a screw top jar and shake until well blended.
4 Toss the dressing through the salad and refrigerate, covered, for several hours. Adjust the seasoning and sprinkle with the fresh coriander before serving.

NUTRITION PER SERVE: *Protein 15 g; Fat 55 g; Carbohydrate 35 g; Dietary Fibre 4 g; Cholesterol 280 mg; 3050 kJ (725 cal)*

ARTICHOKE HEARTS

Artichokes are a thistle and the edible part of a globe artichoke is the flower head. In the centre of this is the choke, a mass of hairs which is, in fact, the flower, and this sits on a tender cup-like base. It is surrounded by fleshy leaves of which the tough, outer ones are discarded to reveal the artichoke's heart, the lower section of delicate inner leaves surrounding the choke and bottom cup. Canned or bottled artichoke hearts retain a good flavour and are a time-saving substitute for fresh ones.

ABOVE: Italian-style chicken and pasta salad

ITALIAN-STYLE CHICKEN AND PASTA SALAD

Preparation time: 30 minutes
  + 3 hours marinating
Total cooking time: 10 minutes
Serves 8

3 chicken breast fillets
$1/4$ cup (60 ml/2 fl oz) lemon juice
1 clove garlic, crushed
100 g ($3^1/2$ oz) thinly sliced prosciutto
1 Lebanese cucumber
2 tablespoons seasoned lemon pepper
2 tablespoons olive oil
$1^1/2$ cups (135 g/$4^1/2$ oz) penne, cooked
$1/2$ cup (80 g/$2^3/4$ oz) thinly sliced sun-dried
  tomatoes
$1/2$ cup (70 g/$2^1/4$ oz) pitted black olives, halved
$1/2$ cup (110 g/$3^1/2$ oz) halved bottled
  artichoke hearts
$1/2$ cup (50 g/$1^3/4$ oz) shaved fresh Parmesan

Creamy basil dressing

$1/3$ cup (80 ml/$2^3/4$ fl oz) olive oil
1 tablespoon white wine vinegar
$1/4$ teaspoon seasoned pepper
1 teaspoon Dijon mustard
3 teaspoons cornflour
$2/3$ cup (170 ml/$5^1/2$ fl oz) cream
$1/3$ cup (20 g/$3/4$ oz) shredded fresh basil

1 Remove the excess fat and sinew from the chicken. Flatten the chicken slightly with a mallet or rolling pin.
2 Combine the lemon juice and garlic in a bowl. Add the chicken and stir until it is coated. Cover with plastic wrap and refrigerate for at least 3 hours or overnight, turning occasionally.
3 Cut the prosciutto into thin strips. Cut the cucumber in half lengthways and cut each half into slices.
4 Drain the chicken and coat in seasoned pepper. Heat the oil in a large heavy-based frying pan. Cook the chicken for 4 minutes on

each side, or until lightly browned and cooked through. Remove from the heat, allow to cool and then cut into small pieces.

5 To make the creamy basil dressing, combine the oil, white wine vinegar, pepper and mustard in a medium pan. Blend the cornflour with ⅓ cup (80 ml/2¾ fl oz) of water in a small bowl or jug until smooth. Add to the pan. Whisk over medium heat for 2 minutes, or until the sauce boils and thickens. Add the cream, basil and salt, to taste. Stir until heated through.

6 Combine the pasta, chicken pieces, cucumber slices, prosciutto, sun-dried tomato, olives and artichoke hearts in a large serving bowl. Pour in the warm creamy basil dressing and toss gently to combine. Serve the salad warm or cold, topped with shaved Parmesan.

NUTRITION PER SERVE: *Protein 15 g; Fat 30 g; Carbohydrate 15 g; Dietary Fibre 2 g; Cholesterol 60 mg; 1555 kJ (370 cal)*

CREAMY SEAFOOD SALAD

Preparation time: 30 minutes
Total cooking time: 5–10 minutes
Serves 8 as a first course, 4 as a main meal

400 g (13 oz) medium-sized conchiglie (shells)
1 cup (250 g/8 oz) whole-egg mayonnaise
3 tablespoons fresh or 2 tablespoons
   dried tarragon
1 tablespoon finely chopped
   fresh parsley
cayenne pepper, to taste
1 teaspoon fresh lemon juice, or to taste
1 kg (2 lb) cooked shellfish flesh: prawns,
   lobster, crab (any one of these or a
   combination), cut into bite-sized pieces
2 mild red radishes, thinly sliced
1 small green pepper (capsicum), julienned

1 Cook the pasta in rapidly boiling salted water until *al dente*. Drain, rinse under cold water and drain again. Place in a large bowl and stir through 1–2 tablespoons of mayonnaise. Cool to room temperature, stirring occasionally to prevent sticking.

2 If using dried tarragon, simmer it in ¼ cup (60 ml/2 fl oz) of milk for 3–4 minutes and then drain. Combine the tarragon, parsley, cayenne pepper and lemon juice in a bowl, with the remaining mayonnaise, and mix well.

3 Add the shellfish to the pasta with the radishes and peppers, and salt and pepper, to taste. Mix with the tarragon mayonnaise, tossing gently to coat. Cover and chill before serving, adding more mayonnaise or extra lemon juice if the mixture is a little dry.

NOTE: To make your own mayonnaise, in a bowl, whisk together 2 egg yolks, 1 teaspoon of Dijon mustard and 2 teaspoons of lemon juice for 30 seconds, until light and creamy. Add 1 cup (250 ml/8 fl oz) of light olive oil, about a teaspoon at a time, whisking continuously. Increase the amount of oil as the mayonnaise thickens. When all the oil has been added, stir in an extra 2 teaspoons of lemon juice and season, to taste, with salt and white pepper. Alternatively, you can use a food processor. Use the same ingredients, but process the yolks, mustard and juice for 10 seconds. With the motor running, add the oil in a slow, thin stream until combined.

NUTRITION PER SERVE (8): *Protein 35 g; Fat 10 g; Carbohydrate 40 g; Dietary Fibre 3 g; Cholesterol 245 mg; 1755 kJ (415 cal)*

ABOVE: Creamy seafood salad

ROCKET, CHERRY TOMATO AND SPICY SALAMI PASTA SALAD

Preparation time: 20 minutes
Total cooking time: 18 minutes
Serves 6

350 g (11 oz) orecchiette
6 slices (50 g/1³⁄₄ oz) spicy Italian salami,
  cut into strips
150 g (5 oz) rocket, shredded
200 g (6¹⁄₂ oz) cherry tomatoes, halved
4 tablespoons olive oil
3 tablespoons white wine vinegar
1 teaspoon sugar

1 Cook the pasta in a large pan of rapidly boiling salted water until *al dente*. Drain, rinse under cold water and drain again. Allow to cool.
2 Heat a frying pan over medium heat, add the prepared salami and cook until crisp. Drain well on paper towels.
3 Combine the salami, pasta, rocket and cherry tomatoes in a large bowl.
4 In a small food processor, combine the oil, vinegar, sugar and ¹⁄₄ teaspoon each of salt and pepper, for 1 minute. Drizzle over the salad just before serving.

NUTRITION PER SERVE: *Protein 9 g; Fat 15 g; Carbohydrate 45 g; Dietary Fibre 4 g; Cholesterol 9 mg; 1505 kJ (360 cal)*

ON THE SIDE

DAMPER Sift 4 cups (500 g/1 lb) of self-raising flour with 1 teaspoon of salt and 1 teaspoon of caster sugar into a large bowl. Use a knife to mix in enough milk, about 1¹⁄₂ cups (375 ml/12 fl oz), to make a fairly stiff dough which leaves the side of the bowl. Knead the dough for about 1 minute, on a floured surface, and form into a ball. Place the ball on a greased baking tray and flatten slightly, cut 2 slits across the top, brush with milk and bake at hot 210°C (415°F/Gas 6–7) for 15 minutes, then turn the oven down to moderate 180°C (350°F/Gas 4) and bake for 20 minutes, or until the damper is golden and the base sounds hollow when tapped.

CHICKEN, PEAR AND PASTA SALAD

Preparation time: 35 minutes
Total cooking time: 30 minutes
Serves 6

350 g (11 oz) gemelli or fusilli
200 g (6¹⁄₂ oz) chicken breast fillets
2 ripe pears
3 spring onions, finely sliced
2 tablespoons toasted slivered almonds
100 g (3¹⁄₂ oz) creamy blue cheese
3 tablespoons sour cream
3 tablespoons ice-cold water

1 Cook the pasta in a large pan of rapidly boiling salted water until *al dente*. Drain, rinse under cold water and drain again. Allow to cool.
2 Place the chicken breasts in a frying pan, cover with cold water and simmer gently for 8 minutes, or until tender, turning the chicken over occasionally. Remove from the pan, allow to cool, slice into fine pieces and place in a bowl with the cooled pasta.
3 Halve the pears and remove the cores. Cut the pears into thin slices, about the same size as the chicken pieces and add to the chicken with the spring onion and almonds.
4 Mix the creamy blue cheese and the sour cream with 3 tablespoons of ice-cold water and ¹⁄₄ teaspoon each of salt and pepper, in a food processor until smooth. Pour the mixture over the salad and stir to combine. Transfer the salad to a serving bowl or arrange on a platter. Garnish with slivers of spring onion, if you like.

NUTRITION PER SERVE: *Protein 20 g; Fat 15 g; Carbohydrate 50 g; Dietary Fibre 5 g; Cholesterol 45 mg; 1655 kJ (395 cal)*

PEARS
The pear is a very versatile fruit. It can be eaten fresh, used in desserts and sweets, or cooked in savoury dishes. The crisp, firm texture reacts well to heat and the flavour is compatible with many other foods. Poultry, cheeses, salad greens and strangely enough, olive oil, make particularly good companions. There is a huge selection of local varieties grown. They can be categorised into dessert pears, those with a clear, crisp sweet flesh intended for eating fresh, and cooking pears, which have a firm, often granular flesh and a more tart taste.

OPPOSITE PAGE: Rocket, cherry tomato and spicy salami pasta salad (top); Chicken, pear and pasta salad

BARBECUED CHICKEN AND PASTA SALAD

Preparation time: 15 minutes
Total cooking time: 15 minutes
Serves 6

1 barbecued chicken
500 g (1 lb) penne
1/4 cup (60 ml/2 fl oz) olive oil
2 tablespoons white wine vinegar
200 g (6 1/2 oz) cherry tomatoes, halved
1/3 cup (20 g/3/4 oz) chopped fresh
   basil leaves
1/2 cup (75 g/2 1/2 oz) chopped pitted
   black olives
freshly ground black pepper, to taste

1 Pull the meat and skin from the barbecued chicken. Cut into fine shreds.
2 Cook the penne in a large pan of rapidly boiling salted water until *al dente*. Drain and transfer to a serving bowl. Combine the oil and vinegar and toss through while the pasta is still warm.
3 Add the chicken, cherry tomatoes, basil and olives to the pasta, and toss thoroughly to combine. Sprinkle with freshly ground black pepper. Serve warm, as a main meal, or at room temperature as part of a selection of salads.
NOTE: The salad can be prepared up to 2 hours in advance. Refrigerate the chicken until close to serving time and add it to the salad at the last minute. Chop and add the basil close to serving time as well, as it discolours when cut.

NUTRITION PER SERVE: *Protein 30 g; Fat 20 g; Carbohydrate 60 g; Dietary Fibre 5 g; Cholesterol 70 mg; 2500 kJ (595 cal)*

ABOVE: Barbecued chicken and pasta salad

LEMON AND VEGETABLE PASTA SALAD

Preparation time: 20 minutes
Total cooking time: 15 minutes
Serves 4

250 g (8 oz) farfalle

1/3 cup (80 ml/2¾ fl oz) olive oil

250 g (8 oz) broccoli, cut into small florets

125 g (4 oz) snow peas (mangetout), topped and tailed

150 g (5 oz) small yellow button squash, cut into quarters

2 tablespoons sour cream

1 tablespoon lemon juice

2 teaspoons finely grated lemon rind

1 celery stick, finely sliced

1 tablespoon chopped chervil

chervil sprigs, to garnish

1 Cook the farfalle in a large pan of rapidly boiling salted water until *al dente*. Drain well, toss with 1 tablespoon of the olive oil and set aside to cool.

2 Combine the broccoli, snow peas and squash in a large bowl, cover with boiling water and leave for 2 minutes. Drain, plunge into iced water, drain again and pat dry with paper towels.

3 Put the sour cream, lemon juice, rind and the remaining oil in a screw top jar and shake for 30 seconds, or until combined. Season with salt and pepper, to taste.

4 Combine the cooled pasta, sliced celery and drained vegetables in a large bowl; sprinkle with chervil. Drizzle the dressing over and toss to combine. Garnish with chervil sprigs. Serve at room temperature.

NUTRITION PER SERVE: *Protein 10 g; Fat 25 g; Carbohydrate 50 g; Dietary Fibre 5 g; Cholesterol 15 mg; 1910 kJ (455 cal)*

CHERVIL

An umbelliferous plant cultivated as a pot-herb, chervil has a delicate, slightly aniseed flavour. It has stiff stems and dainty, curly leaves, which can be chopped for use but are often left whole, like little petals. Its aroma evaporates quickly, so the leaves are best used fresh or added to hot dishes at the last minute. Chervil is folded through omelettes, sprinkled over soup and used as a garnish.

ABOVE: Lemon and vegetable pasta salad

BREAD
Crusty and fresh, in all its delightful varieties, bread is the perfect accompaniment to most meals. Serve plain, or dress it up with garlic, cheese, fresh basil, parsley and other herbs.

GARLIC GRISSINI STICKS
Preheat the oven to moderately hot 200°C (400°F/Gas 6). Combine 2 crushed cloves of garlic with 1 tablespoon of olive oil. Brush over 1 packet of grissini sticks and wrap each in paper-thin strips of prosciutto. Bake for 5 minutes, until the ends crisp. Cool on trays before serving. Makes about 25.

NUTRITION PER SERVE: *Protein 2 g; Fat 2 g; Carbohydrate 6 g; Dietary Fibre 0 g; Cholesterol 4 mg; 210 kJ (50 cal)*

CHEESY HERB ROLLS
Preheat the oven to 220°C (425°F/Gas 7). Combine 125 g (4 oz) of softened butter with 1 tablespoon each of chopped fresh basil, parsley and chives and 1/4 cup (30 g/1 oz) of grated Cheddar cheese. Season with salt and pepper. Cut 4 crusty rosetta rolls into thin slices, but don't cut all the way through. Spread each side of each slice with flavoured butter. Bake for 15 minutes, or until the rolls are crisp and golden. Serves 4.

NUTRITION PER SERVE: *Protein 10 g; Fat 30 g; Carbohydrate 45 g; Dietary Fibre 3 g; Cholesterol 90 mg; 2055 kJ (490 cal)*

CRISPY FOCACCIA TOASTS WITH PESTO

Cut a square of focaccia, about 20 cm (8 inches) in diameter, in half horizontally. Combine 1 cup (50 g/ 1³/4 oz) of basil leaves, 2 cloves of garlic, 3 tablespoons of toasted pine nuts and 4 tablespoons of freshly grated Parmesan in a food processor until roughly chopped. With the motor running, gradually add 1/4 cup (60 ml/2 fl oz) of olive oil and process until the mixture forms a smooth paste. Brush the focaccia squares with olive oil and toast both sides until golden brown. Spread the pesto over the focaccia and cut into small rectangles. Makes 16– 20.

NUTRITION PER SERVE: *Protein 2 g; Fat 6 g; Carbohydrate 4 g; Dietary Fibre 0 g; Cholesterol 3 mg; 340 kJ (80 cal)*

ROASTED PEPPER (CAPSICUM) BRUSCHETTA

Cut a red and a yellow pepper (capsicum) in half, removing the seeds and membrane. Place, skin-side-up, under a hot grill until the skin blackens and blisters. Cover with a damp tea towel and allow to cool. Peel away the skin and cut the flesh into thin strips. Cut 1 loaf of woodfired Italian bread into thin slices and toast lightly until golden. Rub each side of the slices with halved cloves of garlic and brush lightly with extra virgin olive oil. Top with a little of the pepper and sprinkle with fresh lemon thyme. Makes about 30 slices.

NUTRITION PER SERVE: *Protein 2 g; Fat 2 g; Carbohydrate 10 g; Dietary Fibre 1 g; Cholesterol 0 mg; 315 kJ (75 cal)*

ANCHOVY AND TOMATO CROSTINI

Cut 1 French baguette into thick diagonal slices. Brush lightly with olive oil and toast until golden. Spread with 250 g (8 oz) of sun-dried tomato pesto and sprinkle with 50 g (1³/4 oz) of drained, thinly sliced anchovy fillets, 50 g (1³/4 oz) of chopped black olives and some shredded fresh basil. Makes about 15 pieces.

NUTRITION PER SERVE: *Protein 4 g; Fat 5 g; Carbohydrate 15 g; Dietary Fibre 1 g; Cholesterol 4 mg; 535 kJ (125 cal)*

ABOVE, FROM LEFT: Garlic grissini sticks; Cheesy herb rolls; Crispy focaccia toasts with pesto; Roasted pepper bruschetta; Anchovy and tomato crostini

185

FRESH BABY CORN

Fresh baby corn is available from greengrocers and some supermarkets. It should be crisp and dry, have a soft yellowy colour with no blemishes and be no longer than 8 cm (3 inches). It tastes of sweet, fresh corn and the cob is eaten whole. Although made popular in Asian dishes, it is now used in many cooking styles, for the sweet flavour and crunchy texture.

ABOVE: Pasta with Thai-style vegetables

PASTA WITH THAI-STYLE VEGETABLES

Preparation time: 20 minutes
Total cooking time: 15 minutes
Serves 6

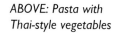

350 g (11 oz) plain or tomato and
  herb fettucine
100 g (3½ oz) fresh baby corn, cut in
  half lengthways
1 carrot, cut into julienne strips
200 g (6½ oz) broccoli, cut into small florets
1 red pepper (capsicum), cut into thin strips
3 tablespoons sweet chilli sauce
2 tablespoons honey
2 teaspoons fish sauce
3 spring onions, julienned
2 teaspoons sesame seeds

1 Cook the pasta in a large pan of rapidly boiling salted water until *al dente*. Drain, rinse under cold water and drain again. Allow to cool.
2 In another pan of boiling water, blanch the corn for 1 minute. Use a slotted spoon to transfer the corn to a bowl of iced water. Blanch the carrot, broccoli and red pepper for 30 seconds, drain and add to the cold water. When the vegetables have cooled, drain and combine with the pasta in a bowl.
3 Whisk together the sweet chilli sauce, honey and fish sauce until well combined. Drizzle over the salad and mix well. Garnish with the spring onion and sesame seeds.

NUTRITION PER SERVE: *Protein 10 g; Fat 2 g; Carbohydrate 60 g; Dietary Fibre 6 g; Cholesterol 0 mg; 1210 kJ (290 cal)*

PASTA WITH MEDITERRANEAN-STYLE VEGETABLES

Preparation time: 30 minutes
Total cooking time: 15 minutes
Serves 6

350 g (11 oz) macaroni

200 g (6¹/2 oz) fried and marinated eggplant
   (aubergine) slices (see note)

100 g (3¹/2 oz) sun-dried or semi-dried
   tomatoes

60 g (2 oz) Kalamata olives, pitted

200 g (6¹/2 oz) double-smoked sliced or
   shaved ham

2 tablespoons sweet chilli sauce

1 tablespoon white wine vinegar

1 tablespoon olive oil

2 tablespoons chopped fresh parsley

1 Cook the pasta in a large pan of rapidly boiling salted water until *al dente*. Drain, rinse under cold water and drain again. Allow to cool and transfer to a bowl.

2 Slice the eggplant, tomato, olives and ham into strips and add to the pasta. Shaved ham can just be separated into smallish pieces.

3 Whisk together the sweet chilli sauce, vinegar, oil, and salt and pepper, to taste, until well combined. Drizzle the dressing over the pasta and vegetables and toss well. Serve scattered with the fresh parsley.

NOTE: Marinated vegetables are available from delicatessens. If preferred, red or green peppers (capsicums) or zucchini (courgettes) can be used.

NUTRITION PER SERVE: *Protein 15 g; Fat 8 g; Carbohydrate 45 g; Dietary Fibre 4 g; Cholesterol 15 mg; 1280 kJ (305 cal)*

SHAVED HAM
Very finely sliced ham is known as shaved ham. It should be wafer-thin, but still in discernible pieces that fall into a loosely bulky heap. This method of preparation gives the ham a delicate texture. Shaved ham is available from delicatessens and should be eaten as soon as possible, as it spoils more quickly than unshaved.

ABOVE: Pasta with Mediterranean-style vegetables

187

BALSAMIC VINEGAR
Balsamic vinegar, *aceto balsamico*, is a speciality of the area around Modena in central northern Italy. It is made from the newly pressed juice of selected white grapes, which is slowly boiled down to one third of its volume. The resulting syrup is aged over a number of years, in a series of wooden casks, until it becomes concentrated, mellow and highly aromatic. It is a dense, almost black sauce which is used sparingly not as a regular vinegar, but as a condiment. A good balsamic vinegar should be sweet and syrupy but not cloying, with an intense fragrance and flavour. There are many imitations being manufactured and a cheap copy bears little resemblance to the real thing. Here is an instance where it is truly worth spending extra for the genuine article.

*OPPOSITE PAGE:
Conchiglie salad with bocconcini, asparagus and oregano (top);
Warm garlic prawn and fettucine salad*

CONCHIGLIE SALAD WITH BOCCONCINI, ASPARAGUS AND OREGANO

Preparation time: 25 minutes
Total cooking time: 10– 15 minutes
Serves 4– 6

350 g (11 oz) conchiglie (shell pasta)
155 g (5 oz) fresh asparagus
200 g (6 1/2 oz) bocconcini cheese, thinly sliced
100 g (3 1/2 oz) cherry tomatoes, quartered
2 tablespoons fresh oregano leaves
4 tablespoons walnut oil
1 tablespoon white wine vinegar
1 tablespoon balsamic vinegar
1/4 teaspoon each salt and freshly ground black pepper

1 Cook the conchiglie in a large pan of rapidly boiling salted water until *al dente*. Drain, rinse under cold water and drain again. Allow to cool.
2 Cut the asparagus into short lengths. Bring a small pan of water to the boil, add the asparagus and blanch for 1 minute. Drain, transfer to a bowl of iced water to cool and then drain again.
3 In a large bowl, combine the conchiglie, asparagus, bocconcini, tomato and oregano. In a small bowl, whisk together the walnut oil, vinegars, salt and pepper until well combined.
4 Drizzle the dressing over the salad and toss thoroughly before serving.

NUTRITION PER SERVE (6): *Protein 15 g; Fat 25 g; Carbohydrate 40 g; Dietary Fibre 5 g; Cholesterol 35 mg; 1900 kJ (455 cal)*

WARM GARLIC PRAWN AND FETTUCINE SALAD

Preparation time: 30 minutes
Total cooking time: 25 minutes
Serves 4– 6

300 g (10 oz) fettucine
2 tablespoons olive oil
4 cloves garlic, crushed
300 g (10 oz) raw prawn meat
2 tablespoons whisky
1/2 cup (125 ml/4 fl oz) cream
3 spring onions, chopped

1 Cook the fettucine in a large pan of rapidly boiling salted water until *al dente*. Drain, rinse under cold water and drain again. Allow to cool and set aside.
2 Heat the olive oil in a heavy-based frying pan. Add the garlic and cook for 30 seconds. Add the prawns and stir-fry over high heat until they change colour. Add the whisky and cook until it evaporates. Add the cream and spring onion and simmer for 2 minutes.
3 Drizzle the sauce over the pasta. Season with plenty of salt and pepper.

NUTRITION PER SERVE (6): *Protein 15 g; Fat 15 g; Carbohydrate 35 g; Dietary Fibre 5 g; Cholesterol 125 mg; 1530 kJ (365 cal)*

ON THE SIDE

PARMESAN BISCUITS Sift 2 cups (250 g/8 oz) of plain flour with 1 teaspoon of baking powder, 1/4 teaspoon of paprika and 1/2 teaspoon of salt into a bowl. Rub in 60 g (2 oz) of butter. Add 1/4 cup (25 g/3/4 oz) of finely grated Parmesan and 3/4 cup (185 ml/6 fl oz) of milk and bring the mixture together. Roll out the mixture to about 2 cm (3/4 inch) thick and cut out the biscuits. Sprinkle with some more Parmesan and bake in a hot 220°C (425°F/Gas 7) oven for 15 minutes.

RIGATONI

Rigatoni is a pasta with many uses: good for salads but also great for serving with chunky sauces, particularly tomato- or meat-based ones. When it is well tossed through, sauce catches inside the tubes and clings to the ribs on the outside surface. Tortiglioni is similar, with a slight bend in the middle.

ABOVE: Rigatoni with tomato, haloumi and spinach

RIGATONI WITH TOMATO, HALOUMI AND SPINACH

Preparation time: 30 minutes
Total cooking time: 1 hour
Serves 6

★

6 egg (Roma) tomatoes, halved
sugar, to sprinkle
4 cloves garlic, chopped
400 g (13 oz) rigatoni
1/4 cup (60 ml/2 fl oz) lemon juice
1/4 cup (60 ml/2 fl oz) olive oil
200 g (6 1/2 oz) haloumi cheese, thinly sliced
100 g (3 1/2 oz) baby English spinach

1 Preheat the oven to moderate 180°C (350°F/Gas 4). Put the tomatoes on a non-stick baking tray, lined with foil if you like, and sprinkle generously with salt, sugar, pepper and the garlic. Bake for 1 hour, or until quite dehydrated and shrunken. Allow to cool. Cut in half again.
2 While the tomatoes are cooking, cook the pasta in a large pan of rapidly boiling salted water until *al dente*. Drain, rinse under cold water and drain again. Allow to cool.
3 Combine the lemon juice and olive oil. Season, to taste, with salt and pepper.
4 Toss the lemon dressing through the cooked, cold pasta and lightly toss the tomato, haloumi cheese and spinach through. Serve sprinkled with freshly cracked black pepper, to taste.

NUTRITION PER SERVE: *Protein 20 g; Fat 35 g; Carbohydrate 50 g; Dietary Fibre 5 g; Cholesterol 25 mg; 2530 kJ (605 cal)*

LEMON AND DATE ZITI

Preparation time: 15– 20 minutes
Total cooking time: 25 minutes
Serves 4– 6

2 cups (360 g/12 oz) dried pitted
 dates, halved
1½ cups (375 ml/12 fl oz) port
375 g (12 oz) ziti
¼ cup (60 ml/2 fl oz) balsamic vinegar
½ cup (125 ml/4 fl oz) olive oil
150 g (5 oz) rocket, trimmed
rind from 3 preserved lemons (see note),
 finely chopped

1 Place the dates and port in a pan. Bring to the boil, reduce the heat and simmer for 10 minutes. Strain the dates, reserving the port. Set aside to cool.
2 Cook the ziti in a large pan of rapidly boiling salted water until *al dente*. Drain, rinse in cold water and drain again. Allow to cool.
3 Combine the balsamic vinegar, reserved port and olive oil in a bowl. Season with a little sugar if necessary.
4 Toss the dressing through the pasta with the dates, rocket and lemon rind.
NOTE: Preserved lemons can be purchased at any good delicatessen or speciality food shop. They are available either per lemon or bottled. This salad is also wonderful served warm.

NUTRITION PER SERVE (6): *Protein 10 g; Fat 20 g; Carbohydrate 95 g; Dietary Fibre 10 g; Cholesterol 0 mg; 2715 kJ (650 cal)*

DATES
Date palms grow in desert regions and have been cultivated for thousands of years. Fresh dates have a fruity, moist pulp and are an excellent source of iron, folic acid and vitamin B6, as well as having a high fibre content. There are hard and soft dates, the latter being preferred for table use. Both dry well, with soft dates maintaining succulent, soft flesh. Fresh and soft dried dates are interchangeable in recipes but dried are sweeter, with a slightly more concentrated flavour.

ABOVE: Lemon and date ziti

and blistered. Remove from the heat and cover with a damp tea towel. When cool, peel away the skin and cut the flesh into thin strips.

3 In a large salad bowl, combine the pasta, pepper strips, onion, parsley, anchovies, oil, lemon juice, and salt and pepper, to taste. Toss until well combined and serve immediately.

NOTE: To prevent pasta sticking together, after rinsing under cold water add a little of the oil to pasta and toss well.

NUTRITION PER SERVE: *Protein 10 g; Fat 10 g; Carbohydrate 65 g; Dietary Fibre 5 g; Cholesterol 0 mg; 1675 kJ (400 cal)*

WARM PASTA AND CRAB SALAD

Preparation time: 20 minutes
Total cooking time: 10 minutes
Serves 6

★

200 g (6¹/2 oz) spaghetti
2 tablespoons olive oil
30 g (1 oz) butter
3 x 200 g (6¹/2 oz) cans crab meat, drained
1 large red pepper (capsicum), cut into
  thin strips
2 teaspoons finely grated lemon rind
3 tablespoons grated fresh Parmesan
2 tablespoons chopped chives
3 tablespoons chopped fresh parsley

1 Break the spaghetti in half and cook it in a large pan of rapidly boiling salted water until *al dente*. Drain.
2 Place the spaghetti in a large serving bowl and toss with the oil and butter. Add all the remaining ingredients and toss to combine. Sprinkle with pepper and serve warm.
NOTE: Substitute 500 g (1 lb) of fresh crab meat for canned if you prefer.

NUTRITION PER SERVE: *Protein 20 g; Fat 15 g; Carbohydrate 25 g; Dietary Fibre 2 g; Cholesterol 100 mg; 1245 kJ (295 cal)*

GRILLED PEPPERS (CAPSICUMS) AND ANCHOVY SALAD

Preparation time: 15 minutes
Total cooking time: 25 minutes
Serves 6

★

500 g (1 lb) penne or spiral pasta
2 large red peppers (capsicums)
1 small red onion, finely chopped
1 cup (20 g/³/4 oz) fresh flat-leaf parsley leaves
2–3 anchovies, whole or chopped
¹/4 cup (60 ml/2 fl oz) olive oil
2 tablespoons lemon juice

1 Cook the pasta in a large pan of rapidly boiling salted water until *al dente*. Drain, rinse under cold water and drain again.
2 Cut the peppers in half and remove seeds and membrane. Place skin-side-up under a hot grill and cook for 8 minutes, or until the skin is black

ABOVE: Grilled peppers and anchovy salad

TUSCAN WARM PASTA SALAD

Preparation time: 15 minutes
Total cooking time: 15 minutes
Serves 6

500 g (1 lb) rigatoni

1/3 cup (80 ml/2¾ fl oz) olive oil

1 clove garlic, crushed

1 tablespoon balsamic vinegar

425 g (14 oz) can artichoke hearts, drained
    and quartered

8 thin slices prosciutto, chopped

1/2 cup (80 g/2¾ oz) sun-dried tomatoes in oil,
    drained and thinly sliced

1/4 cup (15 g/1/2 oz) fresh basil leaves, shredded

2 cups (70 g/2¼ oz) rocket leaves, washed and
    drained well

1/4 cup (40 g/1¼ oz) pine nuts, lightly toasted

1/4 cup (45 g/1½ oz) small black Italian olives

1 Add the rigatoni to a large pan of rapidly boiling water and cook until *al dente*. Drain the pasta thoroughly and transfer to a large serving bowl.
2 While the pasta is cooking, whisk together the oil, garlic and balsamic vinegar.
3 Toss the dressing through the hot pasta. Allow the pasta to cool slightly. Add the artichoke hearts, prosciutto, sun-dried tomato, basil, rocket, pine nuts and olives.
4 Toss all the ingredients together until well combined. Season, to taste, with salt and freshly ground black pepper.
NOTE: To toast the pine nuts, cook in a dry frying pan over medium heat for 1–2 minutes, until lightly golden. Allow to cool.

NUTRITION PER SERVE: *Protein 15 g; Fat 20 g; Carbohydrate 60 g; Dietary Fibre 10 g; Cholesterol 15 mg; 2145 kJ (510 cal)*

SALT
There are two sources of salt, or sodium chloride: rock salt, found in crystalline form in the ground, and sea salt, extracted from sea water. Refined sea salt is available in pure crystal form, which must be ground, in thin flakes ready to use, or already ground. This free running table salt has had products such as phosphate of lime added to prevent the pure salt reverting to crystal form when in humidity. Pure salt provides the best flavour.

*ABOVE: Tuscan
warm pasta salad*

SMOKED SALMON, DILL AND EGG PASTA SALAD

Preparation time: 20 minutes
Total cooking time: 15 minutes
Serves 4– 6

350 g (11 oz) farfalle or fusilli
2 eggs
200 g (6½ oz) smoked salmon, cut into
    thin strips
1 tablespoon finely chopped fresh dill
3 tablespoons sour cream
2 tablespoons lemon juice
¼ teaspoon each salt and freshly ground
    black pepper
1 tablespoon chopped fresh parsley, to garnish

1 Cook the pasta in a large pan of rapidly boiling salted water until *al dente*. Drain, rinse under cold water and drain again. Allow to cool.
2 While the pasta is cooking, cook the eggs for 12 minutes, or until hard-boiled. Allow to cool and then peel, finely grate or chop and set aside.
3 Place the pasta in serving bowls and scatter the strips of smoked salmon and the chopped fresh dill over the top.
4 In a small bowl, whisk together the sour cream, lemon juice, salt and pepper. Drizzle the dressing over the pasta. Sprinkle the egg and parsley over the top and serve immediately.

NUTRITION PER SERVE (6): *Protein 15 g; Fat 10 g; Carbohydrate 40 g; Dietary Fibre 3 g; Cholesterol 90 mg; 1280 kJ (305 cal)*

ON THE SIDE

GARLIC PIZZA BREAD Make up a pizza base using a pizza base mix and roll it out to a thin circle on a baking tray. Brush the surface of the dough with olive oil and sprinkle it with crushed garlic, chopped fresh parsley and coarse salt. Bake until golden brown. Cut into strips with a sharp knife or a pizza cutter.

ORANGE AND OLIVE SALAD Cut 8 peeled oranges into thick slices. Layer the oranges with thinly sliced red (Spanish) onion and chopped fresh mint on a plate. Top with olives and drizzle with a dressing made from orange juice, crushed garlic and a little sesame oil.

MIDDLE-EASTERN HUMMUS, TOMATO AND OLIVE PASTA SALAD

Preparation time: 25 minutes
Total cooking time: 15 minutes
Serves 6

350 g (11 oz) macaroni elbows or
    conchiglie (shell pasta)
200 g (6½ oz) cherry tomatoes, cut
    into quarters
1 large zucchini (courgette), grated
1 small onion, grated
50 g (1¾ oz) black olives, pitted and chopped

Hummus dressing

2 tablespoons hummus
2 tablespoons natural yoghurt
1 tablespoon olive oil
1 clove garlic, finely chopped
1 teaspoon finely grated lemon rind
1 tablespoon chopped fresh parsley

1 Cook the pasta in a large pan of rapidly boiling salted water until *al dente*. Drain, rinse under cold water and drain again. Allow to cool. Place the pasta in a large bowl with the tomato, zucchini, onion and olives.
2 To make the hummus dressing, in a blender or food processor, combine the hummus, yoghurt, olive oil, garlic and lemon rind. Add plenty of salt and pepper and process again briefly.
3 Pour the dressing over the salad, add the parsley and toss well to combine.

NUTRITION PER SERVE: *Protein 8 g; Fat 7 g; Carbohydrate 45 g; Dietary Fibre 5 g; Cholesterol 1 mg; 1145 kJ (270 cal)*

DILL
Dill is a native of the Mediterranean and has been used since ancient times for its medicinal properties and culinary flavours. All of the upper plant is aromatic, but the delicate leaves have the most subtle taste and aroma. Their bitter-sweet flavour nicely complements dairy produce such as cream, butter and cheese, and it enhances fish particularly well. Because its essential oil is extremely volatile, it will quickly evaporate in temperatures above 30°C (86°F), so this means dill should be added to a cooked dish just before serving.

*OPPOSITE PAGE:
Smoked salmon, dill and egg pasta salad (top); Middle-eastern hummus, tomato and olive pasta salad*

GNOCCHI

Simplicity and adaptability are the two characteristics to which gnocchi owes its popularity. While making your own spaghetti may be a daunting task, making gnocchi is a skill that anyone can master. And, once you've perfected the basic potato recipe, you can experiment with other vegetables, such as pumpkin, carrot, spinach or parsnip. Gnocchi also lends itself to buttery, creamy or tomato sauces. Whatever the combination, these little dumplings are simply divine.

GNOCCHI ROMANA
(SEMOLINA GNOCCHI WITH RICH CHEESE SAUCE)

Preparation time: 20 minutes
  + 1 hour refrigeration
Total cooking time: 40 minutes
Serves 4

★ ★

3 cups (750 ml/24 fl oz) milk
1/2 teaspoon ground nutmeg
2/3 cup (85 g/3 oz) semolina
1 egg, beaten
1 1/2 cups (150 g/5 oz) freshly
  grated Parmesan
60 g (2 oz) butter, melted
1/2 cup (125 m/4 fl oz) cream
1/2 cup (75 g/2 1/2 oz) freshly grated
  mozzarella cheese

1 Line a deep Swiss roll tin with baking paper. Combine the milk, half the nutmeg, and salt and freshly ground pepper, to taste, in a medium pan. Bring to the boil, reduce the heat and gradually stir in the semolina. Cook, stirring occasionally, for 5– 10 minutes, or until the semolina is very stiff.
2 Remove the pan from the heat, add the egg and 1 cup of the Parmesan. Stir to combine and then spread the mixture in the tin. Refrigerate for 1 hour, or until the mixture is firm.
3 Preheat the oven to moderate 180°C (350°F/Gas 4). Cut the semolina into rounds using a floured 4 cm (1 1/2 inch) cutter and arrange in a greased shallow casserole dish.
4 Pour the melted butter over the top, followed by the cream. Combine the remaining grated Parmesan with the mozzarella cheese and sprinkle them on the rounds. Sprinkle with the remaining nutmeg. Bake for 20– 25 minutes, or until the mixture is golden. You can serve garnished with a sprig of fresh herbs.
NOTE: Some claim that this traditional dish from Rome can be traced as far back as Imperial Roman times. A crisp garden salad is the ideal accompaniment for this lovely rich recipe.

NUTRITION PER SERVE: *Protein 30 g; Fat 50 g; Carbohydrate 25 g; Dietary Fibre 1 g; Cholesterol 200 mg; 2790 kJ (670 cal)*

SEMOLINA

Semolina is a term that describes a particular meal milled from grain. Usually applied to wheat, it has a coarse, discernible bead, unlike flour which is fine and powdery. It is higher in protein than flour and has a firmer texture that gives 'bite' to the pasta or dough it goes into. Different grades are milled, with fine semolina preferred for the making of gnocchi and a medium grain for baked desserts and puddings.

ABOVE: Gnocchi Romana

ON THE SIDE

TURNIPS WITH TOMATO, WINE AND GARLIC Heat a little olive oil in a frying pan, add some chopped garlic, chilli and onion and cook over low heat until golden. Add a can of peeled, crushed Italian tomatoes in their juice and a little red wine, bring to the boil then reduce the heat to a simmer. Add some thickly sliced turnips and simmer until the sauce thickens and the turnips are tender. Do not overcook or the turnips will start to break up. Stir through some shredded fresh basil just before serving.

POTATO GNOCCHI WITH TOMATO AND BASIL SAUCE

Preparation time: 1 hour
Total cooking time: 45 – 50 minutes
Serves 4 – 6

Tomato sauce

1 tablespoon oil
1 onion, chopped
1 celery stick, chopped
2 carrots, chopped
2 x 425 g (14 oz) cans crushed tomatoes
1 teaspoon sugar
1/2 cup (30 g/1 oz) fresh basil, chopped

Potato gnocchi

1 kg (2 lb) old potatoes
30 g (1 oz) butter
2 cups (250 g/8 oz) plain flour
2 eggs, beaten

freshly grated Parmesan, for serving

1 To make the tomato sauce, heat the oil in a large frying pan, add the onion, celery and carrot and cook for 5 minutes, stirring regularly. Add the tomato and sugar and season with salt and pepper, to taste. Bring to the boil, reduce the heat to very low and simmer for 20 minutes. Cool slightly and process, in batches, in a food processor until smooth. Add the basil; set aside.

2 To make the potato gnocchi, peel the potatoes, chop roughly and steam or boil until very tender. Drain thoroughly and mash until smooth. Using a wooden spoon, stir in the butter and flour, then beat in the eggs. Cool.

3 Turn onto a floured surface and divide into two. Roll each into a long sausage shape. Cut into short pieces and press each piece with the back of a fork.

4 Cook the gnocchi, in batches, in a large pan of boiling salted water for about 2 minutes, or until the gnocchi rise to the surface. Using a slotted spoon, drain the gnocchi, and transfer to serving bowls. Serve with the tomato sauce and freshly grated Parmesan. Garnish with fresh herbs if you like.

NUTRITION PER SERVE (6): *Protein 15 g; Fat 10 g; Carbohydrate 60 g; Dietary Fibre 5 g; Cholesterol 75 mg; 1680 kJ (400 cal)*

POTATO

The best potatoes for gnocchi are old, starchy ones that have a low water content. Their mealy flesh results in a gnocchi that is tender and light. If the potatoes hold a lot of moisture, more flour will be required for the dough, which in turn will cause the gnocchi to be rubbery. The potatoes are best baked, steamed or boiled, and they should not be puréed in a processor as this only results in a gluey texture that is unsuitable for gnocchi dough.

LEFT: Potato gnocchi with tomato and basil sauce

GNOCCHI WITH TOMATO AND FRESH BASIL

Preparation time: 10 minutes
Total cooking time: 15 minutes
Serves 4

1 tablespoon olive oil

1 onion, finely chopped

2 cloves garlic, crushed

410 g (13 oz) can tomatoes

2 tablespoons tomato paste (tomato purée,
   double concentrate)

1 cup (250 ml/8 fl oz) cream

1/4 cup (40 g/1 1/4 oz) chopped
   sun-dried tomatoes

375 g (12 oz) fresh potato gnocchi

1 tablespoon finely chopped fresh basil

60 g (2 oz) pepato cheese, grated

1 Heat the oil in a pan and cook the onion for
2 minutes, or until soft. Add the garlic and cook
for another minute. Stir in the tomato and
tomato paste, increase the heat and cook for
about 5 minutes.
2 Reduce the heat, add the cream and sun-dried
tomatoes and stir through. Simmer gently for
another 3 minutes.
3 Meanwhile, lower batches of the fresh potato
gnocchi into a large pan of boiling salted water.
Cook for about 2 minutes, or until the gnocchi
rise to the surface. Drain, using a slotted spoon,
and add to the sauce with the fresh basil. Season
with salt and freshly ground black pepper.
Transfer to an ovenproof dish and sprinkle with
the pepato cheese. Cook under a hot grill for
5 minutes, until bubbling. Garnish with fresh
herbs, if you like.
NOTE: Pepato cheese is quite a pungent pepper
cheese. Use a milder cheese if you prefer.

NUTRITION PER SERVE: *Protein 10 g; Fat 40 g;*
Carbohydrate 30 g; Dietary Fibre 5 g; Cholesterol 130 mg;
2160 kJ (515 cal)

GNOCCHI

Gnocchi are little
dumplings, sometimes as
tiny as peas, but never
bigger than a mouthful.
Traditionally based on
semolina flour, ricotta
cheese or potato, they are
now made with different
grains such as buckwheat,
and vegetables including
pumpkin and artichokes.
Although nearly always
served with a sauce as
a first course, they make
a good accompaniment.
Once made, they should
be cooked and eaten as
quickly as possible.

ABOVE: Gnocchi
cheese bake

GNOCCHI CHEESE BAKE

Preparation time: 10 minutes
Total cooking time: 15 minutes
Serves 4

500 g (1 lb) fresh potato gnocchi

30 g (1 oz) butter, chopped

1 tablespoon chopped fresh parsley

100 g (3 1/2 oz) fontina cheese, sliced

100 g (3 1/2 oz) provolone cheese, sliced

1 Preheat the oven to moderately hot 200°C
(400°F/Gas 6). Cook the fresh gnocchi, in
batches, in a large pan of boiling water for about
2 minutes, or until the gnocchi rise to the
surface. Carefully remove from the pan with
a slotted spoon and drain well.
2 Put the gnocchi in a lightly greased ovenproof
dish. Scatter with the butter and parsley. Lay the
fontina and provolone cheeses over the top of
the gnocchi. Season with sea salt and cracked
black pepper. Bake for 10 minutes, or until the
cheese has melted.

NUTRITION PER SERVE: *Protein 25 g; Fat 30 g;*
Carbohydrate 10 g; Dietary Fibre 1 g; Cholesterol 115 mg;
1755 kJ (420 cal)

PUMPKIN GNOCCHI WITH SAGE BUTTER

Preparation time: 45 minutes
Total cooking time: 1 hour 30 minutes
Serves 4

500 g (1 lb) pumpkin
1 1/2 cups (185 g/6 oz) plain flour
1/2 cup (50 g/1 3/4 oz) freshly grated Parmesan
1 egg, beaten
100 g (3 1/2 oz) butter
2 tablespoons chopped fresh sage

1 Preheat the oven to warm 160°C (315°F/ Gas 2–3). Brush a baking tray with oil or melted butter. Cut the pumpkin into large pieces, leaving the skin on, and put on the tray. Bake for 1 1/4 hours, or until very tender. Cool slightly. Scrape the flesh from the skin, avoiding any tough or crispy parts. Transfer to a large bowl. Sift the flour into the bowl, add half the Parmesan, the egg and a little black pepper. After mixing thoroughly, turn onto a lightly floured surface and knead for 2 minutes, or until smooth.

2 Divide the dough in half. Using floured hands, roll each half into a sausage about 40 cm (16 inches) long. Cut into 16 equal pieces. Form each piece into an oval shape and press firmly with the floured prongs of a fork, to make an indentation.

3 Lower batches of gnocchi into a large pan of boiling salted water. Cook for about 2 minutes, or until the gnocchi rise to the surface. Drain with a slotted spoon and keep them warm.

4 To make the sage butter, melt the butter in a small pan, remove from the heat and stir in the chopped sage.

5 To serve, divide the gnocchi among four bowls, drizzle with sage butter and sprinkle with the remaining Parmesan.

NUTRITION PER SERVE: *Protein 20 g; Fat 35 g; Carbohydrate 55 g; Dietary Fibre 5 g; Cholesterol 115 mg; 2465 kJ (590 cal)*

ABOVE: Pumpkin gnocchi with sage butter

201

MAKING GNOCCHI

Today, our favourite gnocchi are potato-based but variations can be made using other vegetables such as pumpkin or parsnip, or traditional semolina or cheese.

Gnocchi are little dumplings. No matter what they are based on, the consistency of the dough should be soft and light. When cooking vegetables to be used for gnocchi, ensure that the cooking process doesn't result in soggy vegetables, otherwise you will have to add more flour, thus making the dough too heavy. Work quickly so the dough doesn't become too sticky or soft.

Gnocchi are best eaten as soon after cooking as possible and you should have any accompanying sauce ready before you cook the dumplings.

TRADITIONAL POTATO GNOCCHI

When making potato gnocchi, it is important to use floury potatoes, preferably old boiling potatoes, because

they have a low moisture content. Traditionally, the potatoes are prepared by baking in their skins, thus keeping the potato dry. However, as this is quite time-consuming, most people prefer to steam or boil them. If you do this, make sure you don't overcook the potatoes or they will break up and absorb too much moisture. Also, drain them thoroughly.

Many recipes for potato gnocchi include eggs, to make the gnocchi easier to handle. However, eggs also require the addition of more flour to absorb the extra moisture, thus making the gnocchi a little tougher. Experiment to find which way you prefer to work. The traditional method follows. To make enough for 4–6 people, you will need 1 kg (2 lb) of floury old potatoes, unpeeled, and about 200 g (6½ oz) of plain flour.

1 Prick the unpeeled potatoes all over with a fork and bake in a moderately hot 200°C (400°F/Gas 6) oven for 1 hour, or until tender. Don't wrap in foil. When cool enough to handle but still hot, peel and mash in a bowl with a masher, or put through a ricer or food mill into a bowl.

2 Add three-quarters of the flour and gradually work it in with your hands. When a loose dough forms, transfer it to a lightly floured surface and knead gently. Work in the remaining flour as you knead, but only enough to give a soft, light dough that does not stick to your hands or the work surface, but is still damp to touch. Stop kneading at this stage. Lightly flour the work surface and dust the inside tines of a fork with flour. Take a portion of the dough, about one-fifth, and roll it with your hands on the floured surface to form a long, even rope the thickness of your ring finger. Cut it into 2 cm (¾ inch) pieces.

3 Put a piece on the tines of a fork and press down with your finger, flipping the gnocchi as you do so. It will be rounded into a concave shell shape, ridged on the outer surface. Form a

good hollow in the centre, as this allows the gnocchi to cook evenly and hold the sauce more easily. Continue with the remaining dough.

4 Lower the gnocchi in batches, about 20 at a time, into a large pan of boiling salted water. The gnocchi are cooked when they all rise to the surface, after 2–3 minutes cooking. Remove each batch with a slotted spoon and keep them warm while cooking the remainder. Sauce, and serve.

Potato gnocchi can be frozen, shaped but uncooked, for up to two months. They will need to be first frozen in a single layer, not touching, before being stored in airtight containers. When you are ready to use them, lower them gently, in batches, into boiling water straight from the freezer.

FONTINA CHEESE

A semi-hard cheese from the Italian Alps, fontina has a creamy texture and a sweet, nutty flavour. It is eaten as a table cheese, but is also ideal for cooking because it melts completely to give a thick, rich cream. It is used in sauces for pasta and vegetables, and is the star ingredient of the famous *fonduta*, the Piedmontese version of fondue.

GNOCCHI WITH FONTINA SAUCE

Preparation time: 10 minutes
Total cooking time: 15 minutes
Serves 4

200 g (6½ oz) fontina cheese, finely chopped
½ cup (125 ml/4 fl oz) cream
80 g (2¾ oz) butter
2 tablespoons freshly grated Parmesan
400 g (13 oz) fresh potato gnocchi

1 Combine the fontina cheese, cream, butter and Parmesan in a bowl over a pan of simmering water. Heat, stirring occasionally, for 6– 8 minutes, or until the cheese has melted and the sauce is smooth and hot.

2 When the sauce is halfway through cooking, lower the gnocchi, in batches, into a large pan of boiling salted water and cook for about 2 minutes, or until the gnocchi rise to the surface.

3 Drain the gnocchi, using a slotted spoon, and serve with sauce over the top. Can be garnished with fresh oregano leaves or other fresh herbs.

NUTRITION PER SERVE: *Protein 25 g; Fat 60 g; Carbohydrate 10 g; Dietary Fibre 0 g; Cholesterol 185 mg; 2790 kJ (670 cal)*

ABOVE: Gnocchi with fontina sauce

HERBED POTATO GNOCCHI WITH CHUNKY TOMATO

Preparation time: 1 hour
Total cooking time: 30 minutes
Serves 4

★ ★

500 g (1 lb) floury potatoes, chopped
1 egg yolk
3 tablespoons grated Parmesan
3 tablespoons chopped fresh herbs
   (parsley, basil and chives)
up to 1 cup (125 g/4 oz) plain flour
2 cloves garlic, crushed
1 onion, chopped
4 bacon rashers, roughly chopped
150 g (5 oz) sun-dried tomatoes,
   roughly chopped
425 g (14 oz) can peeled tomatoes
1 teaspoon soft brown sugar
2 teaspoons balsamic vinegar
1 tablespoon shredded fresh basil
shaved Parmesan, for serving

1 To make the gnocchi, steam or boil the potatoes until just tender. Drain thoroughly, cool and mash. Transfer 2 cups of the potato to a large bowl. Add the egg yolk, grated Parmesan and herbs and mix until combined. Gradually add enough flour to form a slightly sticky dough. Knead gently for 5 minutes, adding more flour if necessary, until smooth.

2 Divide the dough into four. Roll each portion on a lightly floured surface to form a sausage 2 cm (¾ inch) thick and cut into 2.5 cm (1 inch) pieces. Roll each piece into an oval shape and roll carefully over lightly floured prongs on the back of a fork. Put on a lightly floured non-stick baking tray and cover until ready to use.

3 To make the sauce, heat a tablespoon of olive oil in a large frying pan, add the garlic and onion and cook over medium heat for 5 minutes, or until the onion is soft and golden.

4 Add the bacon and cook, stirring occasionally, for 5 minutes, or until the bacon has browned.

5 Stir in the sun-dried tomato, tomato, sugar and vinegar, bring to the boil, reduce the heat and simmer for 15 minutes, or until the sauce has thickened. Stir the shredded basil through just before serving.

6 Cook the gnocchi, in batches, in a large pan of boiling salted water for about 2 minutes, or until the gnocchi rise to the surface. Drain well and serve topped with the tomato sauce and Parmesan shavings.

NUTRITION PER SERVE: *Protein 20 g; Fat 6 g; Carbohydrate 45 g; Dietary Fibre 6 g; Cholesterol 70 mg; 1340 kJ (320 cal)*

BELOW: Herbed potato gnocchi with chunky tomato

FETA CHEESE

Feta originated in Greece where it was made in the mountains from ewe's milk. It is a semi-hard, pure white cheese with a crumbly texture, not matured but preserved in a liquid made up of its whey and brine. Its flavour is fresh, mild and slightly salty and this intensifies as the cheese gets older. Feta is an essential ingredient of the Greek salad and is used in fillings for stuffed vegetables, and in pies and tarts.

OPPOSITE PAGE:
Spiced carrot and feta
gnocchi (top); Spinach
and ricotta gnocchi

SPICED CARROT AND FETA GNOCCHI

Preparation time: 45 minutes
Total cooking time: 40 minutes
Serves 6– 8

1 kg (2 lb) carrots, cut into large pieces
200 g (6¹/₂ oz) feta cheese, crumbled
2¹/₄ cups (280 g/9 oz) plain flour
¹/₄ teaspoon ground nutmeg
¹/₄ teaspoon garam masala
1 egg, lightly beaten

Minted cream sauce

30 g (1 oz) butter
2 cloves garlic, crushed
2 spring onions, sliced
1 cup (250 ml/8 fl oz) cream
2 tablespoons shredded fresh mint

1 Steam, boil or microwave the carrot until tender. Drain and allow to cool slightly before transferring to a food processor.
2 Process the carrot and the feta cheese together until smooth. Transfer the mixture to a large bowl. Stir in the sifted flour, spices and egg, and mix to form a soft dough.
3 Lightly coat your fingertips with flour and shape teaspoons of the mixture into flat circles.
4 To make the minted cream sauce, melt the butter in a frying pan, add the garlic and spring onion and cook over medium heat for 3 minutes or until the garlic is soft and golden. Add the cream, bring to the boil, reduce the heat and simmer for 3 minutes, or until the cream has thickened slightly. Remove from the heat, stir the mint through and drizzle over the gnocchi.
5 Cook the gnocchi, in batches, in a large pan of boiling salted water for about 2 minutes, or until they float to the surface. Use a slotted spoon to transfer to warmed serving plates.
NOTE: This mixture is not as firm as some other gnocchi recipes. Make sure the dough is put on a lightly floured surface and keep your fingertips coated in flour when you are shaping the gnocchi.

NUTRITION PER SERVE (8): *Protein 10 g; Fat 25 g; Carbohydrate 35 g; Dietary Fibre 5 g; Cholesterol 90 mg; 1615 kJ (385 cal)*

SPINACH AND RICOTTA GNOCCHI

Preparation time: 45 minutes
  + 1 hour refrigeration
Total cooking time: 30 minutes
Serves 4– 6

4 slices white bread
¹/₂ cup (125 ml/4 fl oz) milk
500 g (1 lb) frozen spinach, thawed
250 g (8 oz) ricotta cheese
2 eggs
¹/₂ cup (50 g/1¾ oz) freshly grated Parmesan, plus some shaved Parmesan, for serving
¹/₄ cup (30 g/1 oz) plain flour

1 Remove the crust from the bread and soak the bread in the milk, in a shallow dish, for 10 minutes. Squeeze out all the excess liquid. Then squeeze excess liquid from the spinach.
2 Combine the bread in a bowl with the spinach, ricotta cheese, eggs, Parmesan and salt and pepper. Use a fork to mix thoroughly. Cover and refrigerate for 1 hour.
3 Lightly dust your hands in flour. Roll heaped teaspoonsful of the mixture into dumplings. Lower batches of the gnocchi into a large pan of boiling salted water. Cook for about 2 minutes, or until the gnocchi rise to the surface. Transfer to serving plates. Drizzle with foaming butter, if you wish, and serve with shaved Parmesan.

NUTRITION PER SERVE (6): *Protein 15 g; Fat 10 g; Carbohydrate 10 g; Dietary Fibre 3 g; Cholesterol 95 mg; 905 kJ (215 cal)*

ON THE SIDE

POPOVERS Process 1 cup (250 g/8 oz) of plain flour with 4 eggs in a food processor until the mixture forms crumbs. While the machine is running, add ¹/₂ cup (125 ml/4 fl oz) of cream, 1 cup (250 ml/8 fl oz) of milk and 45 g (1¹/₂ oz) of melted butter. Butter a muffin tin and divide the mixture among the holes. Bake in a moderately hot 200°C (400°F/Gas 6) oven for 35 minutes, or until golden and puffy.

ABOVE: Parsnip gnocchi

PARSNIPS

Although parsnips are root vegetables, they belong to the *umbelliferae* or parsley family. They are cultivated for their large, tapering ivory taproots, which have a fruity taste and smell. The starchy flesh purées well and whole parsnips add flavour to stews and casseroles. If the parsnip has developed a tough core, remove it before use.

PARSNIP GNOCCHI

Preparation time: 1½ hours
Total cooking time: 45 minutes
Serves 4

★★

500 g (1 lb) parsnip
1½ cups (185 g/6 oz) plain flour
½ cup (50 g/1¾ oz) freshly grated Parmesan

Garlic herb butter

100 g (3½ oz) butter
2 cloves garlic, crushed
3 tablespoons chopped fresh lemon thyme
1 tablespoon finely grated lime rind

1 Peel the parsnip and cut into large pieces. Cook in a large pan of boiling water for 30 minutes, or until very tender. Drain thoroughly and allow to cool slightly.
2 Mash the parsnip in a bowl until smooth. Sift the flour into the bowl and add half the Parmesan. Season with salt and pepper and mix to form a soft dough.
3 Divide the dough in half. Using floured hands, roll each half of the dough out on a lightly floured surface into a sausage 2 cm (¾ inch) wide. Cut each sausage into short pieces, shape each piece into an oval and press the top gently with floured fork prongs.
4 Lower batches of gnocchi into a large pan of boiling salted water. Cook for about 2 minutes, or until the gnocchi rise to the surface. Use a slotted spoon to transfer to serving plates.
5 To make the garlic herb butter, combine all the ingredients in a small pan and cook over medium heat for 3 minutes, or until the butter is nutty brown. Drizzle over the gnocchi and sprinkle with the remaining Parmesan.

NUTRITION PER SERVE: *Protein 10 g; Fat 20 g; Carbohydrate 30 g; Dietary Fibre 4 g; Cholesterol 60 mg; 1450 kJ (345 cal)*

RED PEPPER (CAPSICUM) GNOCCHI WITH GOATS CHEESE

Preparation time: I hour
Total cooking time: 40 minutes
Serves 6– 8

I large red pepper (capsicum)
500 g (I lb) kumera (orange sweet potato), chopped
500 g (I lb) old potatoes, chopped
I tablespoon sambal oelek
I tablespoon grated orange rind
2³/4 cups (340 g/I I oz) plain flour
2 eggs, lightly beaten
2 cups (500 ml/16 fl oz) bottled pasta sauce
100 g (3¹/2 oz) goats cheese
2 tablespoons finely shredded fresh basil leaves

I Cut the red pepper in half and discard the seeds and membrane. Put, skin-side-up, under a hot grill and cook for 8 minutes, or until the skin is black and blistered. Remove from the heat and cover with a damp tea towel. When cool, peel away the skin. Process the pepper in a food processor to form a smooth purée.
2 Steam or boil the kumera and potato in a large pan until very soft. Drain thoroughly, transfer to a large bowl and mash until smooth. Allow to cool slightly.
3 Add the pepper purée, sambal oelek, orange rind, flour and eggs, and mix to form a soft dough. Using floured hands, roll heaped teaspoonsful of the dough into oval shapes. Indent one side using lightly floured prongs on the back of a fork.
4 Lower batches of gnocchi into a large pan of boiling salted water. Cook for about 2 minutes, or until the gnocchi rise to the surface. Remove the gnocchi with a slotted spoon and divide among warmed serving plates. Top with the warmed pasta sauce. Crumble the goats cheese and sprinkle over the top with the shredded basil.

NUTRITION PER SERVE (8): *Protein 15 g; Fat 7 g; Carbohydrate 75 g; Dietary Fibre 7 g; Cholesterol 70 mg; 1830 kJ (435 cal)*

ON THE SIDE

NASTURTIUM AND WATERCRESS SALAD Combine 1 bunch of watercress with the petals from 10 nasturtium flowers, 20 small nasturtium leaves and the separated leaves of 1 Belgian endive. Drizzle with a light Caesar salad dressing. Serve with chopped pecans.

WARM KUMERA, ROCKET AND CRISPY BACON SALAD Roast or boil kumera (orange sweet potato) chunks until tender. Combine with rocket and crispy bacon and sprinkle with crumbled goats cheese. Make up a dressing using wholegrain mustard, red wine vinegar and olive oil. Drizzle over the salad.

GOATS CHEESE
Goats cheese or chevre ranges from fresh, soft and mild to mature and very strong. For cooking, somewhere between these extremes is best, a creamy texture accompanied by a mild but piquant taste. Goats cheese has a fragile texture that tends to crumble. It is made in small loaves or little shapes like logs or pyramids.

ABOVE: Red pepper gnocchi with goats cheese

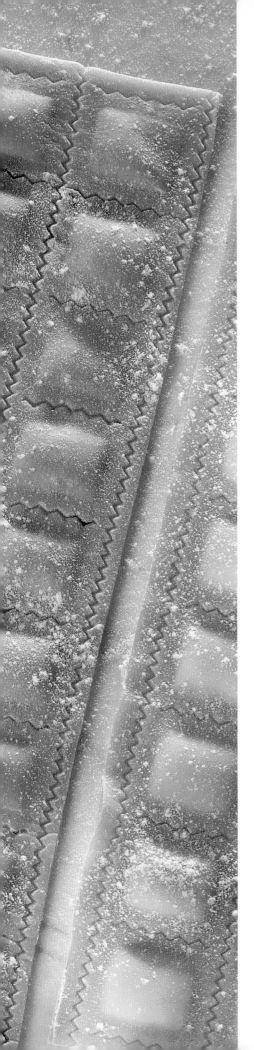

FILLED PASTA

Make your own pasta dough, shape it into delicate pillows of ravioli, wrap it round your finger to make horseshoe tortellini, or roll it out into cannelloni tubes. You can fill tiny parcels of pasta with just about any of your favourite ingredients, from puréed vegetable, spinach and ricotta, to robust meat sauces. In some parts of Italy, just wrapping leftovers in pasta is part of the heritage, so there are no limitations. Of course, if time is short, you can buy the pasta and simply add your own sauce... but that's not half as much fun.

1 egg, beaten

1 tablespoon chopped fresh parsley

1 clove garlic, crushed

1/4 teaspoon mixed spice

Tomato sauce

2 tablespoons olive oil

1 onion, finely chopped

2 cloves garlic, crushed

2 x 425 g (14 oz) cans tomatoes, crushed

3 tablespoons chopped fresh basil

1/2 teaspoon mixed dried herbs

herb sprigs, optional

---

1 To make the pasta, sift the flour and a pinch of salt into a large bowl and make a well in the centre. Whisk together the eggs, oil and 1 tablespoon of water, add gradually to the flour and combine until the mixture forms a ball. Knead on a floured surface for 5 minutes, or until smooth and elastic. Transfer to an oiled bowl, cover with plastic wrap and set aside for 30 minutes.

2 To make the filling, mix all the filling ingredients with salt and pepper, to taste, in a food processor until finely chopped.

3 To make the tomato sauce, heat the oil in a pan, add the onion and garlic and stir over low heat until the onion is tender. Increase the heat, add the tomato, basil, herbs and salt and pepper, to taste. Bring to the boil, reduce the heat and simmer for 15 minutes. Remove from the heat.

4 Roll out half the pasta dough until 1 mm (1/25 inch) thick. Cut with a knife or fluted pastry wheel into 10 cm (4 inch) wide strips. Place teaspoons of filling at 5 cm (2 inch) intervals down one side of each strip. Whisk the extra egg yolk with 3 tablespoons of water and brush along one side of the dough and between the filling. Fold the dough over the filling to meet the other side. Repeat with remaining filling and dough. Press the edges of the dough together firmly to seal. Cut between the mounds with a knife or a fluted pastry wheel. Cook, in batches, in a large pan of rapidly boiling salted water for 10 minutes. Reheat the sauce in a large pan. Add the ravioli and stir until heated through. Garnish and serve.

NUTRITION PER SERVE: *Protein 35 g; Fat 35 g; Carbohydrate 60 g; Dietary Fibre 7 g; Cholesterol 315 mg; 2850 kJ (680 cal)*

RAVIOLI WITH CHICKEN FILLING

Preparation time: 1 hour
  + 30 minutes standing
Total cooking time: 35 minutes
Serves 4

Pasta

2 cups (250 g/8 oz) plain flour

3 eggs

1 tablespoon olive oil

1 egg yolk, extra

Filling

125 g (4 oz) chicken mince

75 g (2 1/2 oz) ricotta or cottage cheese

60 g (2 oz) chicken livers, trimmed and chopped

30 g (1 oz) prosciutto, chopped

1 slice salami, chopped

2 tablespoons freshly grated Parmesan

ABOVE: Ravioli with chicken filling

CHICKEN MEZZELUNE WITH CREAM SAUCE

Preparation time: 45 minutes
Total cooking time: 15 minutes
Serves 4–6 as a first course

250 g (8 oz) packet gow gee wrappers

Chicken and ham filling

250 g (8 oz) chicken breast fillet
1 egg, beaten
90 g (3 oz) cooked ham or prosciutto
2 teaspoons finely snipped chives
2 teaspoons chopped fresh marjoram

Cream sauce

30 g (1 oz) butter
2 spring onions, finely chopped
2 tablespoons white wine
1 1/2 cups (375 ml/12 fl oz) cream

1 To make the filling, remove any excess fat and sinew from the chicken breast. Cut the flesh into pieces and chop in a food processor. Add the egg, 1/2 teaspoon of salt and a pinch of white pepper and process until finely chopped. Transfer to a bowl. Chop the ham or prosciutto finely and stir into the chicken with the herbs.

2 Lay the gow gee wrappers on a work surface, six at a time, and put a teaspoonful of chicken filling in the centre of each. Brush the edges with cold water, fold in half to form a half moon shape (mezzelune), and press the edges together firmly to seal. Place on a tea towel and continue with the remaining circles.

3 If making your own pasta, roll the dough as thinly as possible on a lightly floured surface, or use a pasta machine and pass the dough through 5 or 6 settings. Cut into circles with an 8 cm (3 inch) cutter, fill and seal as above.

4 To make the cream sauce, heat the butter in a small pan, add the spring onion and cook for 2–3 minutes. Add the wine and cream and simmer until reduced. Season, to taste.

5 Cook the mezzelune in batches, in rapidly boiling salted water. Don't crowd the pan. Simmer for 2–3 minutes, until the chicken is cooked. Don't overcook or the chicken will be dry. Drain.

6 Serve the sauce immediately with the mezzelune. Garnish, if you like.

NUTRITION PER SERVE (6): *Protein 10 g; Fat 30 g; Carbohydrate 30 g; Dietary Fibre 2 g; Cholesterol 120 mg; 1810 kJ (430 cal)*

BELOW: Chicken mezzelune with cream sauce

RICOTTA CHEESE

Ricotta is an unsalted, unripened cheese made from the whey of ewe's or cow's milk. It has a limited shelf life and can only be used when fresh. When kept too long it sours and develops an acid flavour. It has a delicate, creamy flavour and a light, crumbly texture that blends well with other ingredients, especially other dairy produce. Ricotta, literally recooked, takes its name from the method by which it is made. In ordinary cheese-making there is left-over hot whey of milk. When this is heated again and the solid milk parts skimmed off and drained, ricotta results.

ABOVE: Spinach and ricotta shells

SPINACH AND RICOTTA SHELLS

Preparation time: 20 minutes
Total cooking time: 15 minutes
Serves 4

20 giant conchiglie (shell pasta)
1 tablespoon oil
2 bacon rashers, finely chopped
1 onion, finely chopped
500 g (1 lb) English spinach, chopped
750 g (1 1/2 lb) ricotta cheese
1/3 cup (35 g/1 1/4 oz) freshly grated Parmesan
1 cup (250 g/8 oz) bottled tomato
    pasta sauce

1 Cook the conchiglie in a large pan of rapidly boiling salted water until *al dente*; drain.
2 Heat the oil in a pan, add the bacon and onion and stir over medium heat for 3 minutes, or until lightly browned. Add the spinach and stir over low heat until wilted. Add the ricotta cheese and stir until combined.
3 Spoon the mixture into the pasta shells and sprinkle with Parmesan. Put the shells on a cold, lightly oiled grill tray. Cook under medium-high heat for 3 minutes, or until lightly browned and heated through.
4 Put the tomato pasta sauce in a small pan and stir over high heat for 1 minute, or until heated through. Spoon the sauce onto serving plates and top with the shells.

NUTRITION PER SERVE: *Protein 45 g; Fat 40 g; Carbohydrate 80 g; Dietary Fibre 10 g; Cholesterol 110 mg; 3470 kJ (830 cal)*

PRAWN TORTELLONI

Preparation time: 40 minutes
Total cooking time: 20–30 minutes
Serves 4

300 g (10 oz) raw prawns
20 g (3/4 oz) butter
I clove garlic, crushed
2 spring onions, chopped
125 g (4 oz) ricotta cheese
I tablespoon chopped fresh basil
200 g (6 1/2 oz) packet gow gee wrappers

Sauce

5 tablespoons olive oil
shells and heads of prawns
I clove garlic, crushed
2 spring onions, including green part, chopped
I dried chilli, crumbled
I firm tomato, finely diced, or
   I tablespoon diced sun-dried tomato

1 Shell the prawns, reserving the heads and shells to flavour the sauce. With a sharp knife, slit down the back of each prawn and discard the vein. Chop the prawns roughly.
2 Heat the butter and gently cook the garlic and spring onion until soft and golden. Allow to cool, mix with the prawns, ricotta and basil and season, to taste. Put a teaspoonful of the mixture on each gow gee wrapper, moisten the edges with water, fold over to form a semi-circle and press firmly to seal. Press the corners together to make a tortelloni shape. For a large circular shape, use more filling and cover with another circle of pasta.
3 To make the sauce, heat 3 tablespoons of the olive oil in a large frying pan. When hot, add the shells and heads of the prawns and toss over high heat until they turn red. Lower the heat and cook for a few minutes, pressing the heads to extract as much flavour as possible. Add 1/2 cup (125 ml/4 fl oz) of water, cover and cook over low heat for 5 minutes. Remove the shells and heads from the pan using a slotted spoon, pressing out as much of the flavoured oil as possible before discarding them.
4 In another pan, heat the remaining 2 tablespoons of olive oil, add the garlic, spring onion and dried chilli and stir over low heat until the garlic is pale golden. Add the prawn stock and diced tomato and heat through.

5 Bring a large pan of salted water to the boil. Drop the tortelloni into the boiling water and cook for 3–4 minutes. Drain, then add to the sauce and toss so the pasta is well coated.
NOTE: Tortelloni are large tortellini.

NUTRITION PER SERVE: *Protein 25 g; Fat 35 g; Carbohydrate 35 g; Dietary Fibre 4 g; Cholesterol 140 mg; 2260 kJ (540 cal)*

ABOVE: Prawn tortelloni

215

Gently twist the ends of the roll to make a shape that resembles a bow. Repeat with the remaining sheets and filling.

3 Lightly brush a large rectangular ovenproof dish with melted butter or oil. Place the bows in the dish, dot with butter and pour the pasta sauce over the centre of the bows, leaving the ends exposed. Cover and bake for 5 minutes, or until the bows are heated through. Serve immediately, generously sprinkled with freshly grated Parmesan and shredded fresh basil leaves.

NUTRITION PER SERVE: *Protein 10 g; Fat 15 g; Carbohydrate 15 g; Dietary Fibre 2 g; Cholesterol 80 mg; 1015 kJ (250 cal)*

SPINACH RAVIOLI WITH SUN-DRIED TOMATO SAUCE

Preparation time: 20 minutes
Total cooking time: 15 minutes
Serves 4

⭐ ⭐

3/4 cup (155 g/5 oz) firmly packed, chopped, cooked English spinach
250 g (8 oz) ricotta cheese, well drained
2 tablespoons freshly grated Parmesan
1 tablespoon chopped fresh chives
1 egg, lightly beaten
200 g (6 1/2 oz) packet gow gee wrappers

Sauce

1/3 cup (80 ml/2 3/4 fl oz) extra virgin olive oil
3 tablespoons pine nuts
100 g (3 1/2 oz) sun-dried tomatoes, sliced

LASAGNE BOWS

Preparation time: 20 minutes
Total cooking time: 20 minutes
Serves 6

⭐ ⭐

four 16 x 24 cm (6 1/2 x 9 1/2 inch) fresh lasagne sheets
400 g (13 oz) fresh ricotta cheese
1 egg, lightly beaten
1/4 teaspoon ground nutmeg
1 cup (50 g/1 3/4 oz) chopped fresh herbs
30 g (1 oz) butter, chopped
300 g (10 oz) bottled tomato pasta sauce
freshly grated Parmesan, for serving
shredded fresh basil leaves, to garnish

1 Preheat the oven to moderately hot 200°C (400°F/Gas 6). Cook the lasagne sheets in a large pan of rapidly boiling salted water until *al dente*, stirring frequently to ensure that they do not stick together.
2 While the pasta is cooking, combine the ricotta cheese, beaten egg, nutmeg and herbs in a bowl. Drain the pasta and carefully lay one sheet on a flat surface. Put 2–3 tablespoons of the ricotta mixture in the centre of the sheet. Fold the top third of the lasagne sheet over the filling, then the bottom third over the top.

*ABOVE: Lasagne bows
RIGHT: Spinach
ravioli with sun-dried
tomato sauce*

1 Combine the spinach, ricotta and Parmesan, chives and half the beaten egg in a medium bowl. Mix well and season with salt and pepper, to taste. Place 1½ teaspoons of the mixture into the centre of a gow gee wrapper. Brush the edge of the wrapper lightly with some of the remaining beaten egg, then cover with another wrapper, until they are all used. Press the edges firmly to seal. Using a 7 cm (2¾ inch) plain scone cutter, cut the ravioli into circles.

2 Cook the ravioli, in batches, in a large pan of rapidly boiling salted water for 4 minutes, or until *al dente*. Don't crowd the pan. Keep each batch warm while cooking the remainder. Carefully drain the ravioli, add to the sauce and toss very gently.

3 To make the sauce, combine the ingredients in a large pan and heat slowly until warm.

NUTRITION PER SERVE: *Protein 20 g; Fat 40 g; Carbohydrate 35 g; Dietary Fibre 5 g; Cholesterol 80 mg; 2440 kJ (580 cal)*

PUMPKIN AND HERB RAVIOLI

Preparation time: 40 minutes
  + 30 minutes resting
Total cooking time: 1 hour 15 minutes
Serves 6

✵ ✵

500 g (1 lb) pumpkin, cut into chunks
1¾ cups (215 g/7 oz) plain flour
3 eggs, lightly beaten
¼ teaspoon ground nutmeg
15 sage leaves
15 fresh flat-leaf parsley leaves
125 g (4 oz) butter, melted
60 g (2 oz) freshly grated Parmesan

1 Preheat the oven to moderate 180°C (350°F/Gas 4). Bake the pumpkin on a baking tray for 1 hour, or until tender. Allow to cool before removing the skin.

2 Process the flour and eggs in a food processor for 30 seconds, or until the mixture forms a dough. Transfer to a lightly floured surface and knead for 3 minutes, until the dough is very smooth and elastic. Cover with a clean cloth and set aside for 30 minutes.

3 Transfer the pumpkin to a bowl with the nutmeg and mash with a fork. Roll out half the dough to a rectangle about 1 mm (¹⁄₂₅ inch) thick. Roll out the remaining half to a rectangle slightly larger than the first.

4 On the first rectangle of dough, put heaped teaspoonful of pumpkin filling at intervals, in straight rows, about 5 cm (2 inches) apart. Flatten each pumpkin mound slightly and place one whole sage or parsley leaf on top of each spoonful of filling.

5 Brush lightly between the mounds of filling with water. Place the second sheet of dough on top, press down gently between pumpkin mounds to seal. Cut into squares with a knife or fluted cutter. Cook the ravioli, in batches, in a large pan of rapidly boiling salted water for 4 minutes, or until *al dente*. Don't crowd the pan. Drain well and serve sprinkled with salt and pepper, to taste, and tossed with melted butter and Parmesan.

NUTRITION PER SERVE: *Protein 15 g; Fat 25 g; Carbohydrate 35 g; Dietary Fibre 5 g; Cholesterol 155 mg; 1645 kJ (390 cal)*

ABOVE: Pumpkin and herb ravioli

FILLING PASTA The benefits of

making your own filled or stuffed pasta are many. You can determine the pasta

flavour, size and shape as well as the ingredients and texture of the filling.

FILLINGS

Ingredients for filled pasta are fresh and interesting. Some, such as cheeses and mashed pumpkin, are smooth, while foods such as shellfish are better in small, discernible pieces. As a general rule, the finer the filling, the smaller the shape. A binding ingredient is usually needed. This is often a soft cheese such as ricotta, but can be cream, sauce or gravy. The moisture content can be controlled by the addition of a little grated Parmesan, breadcrumbs, or even mashed potato. Within a short time, the moisture in the filling will begin to seep through the pasta causing it to become soggy. Therefore, the filling should be quite dry, particularly if the pasta isn't going to be cooked immediately. Fresh filled pasta should be eaten soon after being made.

EQUIPMENT

You will need a long sharp knife, a pastry brush and, ideally, a zig-zag pastry wheel, to give a good seal. A cutter-crimper wheel gives an excellent seal, but can be less manoeuvrable on curved edges. Ravioli stamps or cutters are sometimes available. Moulded ravioli trays give a uniform shape and enable you to make a lot of ravioli quickly, once the technique is mastered.

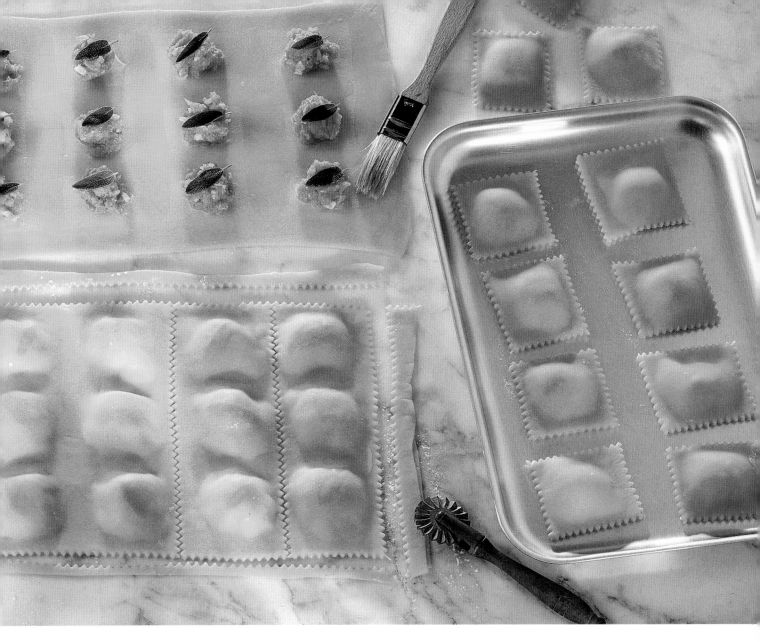

RAVIOLI

To serve 4–6, you will need one batch of basic pasta dough (page 17), about 1½ cups of filling and a beaten egg, for sealing the edges. There are two ways of hand-shaping ravioli: by cutting out the dough and individually folding each one over the filling, or by covering one sheet of dough and the filling with another sheet and cutting shapes from this. The folded method is very simple and has the advantage of a better seal, with only three cut edges which are firmly joined together by hand. The double-sheeted method is quicker, but results in a ravioli with all cut edges, increasing the likelihood of them opening up.

DOUBLE SHEETED METHOD

1 Lightly dust a large work surface with flour. Divide the dough into four. Roll two portions out into very thin (about 2.5 mm / ⅛ inch, or less) sheets, using a hand-cranked pasta machine, or with a rolling pin on the work surface. Roll one sheet slightly bigger than the other and cover this with a tea towel.

2 Spread the smaller sheet out on the work surface. In one corner, lightly mark out two or three ravioli squares for size. Spoon some filling into the centre of each and flatten slightly with the back of the spoon. This will help you determine the amount of filling per square and the spacing between each. The filling should cover about two-thirds of the area of each square. Now spoon equal amounts of filling, evenly spaced, over the sheet. Flatten lightly with the back of the spoon.

3 Brush beaten egg between the filling along the cutting lines. Take the larger sheet and, starting at one end, place it over the first, matching the sides and pressing it here and there so that it sticks to the bottom layer without slipping. Don't stretch it, but let it settle into position naturally.

4 Run your fingers along the cutting lines to press them together, or use the fine edge of a ruler which will also mark the lines as well as seal them. Now cut along these lines using a sharp knife or pastry wheel, or a zig-zag pastry wheel.

5 Transfer to a lightly floured baking tray or large platter and refrigerate while you work the remainder of the dough and filling. Don't put them on top of one another or they'll stick together. They can be refrigerated, covered, for up to 3 hours, depending on the moisture content of the filling. Cooking time varies according to the thickness of the pastry and type of filling.

219

FILLING PASTA

TORTELLINI

These small rounds of pasta dough are filled with anything from cooked meat, chicken and fish, to vegetables and soft cheeses, and then sealed and shaped into rings. To make tortellini for 4–6, you will need one batch of basic pasta dough (page 17), 1½ cups of smooth-textured filling and a beaten egg for sealing.

1 Lightly dust a large work surface with flour. Divide the dough into four, keeping all portions covered until needed. Using a hand-cranked pasta machine or with a rolling pin on the prepared surface, roll out one portion of dough very thinly, about 2.5 mm (1/8 inch) or less.

2 Spread the pasta on a lightly floured work surface and avoid flouring it from now on. With a 6 cm (2½ inch) cutter or an upturned glass, cut out circles.

3 Lightly brush the edge of each circle with beaten egg or water, then spoon about ½ teaspoonful of filling onto the centre of each circle.

4 Working with one circle at a time, fold one side over the other to encase the filling. The cut sides should not match up exactly, but overlap slightly. Press the edges firmly together, slightly easing the filling along the length of the half-moon as you do so. Roll the rim of the cut edge back over itself, with the taller side uppermost. Now, with

the folded rim on the outside, wrap the shape around your index finger and press the two ends together. A dab of water might be needed to help seal them together.

5 Place the completed tortellini on a lightly floured baking tray or large plate and keep chilled while you work the remaining pasta and filling. Depending on the dryness of the filling used, they will keep in the refrigerator for up to 6 hours.

CANNELLONI

These filled tubes of pasta are not at all difficult to make. Suitable fillings include cooked meat with cheese, spinach with

ricotta or mashed pumpkin with pine nuts. As a rough guide, depending on the size of cannelloni you choose to make and the amount of filling you want to use, one batch of basic plain dough (page 17) will make about 20 tubes that are 10 cm (4 inches) long. Cut the pasta for cannelloni wide enough to wrap comfortably around the filling you want to use. Allow for a 2.5 cm (1 inch) overlap at the seam on larger tubes, down to half that on small, finger-sized tubes. Too little overlap, and the cannelloni may expand and open when baked, making serving difficult; too much, and the thickness of the pasta will be unpleasant. It is a good idea to cut one or two extra sheets in case some tear during cooking. To fill 20 tubes, you will need about 4 cups of filling.

1 Roll out fresh pasta sheets to about 2.5 mm (⅛ inch) thick, using a hand-cranked pasta machine or rolling pin.
2 Put a large pan of water on to boil and grease a shallow ovenproof dish.
3 Cut the pasta into sheets of the size you require, bearing in mind that they will increase slightly during cooking. The length of the tube runs with the grain of the pasta.
4 Keep uncooked sheets covered. Drop 3 or 4 at a time, depending on their size, into the water and keep boiling for 1½–2 minutes. Fish them out with a wide strainer or sieve and spread on dry tea towels while the rest of the sheets are being cooked. Turn the sheets over once when partially dry. Do not allow to dry too much as the edges crack when rolling. Trim if necessary. You might like to cut out a paper template to use

as a guide so they will be the same size.
5 Arrange some filling down the centre of each sheet, running it in the same direction as the grain. Roll the pasta tightly around the filling to form a tube. Place the tubes side by side, seam-side-down in the prepared dish, with the overlapping join on the bottom. Cannelloni are nearly always dressed with sauce and topped with cheese before being finished off in the oven, or under the grill.

FREEZING
Filled pastas freeze well and must be cooked straight from the freezer, not defrosted. To freeze filled or stuffed pasta, do so in a single layer or, if necessary, between sheets of baking paper. Cover with a tea towel. When frozen, transfer to an airtight container.

SPINACH AND RICOTTA CANNELLONI

Preparation time: I hour
Total cooking time: I hour I5 minutes
Serves 6

★ ★ ★

375 g (12 oz) fresh lasagne sheets

2 tablespoons olive oil

I large onion, finely chopped

I – 2 cloves garlic, crushed

I kg (2 lb) English spinach, finely chopped

650 g (1 lb 5 oz) fresh ricotta cheese, beaten

2 eggs, beaten

¼ teaspoon freshly ground nutmeg

Tomato sauce

I tablespoon olive oil

I medium onion, chopped

2 cloves garlic, finely chopped

500 g (1 lb) very ripe tomatoes, chopped

2 tablespoons tomato paste (tomato purée, double concentrate)

I teaspoon soft brown sugar

150 g (5 oz) grated mozzarella cheese

CANNELLONI

Cannelloni are simply rectangles of pasta rolled around a filling. The pasta can be sheets of fresh egg dough, or dried lasagne sheets or tubes, which need to be blanched before filling. The dried product is also available in a form that requires no pre-cooking. Once the tubes are filled they may be sauced, then baked with cheese on top.

I Cut the lasagne sheets into 15 even-sized pieces and trim lengthways so that they will fit neatly into a deep-sided, rectangular ovenproof dish when filled. Bring a large pan of water to a rapid boil and cook 1– 2 lasagne sheets at a time until just softened. The amount of time will differ, depending on the type and brand of lasagne, but is usually about 2 minutes. Remove the sheets carefully with a wide strainer or sieve and lay out flat on a clean damp tea towel. Return the water to the boil and repeat the process with the remaining pasta sheets.

2 Heat the oil in a heavy-based frying pan. Cook the onion and garlic until golden, stirring regularly. Add the washed spinach, cook for 2 minutes, cover with a tight-fitting lid and steam for 5 minutes. Drain, removing as much liquid as possible. The spinach must be quite dry or the pasta will be soggy. Combine the spinach with the ricotta, eggs, nutmeg and salt and pepper, to taste. Mix well and set aside.

3 To make the tomato sauce, heat the oil in a frying pan and cook the onion and garlic for 10 minutes over low heat, stirring occasionally. Add the chopped tomato including the juice, the tomato paste, sugar, ½ cup (125 ml/4 fl oz) of water and salt and pepper, to taste. Bring the sauce to the boil, reduce the heat and simmer for 10 minutes. If a smoother sauce is preferred, purée in a food processor until the desired consistency is reached.

4 Preheat the oven to moderate 180°C (350°F/Gas 4). Lightly brush the ovenproof dish with melted butter or oil. Spread about one-third of the tomato sauce over the base of the dish. Working with one piece of lasagne at a time, spoon 2½ tablespoons of the spinach mixture down the centre of the sheet, leaving a border at each end. Roll up and lay, seam-side-down, in the dish. Repeat with the remaining pasta and filling. Spoon the remaining tomato sauce over the cannelloni and scatter the mozzarella over the top.

5 Bake for 30– 35 minutes, or until golden brown and bubbling. Set aside for 10 minutes before serving. Garnish with fresh herb sprigs if you like.

NOTE: Dried cannelloni tubes can be used instead of fresh lasagne sheets. The texture of the pasta will be firmer, but the dish will still be very successful.

NUTRITION PER SERVE: *Protein 35 g; Fat 30 g; Carbohydrate 50 g; Dietary Fibre 10 g; Cholesterol 130 mg; 2555 kJ (610 cal)*

CONCHIGLIE WITH CHICKEN AND PESTO

Preparation time: 45 minutes
Total cooking time: 30 minutes
Serves 4

20 giant conchiglie (shell pasta)
(about 5 cm/2 inches long)
2 tablespoons oil
2 leeks, thinly sliced
500 g (1 lb) chicken mince
1 tablespoon plain flour
1 cup (250 ml/8 fl oz) chicken stock
4 tablespoons chopped pimiento
1/2 cup (50 g/1 3/4 oz) freshly grated Parmesan

Pesto

1 cup (50 g/1 3/4 oz) fresh basil
3 tablespoons pine nuts
2 cloves garlic, crushed
1/4 cup (60 ml/2 fl oz) olive oil

1 Preheat the oven to moderate 180°C (350°F/Gas 4). Brush a shallow baking dish with melted butter or oil. Cook the conchiglie in a large pan of rapidly boiling salted water until *al dente*. Drain well.
2 Heat the oil in a heavy-based pan, add the leek and stir-fry over medium heat for 2 minutes. Add the mince and stir until well browned and all the liquid has evaporated. Use a fork to break up any lumps as the mince cooks. Add the flour and stir over heat for 1 minute. Add the stock and pimiento and stir over medium heat until boiling. Reduce the heat and simmer for 1 minute, or until the mixture has reduced and thickened.
3 To make the pesto, blend the basil, pine nuts, garlic and oil in a food processor or blender for 30 seconds, or until smooth. Spoon into a small bowl or jug and press plastic wrap over the surface to exclude any air.
4 To assemble, spoon the chicken mixture into the cooled pasta shells, transfer to the prepared baking dish and cover with aluminium foil. Bake for 15 minutes, or until heated through. Serve topped with a spoonful of pesto and sprinkled with Parmesan.

NUTRITION PER SERVE: *Protein 45 g; Fat 55 g; Carbohydrate 75 g; Dietary Fibre 10 g; Cholesterol 110 mg; 4090 kJ (975 cal)*

ON THE SIDE

WILD RICE WITH ROASTED PEPPER Seed, quarter and grill 2 red peppers (capsicums) and cut them into thin slices. Cook some mixed wild and long-grain rice until it is tender and then drain. Put 2 tablespoons of olive oil, 2 tablespoons of balsamic vinegar, 1 crushed clove of garlic, 2 chopped spring onions and 2 finely chopped tomatoes in a large bowl. Add the rice mixture and the peppers, season with salt and pepper, to taste, and mix well. Scatter a handful of fresh coriander leaves over the top before serving.

CARAMELIZED LEEKS AND CRISPY BACON Cut leeks in half lengthways and then into long pieces, taking care to keep the leaves together. Cook the leeks over low heat in butter and a little soft brown sugar, turning occasionally, until the leeks are very tender and caramelized. Take care not to overcook them or they will fall apart. Top with pieces of crispy bacon and roughly chopped flat-leaf parsley.

Conchiglie with chicken and pesto

CHICKEN RAVIOLI WITH BUTTERED SAGE SAUCE

Preparation time: 15 minutes
Total cooking time: 10 minutes
Serves 4

500 g (1 lb) fresh or dried chicken-filled
   ravioli or agnolotti
60 g (2 oz) butter
4 spring onions, chopped
2 tablespoons fresh sage, chopped
1/2 cup (50 g/1 3/4 oz) freshly grated Parmesan,
   for serving
fresh sage leaves, extra, for garnish

1 Cook the ravioli in a large pan of rapidly boiling salted water until *al dente*. Drain and return to the pan.

2 While the ravioli is cooking, melt the butter in a heavy-based pan. Add the spring onion and sage and stir for 2 minutes. Add salt and pepper, to taste.
3 Add the sauce to the pasta and toss well. Pour into warmed serving bowls and sprinkle with Parmesan. Serve immediately, garnished with fresh sage leaves.

NUTRITION PER SERVE: *Protein 20 g; Fat 25 g; Carbohydrate 20 g; Dietary Fibre 2 g; Cholesterol 120 mg; 1590 kJ (380 cal)*

TORTELLINI WITH MUSHROOM CREAM SAUCE

Preparation time: 15 minutes
Total cooking time: 10 minutes
Serves 4

500 g (1 lb) tortellini
185 g (6 oz) button mushrooms
1 small lemon
60 g (2 oz) butter
1 clove garlic, crushed
1¼ cups (315 ml/10 fl oz) cream
pinch of nutmeg
3 tablespoons freshly grated Parmesan

1 Cook the tortellini in a large pan of rapidly boiling salted water until *al dente*. Drain, return to the pan and keep warm. Slice the mushrooms finely. Grate the lemon rind.

2 Melt the butter in a pan and cook the mushrooms over medium heat for 2 minutes. Add the garlic, cream, lemon rind, nutmeg and freshly ground black pepper, to taste. Stir over low heat for 1–2 minutes. Stir in the grated Parmesan and cook gently for 3 minutes.

3 Add the sauce to the tortellini and stir gently to combine well. Spoon into serving dishes and top with extra pepper.

NUTRITION PER SERVE: *Protein 10 g; Fat 50 g; Carbohydrate 35 g; Dietary Fibre 5 g; Cholesterol 155mg; 2570 kJ (610 cal)*

CREAM
Cream results from allowing milk to settle. Fats rise to the top and when skimmed off are a pourable single cream with a fat content of 10–20%, or in some countries 35%. Double cream, which contains at least 30% fat, has to be separated mechanically, to give a spoonable cream. Other natural creams, thick and stiff, will contain as much as 60% fat. Thickened cream has had a starch or gelatine added to it.

ABOVE: Tortellini with mushroom cream sauce

FRESH CHILLIES

There are many different types of fresh chilli, ranging from small and fiery to fat and mildly hot. The seeds and the membrane, which are the hottest parts, are generally removed from all but the tiniest. Where a recipe simply calls for fresh chilli, use your experience to select which type. The most fiery are usually small chillies such as birds eye, available in red or green. Serranos, which are red, green or yellow, are also small and very hot. Jalapenos are plump, green or red, and as hot as the serranos weight for weight. Correctly identifying chillies is quite difficult, especially since even growers disagree and the names vary internationally.

BASIL TORTELLINI WITH BACON AND TOMATO SAUCE

Preparation time: 15 minutes
Total cooking time: 25 minutes
Serves 4

500 g (1 lb) fresh or dried basil
   tortellini
1 tablespoon olive oil
4 bacon rashers, chopped
2 cloves garlic, crushed
1 medium onion, chopped
1 teaspoon chopped fresh chillies
425 g (14 oz) can tomatoes
1/2 cup (125 ml/4 fl oz) cream
2 tablespoons chopped fresh basil

1 Cook the pasta in a large pan of rapidly boiling salted water until *al dente*. Drain and return to the pan.

2 While the pasta is cooking, heat the oil in a medium heavy-based pan. Add the bacon, garlic and onion and cook for 5 minutes over medium heat, stirring regularly.

3 Add the chilli and undrained, chopped tomato. Reduce the heat and simmer for 10 minutes. Add the cream and basil and cook for 1 minute. Add the sauce to the pasta and toss well. Serve immediately.

NUTRITION PER SERVE: *Protein 25 g; Fat 25 g; Carbohydrate 95 g; Dietary Fibre 9 g; Cholesterol 60 mg; 2990 kJ (710 cal)*

ON THE SIDE

GREEN BEANS WITH GARLIC AND CUMIN Fry a sliced onion and a crushed clove of garlic in a little olive oil and add a 425 g (14 oz) can of chopped tomatoes and a pinch of ground cumin. Cook this mixture until it has reduced by half and add 300 g (10 oz) of sliced green beans. Cook the beans in the tomato mixture until tender but still vibrant green. Sprinkle with toasted cumin seeds.

RIGHT: Basil tortellini with bacon and tomato sauce

MUSHROOM RAVIOLI

Preparation time: 30 minutes
Total cooking time: 15 minutes
Serves 4

1/2 cup (70 g/2 1/4 oz) hazelnut kernels,
   toasted and skinned
90 g (3 oz) unsalted butter
150 g (5 oz) mushrooms
1 tablespoon olive oil
200 g (6 1/2 oz) packet won ton wrappers

1 Chop the hazelnuts in a food processor. Heat the butter in a pan over medium heat until it sizzles and turns nutty brown. Remove from the heat, stir in the chopped hazelnuts and season with salt and pepper, to taste.

2 Wipe the mushrooms with paper towel. Chop the stems and caps finely. Heat the oil in a pan, add the mushrooms and stir until soft. Add salt and pepper, to taste, and cook until the liquid has evaporated. Allow to cool.

3 Lay 12 won ton wrappers on a work surface and put a small teaspoonful of the mushroom filling on six of them. Brush the edges of the wrappers with water and place another wrapper on top. Press firmly to seal. If desired, trim the edges with a pasta cutter. Lay the ravioli on a tray lined with a clean tea towel and cover with another tea towel. Repeat with 12 more squares. Filling and sealing a few at a time prevents the ravioli from drying out.

4 When all the ravioli are made, cook in batches in a large pan of rapidly boiling salted water. Don't crowd the pan. Very thin pasta will be done in about 2 minutes after the water returns to the boil, so lift out with a slotted spoon and drain in a colander while the next batch is cooking. Serve with the hazelnut sauce.

NOTE: If you can't get toasted and skinned hazelnuts from your health food store, spread the nuts on a baking tray and roast in a moderate oven for 10– 12 minutes. Cool, then rub in a tea towel to remove as many of the skins as possible. Won ton wrappers made with egg are best.

NUTRITION PER SERVE: *Protein 10 g; Fat 35 g; Carbohydrate 35 g; Dietary Fibre 5 g; Cholesterol 60 mg; 2070 kJ (490 cal)*

RAVIOLI
It is thought that ravioli originated in the seaport of Genoa, when thrifty housewives used pasta to wrap around little spoonfuls of leftovers in the hope of disguising it. The sailors happily took their *rabiole* to sea, unaware of the origins of the filling. Today, we are more discerning about the fillings we put in ravioli, and they are stuffed with well-considered combinations of meats, cheese or vegetables.

ABOVE: Mushroom ravioli

227

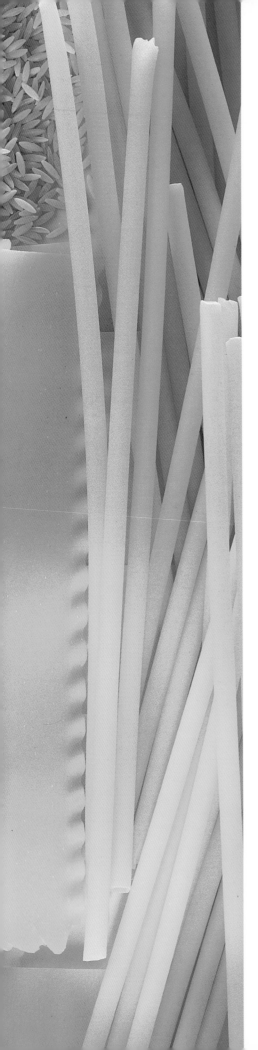

BAKED PASTA

Sheets of pasta layered with ragu or rich tomato sauce and a smooth, creamy béchamel, then finished with grated Parmesan and left in the oven to bubble and melt until the smell becomes irresistible... lasagne is undoubtedly the most famous (and perhaps the favourite) baked pasta dish of our times. But what about pasticcio, cannelloni and macaroni cheese? If you've perfected your lasagne, it could be time to try another little bit of pasta magic.

1 Lightly brush a deep 23 cm (9 inch) round springform tin with oil or butter and line it with baking paper. Cook the macaroni in a large pan of rapidly boiling salted water until *al dente*. Drain and set aside.

2 Arrange the eggplant on trays, sprinkle with salt and allow to stand for 20 minutes. Rinse well and pat dry with paper towels. Heat 2 tablespoons of oil in a frying pan, add the eggplant and cook, in batches, in a single layer, until golden on each side. Add more oil as required. Drain on paper towels.

3 Add the onion and garlic to the same pan and stir over low heat until the onion is tender. Add the mince and brown, breaking up any lumps with a spoon or fork as it cooks. Add the tomato, tomato paste and salt and pepper, to taste, and stir well. Bring to the boil. Reduce the heat and simmer for 15–20 minutes. Set aside.

4 In a bowl, mix together the peas, macaroni, mozzarella and Cheddar cheeses, egg and half the Parmesan. Set aside.

5 Preheat the oven to moderate 180°C (350°F/Gas 4). Place a slice of eggplant in the centre on the base of the prepared tin. Arrange three-quarters of remaining eggplant in an overlapping pattern to completely cover the base and sides of the tin. Sprinkle with half the remaining Parmesan.

6 Combine the mince mixture with the macaroni mixture. Carefully spoon the filling into the eggplant case, packing down well. Arrange the remaining eggplant slices, overlapping, over the filling. Sprinkle with the remaining Parmesan.

7 Bake, uncovered, for 25–30 minutes, or until golden. Allow to rest for 5 minutes before unmoulding onto a serving plate. Serve with salad, if desired.

NOTE: You can omit the mince and add chopped cooked Italian sausage and chopped cooked chicken to the tomato mixture.

Extra tomato sauce can be served with this dish. Make it by simmering canned, crushed tomato with a little garlic, pepper and chopped basil until thickened.

NUTRITION PER SERVE: *Protein 35 g; Fat 20 g; Carbohydrate 20 g; Dietary Fibre 5 g; Cholesterol 115 mg; 1780 kJ (425 cal)*

MACARONI EGGPLANT (AUBERGINE) CAKE

Preparation time: 1 hour
Total cooking time: 1 hour
Serves 6

★★

3/4 cup (115 g/4 oz) macaroni

2–3 eggplant (aubergine), sliced thinly lengthways

1 onion, chopped

1 clove garlic, crushed

500 g (1 lb) pork, beef or chicken mince

425 g (14 oz) can crushed tomatoes

2 tablespoons tomato paste (tomato purée, double concentrate)

1/2 cup (80 g/2 3/4 oz) frozen peas

1 cup (150 g/5 oz) freshly grated mozzarella cheese

1/2 cup (60 g/2 oz) freshly grated Cheddar cheese

1 egg, beaten

1/2 cup (50 g/1 3/4 oz) freshly grated Parmesan

ABOVE: Macaroni eggplant cake

RICOTTA LASAGNE

Preparation time: 1 hour
Total cooking time: 1 hour 30 minutes
Serves 8

500 g (1 lb) fresh spinach lasagne sheets
1/2 cup (30 g/1 oz) fresh basil leaves, chopped
2 tablespoons fresh breadcrumbs
3 tablespoons pine nuts
2 teaspoons paprika
1 tablespoon freshly grated Parmesan

Ricotta filling

750 g (1 1/2 lb) fresh ricotta
1/2 cup (50 g/1 3/4 oz) freshly grated Parmesan
pinch of nutmeg

Tomato sauce

1 tablespoon olive oil
2 onions, chopped
2 cloves garlic, crushed
800 g (1 lb 10 oz) can crushed tomatoes
1 tablespoon tomato paste (tomato purée,
   double concentrate)

Béchamel sauce

60 g (2 oz) butter
1/2 cup (60 g/2 oz) plain flour
2 cups (500 ml/16 fl oz) milk
2 eggs, lightly beaten
1/3 cup (35 g/1 1/4 oz) freshly grated Parmesan

1 Lightly brush a 25 x 32 cm (10 x 13 inch)
baking dish with melted butter or oil. Cut the
pasta sheets into large pieces and cook, 2–3 at
a time, in boiling water for 3 minutes. Drain
and spread on damp tea towels until needed.
2 To make the ricotta filling, mix the ricotta and
Parmesan, nutmeg and a little freshly ground
black pepper in a bowl. Set aside.
3 To make the tomato sauce, heat the oil in
a frying pan, add the onion and cook for
10 minutes, stirring occasionally, until very soft.
Add the garlic and cook for another minute.
Add the tomato and tomato paste and stir until
well combined. Stir until the mixture comes
to the boil. Reduce the heat and simmer,
uncovered, for 15 minutes, or until thickened,
stirring occasionally.

4 To make the béchamel sauce, heat the butter
in a small pan. Add the flour and stir for about
1 minute, until golden and smooth. Remove
from the heat and gradually stir in the milk.
Return to the heat and stir until the sauce boils
and begins to thicken. Remove from the heat
and stir in the eggs. Return to medium heat and
stir until almost boiling, but do not boil. Add
the cheese and season, to taste. Put plastic wrap
onto the surface to prevent a skin forming.
Preheat the oven to moderately hot 200°C
(400°F/Gas 6).
5 Put a layer of lasagne sheets in the dish. Spread
with a third of the ricotta filling, sprinkle with
basil, then top with a third of the tomato sauce.
Repeat the layers, finishing with pasta.
6 Pour the béchamel sauce over the top and
spread until smooth. Sprinkle with the
combined breadcrumbs, pine nuts, paprika
and Parmesan. Bake for 45 minutes, or until
browned. Set the lasagne aside for 10 minutes
before serving.
NOTE: Allowing the lasagne to stand before
serving makes it easier to cut.

NUTRITION PER SERVE: *Protein 30 g; Fat 30 g;
Carbohydrate 60 g; Dietary Fibre 5 g; Cholesterol 130 mg;
2670 kJ (635 cal)*

PAPRIKA
Ground paprika is the
dried and pounded form
of sweet red peppers,
capsicum annuum. It is
bright reddish-orange and
gives a rosy hue to dishes
when used in any quantity.
With a slightly pungent
taste, paprika is the
distinctive flavour in
Hungarian Goulash, and
benefits from slow cooking
to maximise its impact. It
is available in varying
strengths, from very sweet
and mild to fully flavoured
and highly fragrant.

ABOVE: Ricotta lasagne

SEAFOOD WITH PASTA

Preparation time: 30 minutes
Total cooking time: 45 minutes
Serves 6

250 g (8 oz) packet instant lasagne sheets
500 g (1 lb) boneless fish fillets
125 g (4 oz) scallops, cleaned
500 g (1 lb) raw prawns, shelled
    and deveined
125 g (4 oz) butter
1 leek, chopped
2/3 cup (85 g/3 oz) plain flour
2 cups (500 ml/16 fl oz) milk
2 cups (500 ml/16 fl oz) dry white wine
1 cup (125 g/4 oz) freshly grated
    Cheddar cheese
1/2 cup (125 ml/4 fl oz) cream
1/2 cup (50 g/1 3/4 oz) freshly grated Parmesan
2 tablespoons chopped fresh parsley

1 Preheat the oven to moderate 180°C (350°F/Gas 4). Line a greased deep lasagne dish, approximately 30 x 30 cm (12 x 12 inch) with lasagne sheets, breaking them to fill any gaps. Set aside.
2 Chop the fish and scallops into even-sized pieces. Chop the prawns.
3 Melt the butter in a large pan. Add the leek and cook, stirring, for 1 minute. Add the flour and cook, stirring, for 1 minute. Gradually blend in the milk and wine, stirring until the mixture is smooth. Cook, stirring constantly, over medium heat until the sauce boils and thickens. Reduce the heat and simmer for 3 minutes. Remove from the heat and stir in the cheese and salt and pepper, to taste. Add the seafood and simmer for 1 minute. Remove from the heat.
4 Spoon half the seafood mixture over the lasagne sheets. Top with a layer of lasagne sheets. Continue layering, finishing with lasagne sheets.
5 Pour the cream over the top. Sprinkle with the combined Parmesan and parsley. Bake, uncovered, for 30 minutes, or until bubbling and golden.
NOTE: Lasagne sheets are available in straight or ridged sheets.

NUTRITION PER SERVE: *Protein 50 g; Fat 45 g; Carbohydrate 45 g; Dietary Fibre 5 g; Cholesterol 290 mg; 3460 kJ (825 cal)*

CHEDDAR
Cheddar, the most well loved of English cheeses, originated in the small Somerset village of Cheddar. It is a hard cow's milk cheese matured to give well balanced flavours with a mellow aftertaste.

ABOVE: Seafood with pasta

ON THE SIDE

SWEET CHILLI POTATO AND CORIANDER SALAD Cut 1 kg (2 lb) peeled Desiree potatoes into wedges, drizzle with olive oil and sprinkle with sea salt. Roast in a hot oven until crisp and golden. Transfer to a bowl and drizzle generously with sweet chilli sauce. Add about 3 tablespoons of chopped fresh coriander and toss until mixed through.

PASTA PIE

Preparation time: 20 minutes
Total cooking time: 1 hour
Serves 4

★★

250 g (8 oz) macaroni

1 tablespoon olive oil

1 onion, sliced

125 g (4 oz) pancetta, chopped

125 g (4 oz) ham, chopped

4 eggs

1 cup (250 ml/8 fl oz) milk

1 cup (250 ml/8 fl oz) cream

2 tablespoons snipped fresh chives

1 cup (125 g/4 oz) grated Cheddar cheese

125 g (4 oz) bocconcini (approximately 4), chopped

1 Preheat the oven to moderate 180°C (350°F/Gas 4). Cook the macaroni in a large pan of rapidly boiling salted water until *al dente*. Drain. Spread evenly over the base of a 5 cm (2 inch) deep casserole dish.

2 Heat the oil in a large pan, add the onion and stir over low heat until just tender. Stir in the pancetta and cook for 2 minutes. Add the ham to the mixture and stir well. Remove from the heat and allow to cool.

3 In a bowl, whisk together the eggs, milk, cream, chives and salt and pepper, to taste. Mix in the Cheddar cheese, bocconcini and pancetta mixture, stirring thoroughly. Spread evenly over the top of the macaroni. Bake for 35—40 minutes, or until the mixture is set.

NUTRITION PER SERVE: *Protein 40 g; Fat 75 g; Carbohydrate 50 g; Dietary Fibre 5 g; Cholesterol 470 mg; 4335 kJ (1035 cal)*

ABOVE: Pasta pie

DURUM WHEAT

Durum wheat is a hard wheat with high levels of protein and therefore more gluten. It is considered the best wheat for pasta making and by law, all dried pasta made in Italy must be from 100% pure durum wheat semolina, *pasta di semola di grano duro*. As well as the nutritional benefits it provides, it gives pasta good colour, from pale lemon to golden, and more flavour. Durum wheat is necessary for the resilient texture of quality pasta and its presence helps to achieve the desired cooked state known as *al dente*.

BELOW: Pasta souffle

PASTA SOUFFLE

Preparation time: 35 minutes
Total cooking time: 55 minutes
Serves 4

★ ★

2 tablespoons freshly grated Parmesan
60 g (2 oz) butter
1 small onion, finely chopped
2 tablespoons plain flour
2 cups (500 ml/16 fl oz) milk
1/2 cup (125 ml/4 fl oz) chicken stock
3 eggs, separated
3/4 cup (115 g/4 oz) small macaroni, cooked
210 g (7 oz) can salmon, drained and flaked
1 tablespoon chopped fresh parsley
grated rind of 1 lemon

1 Preheat the oven to hot 210°C (415°F/Gas 6–7). Brush a round 6-cup capacity (18 cm/7 inch) soufflé dish with oil. Coat the base and sides with Parmesan. Shake off excess.
2 To collar a soufflé dish, cut a piece of aluminium foil or greaseproof paper 5 cm (2 inches) longer than the circumference of the soufflé dish. Fold the foil in half lengthways. Wrap the foil around the outside of the souffle dish; it should extend 5 cm (2 inches) above the rim. Secure the foil with string.
3 Heat the butter in a large pan. Add the onion and cook over low heat until tender. Add the flour and stir for 2 minutes, or until the mixture is lightly golden. Remove from the heat. Gradually blend in the milk and stock, stirring until the mixture is smooth. Return to the heat. Stir constantly over medium heat until the mixture boils and thickens. Reduce the heat and simmer for 3 minutes. Add the egg yolks and whisk until smooth. Add the macaroni, salmon, parsley, lemon rind and salt and pepper, to taste. Stir until combined. Transfer the mixture to a large bowl.
4 Using electric beaters, beat the egg whites in a small dry mixing bowl until stiff peaks form. Using a metal spoon, fold gently into the salmon mixture. Spoon into the prepared dish. Bake for 40–45 minutes, or until well risen and browned. Serve immediately.
NOTE: Hot soufflés should be made just before you want to serve them as they will collapse very quickly after removal from the oven. The base mixture can be prepared, up to the end of Step 3, well in advance. Soften the mixture before folding in the beaten egg whites. Whites should be folded into the mixture just before cooking.

NUTRITION PER SERVE: *Protein 25 g; Fat 25 g; Carbohydrate 20 g; Dietary Fibre 1 g; Cholesterol 200 mg; 1690 kJ (405 cal)*

CLASSIC LASAGNE

Preparation time: 40 minutes
Total cooking time: 1 hour 40 minutes
Serves 8

★ ★ ★

2 tablespoons oil
30 g (1 oz) butter
1 large onion, finely chopped
1 carrot, finely chopped
1 celery stick, finely chopped
500 g (1 lb) beef mince
150 g (5 oz) chicken livers, finely chopped
1 cup (250 ml/8 fl oz) tomato purée
1 cup (250 ml/8 fl oz) red wine
2 tablespoons chopped fresh parsley
375 g (12 oz) fresh lasagne sheets

Béchamel sauce

60 g (2 oz) butter

$^1/_3$ cup (40 g/1$^1/_4$ oz) plain flour

2$^1/_4$ cups (560 ml/18 fl oz) milk

$^1/_2$ teaspoon nutmeg

1 cup (100 g/3$^1/_2$ oz) freshly grated Parmesan

1 Heat the oil and butter in a heavy-based pan and cook the onion, carrot and celery over medium heat until softened, stirring constantly. Increase the heat, add the mince and brown well, breaking up any lumps with a fork. Add the chicken livers and cook until they change colour. Add the tomato purée, wine, parsley, and salt and pepper, to taste. Bring to the boil, reduce the heat and simmer for 45 minutes; set aside.

2 To make the béchamel sauce, melt the butter in a medium pan over low heat. Add the flour and stir for 1 minute. Remove from the heat and gradually stir in the milk. Return to the heat and stir constantly until the sauce boils and begins to thicken. Simmer for another minute. Add the nutmeg and salt, pepper, to taste. Place a piece of plastic wrap on the surface of the sauce to prevent a skin forming; set aside.

3 Cut the lasagne sheets to fit snugly into a deep, rectangular ovenproof dish. Sometimes the sheets require precooking, so follow the instructions from the manufacturer and drain well before use.

4 To assemble, preheat the oven to moderate 180°C (350°F/Gas 4). Brush the ovenproof dish generously with melted butter or oil. Spread a thin layer of the meat sauce over the base and follow with a thin layer of béchamel. If béchamel has cooled and become too thick, warm it gently to make spreading easier. Lay lasagne sheets on top, gently pressing to push out any air. Continue the layers, finishing with the béchamel. Sprinkle with Parmesan and bake for 35–40 minutes, or until golden brown. Set aside 15 minutes before cutting.

NOTE: A packet of instant lasagne can be used instead of fresh. Follow the manufacturer's instructions. If you prefer, you can leave out the chicken livers and increase the amount of mince.

NUTRITION PER SERVE: *Protein 30 g; Fat 30 g; Carbohydrate 45 g; Dietary Fibre 5 g; Cholesterol 160 mg; 2415 kJ (575 cal)*

BÉCHAMEL SAUCE

Béchamel is known today as a white sauce made by adding milk to a roux, although originally it was produced by adding cream to a thick velouté. The sauce owes its name to a certain Marquis Louis de Béchameil, a rich handsome gourmet who acted as chief steward to Louis XIV. It is unlikely that he created the sauce, but more probable that one of the King's cooks, rather ingratiatingly, named it in his honour.

ABOVE: Classic lasagne

CINNAMON

The best quality cinnamon comes from the Sri Lankan cinnamon tree, *cinnamomum zeylanicum*, which has the most fragrant scent and a delicate and fresh flavour. It is made from the dried inner bark of young shoots where, once exposed, thin layers curl up into a cylinder as they dry. These are slipped together in rolls of ten, then cut into quills of equal length. It is more costly than Chinese cinnamon, *cassia*, where older, outer bark is collected for drying. Cinnamon is used whole, broken into pieces or ground to flavour sweet dishes and baked foods, and it is an ingredient of curry powder and garam masala.

ABOVE: Macaroni cheese

MACARONI CHEESE

Preparation time: 20 minutes
Total cooking time: 35 minutes
Serves 4

2 cups (500 ml/16 fl oz) milk
1 cup (250 ml/8 fl oz) cream
1 bay leaf
1 whole clove
1/2 cinnamon stick
60 g (2 oz) butter
2 tablespoons plain flour
2 cups (250 g/8 oz) freshly grated Cheddar cheese
1/2 cup (50 g/13/4 oz) freshly grated Parmesan
375 g (12 oz) elbow macaroni
1 cup (80 g/23/4 oz) fresh breadcrumbs
2 rashers rindless bacon, chopped and fried until crisp

1 Preheat the oven to moderate 180°C (350°F/Gas 4). Pour the milk and cream into a medium pan with the bay leaf, clove and cinnamon stick. Bring to the boil, then remove from the heat and set aside for 10 minutes. Strain into a jug; remove and discard the flavourings.
2 Melt the butter in a medium pan over low heat. Add the flour and stir for 1 minute. Remove from the heat and gradually add the milk and cream mixture, stirring until smooth. Return to the heat and stir constantly until the sauce boils and thickens. Simmer for 2 minutes, then remove from the heat and add half the Cheddar cheese, half the Parmesan and salt and pepper, to taste. Set aside.
3 Cook the macaroni in a large pan of rapidly boiling salted water until *al dente*. Drain and return to the pan. Add the sauce and mix well. Spoon into a deep casserole dish. Sprinkle with combined breadcrumbs, bacon and remaining cheeses. Bake for 15–20 minutes, or until golden. Serve.
NOTE: You can add chopped cooked chicken to the white sauce before mixing with the pasta.

NUTRITION PER SERVE: *Protein 45 g; Fat 70 g; Carbohydrate 90 g; Dietary Fibre 5 g; Cholesterol 185 mg; 4960 kJ (1185 cal)*

CONCHIGLIE WITH CHICKEN AND RICOTTA

Preparation time: 15 minutes
Total cooking time: 1 hour 10 minutes
Serves 4

500 g (1 lb) conchiglie (shell pasta)
2 tablespoons olive oil
1 onion, chopped
1 clove garlic, crushed
60 g (2 oz) prosciutto, sliced
125 g (4 oz) mushrooms, chopped
250 g (8 oz) chicken mince
2 tablespoons tomato paste (tomato purée, double concentrate)
425 g (14 oz) can crushed tomatoes
1/2 cup (125 ml/4 fl oz) dry white wine
1 teaspoon dried oregano
250 g (8 oz) ricotta cheese
1 cup (150 g/5 oz) grated mozzarella cheese
1 teaspoon snipped fresh chives
1 tablespoon chopped fresh parsley
3 tablespoons freshly grated Parmesan

1 Cook the conchiglie in a large pan of rapidly boiling salted water until *al dente*. Drain well.
2 Heat the oil in a large frying pan. Add the onion and garlic and stir over low heat until the onion is tender. Add the prosciutto and stir for 1 minute. Add the mushrooms and cook for 2 minutes. Add the chicken mince and brown well, breaking up with a fork as it cooks.
3 Stir in the tomato paste, tomato, wine, oregano and salt and pepper, to taste. Bring to the boil, reduce the heat and simmer for 20 minutes.
4 Preheat the oven to moderate 180°C (350°F/Gas 4). Combine the ricotta, mozzarella, chives, parsley and half the Parmesan. Spoon a little of the mixture into each shell. Spoon some of the chicken sauce into the base of a casserole dish. Arrange the conghiglie on top. Spoon the remaining sauce over the top. Sprinkle with the remaining Parmesan. Bake for 25– 30 minutes, or until golden.
NOTE: Conchiglie (shell pasta) vary in size— medium or large shells are best for this dish.

NUTRITION PER SERVE: *Protein 50 g; Fat 40 g; Carbohydrate 95 g; Dietary Fibre 9 g; Cholesterol 115 mg; 3945 kJ (940 cal)*

ON THE SIDE

RASPBERRY BEETROOT SALAD
Cook 1 bunch beetroot in a pan of simmering water until tender, peel and cut into wedges. Make a dressing using raspberry vinegar, orange juice and honey. Toss the beetroot wedges in the dressing and sprinkle with a few caraway seeds.

BABY SPINACH, WALNUT AND CHEDDAR SALAD Combine baby spinach leaves, toasted walnut halves and shavings of vintage Cheddar cheese in a salad bowl. Drizzle with a good-quality French dressing.

CHICKEN MINCE
A good chicken mince will be made of meat from all parts of the chicken. It will have a good proportion of fat and include both white and dark meat. Use it soon after it is made as it will spoil more quickly than regular cuts of meat. Avoid buying pre-minced chicken that looks grey and patchy.

ABOVE: Conchiglie with chicken and ricotta

BAKED SPAGHETTI FRITTATA

Preparation time: 30 minutes
Total cooking time: 35 minutes
Serves 4

★★

30 g (1 oz) butter

125 g (4 oz) mushrooms, sliced

1 green pepper (capsicum), seeded
and chopped

125 g (4 oz) ham, sliced

1/2 cup (80 g/2³/4 oz) frozen peas

6 eggs

1 cup (250 ml/8 fl oz) cream or milk

100 g (3¹/2 oz) spaghetti, cooked and chopped

2 tablespoons chopped fresh parsley

1/4 cup (25 g/³/4 oz) freshly grated Parmesan

*ABOVE: Baked
spaghetti frittata*

1 Preheat the oven to moderate 180°C
(350°F/Gas 4). Lightly brush a 23 cm (9 inch)
flan dish with oil or melted butter.
2 Melt the butter in a frying pan, add the
mushrooms and cook over low heat for
2–3 minutes. Add the pepper and cook for
1 minute. Stir in the ham and peas. Remove
the pan from the heat and allow the mixture
to cool slightly.
3 In a small bowl, whisk the eggs, cream and
salt and pepper, to taste. Stir in the spaghetti,
parsley and mushroom mixture and pour into
the prepared dish. Sprinkle with Parmesan and
bake for 25–30 minutes.
NOTE: Serve with chargrilled vegetables and
leafy salad greens.

NUTRITION PER SERVE: *Protein 25 g; Fat 20 g;
Carbohydrate 10 g; Dietary Fibre 5 g; Cholesterol 300 mg;
1320 kJ (315 cal)*

BAKED CANNELLONI MILANESE

Preparation time: 40 minutes
Total cooking time: 1 hour 50 minutes
Serves 4

500 g (1 lb) pork and veal mince
1/2 cup (50 g/1³/4 oz) dry breadcrumbs
1 cup (100 g/3¹/2 oz) freshly grated Parmesan
2 eggs, beaten
1 teaspoon dried oregano
12–15 cannelloni tubes
375 g (12 oz) fresh ricotta cheese
1/2 cup (60 g/2 oz) freshly grated Cheddar
   cheese

Tomato sauce

425 ml (14 fl oz) can tomato purée (passata)
425 g (14 oz) can crushed tomatoes
2 cloves garlic, crushed
3 tablespoons chopped fresh basil

1 Preheat the oven to moderate 180°C (350°F/Gas 4). Lightly brush a rectangular casserole dish with melted butter or oil.
2 In a bowl, combine the pork and veal mince, breadcrumbs, half the Parmesan, egg, oregano and salt and pepper, to taste. Use a teaspoon to stuff the cannelloni tubes with the mince mixture. Set aside.
3 To make the tomato sauce, bring the tomato purée, tomato and garlic to the boil in a medium pan. Reduce the heat and simmer for 15 minutes. Add the basil and pepper, to taste, and stir well.
4 Spoon half the tomato sauce over the base of the prepared dish. Arrange the stuffed cannelloni tubes on top. Cover with the remaining sauce. Spread with ricotta cheese. Sprinkle with the combined remaining Parmesan and Cheddar cheeses. Bake, covered with foil, for 1 hour. Uncover and bake for another 15 minutes, or until golden. Cut into squares for serving.

NUTRITION PER SERVE: *Protein 60 g; Fat 40 g; Carbohydrate 40 g; Dietary Fibre 5 g; Cholesterol 255 mg; 3190 kJ (762 cal)*

ON THE SIDE

INDIVIDUAL CAULIFLOWER CHEESE Boil, steam or microwave baby cauliflower, allowing 1 per person, until tender. Drain and transfer to an ovenproof dish. Top with a béchamel sauce made by melting 30 g (1 oz) of butter in a small pan and stirring in 1 tablespoon of plain flour. Add 1¹/3 cups (350 ml/11 fl oz) of milk and stir over medium heat for 1 minute, or until the sauce boils and thickens. Add 1/2 cup (60 g/2 oz) of finely grated Cheddar cheese and ¹/4 teaspoon of Dijon mustard and mix to combine. Pour the sauce over the cauliflower, top with finely grated Cheddar cheese and bake in a hot 210°C (415°F/Gas 6–7) oven for 10 minutes, or until the cheese is golden.

ABOVE: Baked cannelloni Milanese

239

3 Add the tomato, oregano, cayenne pepper and olives and simmer gently for 5 minutes. Pour the vegetable sauce over the pasta and toss through with one-third of the mozzarella cheese. Season, to taste, with freshly ground black pepper. Sprinkle with Parmesan and distribute the remaining mozzarella evenly over the top.
4 Bake for 10 minutes, or until the cheese has melted and the top is lightly browned. Serve.

NUTRITION PER SERVE: *Protein 30 g; Fat 35 g; Carbohydrate 75 g; Dietary Fibre 10 g; Cholesterol 45 mg; 3030 kJ (720 cal)*

PASTA AND SPINACH TIMBALES

Preparation time: 25 minutes
Total cooking time: 45 minutes + resting
Serves 6

★★

30 g (1 oz) butter
1 tablespoon olive oil
1 onion, chopped
500 g (1 lb) English spinach, steamed
   and well-drained
8 eggs, beaten
1 cup (250 ml/8 fl oz) cream
100 g (3 1/2 oz) spaghetti or tagliolini, cooked
1/2 cup (60 g/2 oz) grated Cheddar cheese
1/2 cup (50 g/1 3/4 oz) freshly grated Parmesan

RIGATONI GRATIN

Preparation time: 20 minutes
Total cooking time: 30 minutes
Serves 4

★★

375 g (12 oz) rigatoni
1/4 cup (60 ml/2 fl oz) light olive oil
300 g (10 oz) slender eggplant
   (aubergine), chopped
4 small zucchini (courgettes), thickly sliced
1 onion, sliced
410 g (13 oz) can tomatoes
1 teaspoon chopped fresh oregano
pinch of cayenne pepper
8– 10 black olives, pitted and sliced
250 g (8 oz) mozzarella cheese, cut into
   small cubes
2 tablespoons freshly grated Parmesan

1 Preheat the oven to moderate 180°C (350°F/Gas 4). Cook the rigatoni in a large pan of rapidly boiling salted water until *al dente*. Drain the pasta thoroughly and transfer to an oiled, shallow ovenproof dish.
2 While the pasta is cooking, heat the oil in a large pan and fry the eggplant, zucchini and onion for 5 minutes, or until lightly browned.

*ABOVE: Rigatoni gratin
RIGHT: Pasta and spinach timbales*

1 Preheat the oven to moderate 180°C (350°F/Gas 4). Brush six 1-cup capacity dariole moulds with melted butter or oil. Line the bases with baking paper. Heat the butter and oil together in a frying pan. Add the onion and stir over low heat until the onion is tender. Add the well-drained spinach and cook for 1 minute. Remove from the heat and allow to cool. Whisk in the eggs and cream. Stir in the spaghetti or tagliolini, grated cheeses, and salt and freshly ground pepper, to taste; stir well. Spoon into the prepared moulds.

2 Place the moulds in a baking dish. Pour boiling water into the baking dish to come halfway up the sides of the moulds. Bake for 30–35 minutes or until set. Halfway through cooking, you may need to cover the top with a sheet of foil to prevent excess browning. Near the end of cooking time, test the timbales with the point of a knife. When cooked, the knife should come out clean.

3 Allow the timbales to rest for 15 minutes before turning them out. Run the point of a knife around the edge of each mould. Invert onto serving plates.

NUTRITION PER SERVE: *Protein 20 g; Fat 40 g; Carbohydrate 7 g; Dietary Fibre 3 g; Cholesterol 330 mg; 1860 kJ (440 cal)*

BAKED CREAMY CHEESY PASTA

Preparation time: 10–15 minutes
Total cooking time: 35–40 minutes
Serves 4

500 g (1 lb) fusilli
2¹/₂ cups (600 ml/20 fl oz) cream
3 eggs
250 g (8 oz) feta, crumbled
2 tablespoons plain flour
2 teaspoons ground nutmeg
1 cup (125 g/4 oz) grated Cheddar or
    mozzarella cheese

1 Cook the fusilli in a large pan of rapidly boiling salted water until *al dente*. Drain, reserving 1 cup (250 ml/8 fl oz) of the cooking water. Set the pasta aside to cool a little.

2 Preheat the oven to moderate 180°C (350°F/ Gas 4) and brush a 7-cup capacity ovenproof dish with olive oil.

3 Whisk the cream, eggs and reserved water in a large bowl until thoroughly combined. Stir in the crumbled feta, flour, ground nutmeg and salt and pepper, to taste.

4 Transfer the cooled pasta to the prepared dish. Pour the cream mixture over the top and sprinkle with the grated cheese. Bake for 30–35 minutes, or until the mixture is just set and the top is lightly golden.

NUTRITION PER SERVE: *Protein 40 g; Fat 85 g; Carbohydrate 95 g; Dietary Fibre 6 g; Cholesterol 380 g; 5520 kJ 1315 (cal)*

WHITE PEPPER
White peppercorns come from the same tropical vine as black peppercorns, but the berries are treated differently to give a more subdued flavour and a lighter colour. These features are desirable in some dishes, particularly with white sauces and those which are cream based, so the appearance is not spoilt. Surprisingly, white pepper is more aromatic than black.

ABOVE: Baked creamy cheesy pasta

MOZZARELLA CHEESE

Most mozzarella made outside Italy today is intended for cooking, to be sprinkled over pizzas and put into lasagnes and baked dishes. It is a matured, sometimes processed cheese with a rubbery texture, but with great melting qualities. When heated, it breaks down completely and becomes smooth and runny, and forms long strands when stretched, much to the delight of children. It is not eaten as a table cheese. Fresh mozzarella (bocconcini), on the other hand, is enjoyed fresh. It is pure white, has a creamy taste and a limited shelf-life. In Italy, it is sometimes still made from the milk of buffaloes, as it has been for centuries.

ABOVE: Meatballs and pasta

MEATBALLS AND PASTA

Preparation time: 40 minutes
Total cooking time: 55 minutes
Serves 4

2/3 cup (100 g/3 1/2 oz) macaroni

500 g (1 lb) beef mince

1 onion, finely chopped

1 cup (80 g/2 3/4 oz) fresh breadcrumbs

2 tablespoons freshly grated Parmesan

1 tablespoon chopped fresh basil

1 egg, beaten

2 tablespoons olive oil

1 cup (150 g/5 oz) freshly grated mozzarella cheese

Sauce

1 onion, sliced

1 clove garlic, crushed

1 pepper (capsicum), seeded and sliced

125 g (4 oz) mushrooms, sliced

1/4 cup (60 ml/2 fl oz) tomato paste (tomato purée, double concentrate)

1/2 cup (125 ml/4 fl oz) red wine

1 Cook the macaroni in a large pan of rapidly boiling salted water until *al dente*. Drain thoroughly and set aside.

2 In a bowl, combine the mince, onion, half the breadcrumbs, Parmesan, basil and egg. Form heaped teaspoonsful into small balls.

3 Heat the oil in a frying pan. Add the meatballs and cook until well browned. Drain on paper towels. Transfer to an ovenproof dish. Preheat the oven to moderate 180°C (350°F/Gas 4).

4 To make the sauce, add the onion and garlic to the same pan and stir over low heat until the onion is tender. Add the pepper and mushrooms and cook for 2 minutes. Stir in the tomato paste and then the wine and 1 cup (250 ml/8 fl oz) of water. Bring to the boil, stirring continuously. Mix in the macaroni and salt and pepper, to taste. Pour over the top of the meatballs.

5 Bake, uncovered, for 30–35 minutes. Sprinkle with combined mozzarella cheese and remaining breadcrumbs. Bake for another 10 minutes, or until golden.

NUTRITION PER SERVE: *Protein 45 g; Fat 35 g; Carbohydrate 40 g; Dietary Fibre 5 g; Cholesterol 150 mg; 2840 kJ (680 cal)*

PASTA-FILLED VEGETABLES

Preparation time: 40 minutes
Total cooking time: 45 minutes
Serves 6

150 g (5 oz) rissoni
1 tablespoon olive oil
1 onion, finely chopped
1 clove garlic, crushed
3 rindless bacon rashers, finely chopped
1 cup (150 g/5 oz) freshly grated
    mozzarella cheese
1/2 cup (50 g/1 3/4 oz) freshly grated Parmesan
2 tablespoons chopped fresh parsley
4 large red peppers (capsicums), halved
    lengthways, seeds removed
425 g (14 oz) can crushed tomatoes
1/2 cup (125 ml/4 fl oz) dry white wine
1 tablespoon tomato paste (tomato purée,
    double concentrate)
1/2 teaspoon ground oregano
2 tablespoons shredded fresh basil

1 Cook the rissoni in a large pan of boiling salted water until *al dente*. Drain.
2 Preheat the oven to moderate 180°C (350°F/Gas 4). Lightly oil a large shallow ovenproof dish.
3 Heat the oil in a pan. Add the onion and garlic and stir over low heat until the onion is tender. Add the bacon and stir until crisp. Transfer to a large bowl and combine with the rissoni, cheeses and parsley. Spoon the mixture into the pepper halves and arrange in the dish.
4 In a bowl, combine the tomato, wine, tomato paste, oregano and salt and pepper, to taste. Spoon over the rissoni mixture. Sprinkle with basil. Bake for 35–40 minutes.

NUTRITION PER SERVE: *Protein 20 g; Fat 15 g; Carbohydrate 25 g; Dietary Fibre 5 g; Cholesterol 35 mg; 1345 kJ (320 cal)*

ON THE SIDE

BUTTERY CARAWAY CABBAGE

Finely shred cabbage and boil, steam or microwave until tender. Lightly fry some sliced onion with some caraway seeds in lots of butter until the onion is very soft and the caraway seeds are fragrant. Add the cabbage to the pan and toss to combine. Drizzle with a little malt vinegar and season generously with salt and pepper.

RISSONI

Rissoni is dried pasta in the shape of rice. It is good in soups and is perfect for stuffing vegetables. Used in stews, it contributes body and substance without bulk and for this reason it is also ideal as an ingredient of stuffing for poultry.

ABOVE: Pasta-filled vegetables

GARLIC

How garlic is prepared depends on the degree of flavour required for the intended dish. If the cloves are finely chopped or mashed, they will be the most intense as more oils are released this way. For a mild taste without garlicky undertones, the cloves are used whole, often unpeeled, and discarded before the dish is eaten. A stronger flavour without pungency comes from cloves which are peeled and halved.

CANNELLONI

Preparation time: 45 minutes
Total cooking time: 1 hour 10 minutes
Serves 6

Beef and spinach filling

1 tablespoon olive oil
1 onion, chopped
1 clove garlic, crushed
500 g (1 lb) beef mince
250 g (8 oz) packet frozen spinach, thawed
3 tablespoons tomato paste (tomato purée, double concentrate)
1/2 cup (125 g/4 oz) ricotta cheese
1 egg
1/2 teaspoon ground oregano

Béchamel sauce

1 cup (250 ml/8 fl oz) milk
1 sprig of fresh parsley
5 peppercorns
30 g (1 oz) butter
1 tablespoon plain flour
1/2 cup (125 ml/4 fl oz) cream

Tomato sauce

425 g (14 oz) can tomato purée
2 tablespoons chopped fresh basil
1 clove garlic, crushed
1/2 teaspoon sugar

12–15 instant cannelloni tubes
1 cup (150 g/5 oz) freshly grated mozzarella cheese
1/2 cup (50 g/1 3/4 oz) freshly grated Parmesan

1 Preheat the oven to moderate 180°C (350°F/Gas 4). Lightly oil a large shallow ovenproof dish. Set aside.
2 To make the beef and spinach filling, heat the oil in a frying pan, add the onion and garlic and stir over low heat until the onion is tender. Add the mince and brown well, breaking up with a fork as it cooks. Add the spinach and tomato paste. Stir for 1 minute and then remove from the heat. In a small bowl, mix the ricotta, egg, oregano and salt and pepper, to taste. Stir the mixture through the mince until combined. Set aside.
3 To make the béchamel sauce, combine the milk, parsley and peppercorns in a small pan. Bring to the boil. Remove from the heat and

RIGHT: Cannelloni

allow to stand for 10 minutes. Strain, discarding the flavourings. Melt the butter in a small pan over low heat, add the flour and stir for 1 minute, or until smooth. Remove from the heat and gradually stir in the strained milk. Return to the heat and stir constantly over medium heat until the sauce boils and begins to thicken. Reduce the heat, simmer for another minute, then stir in the cream and salt and pepper, to taste.

4 To make the tomato sauce, stir all the ingredients in a pan until combined. Bring to the boil, reduce the heat and simmer for 5 minutes. Season, to taste, with salt and pepper.

5 Spoon the beef and spinach filling into a piping bag and fill the cannelloni tubes or fill using a teaspoon.

6 Spoon a little of the tomato sauce in the base of the casserole dish. Arrange the cannelloni on top. Pour the béchamel sauce over the cannelloni, followed by the remaining tomato sauce. Sprinkle the combined cheeses over the top. Bake, uncovered, for 35–40 minutes, or until golden.

NOTE: Serve with a mixed green salad or steam some vegetables such as broccoli or beans, if desired.

NUTRITION PER SERVE: *Protein 35 g; Fat 40 g; Carbohydrate 25 g; Dietary Fibre 5 g; Cholesterol 150 mg; 2475 kJ (590 cal)*

ITALIAN OMELETTE

Preparation time: 20 minutes
Total cooking time: 15 minutes
Serves 4

2 tablespoons olive oil

1 onion, finely chopped

125 g (4 oz) ham, sliced

6 eggs

¼ cup (60 ml/2 fl oz) milk

2 cups cooked fusilli or spiral pasta
  (150 g/5 oz uncooked)

3 tablespoons grated Parmesan

2 tablespoons chopped fresh parsley

1 tablespoon chopped fresh basil

½ cup (60 g/2 oz) freshly grated
  Cheddar cheese

1 Heat half the oil in a frying pan. Add the onion and stir over low heat until softened. Add the sliced ham to the pan and stir for 1 minute. Transfer to a plate and set aside.

2 In a bowl, whisk the eggs, milk and salt and pepper, to taste. Stir in the pasta, Parmesan, herbs and onion mixture.

3 Heat the remaining oil in the same pan. Pour the egg mixture into the pan. Sprinkle with cheese. Cook over medium heat until the mixture begins to set around the edges. Place under a hot grill to complete the cooking. Cut into wedges for serving.

NOTE: This omelette goes well with a crisp green or mixed salad.

NUTRITION PER SERVE: *Protein 25 g; Fat 25 g; Carbohydrate 30 g; Dietary Fibre 2 g; Cholesterol 310 mg; 1925 kJ (460 cal)*

ABOVE: Italian omelette

ABOVE: Pasticcio

1 tablespoon chopped fresh oregano
1/4 teaspoon nutmeg
1/2 cup (50 g/1 3/4 oz) freshly grated Parmesan

Béchamel sauce

60 g (2 oz) butter
2 tablespoons plain flour
1 1/2 cups (375 ml/12 fl oz) cold milk

150 g (5 oz) bucatini

1 Put the flour, butter, sugar and egg yolk in a food processor with 1 tablespoon of water. Process lightly until the mixture forms a ball, adding more water if necessary. Lightly knead the dough on a floured surface until smooth. Wrap in plastic wrap and refrigerate.
2 To make the filling, heat the oil in a heavy-based pan and cook the onion and garlic until softened and lightly golden. Increase the heat, add the mince and cook until browned, breaking up any lumps with a fork. Add the livers, tomato, red wine, stock, oregano and nutmeg, then season well with salt and pepper. Cook the sauce over high heat until it boils, then reduce to a simmer and cook, covered, for 40 minutes; cool. Stir in the Parmesan.
3 To make the béchamel sauce, heat the butter in a medium pan over low heat. Add the flour and stir for 1 minute, or until the mixture is golden and smooth. Remove from the heat and gradually stir in the milk. Return to the heat and stir constantly until the sauce boils and begins to thicken. Simmer for another minute. Add salt and pepper, to taste.
4 Cook the bucatini in a pan of rapidly boiling salted water until *al dente*. Drain and cool. Brush a 23 cm (9 inch) deep pie dish with melted butter or oil and preheat the oven to warm 160°C (315°F/Gas 2–3). Divide the pastry into two and roll out one piece to fit the base of the prepared dish, overlapping the sides. Spoon about half of the meat mixture into the dish, top with the bucatini and slowly spoon the béchamel sauce over the top, allowing it to seep down and coat the bucatini. Top with the remaining meat. Roll out the remaining pastry and cover the pie. Trim the edges and pinch lightly to seal. Bake for 50–55 minutes, or until dark golden brown and crisp. Set aside for 15 minutes before cutting.

NUTRITION PER SERVE: *Protein 35 g; Fat 50 g; Carbohydrate 65 g; Dietary Fibre 5 g; Cholesterol 270 mg; 3595 kJ (860 cal)*

PASTICCIO

Preparation time: 1 hour
Total cooking time: 1 hour 50 minutes
Serves 6

2 cups (250 g/8 oz) plain flour
125 g (4 oz) cold butter, chopped
1/4 cup (60 g/2 oz) caster sugar
1 egg yolk

Filling

2 tablespoons olive oil
1 onion, chopped
2 cloves garlic, finely chopped
500 g (1 lb) beef mince
150 g (5 oz) chicken livers
2 tomatoes, chopped
1/2 cup (125 ml/4 fl oz) red wine
1/2 cup (125 ml/4 fl oz) rich
   beef stock

PASTITSIO

Preparation time: 1 hour
Total cooking time: 1 hour 25 minutes
Serves 8

2 tablespoons olive oil

4 cloves garlic, crushed

3 onions, chopped

1 kg (2 lb) lamb mince

800 g (1 lb 10 oz) can peeled tomatoes, chopped

1 cup (250 ml/8 fl oz) red wine

1 cup (250 ml/8 fl oz) chicken stock

3 tablespoons tomato paste (tomato purée,
    double concentrate)

2 tablespoons fresh oregano leaves

2 bay leaves

350 g (11 oz) ziti

2 eggs, lightly beaten

750 g (1 1/2 lb) Greek-style yoghurt

3 eggs, extra, lightly beaten

200 g (6 1/2 oz) kefalotyri or manchego cheese,
    grated

1/2 teaspoon ground nutmeg

1/2 cup (50 g/1 3/4 oz) freshly grated Parmesan

1 cup (80 g/2 3/4 oz) fresh breadcrumbs

1 Preheat the oven to moderately hot 200°C (400°F/Gas 6). To make the meat sauce, heat the oil in a large heavy-based pan and cook the garlic and onion over low heat for 10 minutes, or until the onion is soft and golden.

2 Add the mince and cook over high heat until browned, stirring constantly and breaking up any lumps. Add the tomato, wine, stock, tomato paste, oregano and bay leaves. Bring to the boil, reduce the heat and simmer, covered, for 15 minutes. Remove the lid and cook for 30 minutes. Season with salt and pepper.

3 While the meat is cooking, cook the ziti in a large pan of rapidly boiling salted water until *al dente*. Drain well. Transfer to a bowl and stir the eggs through. Spoon into a lightly greased 4-litre capacity ovenproof dish. Top with the meat sauce.

4 Whisk the yoghurt, extra eggs, cheese and nutmeg in a jug to combine and pour the mixture over the meat sauce. Sprinkle with the combined Parmesan and breadcrumbs. Bake for 30–35 minutes, or until the top is crisp and golden brown. Allow to stand for 20 minutes before slicing. Serve with a green salad.

NOTE: Kefalotyri and manchego are firm, grating cheeses. Use Parmesan if they are unavailable.

NUTRITION PER SERVE: *Protein 50 g; Fat 40 g; Carbohydrate 45 g; Dietary Fibre 5 g; Cholesterol 250 mg; 3275 kJ (780 cal)*

PASTICCIO AND PASTITSIO

It is easy to be confused by the terms pasticcio and pastitsio (*pastizio*, or *pastetseo*). In Italian cooking, pasticcio is a generic term used to describe a pie in which the composite parts such as meat, pasta and vegetables are baked in layers. Lasagne is, in fact, one type of pasticcio, and some have a pastry crust. Pasticcio is made for special occasions and can be plain and simple, or quite elaborate in its composition and the ingredients used. It is eaten as a main course and is traditionally served unaccompanied, with a salad or vegetable course following. Pastitsio is the Greek version, and the two are often so similar that it's hard to tell from the recipe which country the cook hails from. Pastitsio is likely to be made with lamb instead of beef, and often Greek favourites such as olives and yoghurt will feature.

LEFT: Pastitsio

BUTTERNUT PUMPKIN FILLED WITH PASTA AND LEEKS

Preparation time: 30 minutes
Total cooking time: 1 hour
Serves 2 as a light meal, or 4 as
  an accompaniment

1 medium butternut pumpkin
20 g (³/4 oz) butter
1 leek, thinly sliced
¹/2 cup (125 ml/4 fl oz) cream
pinch of nutmeg
60 g (2 oz) cooked linguine or stellini
¹/4 cup (60 ml/2 fl oz) olive oil

1 Preheat the oven to moderate 180°C (350°F/Gas 4). Cleanly cut a quarter off the top end of the butternut pumpkin (where the stalk attaches), to make a lid. Level off the other end so that it stands evenly. Scrape out the seeds and sinew from the pumpkin and discard. Hollow out the centre to make room for filling. Sprinkle salt and pepper over the cut surfaces and then transfer the pumpkin to a small baking dish.
2 Melt the butter in a small frying pan and gently cook the leek until softened. Add the cream and nutmeg and cook over low heat for 4– 5 minutes, or until thickened. Season with salt and white pepper, to taste, and stir in the pasta.
3 Fill the butternut pumpkin with the pasta mixture, place the lid on top and drizzle with the olive oil. Bake for 1 hour, or until tender. Test by inserting a skewer through the thickest part of the vegetable.
NOTE: Choose a butternut which is round and fat, not one with a long stem of flesh.

NUTRITION PER SERVE (4): *Protein 10 g; Fat 30 g; Carbohydrate 30 g; Dietary Fibre 6 g; Cholesterol 50 mg; 1885 kJ (450 cal)*

CHICKEN AND VEAL LOAF WITH MUSHROOMS AND SOUR CREAM

Preparation time: 20 minutes
Total cooking time: 1 hour
Serves 6

100 g (3¹/2 oz) pappardelle
¹/4 cup (20 g/³/4 oz) fresh breadcrumbs
1 tablespoon white wine
375 g (12 oz) chicken mince
375 g (12 oz) veal mince
2 cloves garlic, crushed
100 g (3¹/2 oz) button mushrooms,
  finely chopped
2 eggs, beaten
pinch of nutmeg
pinch of cayenne pepper
¹/4 cup (60 ml/2 fl oz) sour cream
4 spring onions, finely chopped
2 tablespoons chopped fresh parsley

1 Grease a 6-cup capacity loaf tin. Cook the pappardelle in a large pan of rapidly boiling salted water until *al dente*. Drain.
2 Preheat the oven to moderately hot 200°C (400°F/Gas 6).
3 Soak the breadcrumbs in the wine. Mix the crumbs in a bowl with the chicken and veal minces, garlic, mushrooms, eggs, nutmeg, cayenne pepper, and salt and freshly ground black pepper, to taste. Mix in the sour cream, spring onion and parsley.
4 Place half the mince mixture into the prepared tin with your hands. Form a deep trough along the entire length. Fill the trough with the pappardelle. Press the remaining mince mixture over the top. Bake for 50– 60 minutes, draining the excess fat and juice from the tin twice during cooking. Cool slightly before slicing.
NOTE: Mushrooms can be chopped in a food processor. Don't prepare too far in advance or they will discolour and darken the loaf.

NUTRITION PER SERVE: *Protein 35 g; Fat 20 g; Carbohydrate 15 g; Dietary Fibre 2 g; Cholesterol 205 mg; 1545 kJ (365 cal)*

BUTTERNUT PUMPKIN
Butternut pumpkins or squash are well named, for they have sweet, buttery and slightly nutty taste. When young, they should be evenly firm, with no cracks or blemishes on the skin. The flesh inside will be crisp, with a good bright colour and a low water content.

OPPOSITE PAGE:
Butternut pumpkin filled with pasta and leeks (top); Chicken and veal loaf with mushrooms and sour cream

GREEN OLIVE PASTE

When the pulp of green olives is mixed with olive oil, salt and herbs, the resulting purée is known as green olive paste or pâté. As is, it makes an excellent dip or spread for bread and it can be used to dress pasta and vegetables. Stirred through soups and sauces, it adds flavour and colour, and is delicious rubbed into the skin of poultry.

ABOVE: Pasta with green olive paste and three cheeses

PASTA WITH GREEN OLIVE PASTE AND THREE CHEESES

Preparation time: 10 minutes
Total cooking time: 20 minutes
Serves 4

400 g (13 oz) mafalda or pappardelle

2 tablespoons olive oil

2 cloves garlic, crushed

1/2 cup (125 g/4 oz) green olive paste

4 tablespoons cream

1/2 cup (50 g/1 3/4 oz) freshly grated Parmesan

1/2 cup (60 g/2 oz) grated Cheddar cheese

1/2 cup (50 g/1 3/4 oz) grated Jarlsberg cheese

1 Preheat the oven to moderately hot 200°C (400°F/Gas 6). Lightly brush a deep ovenproof dish with oil.
2 Cook the pasta in a large pan of rapidly boiling salted water until *al dente*. Drain and return to the pan.
3 Toss the olive oil, garlic and green olive paste through the pasta and then mix in the cream. Season with black pepper. Transfer to the prepared dish.
4 Sprinkle the top with the cheeses. Bake, uncovered, for 20 minutes, or until the top is crisp and cheeses have melted.

NUTRITION PER SERVE: *Protein 25 g; Fat 40 g; Carbohydrate 70 g; Dietary Fibre 6 g; Cholesterol 65 mg; 3055 kJ (725 cal)*

GIANT CONCHIGLIE WITH RICOTTA AND ROCKET

Preparation time: 50 minutes
Total cooking time: 1 hour
Serves 6

☆ ☆

40 giant conchiglie (shell pasta)

Filling

500 g (1 lb) ricotta cheese
1 cup (100 g/3½ oz) grated Parmesan
150 g (5 oz) rocket, finely shredded
1 egg, lightly beaten
180 g (6 oz) marinated artichokes,
    finely chopped
½ cup (80 g/2¾ oz) sun-dried tomatoes,
    finely chopped
½ cup (95 g/3 oz) sun-dried pepper
    (capsicum), finely chopped

Cheese sauce

60 g (2 oz) butter
30 g (1 oz) plain flour
3 cups (750 ml/24 fl oz) milk
100 g (3½ oz) Gruyère cheese, grated
2 tablespoons chopped fresh basil

600 ml (20 fl oz) bottled pasta sauce
2 tablespoons fresh oregano leaves,
    chopped
2 tablespoons fresh basil leaves,
    finely shredded

1 Cook the giant conchiglie in a large pan of rapidly boiling salted water until *al dente*. Drain and arrange the shells on 2 non-stick baking trays to prevent them sticking together. Cover lightly with plastic wrap.
2 To make the filling, mix all the ingredients in a large bowl. Spoon the filling into the shells, taking care not to overfill them or they will split.
3 To make the cheese sauce, melt the butter in a small pan over low heat. Add the flour and stir for 1 minute, or until golden and smooth. Remove from the heat and gradually stir in the milk. Return to the heat and stir constantly until the sauce boils and begins to thicken. Simmer for another minute. Remove from the heat and stir in the Gruyère cheese with the basil and salt and pepper, to taste.

4 Preheat the oven to moderate 180°C (350°F/Gas 4). Spread 1 cup of the cheese sauce over the base of a 3-litre capacity ovenproof dish. Arrange the filled conchiglie over the sauce, top with the remaining sauce and bake for 30 minutes, or until the sauce is golden.
5 Place the bottled pasta sauce and oregano in a pan and cook over medium heat for 5 minutes, or until heated through. To serve, divide the sauce among the warmed serving plates, top with the conchiglie and sprinkle with the shredded fresh basil leaves.

NUTRITION PER SERVE: *Protein 35 g; Fat 35 g; Carbohydrate 70 g; Dietary Fibre 8 g; Cholesterol 145 mg; 3165 kJ (755 cal)*

ABOVE: Giant conchiglie with ricotta and rocket

251

PASTA PRONTO

Forget packet meals and takeaways: pasta is the ultimate convenience food. All of these dishes can be ready in around 30 minutes, some of them so fast they are on the table before the family's had time to sit down. Who knows when friends might call in unexpectedly? A good hoard of dried pasta is the key to quick, fuss-free meals and should be part of every well-stocked store-cupboard. Was that the doorbell? Start grating the Parmesan.

GREEN OLIVES

As the name suggests, green olives are the unripe fruit of the olive tree. When olives begin forming they contain no oil, just sugars and organic acids and it is these which give green olives their tangy flavour. As olives mature, they change from pale green through bright green, rose, deep purple to black, and the oil content increases. The flesh goes from being hard and crisp, to soft and slightly spongy. For these reasons, green olives need to be treated differently to black olives to become edible, and it also helps explain why there is such a contrast in flavour and texture between them.

ABOVE: Linguine with anchovies, olives and capers

LINGUINE WITH ANCHOVIES, OLIVES AND CAPERS

Ready to eat in 30 minutes
Serves 4

★

500 g (1 lb) linguine

2 tablespoons olive oil

2 cloves garlic, crushed

2 very ripe tomatoes, peeled and chopped

3 tablespoons capers

1/2 cup (75 g/2 1/2 oz) pitted black olives, finely chopped

1/4 cup (55 g/2 oz) pitted green olives, finely chopped

1/4 cup (60 ml/2 fl oz) dry white wine

3 tablespoons chopped fresh parsley or basil

90 g (3 oz) can anchovies, drained and chopped

1 Cook the linguine in a large pan of rapidly boiling salted water until *al dente*. Drain and return to the pan.

2 While the pasta is cooking, heat the oil in a large frying pan. Add the garlic and stir over low heat for 1 minute. Add the tomato, capers and olives and cook for 2 minutes.

3 Stir in the wine, parsley or basil, and freshly ground black pepper, to taste. Bring to the boil, reduce the heat and simmer for about 5 minutes. Remove from the heat. Add the anchovies and stir gently to combine.

4 Add to the warm pasta in the pan and toss well to distribute the sauce evenly.

NOTE: For variation or on special occasions, you may like to serve this dish with the following topping. Heat a little olive oil in a small pan and add some fresh breadcrumbs and a crushed clove of garlic. Toss over the heat until crisp and golden and sprinkle over the top with freshly grated Parmesan.

NUTRITION PER SERVE: *Protein 20 g; Fat 15 g; Carbohydrate 90 g; Dietary Fibre 8 g; Cholesterol 15 mg; 2525 kJ (600 cal)*

FETTUCINE WITH SPINACH AND PROSCIUTTO

Ready to eat in 20 minutes
Serves 4–6

500 g (1 lb) spinach or plain fettucine
2 tablespoons olive oil
8 thin slices prosciutto, chopped
3 spring onions, chopped
500 g (1 lb) English spinach
1 tablespoon balsamic vinegar
1/2 teaspoon caster sugar
1/2 cup (50 g/1 3/4 oz) freshly grated Parmesan

1 Cook the pasta in a large pan of rapidly boiling salted water until just *al dente*. Drain and return to the pan.
2 While the pasta is cooking, heat the oil in a large heavy-based deep pan. Add the prosciutto and the spring onion and cook, stirring occasionally, over medium heat for 5 minutes or until crisp.
3 Trim the stalks from the spinach, roughly chop the leaves and add them to the pan. Stir in the vinegar and the sugar, cover and cook for 1 minute or until the spinach has softened. Add salt and pepper, to taste.
4 Add the sauce to the pasta and toss well to distribute sauce evenly. Sprinkle with Parmesan and serve immediately.

NUTRITION PER SERVE (6): *Protein 20 g; Fat 10 g; Carbohydrate 60 g; Dietary Fibre 7 g; Cholesterol 25 mg; 1825 kJ (435 cal)*

PASTA WITH FRAGRANT LIME AND SMOKED TROUT

Ready to eat in 30 minutes
Serves 4

500 g (1 lb) spinach and white linguine
1 tablespoon extra virgin olive oil
3 cloves garlic, crushed
1 tablespoon grated lime rind
2 tablespoons poppy seeds
250 g (8 oz) smoked trout, skin and
    bones removed
400 g (13 oz) camembert cheese, chopped
2 tablespoons chopped fresh dill
lime wedges, for serving

1 Cook the linguine in rapidly boiling salted water until *al dente*. Drain.
2 Heat the olive oil in a large heavy-based frying pan. Add the garlic, cook over low heat for 3 minutes or until fragrant. Add the rind, poppy seeds and pasta to the pan and toss to coat.
3 Fold the trout, camembert and dill through the mixture and cook over low heat until the camembert begins to melt. Toss gently through the pasta and serve immediately with a squeeze of lime.

NUTRITION PER SERVE: *Protein 50 g; Fat 40 g; Carbohydrate 90 g; Dietary Fibre 6 g; Cholesterol 140 mg; 3870 kJ (920 cal)*

ENGLISH SPINACH
English spinach has medium to dark green leaves, smaller than those of swiss chard or silverbeet. The stalks are thin and only the tough lower end needs to be removed. It can be steamed, fried, lightly boiled or baked in a gratin or pie.

ABOVE: Fettucine with spinach and prosciutto

CHICKEN RAVIOLI WITH LIME BALSAMIC DRESSING

Ready to eat in 30 minutes
Serves 4

250 g (8 oz) chicken mince
1 egg, lightly beaten
1 teaspoon finely grated orange rind
1/2 cup (50 g/1 3/4 oz) freshly grated Parmesan
1 tablespoon finely shredded fresh basil
275 g (9 oz) won ton wrappers
2 tablespoons lime juice
2 tablespoons balsamic vinegar
1/2 teaspoon honey
1 tablespoon oil

1 Combine the chicken mince, egg, orange rind, Parmesan and basil in a bowl. Place a heaped tablespoon of chicken mixture in the centre of a won ton wrapper, lightly brush the edges with water and top with another wrapper. Press the edges together to seal. Repeat with remaining filling and wrappers. (This is a quick way to make ravioli.)
2 Cook the chicken ravioli in a large pan of rapidly boiling salted water for 5 minutes.
3 Meanwhile, combine the lime juice, balsamic vinegar, honey and oil in a small jug and whisk to combine. Drain the ravioli. Serve drizzled with the dressing and sprinkled with finely chopped fresh chives. Garnish with lime slices, if you like.

NUTRITION PER SERVE: *Protein 30 g; Fat 20 g; Carbohydrate 50 g; Dietary Fibre 2 g; Cholesterol 120 mg; 2020 kJ (480 cal)*

ZITI WITH ROASTED TOMATOES AND OVOLINI

Ready to eat in 30 minutes
Serves 4

200 g (6 1/2 oz) yellow teardrop tomatoes
200 g (6 1/2 oz) red cherry tomatoes
500 g (1 lb) ziti
200 g (6 1/2 oz) ovolini cheese
100 g (3 1/2 oz) capers
3 tablespoons fresh marjoram leaves
3 tablespoons fresh lemon thyme leaves
2 tablespoons extra virgin olive oil
3 tablespoons balsamic vinegar

1 Preheat the oven to moderately hot 200°C (400°F/Gas 6). Cut all the tomatoes in half and bake, cut-side-up, on an oven tray for 15 minutes.
2 While the tomatoes are baking, cook the ziti in a large pan of rapidly boiling salted water until *al dente*. Drain and return to the pan.
3 Add the tomatoes and remaining ingredients to the drained pasta and toss thoroughly. Serve immediately.
NOTE: Use smaller quantities of fresh herbs if you prefer. Ovolini is a type of small fresh cheese available from speciality shops and some supermarkets. Use bocconcini cut into small pieces, if ovolini is unavailable.

NUTRITION PER SERVE: *Protein 30 g; Fat 30 g; Carbohydrate 90 g; Dietary Fibre 10 g; Cholesterol 50 mg; 3110 kJ (740 cal)*

LIMES
The lime is a tropical citrus tree. The fruit are small, distinctive yellowish-green and almost perfectly rounded, with a thin skin. The taste is pleasantly sharp, with tropical overtones. Slices of the unpeeled fruit make an attractive garnish, while the juice and rind are used to enhance both sweet and savoury dishes. Lime juice works well as a curing agent and is particularly effective on fresh seafood.

ON THE SIDE

HERB SALAD Combine fresh basil leaves, rocket, flat-leaf parsley, coriander and baby English spinach leaves in a bowl. Drizzle with a dressing made of crushed garlic, lemon juice, honey and olive oil. Toss well and serve immediately with loads of freshly cracked black pepper.

MIXED TOMATO SALAD Combine cherry, teardrop and sliced egg (Roma) tomatoes in a bowl with chopped red (Spanish) onion and loads of finely shredded basil leaves. Toss in a little red wine vinegar and olive oil.

OPPOSITE PAGE: Chicken ravioli with lime balsamic dressing (top); Ziti with roasted tomatoes and bocconcini

FARFALLE WITH PEAS

Ready to eat in 20 minutes
Serves 4

500 g (1 lb) farfalle
1 1/2 cups (235 g/7 1/2 oz) frozen baby peas
8 thin slices pancetta
60 g (2 oz) butter
2 tablespoons each shredded fresh
    basil and mint

1 Cook the farfalle in a large pan of rapidly boiling salted water until *al dente*. Drain and return to the pan.
2 While the pasta is cooking, steam, microwave or lightly boil the baby peas until just tender and drain. Chop the pancetta and cook in the butter over medium heat for 2 minutes. Toss the butter and pancetta mixture through the pasta with the peas, basil and mint. Season with cracked black pepper and serve.

NUTRITION PER SERVE: *Protein 20 g; Fat 40 g; Carbohydrate 90 g; Dietary Fibre 10 g; Cholesterol 220 mg; 3470 kJ (830 cal)*

PENNE WITH ROCKET

Ready to eat in 20 minutes
Serves 4

500 g (1 lb) penne
100 g (3 1/2 oz) butter
200 g (6 1/2 oz) rocket, roughly chopped
3 tomatoes, finely chopped
1/2 cup (45 g/1 1/2 oz) grated pecorino cheese
freshly grated Parmesan, for serving

1 Cook the penne in a large pan of rapidly boiling salted water until *al dente*. Drain and return to the pan. Place the pan over low heat. Add the butter, tossing it through until it melts and coats the pasta.
2 Add the rocket leaves to the pasta along with the tomato. Toss through to wilt the rocket. Stir in the pecorino cheese and season with salt and pepper, to taste. Serve sprinkled with freshly grated Parmesan.

NUTRITION PER SERVE: *Protein 20 g; Fat 25 g; Carbohydrate 90 g; Dietary Fibre 10 g; Cholesterol 80 mg; 2885 kJ (690 cal)*

ABOVE, FROM LEFT:
Farfalle with peas; Penne
with rocket; Penne with
olive and pistachio pesto

PENNE WITH OLIVE AND PISTACHIO PESTO

Ready to eat in 20 minutes
Serves 4

500 g (1 lb) penne
125 g (4 oz) unsalted, shelled
   pistachio nuts
4 cloves garlic
1 tablespoon green peppercorns
2 tablespoons lemon juice
150 g (5 oz) pitted black olives
1¹/2 cups (150 g/5 oz) freshly grated Parmesan
   plus extra, shaved, for serving
¹/2 cup (125 ml/4 fl oz) light olive oil

1 Cook the penne in a large pan of rapidly boiling salted water until *al dente*. Drain and return to the pan.
2 While the penne is cooking, combine the pistachio nuts, garlic, peppercorns, lemon juice, black olives and Parmesan in a food processor for 30 seconds, or until roughly chopped.

3 While the motor is running, gradually pour in the olive oil in a thin stream. Blend until the mixture is smooth. Toss the pesto through the hot pasta and serve topped with extra Parmesan.

NUTRITION PER SERVE: *Protein 40 g; Fat 60 g; Carbohydrate 90 g; Dietary Fibre 10 g; Cholesterol 35 mg; 4420 kJ (1055 cal)*

ON THE SIDE

TOMATO, EGG AND OLIVE SALAD Cut 6 ripe tomatoes into thick slices and arrange on a large plate, top with 1 thinly sliced red (Spanish) onion, 6 peeled and sliced hard-boiled eggs, ¹/2 cup (90 g/ 3 oz) of marinated black olives and scatter a few torn fresh basil leaves over the top. Drizzle with some extra virgin olive oil and sprinkle generously with sea salt and freshly cracked black pepper.

SPAGHETTI WITH RICH BEEF AND MUSHROOM SAUCE

Ready to eat in 30 minutes
Serves 6

1 tablespoon light olive oil

1 large onion, finely chopped

2 cloves garlic, crushed

500 g (1 lb) lean beef mince

350 g (11 oz) button mushrooms, halved

1 tablespoon dried mixed herbs

1/2 teaspoon paprika

1/2 teaspoon cracked black pepper

825 g (1 lb 11 oz) can crushed tomatoes

1/2 cup (125 g/4 oz) tomato paste (tomato purée, double concentrate)

1/2 cup (125 ml/4 fl oz) dry red wine

1/2 cup (125 ml/4 fl oz) beef stock

500 g (1 lb) spaghetti

freshly grated Parmesan, for serving

1 Heat the oil in a large, deep pan. Add the onion, garlic and beef and cook for 5 minutes, using a fork to break up any lumps of mince. Add the mushrooms, herbs, paprika and cracked pepper. Reduce the heat to low and stir in the crushed tomato, tomato paste, red wine and stock. Cover and simmer for 15 minutes.
2 While the sauce is cooking, cook the spaghetti in a large pan of rapidly boiling salted water until *al dente*. Drain. Serve the sauce spooned over the spaghetti and top with freshly grated Parmesan.

NUTRITION PER SERVE: *Protein 30 g; Fat 15 g; Carbohydrate 70 g; Dietary Fibre 10 g; Cholesterol 55 mg; 2300 kJ (550 cal)*

ON THE SIDE

PROSCIUTTO, CAMEMBERT AND FIG SALAD Arrange curly oak leaf lettuce leaves on a large plate and top with 4 quartered fresh figs, 100 g (3 1/4 oz) of thinly sliced camembert cheese and 60 g (2 oz) of thinly sliced prosciutto that has been grilled until crisp. Make up a vinaigrette by whisking together 1 crushed clove of garlic, 1 tablespoon of mustard, 2 tablespoons of white wine vinegar and 1/3 cup (80 ml/2 3/4 fl oz) of olive oil. Drizzle over the salad.

PENNE WITH ROASTED PEPPERS (CAPSICUMS)

Ready to eat in 30 minutes
Serves 4

1 red pepper (capsicum)

1 green pepper (capsicum)

1 yellow or orange pepper (capsicum)

1 tablespoon olive oil

2 cloves garlic, crushed

6 anchovy fillets, finely chopped

1 teaspoon seasoned cracked pepper

1/3 cup (80 ml/2 3/4 fl oz) dry white wine

1 cup (250 ml/8 fl oz) vegetable stock

2 tablespoons tomato paste (tomato purée, double concentrate)

500 g (1 lb) penne

1 tablespoon chopped fresh parsley

1 Cut the peppers into large flat pieces and discard the seeds and membrane. Grill, skin-side up, for 8 minutes, or until the skin is black and blistered. Remove from the heat and cover with a damp tea towel. When cool, peel the skin away and cut the flesh into thin strips.
2 Heat the oil in a large pan, add the garlic and anchovy fillets and cook over low heat for 2–3 minutes. Add the strips of pepper, seasoned pepper and wine. Bring to the boil, reduce the heat and simmer for 5 minutes. Stir in the stock and tomato paste and simmer for 10 minutes.
3 While the sauce is cooking, cook the penne in a large pan of rapidly boiling water until *al dente*. Drain, add to the pepper sauce and toss until well combined. Stir in the fresh parsley and serve immediately with crusty Italian bread.
NOTE: If you can't find yellow peppers, use an extra red one, as they are sweeter than green.

NUTRITION PER SERVE: *Protein 20 g; Fat 10 g; Carbohydrate 95 g; Dietary Fibre 10 g; Cholesterol 5 mg; 2245 kJ (535 cal)*

THE DIFFERENCE BETWEEN PEPPERS
Red, yellow, green and purple peppers belong to the same pepper (capsicum) family but have different characteristics. Colour is the most obvious, but texture, flavour and digestive properties also vary. Red peppers have a sweeter flavour and softer flesh, properties which change when subjected to heat. This makes them the best for roasting or grilling. Gold and yellow come next, with green and purple peppers chosen where a crisp flesh and clean taste are required, such as for use in salads and stir-fries.

OPPOSITE PAGE:
Spaghetti with rich beef and mushroom sauce (top); Penne with roasted peppers

SPAGHETTI WITH GARLIC AND CHILLI

Ready to eat in 20 minutes
Serves 4

500 g (1 lb) spaghetti
1/2 cup (125 ml/4 fl oz) extra virgin olive oil
3 cloves garlic, crushed
1 red chilli, finely chopped

1 Cook the spaghetti in a large pan of rapidly boiling salted water until *al dente*. Drain and return to the pan.
2 Just before the spaghetti is cooked, heat the olive oil in a small pan until warm. Add the garlic and red chilli and stir over low heat for 2 minutes. Add the flavoured oil to the pasta and toss to combine.

NUTRITION PER SERVE: *Protein 15 g; Fat 30 g; Carbohydrate 90 g; Dietary Fibre 10 g; Cholesterol 0 mg; 2900 kJ (690 cal)*

FUSILLI WITH SAGE AND GARLIC

Ready to eat in 20 minutes
Serves 4

500 g (1 lb) fusilli
60 g (2 oz) butter
2 cloves garlic, crushed
1/2 cup (10 g/1/4 oz) fresh sage leaves
2 tablespoons cream
freshly grated Parmesan, for serving

1 Cook the fusilli in a large pan of rapidly boiling salted water until *al dente*. Drain and return to the pan.
2 While the pasta is cooking, melt the butter in a frying pan. Add the garlic and fresh sage leaves. Cook over low heat for 4 minutes, stirring frequently.
3 Stir in the cream and season with some salt and freshly ground black pepper, to taste. Stir

the sauce through the drained pasta until thoroughly coated. Top each serving with freshly grated Parmesan.

NUTRITION PER SERVE: *Protein 15 g; Fat 20 g; Carbohydrate 90 g; Dietary Fibre 5 g; Cholesterol 55 mg; 2510 kJ (600 cal)*

RUOTE WITH LEMON, OLIVES AND BACON

Ready to eat in 25 minutes
Serves 4

500 g (1 lb) ruote
6 bacon rashers
1 cup (125 g/4 oz) black olives, sliced
1/3 cup (80 ml/2³/4 fl oz) lemon juice
2 teaspoons finely grated lemon rind
1/3 cup (80 ml/2³/4 fl oz) olive oil
1/3 cup (20 g/³/4 oz) chopped fresh parsley

1 Cook the ruote in a large pan of rapidly boiling salted water until *al dente*. Drain and return to the pan.
2 While the pasta is cooking, discard the bacon rind and cut the bacon into thin strips. Cook in a frying pan until lightly browned.
3 In a bowl, combine the black olives, lemon juice, lemon rind, olive oil, chopped parsley and the bacon. Gently toss the olive and bacon mixture through the pasta until it is evenly distributed. Serve with freshly ground black pepper, to taste.
NOTE: Ruote is a very attractive pasta resembling wagon wheels. Small chunks of sauce are trapped between the spokes.

NUTRITION PER SERVE: *Protein 25 g; Fat 25 g; Carbohydrate 90 g; Dietary Fibre 10 g; Cholesterol 30 mg; 2900 kJ (690 cal)*

BELOW, FROM LEFT: Spaghetti with garlic and chilli; Fusilli with sage and garlic; Ruote with lemon, olives and bacon

PARSLEY

Curly-leafed and flat-leafed parsley are commonly used in everyday cooking. Parsley adds flavour as well as colour to a dish, is equally at home fresh or cooked, and is ideal as a garnish for savoury foods. If you don't grow your own, buy parsley with unwilted leaves and firm stems. For storage, immerse the stalks in cold water for up to a week, or put the parsley in the vegetable section of the refrigerator, wrapped in paper towels. Parsley is a rich source of iron as well as vitamins A, B and C.

SPAGHETTI PUTTANESCA

Ready to eat in 25 minutes
Serves 4 – 6

✯ ✯

500 g (1 lb) spaghetti
2 tablespoons olive oil
3 cloves garlic, crushed
2 tablespoons chopped fresh parsley
$1/4 - 1/2$ teaspoon chilli flakes or powder
2 x 425 g (14 oz) cans crushed tomatoes
1 tablespoon capers
3 anchovy fillets, chopped
3 tablespoons black olives
freshly grated Parmesan, for serving

1 Cook the spaghetti in a large pan of rapidly boiling salted water until *al dente*. Drain and return to the pan.
2 While the spaghetti is cooking, heat the oil in a large heavy-based frying pan. Add the garlic, parsley and chilli flakes and cook, stirring constantly, for 1 minute, over medium heat.
3 Add the crushed tomato to the pan, bring to the boil, reduce the heat and simmer for 5 minutes.
4 Add the capers, anchovies and olives and cook, stirring, for 5 minutes. Season with black pepper. Toss gently with the pasta until the sauce is evenly distributed. Serve with Parmesan.

NUTRITION PER SERVE (6): *Protein 15 g; Fat 10 g; Carbohydrate 65 g; Dietary Fibre 5 g; Cholesterol 5 mg; 1650 kJ (395 cal)*

ABOVE: Spaghetti puttanesca

SPAGHETTI WITH PEAS AND ONIONS

Ready to eat in 25 minutes
Serves 4 – 6

500 g (1 lb) spaghetti or vermicelli

1 kg (2 lb) large bulb spring onions

1 tablespoon olive oil

4 bacon rashers, chopped

2 teaspoons plain flour

1 cup (250 ml/8 fl oz) chicken stock

1/2 cup (125 ml/4 fl oz) white wine

1 cup (155 g/5 oz) shelled fresh peas

1 Cook the pasta in a large pan of rapidly boiling salted water until *al dente*. Drain and return to the pan.
2 While the pasta is cooking, trim the outer skins and ends from the onions, leaving only a small section of the green stem attached.
3 Heat the oil in a large heavy-based pan. Add the bacon and onions and stir over low heat for 4 minutes or until golden. Sprinkle the flour lightly over the top and stir for 1 minute.
4 Add the combined stock and wine and stir until the mixture boils and thickens slightly. Add the peas and cook for 5 minutes or until the onions are tender. Add black pepper, to taste. Add the mixture to the pasta and toss gently. Garnish with sprigs of fresh herbs if you like.

NUTRITION PER SERVE (6): *Protein 20 g; Fat 5 g; Carbohydrate 70 g; Dietary Fibre 10 g; Cholesterol 15 mg; 1770 kJ (420 cal)*

ABOVE: Spaghetti with peas and onions

BABY YELLOW SQUASH
Baby yellow squash belong to the vegetable marrow family. They are chosen for their colour, size and texture and are easy to prepare, with no wastage. They lend themselves equally well to baking, steaming, boiling and stir-frying and this versatility has made them popular in many cuisines.

SPICY SAUSAGE AND FENNEL RIGATONI

Ready to eat in 25 minutes
Serves 4–6

500 g (1 lb) rigatoni
30 g (1 oz) butter
1 tablespoon oil
500 g (1 lb) chorizo sausage, thickly sliced diagonally
1 bulb fennel, thinly sliced
2 cloves garlic, crushed
1/3 cup (80 ml/2 3/4 fl oz) lime juice
400 g (13 oz) can red pimientos, sliced
100 g (3 1/2 oz) small rocket leaves, chopped
shavings of fresh Parmesan, for serving

1 Cook the rigatoni in a large pan of rapidly boiling salted water until *al dente*. Drain and return to the pan.
2 While the rigatoni is cooking, heat the butter and oil in a large frying pan. Add the chorizo sausage slices and cook over medium heat until well browned. Add the fennel to the pan and cook, stirring occasionally, for 5 minutes.
3 Add the garlic to the pan and stir for 1 minute. Stir in the lime juice and pimientos, bring to the boil, reduce the heat and simmer for another 5 minutes.
4 Add the sausage mixture and rocket to the pasta and toss to combine. Serve topped with shavings of fresh Parmesan.
NOTE: Chorizo is a spicy dried sausage, heavily flavoured with garlic and chilli. It is similar to salami, which can be substituted if chorizo sausage is not available.

NUTRITION PER SERVE (6): *Protein 25 g; Fat 35 g; Carbohydrate 60 g; Dietary Fibre 5 g; Cholesterol 80 mg; 2945 kJ (705 cal)*

FUSILLI WITH VEGETABLES

Ready to eat in 30 minutes
Serves 4–6

500 g (1 lb) fusilli
3 tablespoons olive oil
6 yellow squash, sliced
3 zucchini (courgettes), sliced
2 cloves garlic, crushed
3 spring onions, chopped
1 red pepper (capsicum), cut into strips
1/3 cup (65 g/2 1/4 oz) corn kernels
4 tomatoes, chopped
2 tablespoons chopped fresh parsley

1 Cook the fusilli in a large pan of rapidly boiling salted water until *al dente*. Drain and return to the pan.
2 While the fusilli is cooking, heat 2 tablespoons of the oil in a wok or frying pan, add the squash and zucchini and stir-fry for 3 minutes, or until the vegetables are just tender. Add the garlic, spring onion, red pepper and corn kernels to the wok and stir-fry for another 2–3 minutes. Add the tomato and stir until combined.
3 Add the remaining olive oil and fresh parsley to the pasta and toss well. Serve the pasta topped with the vegetable mixture.
NOTE: This is a good recipe to use up any vegetables you have on hand. Mushrooms, broccoli, snow peas (mangetout) and asparagus are all suitable, and other fresh herbs such as chives or coriander can be added.

NUTRITION PER SERVE (6): *Protein 20 g; Fat 20 g; Carbohydrate 100 g; Dietary Fibre 15 g; Cholesterol 5 mg; 2740 kJ (654 cal)*

ON THE SIDE

ASPARAGUS AND PARMESAN SALAD Cook 300 g (10 oz) of asparagus in a pan of boiling water until bright green and tender. Refresh in iced water and drain well. Arrange the asparagus on a plate and top with shavings of Parmesan cheese. Drizzle with a little balsamic vinegar and extra virgin olive oil and sprinkle generously with cracked black pepper.

OPPOSITE PAGE: Spicy sausage and fennel rigatoni (top); Fusilli with vegetables

CREAM OF ONION PASTA

Ready to eat in 30 minutes
Serves 4

500 g (1 lb) fettucine or linguine
50 g (1³/4 oz) butter
6 onions, thinly sliced
¹/2 cup (125 ml/4 fl oz) beef stock
¹/2 cup (125 ml/4 fl oz) cream
shavings of Parmesan cheese, for serving
spring onion, to garnish, optional

1 Cook the fettucine in a large pan of rapidly boiling salted water until *al dente*. Drain and return to the pan.
2 While the pasta is cooking, melt the butter, add the onion and cook over medium heat for 10 minutes, until soft. Stir in the stock and cream and simmer for 10 minutes. Season with salt and pepper, to taste.
3 Stir the sauce through the fettucine and serve with shavings of Parmesan. Garnish with chopped spring onion if you wish.

NUTRITION PER SERVE: *Protein 20 g; Fat 25 g; Carbohydrate 95 g; Dietary Fibre 10 g; Cholesterol 80 mg; 2935 kJ (700 cal)*

ORIENTAL FRICELLI

Ready to eat in 30 minutes
Serves 4–6

500 g (1 lb) multicoloured fricelli
2 tablespoons peanut oil
1 teaspoon sesame oil
2 garlic cloves, crushed
1 tablespoon grated fresh ginger
¹/2 Chinese cabbage, finely shredded
1 red pepper (capsicum), thinly sliced
200 g (6¹/2 oz) sugar snap peas
3 tablespoons soy sauce
3 tablespoons sweet chilli sauce
2 tablespoons chopped fresh coriander
chopped peanuts or cashews,
   to garnish

1 Cook the fricelli in a large pan of rapidly boiling salted water until *al dente*. Drain and keep warm.

2 While the fricelli is cooking, heat the oils in a pan, add the garlic and ginger and cook over medium heat for 1 minute.
3 Add the cabbage, red pepper and peas to the wok and stir-fry for 3 minutes over high heat. Stir in the sauces and coriander and cook for 3 minutes, or until heated through. Add the fricelli to the wok and toss to combine. Serve sprinkled with chopped peanuts or cashews.

NUTRITION PER SERVE (6): *Protein 15 g; Fat 10 g; Carbohydrate 65 g; Dietary Fibre 10 g; Cholesterol 0 mg; 1780 kJ (425 cal)*

SPAGHETTI WITH CREAMY LEMON SAUCE

Ready to eat in 20 minutes
Serves 4

500 g (1 lb) spaghetti
1 cup (250 ml/8 fl oz) cream
³/4 cup (185 ml/6 fl oz) chicken stock
1 tablespoon finely grated lemon rind plus
   some shredded, to garnish
2 tablespoons finely chopped fresh parsley
2 tablespoons chopped fresh chives

1 Cook the spaghetti in a large pan of rapidly boiling salted water until *al dente*. Drain and return to the pan.
2 While the spaghetti is cooking, combine the cream, chicken stock and lemon rind in a pan over medium heat. Bring to the boil, stirring occasionally. Reduce the heat and simmer gently for 10 minutes, or until the sauce is reduced and thickened slightly.
3 Add the sauce and herbs to the spaghetti and toss to combine. Serve immediately, garnished with finely shredded lemon rind.

NUTRITION PER SERVE: *Protein 15 g; Fat 30 g; Carbohydrate 90 g; Dietary Fibre 5 g; Cholesterol 85 mg; 2850 kJ (680 cal)*

CHIVES
Chives are related to the onion, but used as a herb, either for seasoning or for garnishing. Only the green stalks, with their mild flavour, are eaten and they should be freshly cut as you need them. If they are intended as a garnish for hot food, sprinkle them on just before serving. Dried chives bear little resemblance in taste or texture to fresh.

OPPOSITE PAGE, FROM TOP: Cream of onion pasta; Oriental fricelli; Spaghetti with creamy lemon sauce

SORREL

Sorrel is a bitter leaf vegetable rich in vitamins A and C, as well as in essential minerals. Young, glossy leaves are simply rinsed and trimmed of their tough stems before being tossed in a green salad. Sorrel's clean, sharp flavour makes it a good companion to fish and rich poultry such as goose and duck, and it is used to flavour stews and sauces. When subjected to prolonged heat, it breaks down to a pulp, so it is good for puréeing. Avoid iron or aluminium pans when cooking with sorrel, as the chemical reaction that results leaves the sorrel acrid.

TORTELLINI BROTH

Ready to eat in 20 minutes
Serves 4

250 g (8 oz) tortellini
4 cups (1 litre) good-quality beef stock
1/2 cup (30 g/2 oz) sliced spring onions, plus extra, for garnish

1 Cook the tortellini in a large pan of rapidly boiling salted water until *al dente*. Drain and divide among 4 deep soup bowls.
2 While the tortellini is cooking, bring the beef stock to the boil in a pan. Add the spring onion and simmer for 3 minutes. Ladle the stock over the tortellini and garnish with the extra spring onion, finely sliced.

NUTRITION PER SERVE: *Protein 10 g; Fat 1 g; Carbohydrate 45 g; Dietary Fibre 3 g; Cholesterol 0 mg; 945 kJ (225 cal)*

ARTICHOKE, EGG AND SORREL PASTA

Ready to eat in 25 minutes
Serves 4

500 g (1 lb) conchiglie (shell pasta)
2 tablespoons oil
3 cloves garlic, crushed
315 g (10 oz) marinated artichoke hearts, halved
3 tablespoons chopped fresh parsley
160 g (5½ oz) sorrel leaves, roughly chopped
4 hard-boiled eggs, chopped
fresh Parmesan shavings, for serving

1 Cook the conchiglie in a large pan of rapidly boiling salted water until *al dente*. Drain and keep warm.
2 While the pasta is cooking, heat the oil in a frying pan, add the garlic and cook over medium heat until golden. Add the artichoke hearts and chopped parsley and cook over low

heat for 5 minutes, or until the artichoke hearts are heated through.

3 Transfer the pasta to a large bowl. Add the sorrel leaves, eggs and artichoke hearts and toss to combine. Serve immediately, topped with shavings of fresh Parmesan and cracked black pepper, to taste.

NUTRITION PER SERVE: *Protein 25 g; Fat 20 g; Carbohydrate 90 g; Dietary Fibre 10 g; Cholesterol 210 mg; 2620 kJ (625 cal)*

CHEESY BUCKWHEAT AND BEAN PASTA

Ready to eat in 30 minutes
Serves 4

500 g (1 lb) buckwheat fusilli
1 tablespoon oil
2 cloves garlic, crushed
1 onion, chopped
300 g (10 oz) bottled pasta sauce
¹/₃ cup (80 ml/2³/₄ fl oz) orange juice
400 g (13 oz) can kidney beans, drained
1 cup (125 g/4 oz) grated Cheddar cheese
    plus extra, for serving
3 tablespoons chopped fresh herbs

1 Cook the fusilli in a large pan of rapidly boiling salted water until *al dente*. Drain and return to the pan.

2 While the pasta is cooking, heat the oil in a frying pan. Add the garlic and onion and cook over medium heat for 3 minutes, or until the onion is golden but not brown.

3 Add the pasta sauce, orange juice and kidney beans. Bring to the boil, reduce the heat and simmer for 5 minutes, or until the sauce is heated through.

4 Add the sauce to the pasta with the Cheddar cheese and fresh herbs. Stir until the cheese melts and serve immediately. Top with extra grated Cheddar cheese.

NUTRITION PER SERVE: *Protein 20 g; Fat 15 g; Carbohydrate 65 g; Dietary Fibre 15 g; Cholesterol 25 mg; 2015 kJ (480 cal)*

ABOVE, FROM LEFT: Tortellini broth; Artichoke, egg and sorrel pasta; Cheesy buckwheat and bean pasta

PREPARING AND COOKING BLACK MUSSELS

Black mussels are a variety of bivalve mollusc with a rounded black shell and plump, succulent flesh. Like all shellfish, they must be bought and eaten fresh and cleaned before cooking. First, discard those which have already opened. Scrub the unopened mussels with a stiff brush and remove the beard. If the mussels are gritty, they can be soaked in clean, salted water for 1–2 hours to make them expel grit and sand. After a final rinse, put them in a pan to steam open. By the time they have all opened, they will be cooked. Before using, discard any unopened mussels and those with flat and dried out flesh.

OPPOSITE PAGE: Tomato mussels on spaghetti (top); Gorgonzola and toasted walnuts on linguine

TOMATO MUSSELS ON SPAGHETTI

Ready to eat in 30 minutes
Serves 4

16 fresh black mussels
500 g (1 lb) spaghetti
4 tablespoons olive oil
1 large onion, finely chopped
2 cloves garlic, crushed
850 g (1 lb 12 oz) can crushed tomatoes
1/2 cup (125 ml/4 fl oz) white wine

1 Scrub the mussels thoroughly and remove the beards. Discard any open mussels.
2 Cook the spaghetti in a large pan of rapidly boiling salted water until *al dente*. Drain, return to the pan and toss with half the olive oil.
3 While the pasta is cooking, heat the remaining olive oil in a pan, add the onion and cook until soft, but not brown. Add the garlic and cook for another minute. Stir in the tomato and wine and bring to the boil. Reduce the heat and simmer gently.
4 Meanwhile, put the mussels in a large pan and just cover with water. Cook over high heat for a few minutes, until the mussels have opened. Shake the pan often and discard any mussels that have not opened after 5 minutes.
5 Add the mussels to the tomato sauce and stir to combine. Serve the pasta with mussels and sauce over the top. Garnish with sprigs of thyme, if desired.

NUTRITION PER SERVE: *Protein 20 g; Fat 20 g; Carbohydrate 95 g; Dietary Fibre 10 g; Cholesterol 8 mg; 2825 kJ (670 cal)*

ON THE SIDE

SPINACH, PANCETTA AND PECAN NUT SALAD Mix together 250 g (8 oz) of baby spinach leaves, 50 g (1 3/4 oz) of toasted pecan nuts and 3 peeled and chopped hard-boiled eggs. Fry or grill 6 paper-thin slices of pancetta until crispy. Break the pancetta into bite-size pieces and toss through the salad. To make the dressing, thoroughly combine 100 g (3 1/2 oz) of blue cheese with 1/4 cup (60 ml/2 fl oz) of cream, 2 tablespoons of milk and 2 tablespoons of oil. When mixed, drizzle over the salad and serve immediately.

GORGONZOLA AND TOASTED WALNUTS ON LINGUINE

Ready to eat in 25 minutes
Serves 4

3/4 cup (75 g/2 1/2 oz) walnut halves
500 g (1 lb) linguine
75 g (2 1/2 oz) butter
150 g (5 oz) gorgonzola cheese, chopped or crumbled
2 tablespoons cream
1 cup (155 g/5 oz) shelled fresh peas

1 Preheat the oven to moderate 180°C (350°F/Gas 4). Lay the walnuts on an oven tray in a single layer and bake for about 5 minutes, until lightly toasted. Set the walnuts aside to cool.
2 Cook the linguine in a large pan of rapidly boiling water until *al dente*. Drain and return to the pan.
3 While the pasta is cooking, melt the butter in a small pan over low heat and add the gorgonzola, cream and peas. Stir gently for 5 minutes, or until the sauce has thickened. Season, to taste, with salt and pepper. Add the sauce and the walnuts to the pasta and toss until well combined. Serve immediately, sprinkled with freshly ground black pepper.
NOTE: You can use frozen peas if you prefer. Don't bother to thaw them, just add them as directed in the recipe. Use a milder blue cheese such as Castello in place of the gorgonzola, if you don't like really strong blue cheese.

NUTRITION PER SERVE: *Protein 30 g; Fat 50 g; Carbohydrate 90 g; Dietary Fibre 10 g; Cholesterol 95 mg; 3870 kJ (920 cal)*

SPAGHETTI WITH HERBS

Ready to eat in 20 minutes
Serves 4

500 g (1 lb) spaghetti
50 g (1 3/4 oz) butter
1/2 cup (30 g/1 oz) shredded fresh basil
1/3 cup (10 g/1/4 oz) chopped fresh oregano
1/3 cup (20 g/3/4 oz) chopped fresh chives

1 Cook the spaghetti in a large pan of rapidly boiling salted water until *al dente*. Drain and return to the pan.
2 Add the butter to the pan, tossing it through until it melts and coats the strands of spaghetti. Add the basil, oregano and chives to the pan and toss the herbs through the buttery pasta until well distributed. Season, to taste, and serve immediately.

NUTRITION PER SERVE: *Protein 15 g; Fat 10 g; Carbohydrate 90 g; Dietary Fibre 5 g; Cholesterol 30 mg; 2175 kJ (520 cal)*

PASTA WITH PESTO AND PARMESAN

Ready to eat in 15 minutes
Serves 4

500 g (1 lb) linguine or taglierini
1/4 cup (40 g/1 1/4 oz) pine nuts
2 firmly packed cups (100 g/3 1/2 oz) fresh basil leaves
2 cloves garlic, chopped
1/4 cup (25 g/3/4 oz) freshly grated Parmesan plus shavings, to garnish
1/2 cup (125 ml/4 fl oz) extra virgin olive oil

1 Cook the pasta in a large pan of rapidly boiling salted water until *al dente*. Drain and return to the pan.
2 While the pasta is cooking, mix the pine nuts, fresh basil leaves, garlic and Parmesan in a food processor until finely chopped. With the motor running, add the extra virgin olive

BELOW, FROM LEFT:
Spaghetti with herbs;
Pasta with pesto
and Parmesan;
Calabrian spaghetti

oil in a slow stream until a smooth paste is formed. Season with salt and freshly ground black pepper, to taste. Toss the pesto through the hot pasta until it is thoroughly distributed. Garnish with shavings of fresh Parmesan.

NUTRITION PER SERVE: *Protein 20 g; Fat 45 g; Carbohydrate 90 g; Dietary Fibre 5 g; Cholesterol 15 mg; 3390 kJ (810 cal)*

CALABRIAN SPAGHETTI

Ready to eat in 20 minutes
Serves 4

500 g (1 lb) spaghetti

1/3 cup (80 ml/2 3/4 fl oz) olive oil

3 cloves garlic, crushed

50 g (1 3/4 oz) anchovy fillets, finely chopped

1 teaspoon finely chopped fresh red chillies

3 tablespoons chopped fresh parsley

1 Cook the spaghetti in a large pan of rapidly boiling salted water until *al dente*. Drain and return to the pan.

2 While the spaghetti is cooking, heat the olive oil in a small pan. Add the garlic, anchovy fillets and red chillies and cook over low heat for 5 minutes. Be careful not to burn the garlic or brown it too much as it will become bitter. Add the parsley to the garlic mixture and cook for a few more minutes. Season with salt and freshly ground black pepper, to taste.

3 Add the sauce to the pasta and toss through until well combined. Serve garnished with extra anchovies and sliced red chillies as well as a sprig of fresh herbs, if desired.

NUTRITION PER SERVE: *Protein 15 g; Fat 20 g; Carbohydrate 90 g; Dietary Fibre 5 g; Cholesterol 10 mg; 2600 kJ (620 cal)*

PESTO

When a fully made pesto is stored for any length of time, the composition of the ingredients alters. The cheese component reacts with other ingredients, in particular the basil, and starts to turn rancid. It will keep, at best, for 5–7 days, if refrigerated in an airtight jar with a layer of olive oil or plastic wrap covering the exposed surface. A more successful option when making pesto to put away is to leave out the cheeses and stir them through when the sauce is to be used. In this way, your pesto will keep for 2–3 months refrigerated, or 5–6 months frozen.

RAVIOLI WITH PEAS AND ARTICHOKES

Ready to eat in 30 minutes
Serves 4

650 g (1 lb 5 oz) fresh cheese and
   spinach ravioli
1 tablespoon olive oil
8 marinated artichoke hearts, quartered
2 large cloves garlic, finely chopped
1/2 cup (125 ml/4 fl oz) dry white wine
1/2 cup (125 ml/4 fl oz) chicken stock
2 cups (310 g/10 oz) frozen peas
125 g (4 oz) thinly sliced prosciutto, chopped
1/4 cup (7 g/1/4 oz) chopped fresh flat-leaf parsley
1/2 teaspoon seasoned cracked pepper

1 Cook the ravioli in a large pan of rapidly boiling salted water until *al dente*. Drain.
2 While the ravioli is cooking, heat the olive oil in a pan and cook the artichoke hearts and garlic over medium heat for 2 minutes, stirring frequently. Add the wine and stock and stir until well mixed. Bring to the boil, reduce the heat slightly and simmer for 5 minutes. Add the peas (they don't need to be thawed first) and simmer for another 2 minutes.
3 Stir the prosciutto, parsley and pepper into the artichoke mixture. Serve the ravioli topped with the artichoke mixture.
NOTE: You can buy marinated artichoke hearts in jars from supermarkets and delicatessens.

NUTRITION PER SERVE: *Protein 25 g; Fat 15 g; Carbohydrate 30 g; Dietary Fibre 10 g; Cholesterol 45 mg; 1540 kJ (370 cal)*

ON THE SIDE

PEACH SALSA SALAD Cut 6 large fresh peaches into wedges and put them in a bowl. Add 1 thinly sliced red (Spanish) onion, 6 quartered egg (Roma) tomatoes, 1 cup (200 g/6½ oz) of corn kernels and 1 sliced green pepper (capsicum). Make a dressing by thoroughly mixing 1 crushed clove of garlic, 1 teaspoon of ground cumin, 1 finely chopped red chilli, 2 tablespoons of freshly squeezed lime juice and 1/4 cup (60 ml/2 fl oz) of oil. Pour over the salad and toss to combine. Fold through 1/2 cup (15 g/1/2 oz) of fresh coriander leaves just before serving.

BRANDIED CREAM AND SALMON FUSILLI

Ready to eat in 30 minutes
Serves 2

375 g (12 oz) fusilli
45 g (1 1/2 oz) butter
1 leek, finely sliced
1 large clove garlic, crushed
1/4 cup (60 ml/2 fl oz) brandy
1/2 teaspoon sambal oelek
2 tablespoons finely chopped fresh dill
1 tablespoon tomato paste (tomato purée, double concentrate)
1 cup (250 ml/8 fl oz) cream
250 g (8 oz) smoked salmon, thinly sliced
red caviar or lumpfish roe, to garnish, optional

1 Cook the fusilli in a large pan of rapidly boiling salted water until *al dente*. Drain.
2 Heat the butter in a large pan and cook the leek over medium heat for a few minutes, until soft. Add the garlic and cook for another minute. Add the brandy and cook for another minute. Stir in the sambal oelek, dill, tomato paste and cream. Simmer gently for 5 minutes, until the sauce reduces and thickens slightly.
3 Add the pasta and smoked salmon to the sauce. Toss to combine and season with freshly ground black pepper, to taste. Divide the mixture between two serving bowls. Garnish with a spoonful of caviar, if you like, and a sprig of dill. Serve immediately.
NOTE: Wash the leek thoroughly, as dirt and grit can sometimes be difficult to remove from the inner leaves.

NUTRITION PER SERVE: *Protein 55 g; Fat 80 g; Carbohydrate 140 g; Dietary Fibre 10 g; Cholesterol 290 mg; 6500 kJ (1550 cal)*

SAMBAL OELEK
Sambal oelek is an indispensable paste used in Indonesian cooking. Traditionally, it is made from red chillies and salt. The commercially available product is often mixed with vinegar. As well as being used to flavour dishes, sambal oelek can be served as a dipping sauce or an accompaniment. Sometimes labelled sambal ulek, it can be found in supermarkets and Asian food stores. It is handy to have to use whenever chilli is called for. Store in the refrigerator.

OPPOSITE PAGE: Ravioli with peas and artichokes (top); Brandied cream and salmon fusilli

PASTA NIÇOISE

Ready to eat in 25 minutes
Serves 4

☆

500 g (I lb) farfalle
350 g (II oz) green beans
1/3 cup (80 ml/2¾ fl oz) olive oil
60 g (2 oz) sliced anchovy fillets
2 garlic cloves, finely sliced
250 g (8 oz) cherry tomatoes, halved
freshly grated Parmesan, for serving

I Cook the farfalle in a large pan of rapidly boiling salted water until *al dente*. Drain and return to the pan.
2 While the pasta is cooking, place the beans in a heatproof bowl and cover with boiling water. Set aside for 5 minutes, drain and rinse under cold water.
3 Heat the olive oil in a frying pan and stir-fry the beans and anchovy fillets for 2– 3 minutes. Add the garlic and cook for 1 minute. Add the cherry tomatoes and stir through.

4 Add the sauce to the pasta, toss well and warm through. Serve with freshly grated Parmesan.

NUTRITION PER SERVE: *Protein 20 g; Fat 25 g; Carbohydrate 90 g; Dietary Fibre 10 g; Cholesterol 15 mg; 2810 kJ (670 cal)*

GARLIC BUCATINI

Ready to eat in 15 minutes
Serves 4

☆

500 g (I lb) bucatini
1/3 cup (80 ml/2¾ fl oz) olive oil
8 garlic cloves, crushed
2 tablespoons chopped fresh parsley
freshly grated Parmesan, for serving

I Cook the bucatini in a large pan of rapidly boiling water until *al dente*. Drain and return to the pan.
2 When the pasta is almost finished cooking, heat the olive oil over low heat in a frying pan and add the garlic. Cook for 1 minute before

ABOVE, FROM LEFT:
Pasta Niçoise; Garlic bucatini; Spaghetti Mediterranean

removing from the heat. Add the garlic oil and the parsley to the pasta and toss to distribute thoroughly. Serve with Parmesan.

NOTE: Olives or diced tomato can be added. Do not overcook the garlic or it will be bitter.

NUTRITION PER SERVE: *Protein 15 g; Fat 20 g; Carbohydrate 90 g; Dietary Fibre 5 g; Cholesterol 5 mg; 2605 kJ (620 cal)*

SPAGHETTI MEDITERRANEAN

Ready to eat in 30 minutes
Serves 4– 6

500 g (1 lb) spaghetti
750 g (1 1/2 lb) tomatoes
1/2 cup (125 ml/4 fl oz) extra virgin
    olive oil
2 garlic cloves, crushed
4 spring onions, finely sliced
6 anchovy fillets, chopped
1/2 teaspoon grated lemon rind

1 tablespoon fresh thyme leaves
12 stuffed green olives, thinly sliced
shredded fresh basil, for serving

1 Cook the spaghetti in a large pan of rapidly boiling salted water until *al dente*. Drain and return to the pan.
2 While the pasta is cooking, score small crosses in the bases of the tomatoes. Add to a pan of boiling water for 1– 2 minutes, drain and plunge into cold water. Peel down from the cross and discard the skin. Cut the tomatoes in half horizontally. Place a sieve over a small bowl and squeeze the tomato seeds and juice into it; discard the seeds. Chop the tomatoes roughly and set aside.
3 In a bowl, combine the olive oil, garlic, spring onion, anchovies, lemon rind, thyme leaves and stuffed green olives. Add the chopped tomato and tomato juice, mix well and season with salt and freshly ground black pepper, to taste. Add the sauce to the pasta, toss to combine and sprinkle with shredded fresh basil.

NUTRITION PER SERVE (6): *Protein 10 g; Fat 20 g; Carbohydrate 60 g; Dietary Fibre 5 g; Cholesterol 3 mg; 2060 kJ (490 cal)*

THYME
There are many different types of thyme used in cooking and they range from having grey-green leaves and a pungent scent, to tiny bright green leaves with a more evasive perfume. In fact, the fragrance that thyme imparts to a dish is just as important as the flavour. Wild thyme is refined and aromatic while lemon thyme gives off a subtle lemony fragrance when heated. With small leaves of low moisture content, thyme is one herb which is easy to dry.

279

SPAGHETTI WITH TOMATO SAUCE

Ready to eat in 30 minutes
Serves 4

500 g (1 lb) spaghetti
1 tablespoon olive oil
1 onion, finely chopped
2 cloves garlic, crushed
825 g (1 lb 11 oz) can crushed tomatoes
1 teaspoon dried oregano
2 tablespoons tomato paste (tomato purée, double concentrate)
2 teaspoons sugar
shavings fresh Parmesan, for serving

1 Cook the spaghetti in a large pan of rapidly boiling salted water until *al dente*. Drain.
2 Heat the oil in a pan, add the onion and cook for 3 minutes, until soft. Add the garlic and cook for another minute.
3 Add the tomato and bring to the boil. Add the oregano, tomato paste and sugar; reduce the heat and simmer for 15 minutes. Season with salt and pepper, to taste. Serve the pasta topped with the tomato sauce and shavings of fresh Parmesan.

NUTRITION PER SERVE: *Protein 20 g; Fat 10 g; Carbohydrate 100 g; Dietary Fibre 10 g; Cholesterol 5 mg; 2300 kJ (550 cal)*

RICOTTA AND BASIL WITH TAGLIATELLE

Ready to eat in 25 minutes
Serves 4

500 g (1 lb) tagliatelle
1 cup (20 g/³/₄ oz) fresh flat-leaf parsley
1 cup (50 g/1³/₄ oz) fresh basil leaves
1 teaspoon olive oil
¹/₃ cup (50 g/1³/₄ oz) chopped sun-dried pepper (capsicum)
1 cup (250 g/8 oz) sour cream
250 g (8 oz) fresh ricotta cheese
¹/₄ cup (25 g/³/₄ oz) freshly grated Parmesan

1 Cook the tagliatelle in a large pan of rapidly boiling salted water until *al dente*. Drain and return to the pan.

2 While the pasta is cooking, process the parsley and basil in a food processor or blender until just chopped.
3 Heat the oil in a pan. Add the sun-dried pepper and fry for 2– 3 minutes. Stir in the sour cream, ricotta and Parmesan and stir over low heat for 4 minutes, or until heated through. Do not allow to boil.
4 Add the herbs and sauce to the pasta, toss to combine and serve.

NUTRITION PER SERVE: *Protein 25 g; Fat 35 g; Carbohydrate 90 g; Dietary Fibre 5 g; Cholesterol 120 mg; 3330 kJ (800 cal)*

SPAGHETTI CARBONARA WITH MUSHROOMS

Ready to eat in 25 minutes
Serves 4

500 g (1 lb) spaghetti
8 bacon rashers
2 cups (180 g/6 oz) sliced button mushrooms
2 teaspoons chopped fresh oregano
4 eggs, lightly beaten
1 cup (250 ml/8 fl oz) cream
²/₃ cup (65 g/2¹/₄ oz) freshly grated Parmesan

1 Cook the spaghetti in a large pan of rapidly boiling salted water until *al dente*. Drain and return to the pan.
2 While the spaghetti is cooking, trim the bacon and cut into small pieces. Fry until lightly browned and then set aside on paper towels. Add the mushrooms to the pan and fry for 2– 3 minutes, until soft.
3 Add the mushrooms, bacon, oregano and the combined eggs and cream to the drained spaghetti. Cook over low heat, stirring, until the mixture starts to thicken slightly. Remove from the heat and stir in the cheese. Season with salt and cracked black pepper; to taste.

NUTRITION PER SERVE: *Protein 45 g; Fat 40 g; Carbohydrate 90 g; Dietary Fibre 5 g; Cholesterol 320 mg; 3844 kJ (920 cal)*

TOMATO PASTE
Tomato paste, also known in the U.K. as tomato purée, is made by simmering whole tomatoes until very thick, dark and no longer liquid. Only salt is added, and sometimes a little sugar. The resulting paste has an intense flavour that is used sparingly to flavour sauces, stocks, stews and soups. The many commercial brands have varying degrees of concentration, so it is a matter of trying different ones until you find one that best suits your needs. Italian tomato paste is graded, so look for *doppio concentrato* (double concentrate), or *triplo concentrato* (triple concentrate) on the label.

OPPOSITE PAGE, FROM TOP: Spaghetti with tomato sauce; Ricotta and basil with tagliatelle; Spaghetti carbonara with mushrooms

281

FARFALLE WITH PEAS, PROSCIUTTO AND MUSHROOMS

Ready to eat in 20 minutes
Serves 4

★

375 g (12 oz) farfalle
60 g (2 oz) butter
1 onion, chopped
200 g (6 1/2 oz) mushrooms, thinly sliced
250 g (8 oz) frozen peas
3 slices of prosciutto, sliced
1 cup (250 ml/8 fl oz) cream
1 egg yolk
fresh Parmesan, optional, for serving

1 Cook the farfalle in a large pan of rapidly boiling salted water until *al dente*. Drain and return to the pan.
2 While the pasta is cooking, heat the butter in a pan, add the onion and mushrooms and stir over medium heat for 5 minutes or until tender.

BELOW: Farfalle with peas, prosciutto and mushrooms

3 Add the peas and prosciutto to the pan. Combine the cream and the yolk in a small jug and pour into the pan. Cover and simmer for 5 minutes or until heated through.
4 Mix the sauce through the pasta or serve the sauce over the top of the pasta. Can be topped with shaved or grated fresh Parmesan.

NUTRITION PER SERVE: *Protein 25 g; Fat 45 g; Carbohydrate 75 g; Dietary Fibre 10 g; Cholesterol 180 mg; 3280 kJ (785 cal)*

ON THE SIDE

FENNEL, ORANGE AND ALMOND SALAD Finely slice 1 or 2 fennel bulbs. Peel 3 oranges, removing all the white pith, and cut into segments. Toast 100 g (3 1/2 oz) of flaked almonds in a frying pan until golden. Combine the fennel, oranges and almonds in a bowl. Add 150 g (5 oz) of crumbled creamy blue cheese and 50 g (1 3/4 oz) of thinly sliced sun-dried pepper (capsicum). Make a dressing by combining 3 tablespoons of orange juice, 1 teaspoon of sesame oil and 1 tablespoon of red wine vinegar. Drizzle over the salad and serve.

PENNE WITH SUN-DRIED TOMATOES AND LEMON

Ready to eat in 25 minutes
Serves 4

250 g (8 oz) penne
¼ cup (60 ml/2 fl oz) olive oil
3 bacon rashers, chopped
I onion, chopped
⅓ cup (80 ml/2¾ fl oz) lemon juice
I tablespoon fresh thyme leaves
⅓ cup (50 g/1¾ oz) chopped
   sun-dried tomatoes
½ cup (80 g/2¾ oz) pine nuts, toasted

I Cook the pasta in a large pan of rapidly boiling salted water until *al dente*. Drain.
2 While the pasta is cooking, heat the olive oil in a large pan, add the chopped bacon and onion and stir over medium heat for 4 minutes or until the bacon is brown and the onion has softened.
3 Add the pasta to the pan with the lemon juice, thyme leaves, sun-dried tomato and pine nuts. Stir over low heat for 2 minutes, or until heated through.
NOTE: You can use pancetta instead of bacon, if preferred.

NUTRITION PER SERVE: *Protein 15 g; Fat 30 g; Carbohydrate 50 g; Dietary Fibre 5 g; Cholesterol 15 mg; 2200 kJ (530 cal)*

FARFALLE WITH PINK PEPPERCORNS AND SUGAR SNAP PEAS

Ready to eat in 30 minutes
Serves 4

400 g (13 oz) farfalle
I cup (250 ml/8 fl oz) white wine
I cup (250 ml/8 fl oz) cream
100 g (3½ oz) pink peppercorns in
   vinegar, drained
300 ml (9½ fl oz) crème fraîche
200 g (6½ oz) sugar snap peas,
   topped and tailed

I Cook the pasta in a large pan of rapidly boiling salted water until *al dente*. Drain and return to the pan.
2 While the pasta is cooking, pour the wine into a large saucepan, bring to the boil, reduce the heat and simmer until reduced by half.
3 Add the cream, bring to the boil, reduce the heat and simmer until reduced by half.
4 Remove from the heat and stir in the pink peppercorns and crème fraîche. Return to the heat and add the sugar snap peas, simmering until the peas turn bright green. Season with salt, if necessary. Stir through the pasta and serve immediately.

NUTRITION PER SERVE: *Protein 15 g; Fat 55 g; Carbohydrate 80 g; Dietary Fibre 8 g; Cholesterol 175 mg; 3855 kJ (915 cal)*

ABOVE: Penne with sun-dried tomatoes and lemon

PASTA DESSERTS

Never had pasta as a dessert? You're probably not alone. But once you've tasted these luscious desserts, you'll begin to wonder why. Combined with fresh fruit, cream or chocolate, pasta becomes the finale rather than the beginning. If you're a die-hard pasta fan you can even start and end your meal with pasta. While the concept is not strictly conventional, the possibilities are endless. As they say, the proof of the pudding's in the eating... so what are you waiting for?

CANDIED LEMON PEEL
Candied or crystallized lemon peel is fresh peel that has been preserved in sugar. A sugar syrup is introduced to replace the moisture content and this process is done gradually to allow the lemon rind to keep its shape and tenderness. When enough sugar has been absorbed, the peel is allowed to dry out so that it will be easy to store. Candied lemon peel is used in puddings and desserts, and as a decoration for cakes and sweets.

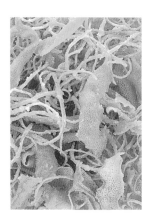

ABOVE: Sweet cheese in lemon pasta

SWEET CHEESE IN LEMON PASTA

Preparation time: I hour + standing
Total cooking time: 25 minutes
Serves 4– 6

★★

2 cups (250 g/8 oz) plain flour
1/2 teaspoon salt
I teaspoon caster sugar
grated rind of 2 lemons
2 tablespoons fresh lemon juice
2 eggs, lightly beaten
I tablespoon currants
I tablespoon brandy
600 g (1 1/4 lb) ricotta cheese
5 tablespoons icing sugar
3/4 teaspoon grated lemon rind
3/4 teaspoon vanilla essence
beaten egg, for glazing
4 tablespoons flaked almonds, toasted
vegetable oil, for frying
I cup (250 ml/8 fl oz) cream, flavoured
   with brandy, to taste
mint leaves and thin strips of lemon rind or
   candied lemon peel, to garnish, optional

I Pile the combined flour, salt, sugar and lemon rind on a work surface and make a well in the centre. Add 1– 2 tablespoons of water, the lemon juice and egg and gradually blend them into the flour, using a fork. The dough can be made in a processor up to this point. When a loosely combined dough forms, use your hands and begin kneading. Incorporate a little extra flour if the dough feels moist. Knead for 5– 8 minutes, or until smooth and elastic. Cover with plastic and set aside for 15 minutes.

2 Soak the currants in the brandy in a bowl. In a larger bowl, combine the ricotta cheese, icing sugar, lemon rind and vanilla. Set aside.

3 Divide the dough into eight equal portions. Roll each out to a thin sheet about 18 cm (7 inches) square. Cover each as it is completed.

4 Trim the pasta into neat squares. Working with a few at a time, brush around the edges with beaten egg. Add the currants and toasted almonds to the ricotta filling, then put one-eighth of the filling in the middle of each square of dough. Fold the edges over to completely enclose the filling. Press the edges down to seal.

5 Heat oil in a pan to 1– 2 cm (about 1/2 inch) depth. Drop a piece of scrap pasta in to check that it turns golden without burning. Fry the parcels, two or three at a time, until golden. Remove with a slotted spoon, drain on paper towels and keep warm. Serve with brandy cream, sprinkled with icing sugar and garnished with mint leaves and lemon rind.

NUTRITION PER SERVE (6): *Protein 20 g; Fat 45 g; Carbohydrate 50 g; Dietary Fibre 3 g; Cholesterol 185 mg; 2965 kJ (705 cal)*

CREAMY FRESH STRAWBERRY ROLLS

Preparation time: 40 minutes
Total cooking time: 50 minutes
Serves 6

250 g (8 oz) strawberries, hulled
60 g (2 oz) butter
2 egg yolks
1/3 cup (80 ml/2³/4 fl oz) cream
1/3 cup (90 g/3 oz) sugar
1 teaspoon lemon juice
6 sheets fresh lasagne, 16 cm x 21 cm
   (6¹/2 x 8¹/2 inches)
1/3 cup (40 g/1¹/4 oz) toasted slivered almonds,
   plus 1 tablespoon for decoration
icing sugar, for dusting

1 Preheat the oven to moderate 180°C (350°F/Gas 4) and grease a gratin dish. Halve the strawberries, slicing from top to bottom. Melt 20 g (³/4 oz) of butter in a pan and lightly toss the strawberries for 20 seconds. Remove from the pan. Melt another 20 g (³/4 oz) of butter in the pan. Mix the egg yolks with the cream, then add to the pan with the sugar and lemon juice. Cook, stirring often, until very thick. Remove from the heat and stir in the strawberries. Cool.
2 Cook the fresh lasagne sheets, two at a time, in plenty of boiling water for 3 minutes, or until *al dente*. Transfer to a bowl of cold water and leave for 1 minute before placing on tea towels to dry.
3 Divide the strawberry mixture and the almonds among the pasta sheets, leaving a 3 cm (1¹/4 inch) border all around. Fold in the long edges first, then carefully fold up the end closest to you and roll. As the mixture begins to ooze, bring the top end over and towards you. Carefully place, seam-side-down, in the prepared dish. Position the rolls closely side-by-side.
4 Dot the top with pieces of the remaining butter. Sprinkle with extra almonds and 2 teaspoons of sifted icing sugar. Bake for 15 minutes, then place under a preheated grill for 5 minutes or until lightly browned.
NOTE: This dessert is delicious accompanied by vanilla ice cream and a strawberry coulis. For a change, you can use fresh raspberries when they are in season. They will not need to be cooked, so just add them to the prepared cream

mixture. Blueberries can also be used and should be prepared the same way as the strawberries, but not sliced. You can use dry lasagne sheets instead of fresh, but they are often thicker, less pliable and slippery to handle. If you use them, cook them as they come from the packet, then trim to the dimensions above.

NUTRITION PER SERVE: *Protein 9 g; Fat 20 g; Carbohydrate 50 g; Dietary Fibre 4 g; Cholesterol 100 mg; 1775 kJ (420 cal)*

STRAWBERRIES
All the strawberry varieties grown today for the mass market are hybrids, descendants of an original cross between a large fruited North American berry and one with intense flavour from Chile.

ABOVE: Creamy fresh strawberry rolls

BLANCHED ALMONDS

Almonds which have had their skins removed are known as blanched almonds. They are readily available, sold in bulk or pre-packaged, but the skins can be easily removed at home. Drop the shelled almonds into boiling water and simmer for 1 minute. Drain, and as soon as they are cool enough to handle, squeeze each almond between your thumb and forefinger. The nut will pop out. Where ground almonds are called for in a recipe it might be worth buying them ready ground, as it is difficult to achieve a uniform and fine grind with most home equipment, and oil can be extracted which makes the almonds moist and clump into little balls. This problem can be partly avoided by adding about 2 tablespoons of the recipe's sugar to the almonds when grinding.

ABOVE: Coconut and lemon rissoni cake

COCONUT AND LEMON RISSONI CAKE

Preparation time: 20 minutes
Total cooking time: 1 hour
Serves 6– 8

1/3 cup (70 g/2 1/4 oz) rissoni
1/4 cup (30 g/1 oz) plain flour
3/4 cup (90 g/3 oz) self-raising flour
1/2 cup (95 g/3 1/4 oz) ground almonds
1/2 cup (45 g/1 1/2 oz) desiccated coconut
1 tablespoon firmly packed grated lemon rind
185 g (6 oz) butter
1/2 cup (160 g/5 1/2 oz) apricot jam
1 cup (250 g/8 oz) caster sugar
3 eggs, lightly beaten

1 Preheat the oven to warm 160°C (315°F/ Gas 2– 3). Brush a deep 20 cm (8 inch) round cake tin with melted butter or oil. Line the base and sides with baking paper.
2 Cook the rissoni in a large pan of rapidly boiling water for 3– 4 minutes, or until *al dente*. Drain well.
3 While the rissoni is cooking, combine the flours, almonds, coconut and lemon rind in a large bowl. Make a well in the centre.
4 Melt the butter, jam and sugar in a medium pan over low heat, or in a heatproof bowl in the microwave oven, until smooth. Stir in the rissoni, then using a large metal spoon, stir into the dry ingredients. Stir in the eggs until smooth. Pour into the tin and bake for 50– 55 minutes or until firm and a skewer comes out clean when inserted in the centre. Leave in the tin for 10– 15 minutes before turning out. Serve warm or cold, topped with candied lemon slices.

NUTRITION PER SERVE (8): *Protein 8 g; Fat 30 g; Carbohydrate 60 g; Dietary Fibre 3 g; Cholesterol 125 mg; 2280 kJ (540 cal)*

BAKED RISSONI PUDDING

Preparation time: 15 minutes
Total cooking time: 1 hour
Serves 4– 6

¹/4 cup (50 g/1³/4 oz) rissoni

2 eggs, lightly beaten

¹/3 cup (80 ml/2³/4 fl oz) maple syrup

2 cups (500 ml/16 fl oz) cream

¹/4 cup (30 g/1 oz) sultanas

1 teaspoon vanilla essence

pinch of nutmeg

¹/4 teaspoon ground cinnamon

1 Preheat the oven to slow 150°C (300°F/ Gas 2). Cook the rissoni in a large pan of rapidly boiling water for 3– 4 minutes, or until *al dente*. Drain well.

2 Whisk together the eggs, maple syrup and cream in a bowl.

3 Stir in the rissoni, sultanas, vanilla essence, nutmeg and cinnamon. Pour the mixture into a deep round or oval ovenproof dish. Sit the dish in a large baking dish and pour enough water into the baking dish to come halfway up the sides of the ovenproof dish. Bake for 50– 55 minutes, or until a knife comes out clean when inserted into the centre.

NOTE: As a variation, replace the sultanas with chopped dried apricots or raisins. Or, use fresh pitted and chopped dates or whole raspberries and blueberries. The cooking time may need to be a little longer with the fresh fruit, because some of the juice will ooze out.

NUTRITION PER SERVE (6): *Protein 5 g; Fat 30 g; Carbohydrate 25 g; Dietary Fibre 1 g; Cholesterol 155 mg; 1700 kJ (405 cal)*

ABOVE: Baked rissoni pudding

ABOVE: Berries and cream pasta stack

BERRIES AND CREAM PASTA STACK

Preparation time: 15 minutes
Total cooking time: 15 minutes
Serves 4

★

4 fresh or dried lasagne sheets
oil, for deep-frying
2 cups (500 ml/16 fl oz) cream
250 g (8 oz) punnet strawberries
250 g (8 oz) punnet blueberries
250 g (8 oz) punnet raspberries
4 passionfruit
icing sugar, for dusting

1 Cook the lasagne sheets two at a time in a large pan of rapidly boiling water until *al dente*. Add a little oil to the water to prevent the pasta from sticking together. Drain, then carefully rinse the pasta sheets under cold running water. Carefully cut each sheet into three, crossways. Pat dry with a tea towel.

2 Half fill a medium pan with oil. Heat the oil until moderately hot. Cook the pasta pieces one at a time until crisp and golden. Drain on paper towels.

3 Whip the cream until soft peaks form. Place one piece of fried lasagne sheet on each serving plate. Top with some cream, berries and passionfruit pulp. Dust with a little icing sugar. Continue layering once more for each, finishing with a lasagne sheet. Dust again with icing sugar and serve immediately.

NOTE: Any fruits in season are suitable to use for this dessert. Chop or slice the way you like. If you prefer, you can add a little sugar and vanilla to the whipped cream to sweeten.

NUTRITION PER SERVE: *Protein 7 g; Fat 50 g; Carbohydrate 35 g; Dietary Fibre 10 g; Cholesterol 145 mg; 2520 kJ (600 cal)*

PASTA CASES WITH FRUITY RICOTTA FILLING

Preparation time: 35 minutes
Total cooking time: 30 minutes
Serves 4

oil, for deep-frying
6 dried lasagne sheets

Ricotta fruit filling

350 g (11 oz) fresh ricotta cheese
1 tablespoon caster sugar
60 g (2 oz) mixed candied fruit (cherries,
  orange and lemon peel), chopped
30 g (1 oz) dark chocolate shavings

1 Heat the oil. It will need to be at least 10 cm (4 inches) deep. Cook the lasagne sheets one at a time in plenty of boiling salted water until *al dente*. Remove with a sieve and place in a bowl of cold water for a minute or two, then transfer to a tea towel and dry both sides. Trim the end of each sheet to make a square.
2 For the next step you will need 3 implements able to withstand boiling oil: a soup ladle of approximately 9 cm (3½ inch) diameter or a wire scoop of the same dimensions; a utensil such as an egg whisk or a mixmaster beater which fits into the scoop to hold the pasta in shape; a pair of tongs. Take one pasta square and gently push it into the ladle by hand. Form a cup shape, with the corners sticking out and with flutes between them.
3 Test the oil for frying by dropping in a piece of scrap pasta. It should bubble immediately and rise to the top. Lower the ladle into the oil. Use tongs to lift the pasta away from the ladle to prevent it sticking initially, then use the egg whisk to maintain the shape. The cases are quite sturdy so don't be afraid to manhandle them. They are ready when crisp and golden with bubbles forming on the surface. Practise with the first two, as these are spares.
4 As each case is ready, remove from the oil and drain upside-down on paper towels. Allow to cool before serving.
5 To make the sweet ricotta filling, mix the ricotta with the sugar until combined. Don't use a food processor as it will make the texture too smooth. Fold in the fruit and chocolate. Spoon into the pasta shells just before serving. Top with shaved curls of chocolate.

NOTE: If the cases become limp or have spots of surface oil, put them in a hot oven to crisp up again. These cases are perfect for turning a humble dessert such as ice cream or fruit salad into an elegant course. Dress the dish up further with a simple sauce and finish off with a dusting of icing sugar. Wire gaufrette baskets, suitable for making the pastry cases, are available from speciality kitchenware shops.

NUTRITION PER SERVE: *Protein 15 g; Fat 15 g; Carbohydrate 45 g; Dietary Fibre 2 g; Cholesterol 40 mg; 1585 kJ (375 cal)*

CASTER SUGAR
When granulated sugar is crushed to a very fine grain it is called caster sugar. Also known as superfine sugar, it is preferred in cooking because the grains melt quickly and dissolve completely. Caster sugar has good visual appeal and so is sprinkled on the top of cakes, puddings and sweet breads. It is also used to coat sweets and candies.

ABOVE: Pasta cases with fruity ricotta filling

HAZELNUTS

Hazelnuts are the edible nut of the hazel tree, *Corylus*, a member of the birch family. They are rich in oil and pleasant tasting, and are used in baking and confectionery. In recipes, skinned and roasted hazelnuts are often called for, and it is possible to do this at home. Spread them on a baking tray and bake at moderate 180°C (350°F/Gas 4) until the skins shrivel and flake, about 10 minutes. Wrap the hazelnuts in a tea towel for 5 minutes and then rub them vigorously with the tea towel to start dislodging the skins. Then each one has to be skinned separately, rubbing between your fingers.

ABOVE: Chocolate nut cake

CHOCOLATE NUT CAKE

Preparation time: 30 minutes
  + overnight refrigeration
Total cooking time: 5– 10 minutes
Serves 6– 8

250 g (8 oz) stellini

1 cup (140 g/5¹/2 oz) roasted hazelnuts, skinned

1¹/2 cups (150 g/4¹/2 oz) walnuts

³/4 cup (100 g/3¹/2 oz) blanched almonds

3 tablespoons cocoa powder

1 teaspoon ground cinnamon

²/3 cup (155 g/5 oz) sugar

1 tablespoon mixed peel

grated rind of 1 lemon

1 teaspoon vanilla essence

2 tablespoons Cognac

60 g (2 oz) butter

100 g (3¹/2 oz) dark chocolate, chopped

1 Grease and line the base of a deep 20 cm (8 inch) round springform tin. Cook the pasta in boiling water until *al dente*. Rinse under cold water to cool. Drain thoroughly.

2 Place the nuts, cocoa powder, cinnamon, sugar, mixed peel, rind, vanilla essence and Cognac in a food processor. Process in short bursts until finely ground.

3 Melt the butter and chocolate in a small pan over low heat or in the microwave, until smooth.

4 Combine the pasta, nut mixture and melted chocolate and butter. Mix well. Spoon the mixture into the prepared tin. Press down firmly with a wet hand. Smooth the surface with the back of a wet spoon. Refrigerate overnight to firm. Remove from the tin and cut into wedges. Dust with a little cocoa powder and icing sugar for serving. Delicious with whipped cream.

NUTRITION PER SERVE (8): *Protein 15 g; Fat 45 g; Carbohydrate 55 g; Dietary Fibre 7 g; Cholesterol 20 mg; 2795 kJ (665 cal)*

INDEX

Page numbers in *italics* refer to photographs. Page numbers in **bold** type refer to margin notes.

On the Side
Accompaniments

Antipasto Salad, 157

Asparagus and Parmesan Salad, 266

Asparagus with Lemon Hazelnut Butter, 63

Baby Spinach, Walnut and Cheddar Salad, 237

Bacon, Lettuce and Tomato Salad, 83

Bean Salad with Vinaigrette, 61

Beans with Parsley Butter, 91

Beetroot and Nectarine Salad, 131

Beetroot, Goats Cheese and Pistachio Nut Salad, 73

Black Beans with Tomato, Lime and Coriander, 97

Braised Leeks with Pine Nuts, 164

Buttery Caraway Cabbage, 243

Caramelized Leeks and Crispy Bacon, 223

Cauliflower Cheese, Individual, 239

Cherry Tomatoes with Butter and Dill, 89

Chive and Garlic Corn Cobs, 63

Crispy Zucchini Ribbons, 139

Cucumber with Toasted Sesame Seeds, 57

Damper, 181

Dilled Orange Carrots, 164

Fennel, Orange and Almond Salad, 282

Garlic Dill Mushrooms, 64

Garlic Pizza Bread, 195

Greek Salad, 146

Green Beans with Garlic and Cumin, 226

Green Herb Pilaf, 162

Herb Bread, 43

Herb Salad, 256

Kumera and Parsnip Chips, 175

Kumera, Yoghurt and Dill Salad, 150

Marinated Mushroom Salad, 96

Mixed Tomato Salad, 256

Nasturtium and Watercress Salad, 209

Orange and Olive Salad, 195

Panzanella, 91

Parmesan Biscuits, 188

Peach Salsa Salad, 276

Polenta Bread, 175

Popovers, 206

Potato Salad, 59

Potato, Egg and Bacon Salad, 113

Prosciutto, Camembert and Fig Salad, 261

Pumpkin and Sage Scones, 173

Raspberry Beetroot Salad, 237

Roast Broccoli with Cumin Seeds, 89

Roast Pumpkin with Sage, 57

Roasted Tomatoes Topped with Herbed Goats Cheese, 87

Roasted Vegetable and Brie Salad, 110

Sesame Coleslaw, 160

Spicy Cucumber Salad, 64

Spinach, Pancetta and Pecan Nut Salad, 272

Sweet Chilli Potato and Coriander Salad, 232

Tabouli, 107

Tomato and Bocconcini Salad, 157

Tomato and Feta Salad, 150

Tomato, Egg and Olive Salad, 259

Turnips with Tomato, Wine and Garlic, 198

Waldorf Salad, 130

Warm Broccoli Florets with Almonds, 131

Warm Ginger and Sesame Carrot Salad, 136

Warm Kumera, Rocket and Crispy Bacon Salad, 209

Warm Spring Vegetable Salad, 146

Warm Vegetable Salad, 120

Watercress, Salmon and Camembert Salad, 96

Wild Rice with Roasted Pepper, 223

Zucchini with Tomato and Garlic, 97

Pasta dishes

A

Alfredo, 25, *25*
Alfredo sauce, **162**
almonds, blanched, **288**
Amatriciana, 29, *29*
Anchovy and Tomato Crostini, 185, *185*
anchovy fillets, **152**
antipasto
  Balsamic Tomatoes, Slow-Roasted, 53, *53*
  Barbecued Sardines, 51, *51*
  Bruschetta, 53, *53*
  Cauliflower Fritters, 53, *53*
  Grilled Eggplant and Peppers, 52, *52*
  Mussels, Stuffed, 50, *50*
  Pesto Bocconcini Balls, 52, *52*
  Polenta Shapes with Chorizo and Salsa, 51, *51*
  Salami and Potato Frittata Wedges, 50, *50*
Arrabbiata, 32, *32*
Artichoke, Egg and Sorrel Pasta, 270, *270*
artichokes, **178**
  Farfalle and Olives, with, 117, *117*
  Ravioli with Peas and, 276, *277*
asiago, 169, *169*
asparagus, **154**
  Conchiglie Salad with Bocconcini, Asparagus and Oregano, 188, *189*
  Creamy Asparagus Linguine, 118, *119*
  Tagliatelle with Asparagus and Fresh Herbs, 154, *154*
aubergine *see* eggplants

B

bacon
  Basil Tortellini with Bacon and Tomato Sauce, 226, *226*
  Carbonara, 27, *27*
  Ruote with Lemon, Olives and, 263, *263*
  Spaghetti Carbonara, 155, *155*, **155**

Spaghetti Carbonara with Mushrooms, 280, 281
Bacon and Pea Soup, 43, *43*
Baked Cannelloni Milanese, 239, *239*
Baked Creamy Cheesy Pasta, 241, *241*
baked pasta
  Butternut Pumpkin Filled with Pasta and Leeks, *248*, 249
  Cannelloni, 244, *244*
  Cannelloni Milanese, 239, *239*
  Chicken and Veal Loaf with Mushrooms and Sour Cream, *248*, 249
  Classic Lasagne, 234, *235*
  Conchiglie with Chicken and Ricotta, 237, *237*
  Creamy Cheesy Pasta, 241, *241*
  Giant Conchiglie with Ricotta and Rocket, 251, *251*
  Italian Omelette, 245, *245*
  Macaroni Cheese, 236, *236*
  Macaroni Eggplant Cake, 230, *230*
  Meatballs and Pasta, 242, *242*
  Pasta and Spinach Timbales, 240, *240*
  Pasta Pie, 233, *233*
  Pasta Souffle, 234, *234*
  Pasta with Green Olive Paste and Three Cheeses, 250, *250*
  Pasta-filled Vegetables, 243, *243*
  Pasticcio, 246, *246*, **247**
  Pastitsio, 247, *247*, **247**
  Ricotta Lasagne, 231, *231*
  Rigatoni Gratin, 240, *240*
  Seafood with Pasta, 232, *232*
  Spaghetti Frittata, 238, *238*
Baked Pasta and Mince, 61, *61*
Baked Rissoni Pudding, 289, *289*
Baked Spaghetti Frittata, 238, *238*

balsamic vinegar, **188**
  Chicken Ravioli with Lime Balsamic Dressing, 256, *257*
  Slow-roasted Balsamic Tomatoes, 53, *53*
Barbecued Chicken and Pasta Salad, 182, *182*
Barbecued Sardines, 51, *51*
basil, **41**
  Fettucine with Zucchini and Crisp-fried, 116, *116*
  Gnocchi with Tomato and Fresh, 200
  Linguine in Honey Basil Cream, 158, *158*
  Potato Gnocchi with Tomato and Basil Sauce, 199, *199*
  Prawn and Basil Soup, 42, *42*
  Ricotta and Basil with Tagliatelle, *280*, 281
  Tomato and Basil Pasta Salad, 174, *174*
  Tomato Soup with Pasta and Basil, 41, *41*
  Vegetable Soup with Basil Sauce, 45, *45*
Basil Tortellini with Bacon and Tomato Sauce, 226, *226*
bay leaves, **80**
Bean Soup with Sausage, 39, *39*
beans
  and pasta, **46**
  borlotti, **37**
  broad, **45**
  Cheesy Buckwheat and Bean Pasta, 271, *271*
  Fettucine with Creamy Mushroom and Bean Sauce, 151, *151*
  Fusilli with Broad Bean Sauce, 146, *146*
  pasta and beans, **46**
  Pasta and Bean Soup, 46, *46*
  Rigatoni with Kidney Beans and Italian Sausage, 65, *65*
  Tuna, Green Bean and Onion Salad, 176, *177*
Béchamel sauce, 231, 235, **235,** 244, 246

beef
 Meatballs Stroganoff, 76, *76*
 Spaghetti with Rich Beef and
  Mushroom Sauce, *260,* 261
 Stir-fried Chilli Beef with
  Spaghettini, 70, *71*
beef stock, **49**
bel paese, 168, *168*
Berries and Cream Pasta Stack,
 290, *290*
black mussels, 272, *272*
black olives, **118,** *118*
 sautéed, 135, *135*
black pepper, **148**
blue cheese
 Caramelized Onion and Blue
  Cheese Rissoni, 159, *159*
 Blue Cheese and Broccoli with
  Rigatoni, *138,* 139
bocconcini, 166, *167*
 Conchiglie Salad with
  Bocconcini, Asparagus and
  Oregano, 188, *189*
 Pesto Bocconcini Balls, 52, *52*
bolognese
 Classic, 24, *24*
 Quick Spaghetti, 60, *60*
 Spaghetti, 56, *56*
 Spaghetti with Chicken,
  85, *85*
borlotti beans, **37**
Boscaiola, Creamy, 30, *30*
Brandied Cream and Salmon
 Fusilli, 276, *277*
Brandy Chicken Fettucine,
 91, *91*
breadcrumbs, **130**
broad beans, **45**
broccoli, **42**
 Blue Cheese and Broccoli
  with Rigatoni, *138,* 139
 Conchiglie with Broccoli and
  Anchovy, 152, *153*
 Broccoli Soup, 42, *42*
Bruschetta, 53, *53*
Bucatini with Gorgonzola
 Sauce, 150, *150*
butternut pumpkin, **249**
Butternut Pumpkin Filled with
 Pasta and Leeks, *248,* 249
button mushrooms, **137**

C

Cacciatore, 67, *67*
Calabrian Spaghetti, 275, *275*
calamari, **94**

candied lemon peel, **286**
cannelloni, 220, *221,* **222**
Cannelloni, 244, *244*
cannelloni
 Spinach and Ricotta,
  222, *222*
capers, **125**
 Linguine with Anchovies,
  Olives and Capers,
  254, *254*
 Orecchiette with Tuna,
  Lemon and Caper Sauce,
  160, *161*
 Spaghetti with Olives and
  Capers, 125, *125*
cappelletti, **81**
capsicums *see* peppers
Caramelized Onion and
 Blue Cheese Rissoni,
 159, *159*
carbonara, 27, *27,* **155**
Carbonara
 Grilled, 160, *161*
carbonara
 Spaghetti, 155, *155*
 Spaghetti Carbonara with
  Mushrooms, *280,* 281
carrots
 Spiced Carrot and Feta
  Gnocchi, 206, *207*
caster sugar, **291**
Cauliflower Fritters, 53, *53*
caviar, red, **102**
cayenne pepper, **157**
celery, **43**
 Pasta with Braised Oxtail and,
  58, *58*
Cheddar, **232**
cheese dishes
 Blue Cheese and Broccoli
  with Rigatoni, *138,* 139
 Caramelized Onion and Blue
  Cheese Rissoni, 159, *159*
 Fettucine with Smoked
  Cheese and Salami,
  156, 157
 Gnocchi Cheese Bake,
  200, *200*
 Macaroni Cheese, 236, *236*
 Pasta with Green Olive Paste
  and Three Cheeses,
  250, *250*
 Red Pepper Gnocchi with
  Goats Cheese, 209, *209*
 Sweet Cheese in Lemon
  Pasta, 286, *286*
Cheese sauce, 82, 123

cheeses
 asiago, 169, *169*
 bel paese, 168, *168*
 bocconcini, 166, *167*
 Cheddar, **232**
 feta, **206**
 fontina, 168, *168,* **204**
 goats cheese, 169, *169,*
  209
 gorgonzola, **150,** *166,*
  167
 grana, 168, *169*
 mascarpone, 167, *167*
 mozzarella, 166, *166,* **242**
 ovolini, 166, *167*
 parmigiano reggiano, 168,
  168
 pecorino, 167, *167*
 provolone, 167, *167*
 ricotta, 166, *166,* **214**
 taleggio, 169
Cheesy Buckwheat and Bean
 Pasta, 271, *271*
Cheesy Herb Rolls, 184,
 184
cherry tomatoes, **140**
chervil, **183**
chicken
 Barbecued Chicken and Pasta
  Salad, 182, *182*
 Brandy Chicken Fettucine,
  91, *91*
 Conchiglie with Chicken and
  Pesto, 223, *223*
 Conchiglie with Chicken and
  Ricotta, 237, *237*
 Fettucine, and Mushroom
  Sauce with, 86, *86*
 Italian-style Chicken and
  Pasta Salad, 178, *178*
 Lasagnette with Mushrooms
  and Chicken, 88, *88*
 Lemon, Parsley and
  Orecchiette, 83, *83*
 mince, **237**
 Oriental Chicken Pasta, 84,
  84
 Pear and Pasta Salad,
  180, 181
 Penne with Chicken and
  Mushrooms, 148, *149*
 Pesto Chicken Pasta, 87,
  87
 Ravioli with Chicken Filling,
  212, *212*
 Ravioli with Fresh Tomato
  Sauce, 90, *90*

chicken *continued*
  Spaghetti with Chicken
    Meatballs, 80, *80*
  Spaghetti with Chicken
    Bolognese, 85, *85*
  Spicy Chicken Broth with
    Coriander Pasta, 40, *40*
  Tagliatelle with Chicken
    Livers and Cream, 147, *147*
  Tortellini with Tomato Sauce,
    81, *81*
Chicken and Macaroni Bake,
  88, *88*
Chicken and Pasta Soup, 47, *47*
Chicken and Spinach Lasagne,
  82, *82*
Chicken and Veal Loaf with
  Mushrooms and Sour Cream,
  248, 249
Chicken Livers with Penne,
  89, *89*
Chicken Mezzelune with Cream
  Sauce, 213, *213*
Chicken Ravioli with Buttered
  Sage Sauce, 224, *224*
Chicken Ravioli with Fresh
  Tomato Sauce, 90, *90*
Chicken Ravioli with Lime
  Balsamic Dressing, 256, *257*
Chicken Tortellini with Tomato
  Sauce, 81, *81*
Chicken with Lemon, Parsley
  and Orecchiette, 83, *83*
Chicken, Barbecued, and Pasta
  Salad, 182, *182*
Chicken, Leek and Chickpea
  Soup, 36
Chicken, Pear and Pasta Salad,
  180, 181
Chicken, Warm, and Pasta
  Salad, 174, *174*
chickpeas, **132**
  Conchiglie with, 132, *133*
chilli dishes
  Spaghetti with Chilli
    Calamari, 99, *99*
  Spaghetti with Garlic and
    Chilli, 262, *262*
  Stir-fried Chilli Beef with
    Spaghettini, 70, *71*
chilli garlic olives, 135, *135*
Chilli Seafood in Tomato Sauce,
  103, *103*
chillies, **226**
chives, **269,** *269*
Chocolate Nut Cake,
  292, *292*

chorizo, **62,** 67, *67*
Chunky Spaghetti Napolitana,
  124, *124*
cinnamon, **236**
clams, **112**
Classic Bolognese, 24, *24*
Classic Lasagne, 234, *235*
Coconut and Lemon Rissoni
  Cake, 288, *288*
cod
  Tomato Pasta with Smoked
    Cod and Sesame, *106,* 107
cold meats
  cacciatore, 67, *67*
  chorizo, 67, *67*
  coppa, 67, *67*
  finocchiona Toscana, 67, *67*
  ham, shaved, **187**
  Milano salami, 67, *67*
  mortadella, 67, *67*
  pancetta, 66, *66*
  pastrami, **176,** *176*
  pepperoni, 67, *67*
  prosciutto, 66, *66*
  salami, 67, *67*
  speck, 67, *67*
conchiglie
  Giant Conchiglie with
    Ricotta and Rocket,
    251, *251*
Conchiglie Salad with
  Bocconcini, Asparagus and
  Oregano, 188, *189*
Conchiglie with Broccoli and
  Anchovy, 152, *153*
Conchiglie with Chicken and
  Pesto, 223, *223*
Conchiglie with Chicken and
  Ricotta, 237, *237*
Conchiglie with Chickpeas,
  132, *133*
coppa, 67, *67*
coriander, **40**
  Spicy Chicken Broth with
    Coriander Pasta, 40, *40*
corn, **186**
Country Pumpkin and Pasta
  Soup, 48, *48*
courgettes *see* zucchini
crab, **97**
Crab Cakes with Hot Salsa,
  97, *97*
cream, **225**
Cream of Onion Pasta, *268,*
  269
Creamy Asparagus Linguine,
  118, *119*

Creamy Boscaiola, 30, *30*
creamy pasta
  Alfredo, 25, *25*
  Baked Creamy Cheesy Pasta,
    241, *241*
  Brandied Cream and Salmon
    Fusilli, 276, *277*
  Bucatini with Gorgonzola
    Sauce, 150, *150*
  Caramelized Onion and Blue
    Cheese Rissoni, 159, *159*
  Chicken and Veal Loaf with
    Mushrooms and Sour
    Cream, 248, *249*
  Chicken Mezzelune with
    Cream Sauce, 213, *213*
  Conchiglie with Broccoli and
    Anchovy, 152, *153*
  Farfalle with Tuna,
    Mushrooms and Cream,
    95, *95*
  Fettucine Alfredo, 162, *162*
  Fettucine with Creamy
    Mushroom and Bean Sauce,
    151, *151*
  Fusilli with Broad Bean
    Sauce, 146, *146*
  Grilled Carbonara, 160, *161*
  Lemon Grass and Lime
    Scallop Pasta, 165, *165*
  Linguine in Honey Basil
    Cream, 158, *158*
  Linguine with Creamy
    Lemon Sauce, 163, *163*
  Orecchiette with Tuna,
    Lemon and Caper Sauce,
    160, *161*
  Penne with Chicken and
    Mushrooms, 148, *149*
  Penne with Creamy Tomato
    Sauce, 126, *126*
  Pork and Veal Ravioli with
    Cheesy Sauce, 164, *164*
  Rigatoni with Sausage and
    Parmesan, 148, *149*
  Spaghetti with Creamy Garlic
    Mussels, 110, *110*
  Spaghetti with Creamy
    Lemon Sauce, *268,* 269
  Tagliatelle with Chicken
    Livers and Cream, 147, *147*
  Tagliatelle with Veal, Wine
    and Cream, 57, *57*
  Tortellini with Mushroom
    Cream Sauce, 225, *225*
Creamy Prawns with Fettucine,
  96, *96*

Creamy Seafood Ravioli, 108, *108*
Creamy Seafood Salad, 179, *179*
Crispy Focaccia Toasts with Pesto, 185, *185*
cumin
  Parsee Lamb with Cumin, Eggs and Tagliatelle, 75, *75*

D

dates, **191**
desserts
  Baked Rissoni Pudding, 289, *289*
  Berries and Cream Pasta Stack, 290, *290*
  Chocolate Nut Cake, 292, *292*
  Coconut and Lemon Rissoni Cake, 288, *288*
  Pasta Cases with Fruity Ricotta Filling, 291, *291*
  Strawberry Rolls, Creamy Fresh, 287, *287*
  Sweet Cheese in Lemon Pasta, 286, *286*
dill, **195**
  Smoked Salmon, Dill and Egg Pasta Salad, *194*, 195
durum wheat, **234**

E

egg tomatoes, **122**
eggplants, **44**
  Green Olive and Eggplant Toss, 120, *120*
  Grilled Eggplant and Peppers, 52, *52*
  Macaroni Eggplant Cake, 230, *230*
  Tortellini with Eggplant, 143, *143*
English spinach, **255**

F

Farfalle Salad with Sun-Dried Tomatoes and Spinach, 172, *172*
Farfalle with Artichoke Hearts and Olives, 117, *117*
Farfalle with Mushrooms, 126
Farfalle with Peas, 258, *258*
Farfalle with Peas, Prosciutto and Mushrooms, 282, *282*

Farfalle with Pink Peppercorns and Sugar Snap Peas, 283
Farfalle with Tuna, Mushrooms and Cream, 95, *95*
fennel, **107**
  Spicy Sausage and Fennel Rigatoni, 266, *267*
  Trout, Fettucine and Fennel Frittata, *106*, 107
feta cheese, **206**
fettucine
  Brandy Chicken, 91, *91*
  with Chicken and Mushroom Sauce, 86, *86*
  Creamy Prawns with, 96, *96*
  Spinach Fettucine with Mushroom Sauce, 152, *153*
  Trout, Fettucine and Fennel Frittata, *106*, 107
  Warm Garlic Prawn and Fettucine Salad, 188, *189*
Fettucine Alfredo, 162, *162*
Fettucine Boscaiola, 137, *137*
Fettucine Primavera, 131, *131*
Fettucine with Caviar, 102, *102*
Fettucine with Chicken and Mushroom Sauce, 86, *86*
Fettucine with Creamy Mushroom and Bean Sauce, 151, *151*
Fettucine with Smoked Cheese and Salami, *156*, 157
Fettucine with Smoked Salmon, 111, *111*
Fettucine with Snow Peas and Walnuts, 140, *141*
Fettucine with Spinach and Prosciutto, 255, *255*
Fettucine with Zucchini and Crisp-fried Basil, 116, *116*
filling pasta, 218-21, *218-21*
  Basil Tortellini with Bacon and Tomato Sauce, 226, *226*
  Chicken Mezzelune with Cream Sauce, 213, *213*
  Chicken Ravioli with Buttered Sage Sauce, 224, *224*
  Conchiglie with Chicken and Pesto, 223, *223*
  Lasagne Bows, 216, *216*
  Mushroom Ravioli, 227, *227*
  Prawn Tortelloni, 215, *215*
  Pumpkin and Herb Ravioli, 217, *217*

Ravioli with Chicken Filling, 212, *212*
Spinach and Ricotta Cannelloni, 222, *222*
Spinach and Ricotta Shells, 214, *214*
Spinach Ravioli with Sun-dried Tomato Sauce, 216, *216*
Tortellini with Mushroom Cream Sauce, 225, *225*
Finocchiona Toscana, 67, *67*
fish stock, **99**
flour, seasoned, **73**
focaccia, crispy, toasts with pesto, 185, *185*
fontina, 168, *168*, **204**
Fragrant Herb Tagliatelle with Kaffir Lime and Prawns, 100, *101*
Fragrant Seafood Pasta, 102, *103*
Fricelli, Oriental, 268, 269
frittata
  Baked Spaghetti, 238, *238*
  Salami and Potato Frittata Wedges, 50, *50*
  Trout, Fettucine and Fennel, *106*, 107
fusilli
  Brandied Cream and Salmon, 276, *277*
  Lamb and Fusilli Soup, 49, *49*
  Meatballs with, 73, *73*
  Moroccan Lamb and Roasted Pepper with, 70, *71*
Fusilli with Broad Bean Sauce, 146, *146*
Fusilli with Green Sauce, *128*, 129
Fusilli with Sage and Garlic, 262, *262*
Fusilli with Vegetables, 266, *267*

G

garam masala, **75**
garlic, **77, 244**
  chilli garlic olives, 135, *135*
  Fusilli with Sage and, 262, *262*
  Spaghetti with Creamy Garlic Mussels, 110, *110*
  Spaghetti with Garlic and Chilli, 262, *262*
  Spaghettini with Roasted Salmon and, 104

garlic *continued*
Warm Garlic Prawn and Fettucine Salad, 188, *189*
Garlic Bucatini, 278, *278*
Garlic Grissini Sticks, 184, *184*
Garlic, Pasta and Fish Soup, 47
Giant Conchiglie with Ricotta and Rocket, 251, *251*
ginger, **70**
gnocchi, **200**
Herbed Potato Gnocchi with Chunky Tomato, 205, *205*
Parsnip, 208, *208*
potato, 202, *202*
Potato Gnocchi with Tomato and Basil Sauce, 199, *199*
Pumpkin Gnocchi with Sage Butter, 201, *201*
Red Pepper Gnocchi with Goats Cheese, 209, *209*
Spiced Carrot and Feta, 206, *207*
Spinach and Ricotta, 206, *207*
Gnocchi Cheese Bake, 200, *200*
Gnocchi Romana, 198, *198*
Gnocchi with Fontina Sauce, 204, *204*
Gnocchi with Tomato and Fresh Basil, 200
goats cheese, 169, *169*, **209**
Red Pepper Gnocchi with, 209, *209*
gorgonzola, **150,** *166,* 167
Bucatini with Gorgonzola Sauce, 150, *150*
Gorgonzola and Toasted Walnuts on Linguine, 272, *273*
grana, 168, *169*
Green Olive and Eggplant Toss, 120, *120*
green olives, **254**
paste, **250**
gremolata, **113**
Grilled Carbonara, 160, *161*
Grilled Eggplant and Peppers, 52, *52*
Grilled Peppers and Anchovy Salad, 192, *192*
Grilled Vegetables on Pasta, 122, *122*

H

ham, shaved, **187**
hazelnuts, **292**

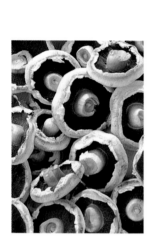

Herb Tagliatelle with Kaffir Lime and Prawns, 100, *101*
Herbed Potato Gnocchi with Chunky Tomato, 205, *205*
honey, **158**
Linguine in Honey Basil Cream, 158, *158*

I–J

Italian Omelette, 245, *245*
Italian sausages, **65**
Italian-style Chicken and Pasta Salad, 178, *178*

K

Kaffir lime leaves, **101**

L

lamb
Moroccan Lamb and Roasted Pepper with Fusilli, 70, *71*
Parsee Lamb with Cumin, Eggs and Tagliatelle, 75, *75*
Pasta with Lamb and Vegetables, 77, *77*
Turkish Ravioli, 69, *69*
Lamb and Fusilli Soup, 49, *49*
lasagne, **82**
Chicken and Spinach, 82, *82*
Classic, 234, *235*
Ricotta, 231, *231*
Vegetable, 123, *123*
Lasagne Bows, 216, *216*
Lasagnette with Mushrooms and Chicken, 88, *88*
leeks, **39**
Butternut Pumpkin Filled with Pasta and, *248,* 249
Chicken, Leek and Chickpea Soup, 36
Lemon and Date Ziti, 191, *191*
Lemon and Vegetable Pasta Salad, 183, *183*
lemon grass, **165**
Lemon Grass and Lime Scallop Pasta, 165, *165*
Lemon-Scented Broth with Tortellini, 36, *36*
lemons, **83**
candied peel, **286**
Coconut and Lemon Rissoni Cake, 288, *288*
Linguine with Creamy Lemon Sauce, 163, *163*

Orecchiette with Tuna, Lemon and Caper Sauce, 160, *161*
Penne with Sun-dried Tomatoes and, 283, *283*
Ruote with Lemon, Olives and Bacon, 263, *263*
Spaghetti with Creamy Lemon Sauce, *268,* 269
Sweet Cheese in Lemon Pasta, 286, *286*
limes, **256**
Chicken Ravioli with Lime Balsamic Dressing, 256, *257*
Herb Tagliatelle with Kaffir Lime and Prawns, 100, *101*
Lemon Grass and Lime Scallop Pasta, 165, *165*
Pasta with Fragrant Lime and Smoked Trout, 255
linguine
Creamy Asparagus, 118, *119*
Gorgonzola and Toasted Walnuts on, 272, *273*
Linguine in Honey Basil Cream, 158, *158*
Linguine with Anchovies, Olives and Capers, 254, *254*
Linguine with Creamy Lemon Sauce, 163, *163*
Linguine with Red Pepper Sauce, *128,* 129
Linguine with Roasted Vegetable Sauce, 121

M

macaroni, **74**
Chicken and Macaroni Bake, 88, *88*
Macaroni Cheese, 236, *236*
Macaroni Eggplant Cake, 230, *230*
Marinara, 33, *33*
Spaghetti, 94, *94*
marjoram, **72**
mascarpone, 167, *167*
meat
Baked Pasta and Mince, 61, *61*
Basil Tortellini with Bacon and Tomato Sauce, 226, *226*
Bean Soup with Sausage, 39, *39*
Carbonara, 27, *27*
Chicken and Veal Loaf with Mushrooms and Sour Cream, *248,* 249

Classic Bolognese, 24, *24*

Classic Lasagne, 234, *235*

Farfalle with Peas, Prosciutto and Mushrooms, 282, *282*

Fettucine with Smoked Cheese and Salami, *156,* 157

Fettucine with Spinach and Prosciutto, 255, *255*

Italian sausages, **65**

Lamb and Fusilli Soup, 49, *49*

Moroccan Lamb and Roasted Pepper with Fusilli, 70, *71*

Parsee Lamb with Cumin, Eggs and Tagliatelle, 75, *75*

Pasta with Braised Oxtail and Celery, 58, *58*

Pasta with Lamb and Vegetables, 77, *77*

Penne with Prosciutto, 74, *74*

Pork and Veal Ravioli with Cheesy Sauce, 164, *164*

Pork, Paprika and Poppy Seeds with Pasta, 68, *68*

Quick Spaghetti Bolognese, 60, *60*

Rigatoni with Chorizo and Tomato, 62, *62*

Rigatoni with Italian-style Oxtail Sauce, 64, *64*

Rigatoni with Kidney Beans and Italian Sausage, 65, *65*

Rigatoni with Salami and Fresh Herbs, 72, *72*

Rigatoni with Sausage and Parmesan, 148, *149*

Rocket, Cherry Tomato and Spicy Salami Pasta Salad, *180,* 181

Salami and Potato Frittata Wedges, 50, *50*

Spaghetti Bolognese, 56, *56*

Spaghetti with Rich Beef and Mushroom Sauce, *260,* 261

Spaghetti with Salami and Peppers, 59, *59*

Spicy Sausage and Fennel Rigatoni, 266, *267*

Stir-fried Chilli Beef with Spaghettini, 70, *71*

Tagliatelle with Veal Wine and Cream, 57, *57*

Ziti with Vegetables and Sausage, 63, *63*

Meatball and Pasta, 242, *242*

Meatballs Stroganoff, 76, *76*

Meatballs with Fusilli, 73, *73*

meats *see also* cold meats

Middle-Eastern Hummus, Tomato and Olive Pasta Salad, *194,* 195

Milano Salami, 67, *67*

Minestrone, 37, *37*

Moroccan Lamb and Roasted Pepper with Fusilli, 70, *71*

mortadella, 67, *67*

mozzarella cheese, 166, *166,* **242** *see also* bocconcini

Olive and Mozzarella Spaghetti, 116, *117*

Mushroom Ravioli, 227, *227*

mushrooms

button, **137,** *137*

Chicken and Veal Loaf with Mushrooms and Sour Cream, *248,* 249

Chicken Fettucine and Mushroom Sauce, 86, *86*

Farfalle with, 126

Farfalle with Peas, Prosciutto and, 282, *282*

Farfalle with Tuna, Mushrooms and Cream, 95, *95*

Fettucine with Creamy Mushroom and Bean Sauce, 151, *151*

Lasagnette with Mushrooms and Chicken, 88, *88*

Pastrami, Mushroom and Cucumber Salad, 176, *177*

Rissoni and Mushroom Broth, 38, *38*

Spaghetti Carbonara with, *280,* 281

Spaghetti with Rich Beef and Mushroom Sauce, *260,* 261

Spinach Fettucine with Mushroom Sauce, 152, *153*

Tortellini with Mushroom Cream Sauce, 225, *225*

mussels

black, **272**

Spaghetti and Mussels in Tomato and Herb Sauce, 113, *113*

Spaghetti with Creamy Garlic, 110, *110*

Stuffed, 50, *50*

Tomato Mussels on Spaghetti, 272, *273*

Mussels with Tomato Sauce, 109, *109*

mustard, **147**

N

Napolitana, 26, *26*

O

octopus

Tagliatelle with, 105, *105*

Olive and Mozzarella Spaghetti, 116, *117*

Olive and Tomato Tapenade, 135, *135*

olive oil, **60**

olives, **118,** 134, *134, 135,* **254**

and Mozzarella Spaghetti, 116, *117*

Farfalle with Artichoke Hearts and, 117, *117*

Green Olive and Eggplant Toss, 120, *120*

green olive paste, **250**

Linguine with Anchovies, Olives and Capers, 254, *254*

Middle-Eastern Hummus, Tomato and Olive Pasta Salad, *194,* 195

Pasta with Green Olive Paste and Three Cheeses, 250, *250*

Penne with Olive and Pistachio Pesto, 259, *259*

Ruote with Lemon, Olives and Bacon, 263, *263*

Spaghetti with Olives and Capers, 125, *125*

Omelette, Italian, 245, *245*

onions

Caramelized Onion and Blue Cheese Rissoni, 159, *159*

Spaghetti with Peas and Onions, 265, *265*

orecchiette

Chicken with Lemon, Parsley and, 83, *83*

Orecchiette with Tuna, Lemon and Caper Sauce, 160, *161*

oregano, **172**

Oriental Chicken Pasta, 84, *84*

Oriental Fricelli, *268,* 269

ovolini, 166, *166*

oxtail

Pasta with Braised Oxtail and Celery, 58, *58*

Rigatoni with Italian-style Oxtail Sauce, 64, *64*

P

Pancetta, 66, *66*

pappardelle, **104**

Pappardelle with Salmon, 104, *104*

paprika, **231**

Parmesan, **164**

   Pasta with Pesto and, 274, *274*

   Rigatoni with Sausage and, 148, *149*

parmigiano reggiano, 168, *168*

Parsee Lamb with Cumin, Eggs and Tagliatelle, 75, *75*

parsley, **264**

   Chicken with Lemon, Parsley and Orecchiette, 83, *83*

   flat-leaf, **124**

Parsnip Gnocchi, 208, *208*

parsnips, **208**

pasta

   cooking, 9

   dried, 10–13

   fresh, 14

   making, 16

   re-heating, **86**

Pasta and Bean Soup, 46, *46*

Pasta and Mince, Baked, 61, *61*

Pasta and Spinach Timbales, 240, *240*

Pasta Cases with Fruity Ricotta Filling, 291, *291*

Pasta Niçoise, 278, *278*

Pasta Pie, 233, *233*

Pasta Souffle, 234, *234*

Pasta with Braised Oxtail and Celery, 58, *58*

Pasta with Fragrant Lime and Smoked Trout, 255

Pasta with Green Olive Paste and Three Cheeses, 250, *250*

Pasta with Lamb and Vegetables, 77, *77*

Pasta with Mediterranean-style Vegetables, 187, *187*

Pasta with Pesto and Parmesan, 274, *274*

Pasta with Thai-style Vegetables, 186, *186*

Pasta-filled Vegetables, 243, *243*

Pasticcio, 246, *246,* **247**

Pastitsio, 247, *247,* **247**

pastrami, **176,** *176*

Pastrami, Mushroom and Cucumber Salad, 176, *177*

pears, **181**

pecorino, 167, *167*

penne

   Livers with, 89, *89*

   Spicy Penne with Peppers, 140, *141*

Penne with Chicken and Mushrooms, 148, *149*

Penne with Creamy Tomato Sauce, 126, *126*

Penne with Olive and Pistachio Pesto, 259, *259*

Penne with Prosciutto, 74, *74*

Penne with Pumpkin and Cinnamon Sauce, 132, *133*

Penne with Roasted Peppers, *260,* 261

Penne with Rocket, 258, *258*

Penne with Sun-dried Tomatoes and Lemon, 283, *283*

pepper

   black, **148**

   cayenne, **157**

   white, **241**

Pepperoni, 67, *67*

peppers, **261**

   Grilled Peppers and Anchovy Salad, 192, *192*

   Linguine with Red Pepper Sauce, *128,* 129

   Spicy Penne with, 140, *141*

pesto, 28, *28,* **275**

   Conchiglie with Chicken and, 223, *223*

   Pasta with Pesto and Parmesan, 274, *274*

   Penne with Olive and Pistachio, 259, *259*

   Pesto Bocconcini Balls, 52, *52*

   Pesto Chicken Pasta, 87, *87*

pine nuts, **139**

   Pumpkin and Pine Nut Tagliatelle, *138,* 139

Pistou Soupe au, 45

Polenta Shapes with Chorizo and Salsa, 51, *51*

Pomodoro, 23, *23*

pork

   Paprika and Poppy Seeds with Pasta, 68, *68*

   Pork and Veal Ravioli with Cheesy Sauce, 164, *164*

   Pork, Paprika and Poppy Seeds with Pasta, 68, *68*

potato gnocchi, 202, *202*

Potato Gnocchi with Tomato and Basil Sauce, 199, *199*

potatoes, **199**

   Herbed Potato Gnocchi with Chunky Tomato, 205, *205*

   Salami and Potato Frittata Wedges, 50, *50*

Prawn and Basil Soup, 42, *42*

Prawn Tortelloni, 215, *215*

prawns

   Creamy Prawns with Fettucine, 96, *96*

   Fragrant Herb Tagliatelle with Kaffir Lime and, 100, *101*

   Snow Pea, Prawn and Pasta Soup, 38, *38*

   Spicy Prawn Mexicana, 100, *100*

   Warm Garlic Prawn and Fettucine Salad, 188, *189*

Primavera, 22, *22*

   Fettucine, 131, *131*

prosciutto, 66, *66,* **160**

   Farfalle with Peas, Prosciutto and Mushrooms, 282, *282*

   Fettucine with Spinach and, 255, *255*

   Penne with, 74, *74*

provolone, 166, *167*

Pumpkin and Herb Ravioli, 217, *217*

Pumpkin and Pine Nut Tagliatelle, *138,* 139

Pumpkin Gnocchi with Sage Butter, 201, *201*

pumpkins, **48, 201**

   butternut, **249**

   Butternut Pumpkin Filled with Pasta and Leeks, *248,* 249

   Country Pumpkin and Pasta Soup, 48, *48*

   Penne with Pumpkin and Cinnamon Sauce, 132, *133*

   Rigatoni with Pumpkin Sauce, 127, *127*

Puttanesca, 31, *31*

Q

Quick Spaghetti Bolognese, 60, *60*

R

Ratatouille and Pasta Soup, 44, *44*
ravioli, 219, *219,* **227**
  Chicken Ravioli with Buttered Sage Sauce, 224, *224*
  Chicken Ravioli with Fresh Tomato Sauce, 90, *90*
  Chicken Ravioli with Lime Balsamic Dressing, 256, *257*
  Mushroom, 227, *227*
  Pork and Veal Ravioli with Cheesy Sauce, 164, *164*
  Pumpkin and Herb, 217, *217*
  Spinach Ravioli with Sun-dried Tomato Sauce, 216, *216*
  Turkish, 69, *69*
Ravioli with Chicken Filling, 212, *212*
Ravioli with Mascarpone and Pancetta, *156,* 157
Ravioli with Peas and Artichokes, 276, *277*
red caviar, **102**
Red Pepper Gnocchi with Goats Cheese, 209, *209*
red wine, **64**
ricotta, 166, *167*
  Conchiglie with Chicken and, 237, *237*
  Giant Conchiglie with Ricotta and Rocket, 251, *251*
  Pasta Cases with Fruity Ricotta Filling, 291, *291*
  Spinach and Ricotta Cannelloni, 222, *222*
  Spinach and Ricotta Gnocchi, 206, *207*
  Spinach and Ricotta Shells, 214, *214*
Ricotta and Basil with Tagliatelle, *280,* 281
ricotta cheese, **214**
Ricotta Lasagne, 231, *231*
rigatoni, **190**
  Blue Cheese and Broccoli with, *138,* 139
  Spicy Sausage and Fennel, 266, *267*
Rigatoni Gratin, 240, *240*
Rigatoni with Chorizo and Tomato, 62, *62*
Rigatoni with Italian-style Oxtail Sauce, 64, *64*

Rigatoni with Kidney Beans and Italian Sausage, 65, *65*
Rigatoni with Pumpkin Sauce, 127, *127*
Rigatoni with Salami and Fresh Herbs, 72, *72*
Rigatoni with Sausage and Parmesan, 148, *149*
Rigatoni with Tomato, Haloumi and Spinach, 190, *190*
rissoni, **243**
  Baked Rissoni Pudding, 289, *289*
  Caramelized Onion and Blue Cheese, 159, *159*
  Coconut and Lemon Rissoni Cake, 288, *288*
Rissoni and Mushroom Broth, 38
Roasted Pepper Bruschetta, 185, *185*
Rocket, Cherry Tomato and Spicy Salami Pasta Salad, *180,* 181
rosemary, **85**
Ruote with Lemon, Olives and Bacon, 263, *263*

S

saffron, **163**
salads
  Barbecued Chicken and Pasta Salad, 182, *182*
  Chicken, Pear and Pasta Salad, *180,* 181
  Conchiglie Salad with Bocconcini, Asparagus and Oregano, 188, *189*
  Grilled Peppers and Anchovy Salad, 192, *192*
  Italian-style Chicken and Pasta Salad, 178, *178*
  Lemon and Date Ziti, 191, *191*
  Lemon and Vegetable Pasta Salad, 183, *183*
  Middle-Eastern Hummus, Tomato and Olive Pasta Salad, *194,* 195
  Pasta with Mediterranean-style Vegetables, 187, *187*
  Pasta with Thai-style vegetables, 186, *186*

Pastrami, Mushroom and Cucumber Salad, 176, *177*
Rigatoni with Tomato, Haloumi and Spinach, 190, *190*
Rocket, Cherry Tomato and Spicy Salami Pasta Salad, *180,* 181
Seafood Salad, Creamy, 179, *179*
Smoked Salmon, Dill and Egg Pasta Salad, *194,* 195
Tuna, Green Bean and Onion Salad, 176, *177*
Tuscan Warm Pasta Salad, 193, *193*
warm, **174**
Warm Garlic Prawn and Fettucine Salad, 188, *189*
Warm Pasta and Crab Salad, 192
salami, **59,** 67, *67*
  Fettucine with Smoked Cheese and, *156,* 157
  Rigatoni with Salami and Fresh Herbs, 72, *72*
  Rocket, Cherry Tomato and Spicy Salami Pasta Salad, *180,* 181
  Spaghetti with Salami and Peppers, 59, *59*
Salami and Potato Frittata Wedges, 50, *50*
salmon, **98**
  Brandied Cream and Salmon Fusilli, 276, *277*
  Fettucine with Smoked Salmon, 111, *111*
  Pappardelle with Salmon, 104, *104*
  Smoked Salmon, Dill and Egg Pasta Salad, *194,* 195
  Spaghettini with Roasted Salmon and Garlic, 104
Salmon and Pasta Mornay, 98, *98*
salt, **193**
sambal oelek, **276**
Sardines, Barbecued, 51, *51*
sauces
  Alfredo, **162**
  Béchamel, 231, 235 **235,** 244, 246
  Cheese, 82, 123
  Tomato, 81, 94, 212, 231, 244

sausages
 Bean Soup with, 39, *39*
 fresh Italian, **65**
 Rigatoni with Sausage and
  Parmesan, 148, *149*
 Spicy Sausage and Fennel
  Rigatoni, 266, *267*
 Ziti with Vegetables and,
  63, *63*
scallops, **108**
seafood
 Anchovy and Tomato
  Crostini, 185, *185*
 anchovy fillets, **152**
 Barbecued Sardines, 51, *51*
 black mussels, **272**
 Brandied Cream and Salmon
  Fusilli, 276, *277*
 Chilli Seafood in Tomato
  Sauce, 103, *103*
 clams, **112**
 Creamy Prawns with
  Fettucine, 96, *96*
 Creamy Seafood Ravioli,
  108, *108*
 Creamy Seafood Salad,
  179, *179*
 Farfalle with Tuna,
  Mushrooms and Cream,
  95, *95*
 Fettucine with Smoked
  Salmon, 111, *111*
 Fragrant Herb Tagliatelle with
  Kaffir Lime and Prawns,
  100, *101*
 Fragrant Seafood Pasta,
  102, *103*
 Garlic, Pasta and Fish Soup,
  47
 Linguine with Anchovies,
  Olives and Capers, 254,
  254
 Orecchiette with Tuna,
  Lemon and Caper Sauce,
  160, *161*
 Pappardelle with Salmon, 104,
  104
 Pasta with Fragrant Lime and
  Smoked Trout, 255
 scallops, **108**, *108*
 Smoked Salmon, Dill and Egg
  Pasta Salad, *194,* 195
 Snow Pea, Prawn and Pasta
  Soup, 38, *38*
 Spaghetti and Mussels in
  Tomato and Herb Sauce,
  113, *113*

Spaghetti with Creamy Garlic
 Mussels, 110, *110*
Spaghetti with Olives and
 Capers, 125, *125*
Spaghettini with Roasted
 Salmon and Garlic, 104
Spicy Prawn Mexicana,
 100, *100*
Stuffed Mussels, 50, *50*
Tagliatelle with Octopus,
 105, *105*
Tomato Mussels on Spaghetti,
 272, *273*
Tomato Pasta with Smoked
 Cod and Sesame, *106,* 107
Trout, Fettucine and Fennel
 Frittata, *106,* 107
Tuna and Pasta Salad,
 175, *175*
Tuna, Green Bean and Onion
 Salad, 176, *177*
Warm Garlic Prawn and
 Fettucine Salad, 188, *189*
Seafood with Pasta, 232, *232*
semolina, **198**
silverbeet, **129**
Slow-roasted Balsamic
 Tomatoes, 53, *53*
Smoked Salmon, Dill and Egg
 Pasta Salad, *194,* 195
Snow Pea, Prawn and Pasta
 Soup, 38, *38*
snow peas, **84**
 Fettucine with Snow Peas and
  Walnuts, 140, *141*
sorrel, **270**
Souffle, Pasta, 234, *234*
Soupe au Pistou, 45, *45*
soups
 Bacon and Pea, 43, *43*
 Bean Soup with Sausage,
  39, *39*
 Beef Stock, **49**
 Broccoli, 42, *42*
 Chicken and Pasta,
  47, *47*
 Chicken, Leek and Chickpea,
  36
 Garlic, Pasta and Fish, 47
 Lamb and Fusilli, 49, *49*
 Lemon-Scented Broth with
  Tortellini, 36, *36*
 Minestrone, 37, *37*
 Pasta and Bean, 46, *46*
 Prawn and Basil, 42, *42*
 Rissoni and Mushroom
  Broth, 38

Snow Pea, Prawn and Pasta,
 38, *38*
Soupe au Pistou, 45, *45*
Spicy Chicken Broth with
 Coriander Pasta, 40, *40*
Tomato Soup with Pasta and
 Basil, 41, *41*
Vegetable Soup with Basil
 Sauce, 45, *45*
spaghetti, **110**
 Baked Spaghetti Frittata,
  238, *238*
 Calabrian, 275, *275*
 Chunky Spaghetti Napolitana,
  124, *124*
 Olive and Mozzarella,
  116, *117*
 Quick Spaghetti Bolognese,
  60, *60*
 Tomato Mussels on, 272, *273*
Spaghetti and Mussels in
 Tomato and Herb Sauce,
 113, *113*
Spaghetti Bolognese, 56, *56*
Spaghetti Carbonara, 155,
 155, **155**
Spaghetti Carbonara with
 Mushrooms, *280,* 281
Spaghetti Marinara, 94, *94*
Spaghetti Mediterranean,
 279, *279*
Spaghetti Puttanesca, 264, *264*
Spaghetti Siracusani, 136, *136*
Spaghetti Tomato Salad,
 173, *173*
Spaghetti Vongole, 112, *112*
Spaghetti with Chicken
 Bolognese, 85, *85*
Spaghetti with Chicken
 Meatballs, 80, *80*
Spaghetti with Chilli Calamari,
 99, *99*
Spaghetti with Creamy Garlic
 Mussels, 110, *110*
Spaghetti with Creamy Lemon
 Sauce, *268,* 269
Spaghetti with Fresh Tomato
 Sauce, 121, *121*
Spaghetti with Garlic and Chilli,
 262, *262*
Spaghetti with Herbs, 274, *274*
Spaghetti with Herbs and
 Tomato, 130, *130*
Spaghetti with Olives and
 Capers, 125, *125*
Spaghetti with Peas and Onions,
 265, *265*

Spaghetti with Rich Beef and Mushroom Sauce, *260, 261*

Spaghetti with Salami and Peppers, 59, *59*

Spaghetti with Tomato Sauce, *280,* 281

spaghettini

Stir-fried Chilli Beef with Spaghettini, 70, *71*

Spaghettini with Roasted Salmon and Garlic, 104

Speck, 67, *67*

Spiced Carrot and Feta Gnocchi, 206, *207*

Spicy Chicken Broth with Coriander Pasta, 40, *40*

Spicy Penne with Peppers, 140, *141*

Spicy Prawn Mexicana, 100, *100*

Spicy Sausage and Fennel Rigatoni, 266, *267*

spinach

Chicken and Spinach Lasagne, 82, *82*

English, **255**

Farfalle Salad with Sun-Dried Tomatoes and, 172, *172*

Fettucine with Spinach and Prosciutto, 255, *255*

Pasta and Spinach Timbales, 240, *240*

Rigatoni with Tomato, Haloumi and, 190, *190*

Spinach and Ricotta Cannelloni, 222, *222*

Spinach and Ricotta Gnocchi, 206, *207*

Spinach and Ricotta Shells, 214, *214*

Spinach Fettucine with Mushroom Sauce, 152, *153*

Spinach Ravioli with Sun-dried Tomato Sauce, 216, *216*

squash, baby yellow, 266

Stir-Fried Chilli Beef with Spaghettini, 70, *71*

stocks

beef, **49**

fish, **99**

vegetable, **151**

strawberries, **287**

Strawberry Rolls, Creamy Fresh, 287, *287*

Stuffed Mussels, 50, *50*

sugar, caster, **291**

Sun-dried Tomato Sauce on Tagliatelle, 118, *119*

sun-dried tomatoes, **111**

Sweet Cheese in Lemon Pasta, 286, *286*

T

Tagliatelle with Asparagus and Fresh Herbs, 154, *154*

Tagliatelle with Chicken Livers and Cream, 147, *147*

Tagliatelle with Octopus, 105, *105*

Tagliatelle with Tomato and Walnuts, 142, *142*

Tagliatelle with Veal Wine and Cream, 57, *57*

taleggio, 169, *169*

thyme, **279**

Tomato and Basil Pasta Salad, 174, *174*

Tomato Mussels on Spaghetti, 272, *273*

Tomato Pasta with Smoked Cod and Sesame, *106,* 107

Tomato Sauce, 81, 94, 212, 231, 244

Tomato Soup with Pasta and Basil, 41, *41*

tomatoes

Anchovy and Tomato Crostini, 185, *185*

Basil Tortellini with Bacon and Tomato Sauce, 226, *226*

cherry, **140**

Chicken Ravioli with Fresh Tomato Sauce, 90, *90*

Chicken Tortellini with Tomato Sauce, 81, *81*

Chilli Seafood in Tomato Sauce, 103, *103*

egg, **122**

Farfalle Salad with Sun-dried Tomatoes and Spinach, 172, *172*

Gnocchi with Tomato and Fresh Basil, 200

Herbed Potato Gnocchi with Chunky Tomato, 205, *205*

Middle-Eastern Hummus, Tomato and Olive Pasta Salad, *194,* 195

Olive and Tomato Tapenade, 135, *135*

paste, **281**

Penne with Creamy Tomato Sauce, 126, *126*

Penne with Sun-dried Tomatoes and Lemon, 283, *283*

Rigatoni with Chorizo and, 62, *62*

Rigatoni with Tomato, Haloumi and Spinach, 190, *190*

Rocket, Cherry Tomato and Spicy Salami Pasta Salad, *180,* 181

Slow-roasted Balsamic, 53, *53*

Spaghetti Tomato Salad, 173, *173*

Spaghetti with Fresh Tomato Sauce, 121, *121*

Spaghetti with Herbs and, 130, *130*

Spinach Ravioli with Sun-dried Tomato Sauce, 216, *216*

sun-dried, **111**

Sun-dried Tomato Sauce on Tagliatelle, 118, *119*

Tagliatelle with Tomato and Walnuts, 142, *142*

Ziti with Roasted Tomatoes and Ovolini, 256, *257*

tortellini, **81, 143,** 220, *220*

Basil Tortellini with Bacon and Tomato Sauce, 226, *226*

Chicken Tortellini with Tomato Sauce, 81, *81*

Lemon-Scented Broth with, 36, *36*

Prawn, 215, *215*

Tortellini Broth, 270, *270*

Tortellini with Eggplant, 143, *143*

Tortellini with Mushroom Cream Sauce, 225, *225*

trout

Pasta with Fragrant Lime and Smoked, 255

Trout, Fettucine and Fennel Frittata, *106,* 107

tuna, **95**

Farfalle with Tuna, Mushrooms and Cream, 95, *95*

tuna *continued*
    Orecchiette with Tuna,
      Lemon and Caper Sauce,
      160, *161*
Tuna and Pasta Salad, 175, *175*
Tuna, Green Bean and Onion
    Salad, 176, *177*
Turkish Ravioli, 69, *69*
Tuscan Warm Pasta Salad,
    193, *193*

U – V

veal
    Chicken and Veal Loaf with
      Mushrooms and Sour
      Cream, *248,* 249
    Pork and Veal Ravioli with
      Cheesy Sauce, 164, *164*
    Tagliatelle with Veal Wine
      and Cream, 57, *57*
Vegetable Lasagne, 123, *123*
Vegetable Soup with Basil
    Sauce, 45, *45*
vegetable stock, **151**
vegetables with pasta
    Chunky Spaghetti Napolitana,
      124, *124*
    Conchiglie with Chickpeas,
      132, *133*
    Creamy Asparagus Linguine,
      118, *119*
    Farfalle with Artichoke Hearts
      and Olives, 117, *117*
    Farfalle with Mushrooms,
      126

    Fettucine with Zucchini and
      Crisp-fried Basil, 116, *116*
    Fusilli with Green Sauce,
      128, 129
    Fusilli with Vegetables,
      266, *267*
    Green Olive and Eggplant
      Toss, 120, *120*
    Grilled Vegetables on Pasta,
      122, *122*
    Lemon and Vegetable Pasta
      Salad, 183, *183*
    Linguine with Red Pepper
      Sauce, *128,* 129
    Linguine with Roasted
      Vegetable Sauce, 121
    Olive and Mozzarella
      Spaghetti, 116, *117*
    Pasta with Mediterranean-
      style Vegetables, 187, *187*
    Pasta with Thai-style
      Vegetables, 186, *186*
    Pasta-filled Vegetables,
      243, *243*
    Penne with Creamy Tomato
      Sauce, 126, *126*
    Penne with Pumpkin and
      Cinnamon Sauce, 132, *133*
    Rigatoni with Pumpkin
      Sauce, 127, *127*
    Spaghetti with Herbs and
      Tomato, 130, *130*
    Spaghetti with Olives and
      Capers, 125, *125*
    Spicy Penne with Peppers,
      140, *141*

    Sun-dried Tomato Sauce on
      Tagliatelle, 118, *119*

W

walnuts, **142**
    Fettucine with Snow Peas
      and Walnuts, 140, *141*
    Tagliatelle with Tomato
      and Walnuts, 142, *142*
Warm Chicken and Pasta
    Salad, 174, *174*
Warm Garlic Prawn and
    Fettucine Salad, 188, *189*
Warm Pasta and Crab Salad,
    192, *192*
white pepper, **241**
white wine, **57**
wine, **57, 64**

Y

yoghurt, **69**

Z

Ziti with Roasted Tomatoes
    and Ovolini, 256, *257*
Ziti with Vegetables and
    Sausage, 63, *63*
zucchini, **116**
    Fettucine with Zucchini
      and Crisp-fried Basil,
      116, *116*
    Fettucine, and Crisp-fried
      Basil with, 116, *116*

ACKNOWLEDGEMENTS

HOME ECONOMISTS: Jo Forrest, Michelle Lawton, Kerrie Mullins, Justine Poole, Kerrie Ray, Chris Sheppard, Dimitra Stais, Alison Turner, Jody Vassallo

RECIPE DEVELOPMENT: Wendy Berecry, Rebecca Clancy, Amanda Cooper, Alex Diblasi, Michelle Earl, Joanne Glynn, Lulu Grimes, Michelle Lawton, Barbara Lowery, Angela Nahas, Sally Parker, Jennene Plumber, Tracey Port, Jo Richardson, Tracy Rutherford, Dimitra Stais, Jody Vassallo

PHOTOGRAPHY: Jon Bader, Ashley Barber, Joe Filshie, Chris Jones, Luis Martin, Reg Morrison

STYLISTS: Amanda Cooper, Carolyn Fienberg, Michelle Gorry, Mary Harris, Donna Hay, Rosemary Mellish

The publisher wishes to thank the following for their assistance in the photography for this book: Antico's Northbridge Fruitworld, NSW; Bush Wa Zee Pty Ltd Ceramics, NSW; Dee Why Fruitworld, NSW; Nick Greco Family Delicatessen, NSW; Ma Maison en Provence, NSW; Pasta Vera, NSW.